Intelligent Life
in the Universe

INTELLIGENT LIFE

I. S. SHKLOVSKII

Being a translation, extension, and revision
of I. S. Shklovskii's UNIVERSE, LIFE, MIND

IN THE UNIVERSE

AND CARL SAGAN

Authorized translation by Paula Fern

 A DELTA BOOK

A DELTA BOOK

Published by
DELL PUBLISHING CO., INC.
1 Dag Hammarskjold Plaza
New York, N.Y. 10017
Copyright 1966 by Holden-Day, Inc.

Delta ® TM 755118, Dell Publishing Co., Inc.
Reprinted by arrangement with Holden-Day, Inc.
Library of Congress Catalog Card Number 64-18404
Printed in the United States of America

Tenth Printing

To the memory of John Burdon Sanderson Haldane, F.R.S., member of the National Academies of Sciences of the United States and of the Soviet Union, member of The Order of the Dolphins, and a local example of what this book is about.

Preface

"The prey runs to the hunter," wrote Iosef Shmuelovich Shklovskii in a letter to me in 1962. Knowing his wide-ranging interests, I had sent him a preprint of a paper of mine called "Direct Contact Among Galactic Civilizations by Relativistic Interstellar Spaceflight," a speculative exercise on a topic which I thought might interest him. Shklovskii wrote to tell me that he was completing a semipopular book, *Vselennaia, Zhizn, Razum* (in English, *Universe, Life, Mind*). It was being written for the fifth anniversary of the launching of the first Soviet artificial satellite on October 4, 1957. Shklovskii had been about to write a chapter on the possibility of interstellar spaceflight when my preprint arrived, just in time to be partially incorporated into the text. *Vselennaia, Zhizn, Razum* was published in Moscow in early 1963. Parts of it were also serialized in *Komsomolskaya Pravda,* and extracts published in the Soviet scientific journal *Priroda.* It has received enthusiastic acclaim in the Soviet Union and elsewhere, and is being translated into a variety of languages, including Chinese.

When I received a copy of the book, I was struck by its broad scope and novel insights. I wrote to Shklovskii, asking him if we might translate it into English. Shklovskii readily consented, and invited me to add additional material as I saw fit. As the translation proceeded, in the capable hands of Paula Fern, I found myself unable to resist the temptation to annotate the text, clarify concepts for the scientific layman, comment at length, and introduce new material. The delay in the publication of the English edition is attributable entirely to this cause. I have added about as much material as there was in the work initially, and the figures and captions are solely my responsibility. I hope that the book is, as a result, of somewhat wider appeal. Shklovskii also has made a large number of changes and additions which have been incorporated into the English edition.

The result is a peculiar kind of cooperative endeavor. I have sent much of the entirely new material to Shklovskii for his comment, and he has sent much new material to me for inclusion. Since he does not travel out of the Soviet Union and I have never traveled to the Soviet Union, we have been unable to discuss the present edition in person. "The probability of our meeting is unlikely to be smaller than the probability of a visit to the Earth by an extraterrestrial cosmonaut," he once wrote, in a puckish mood. Consequently, there are places in the present work where Shklovskii and I alternate sentences, or even occasionally insert clauses into each other's sentences. Shklovskii and I agree on almost all the substantive issues of this book, but to avoid the possibility of attribution to Shklovskii of a view which he does not hold, I have adopted the following strategem: Sentences or paragraphs which appeared either in the Russian edition of this book, or in additions provided by Shklovskii, are presented in ordinary type. Annotations, additions, and discussions of my devising are surrounded by the symbols ▽ and △, the first preceding and the second following my contribution. In those cases where Shklovskii uses the word "we," as in "we believe" or "we feel," this generally represents a sentiment shared by both of us.

As the reader might expect for a book written by two authors, one in the Soviet Union and one in the United States, there are occasional ideological differences. I have not tried to avoid these problems, but I also have not tried, in what is primarily a scientific work, to rebut each ideological assertion. When Shklovskii expresses his belief that lasting world peace is impossible while capitalism survives, or implies that lasers are being actively developed in the United States for their possible military applications alone, I have let the content of these statements stand, despite their political intent. I have occasionally interjected some remarks on related subjects, with which, perhaps, Shklovskii would disagree. I do not think the reader will be distressed by the occasional appearance of a dialogue.

The possibility of extraterrestrial life has caused some ideological embarrassment in the Soviet Union. There used to be, at Alma Ata, in the Kazakh Soviet Socialist Republic, an Institute of Astrobotany, some of whose members argued that the existence of extraterrestrial life was required by dialectical materialism, and implied strongly that the absence of life on Mars, or even on Jupiter, would be a clear disproof of the philosophical basis of Communism. This dangerous situation prompted an article in the September–October 1958 issue of the Soviet astronomical journal *Astronomicheskii Zhurnal,* called "Concerning the 'Philosophical Foundation' of One Question," by I. G. Perel', in which Perel' points out that both the materialist and the idealist philosophical schools seem to strongly support the likelihood of extraterrestrial life. He argues that dialectical materialism is a method, not a body of knowledge, much as Shklovskii does on p. 136 of this book; and in particular, that even if Mars or Jupiter is lifeless, dialectical materialism is not disproved. This debate has been echoed by other discussions in the United States, which, while on a different ideological basis, turn out to have very similar content.

The present work has ten more chapters than the original Russian edition. This is due almost entirely to new material. The over-all organization remains as in the Russian edition: a discussion first of the astronomical background, then of the nature of life and its possible occurrence in our solar system, and finally, a treatment of the possibility that advanced communicative technical civilizations exist on planets of other stars. A more detailed overview of the book appears in the introductory chapter by Shklovskii. I have added an introductory chapter on the psychological perils of the study of extraterrestrial life.

It is impossible for me to thank all those who have helped to shape my views on the topics of this book. I would, however, like to acknowledge my debt to the following people for specific discussion of relevant material or for reading and commenting on various parts of the present work in manuscript form: Dr. Elso Barghoorn, Dr. Geoffrey Burbidge, Dr. Frank Drake, Dr. Freeman Dyson, Dr. Owen Gingerich, Dr. J. B. S. Haldane, Dr. William Irvine, Dr. Luigi Jacchia, Dr. G. P. Kuiper, Dr. David Layzer, Dr. A. E. Lilley, Dr. Phillip Morrison, Dr. H. J. Muller, Dr. James B. Pollack, Dr. Lynn Sagan, Dr. Evry Schatzmann, Dr. Ellie Shneour, Dr. Charles H. Townes, and Dr. Andrew T. Young. I am also grateful to Dr. Leo Goldberg for editorial advice. None of the foregoing are, of course, responsible for any errors of fact or interpretation which may have crept into the manuscript. Several colleagues have been kind enough to point out typographical and other errors in the first printing; these errors have been corrected in the present edition.

In addition to credits referenced through the text the following acknowledgements are made: the jacket composite photograph is by courtesy of NASA and Mt. Wilson and Palomar Observatories. The frontispiece cartoon, from POGO is © by Walt Kelly and reprinted by kind permission of the Hall Syndicate, Inc. Cartoons, page 24, by Charles Schulz, © by United Features Syndicate and also published in *It's A Dog's Life, Charlie Brown* by Holt, Rinehart and Winston. Quotations from Loren Eiseley's *The Immense Journey* (1946) pages 25, 182, 356 and 432 are © by Random House, Inc., and reproduced through their permission. Mt. Wilson and Palomar Observatories through whose courtesy the photographs on page 7 and in many other places in the book are reproduced, are associated with the Carnegie Institution of Washington and the California Institute of Technology. Yerkes Observatory through whose courtesy the illustrations on page 41 and elsewhere are reproduced, is a unit of the University of Chicago. The diagram on page 80 is reproduced through the courtesy of Professor Chushiro Hayashi. The diagrams from the *Astrophysical Journal* on pages 81 and 84 are © in the years indicated by the University of Chicago. The diagram on page 86 also appeared in the volume "Stellar Populations," *Specola Vaticana Richerche Astronomiche,* volume 5, page 227. The figures from the *Astrophysical Journal* on pages 118 and 119 are © 1963 by the University of Chicago. The diagram on page 150 first appeared in *Sky and Telescope 26:* 3. The diagram on page 163 first appeared in *Physics Today 1:* 12–28, 1948. The illustration on page 180 is reproduced through the courtesy of Mr. Charles Addams and the *New Yorker* Magazine, Inc. The quotation on page 184 appears on page 1–9 of *The Feynman Lectures on Physics,* volume 1, by R. P. Feynman, R. Leighton and M. Sands, Addison-Wesley, 1963, through the kind permission of Professor Feynman and the publisher. The photographs on pages 338 and 339 appeared in *Science 138:* 1392–99 (1962), and are reproduced by permission. The upper illustration on page 354 is reproduced through the courtesy of Mr. Herbert Block; the lower through the courtesy of Mr. Charles Addams and the *New Yorker* Magazine, Inc. Parts of Chapters 29, 32, and 33, as well as Figure 32–1, are taken from an article by Carl Sagan in *Planetary and Space Science,* volume 11, p. 45 (1963) and are reproduced through the courtesy of Professor D. R. Bates, the editor. The illustrations on pages 458, 461 and 462 are reproduced through the courtesy of Macmillan and Co., Ltd., London. The quotations on pages 459 and 460 are reproduced from H. Frankfort *et al., Before Philosophy, The Intellectual Adventure of Ancient Man,* © 1946 by the University of Chicago Press.

Dr. Charles Federer and Dr. Joseph Ashbrook of *Sky and Telescope* have generously assisted in tracking down illustrative material.

Collecting the epigraphs for the chapters of this book has been a source of considerable pleasure for me. Some of these epigraphs have been suggested by others. The quotations from Pasternak, on page 26, and by Smelianov on page 272 appeared in the Russian edition. The quote from Herschel on page 110 was suggested by Dr. Owen Gingerich, as was the epigraph of Chapter 11. Dr. Sidney Coleman recommended the epigraph of Chapter 28. Dr. Robert B. Leighton called my attention to the Walt Kelly strip used as one of the frontispieces. The dedication of this book, while of my devising, was approved by Professor Shklovskii.

I would like, finally, to express my thanks to Mrs. Ruth Ellen Galper for intelligent commentary on and typing of what proved to be an unexpectedly long manuscript; and to Miss Jean Swift for reading and providing useful editorial comments on the entire work, and to the other members of the publisher's staff. Other assistance with the manuscript was generously provided by Mrs. Terry Brown, Mrs. Sondra Cohen, Mrs. Elinore Green, and Miss Kathryn Bloom.

Carl Sagan
Cambridge, Mass.
May 15, 1966

A note on
mathematical and physical units

▽ In this book, we are concerned with quantities ranging from the immensely large to the minutely small. If we were to write out these sizes in the conventional way, using any unit of length we wish—miles or inches, for example—the pages of the book would be filled with large numbers of zeros, either before or after the decimal place. For any one of these numbers, such as 33 000 000 000 000 000, there is always the tedious problem of counting the number of zeros.

▽ To avoid these difficulties, mathematicians devised, some centuries ago, a very simple exponential notation for large and small numbers. The expression a^n means that we are to multiply the number a by itself n times. For example, $2^2 = 4$; $10^3 = 1000$; etc. a is called the base, and n, the exponent. A negative exponent denotes a reciprocal. Thus, $a^{-n} = 1/a^n$. In this way, $\frac{1}{8}$ can be written as 2^{-3}; $\frac{1}{10\,000}$, 10^{-4}; etc. A fractional exponent, such as $a^{1/2}$, indicates that we must multiply a by itself less than one time; therefore, we should obtain a number which is less than a. For example, an exponent of $\frac{1}{2}$ denotes the square root; an exponent of $\frac{1}{10}$ denotes the tenth root, etc. Therefore, $8^{1/3} = 2$; $10000^{1/4} = 10$; etc. Since $2^3 = 8$, and $10^4 = 10000$, these results can also be written as $(2^3)^{1/3} = 2^1 = 2$, and $(10^4)^{1/4} = 10^1 = 10$.

▽ With this notation, multiplication and division become very easy, provided we compare quantities with the same base. In multiplication, we add exponents; in division, we subtract exponents. $100 \times 1000 = 100000$; or, in our notation, $10^2 \times 10^3 = 10^5$. Such addition of exponents becomes very useful for extremely large numbers. For example, the product of 2 million and 4.5 billion may be written as

$$(2 \times 10^6) \times (4.5 \times 10^9) = 9 \times 10^{15}.$$

The expression 9×10^{15} is a much neater way of describing the number, which otherwise we might have to call "nine million trillion."

▽ Similarly, 7 billion divided by 2000 can be expressed as

$$\frac{7 \times 10^9}{2 \times 10^3} = \frac{7}{2} \times 10^6 = 3.5 \times 10^6.$$

Since division is equivalent to multiplication by reciprocals, we can write this as

$$(7 \times 10^9) \times (2^{-1}) \times (10^{-3}) = 3.5 \times 10^6.$$

▽ Our arithmetic is based upon the base 10, probably because we have ten fingers on our hands, and mathematics developed among people who counted on their fingers. The metric system of units, introduced in France at the time of the French Revolution, is also constructed on the base 10. For example, there are 10 millimeters to a centimeter; 1000 grams to a kilogram; and so forth. The United States, United Kingdom, and a few other countries are still stuck in the morass of what is called the English system of units, in which, for example, 12 inches make a foot; 16 ounces make a pound; and 5280 feet make a mile—as if the English system had developed among some species of animal with a strange and variable number of appendages. In this book we use primarily the metric system. Distances will be measured in centimeters, meters, kilometers, and so forth; masses will be measured in grams and their multiples; and time will be measured in seconds. A conversion from metric to English units will be made where the metric units are first introduced in the body of the text. The reader is encouraged to adopt the metric system of units in his thinking about the contents of this book.

▽ The exponential system of notation can also be used for the physical units. For example, a light year is defined as the distance which light travels in one year. In metric units, light travels 3×10^{10} cm in each second (or per second). This is the velocity of light. We may also write this as 3×10^{10} cm/sec, or 3×10^{10} cm sec^{-1}, where, as with numbers, the exponent -1 indicates a reciprocal. To determine the number of centimeters that light travels in a year from the number of centimeters that it travels in a second, we must find the number of seconds in a year. There are 60 seconds in a minute, 60 minutes in an hour, 24 hours in a day, about 365 days in a year. Thus, a light year may be written as

$$(3 \times 10^{10} \text{ cm sec}^{-1}) \times (6 \times 10 \text{ sec min}^{-1}) \times (6 \times 10 \text{ min hr}^{-1})$$
$$\times (2.4 \times 10 \text{ hr day}^{-1}) \times (3.65 \times 10^2 \text{ days yr}^{-1}).$$

If we perform the multiplication and cancel units—(sec^{-1}) × (sec) = 1, etc.—we find that a light year is about 10^{18} cm, a very large distance.

▽ As another problem, consider the density of the Sun. The volume of a sphere is $\frac{4}{3} \pi R^3$, where R is its radius. The density is simply the mass, M, divided by the volume. Therefore, the density of the Sun is $M/(\frac{4}{3} \pi R^3)$, or $3(4\pi)^{-1} M R^{-3}$. The mass of the Sun is 2×10^{33} gm; its radius is 7×10^{10} cm. If you substitute these values for M and R in the above equation and find that the density of the Sun is about 1.4 gm cm^{-3}, you will have no difficulty with any of the mathematics in this book. (Since the density of water is about 1 gm cm^{-3}, we have derived the somewhat surprising result that the Sun is only slightly more dense than water.) △

A NOTE ON MATHEMATICAL AND PHYSICAL UNITS

Table of contents

III: INTELLIGENT LIFE IN THE UNIVERSE

The color slides appearing between pages 224 and 226 in the hard cover edition do not appear in this edition.

A star cloud in the region of the galactic center. There are approximately a million stars in this photograph. According to the estimates of Chapter 29, a planet of one of these stars holds a technical civilization vastly in advance of our own. (Courtesy of Mount Wilson and Palomar Observatories.)

There is one
race of men, one race of gods; both have breath
of life from a single mother. But sundered power
holds us divided, so that the one is nothing, while for the
other the brazen sky is established
their sure citadel forever. Yet we have some likeness in great
intelligence, or strength, to the immortals,
though we know not what the day will bring, what course
after nightfall
destiny has written that we must run to the end.

Pindar, *Sixth Nemean Ode*

1

Perspectives

Numberless are the world's wonders, but none
More wonderful than man; the stormgrey sea
Yields to his prows, the huge crests bear him high . . .
The lion on the hill, the wild horse windy-maned,
Resign to him; and his blunt yoke has broken
The sultry shoulders of the mountain bull.
Words also, and thought as rapid as air,
He fashions to his good use . . .

Sophocles, *Antigone*

My surprise reached a climax, however, when I found that [Sherlock Holmes] was ignorant of the Copernican Theory, and of the composition of the Solar System. That any civilized human being in the nineteenth century should not be aware that the Earth travelled round the sun appeared to me to be such an extraordinary fact that I could hardly realize it.

"You appear to be astonished," he said, smiling at my expression of surprise. "Now that I do know it, I shall do my best to forget it . . ."

"But the Solar System!" I protested.

"What the deuce is it to me?" he interrupted impatiently: "you say that we go round the sun. If we went round the moon it would not make a pennyworth of difference to me . . ."

Sir Arthur Conan Doyle, *A Study in Scarlet*

Since the dawn of history, man has speculated about the possibility that intelligent life may exist on other worlds beyond the Earth. This idea probably originated from the often unsuccessful attempts of primitive religions to give meaning to those aspects of the environment which had no simple explanations. In the ancient Vedda culture of Ceylon, the belief in the migration of the soul after death was linked with the concept of a plurality of habitable worlds. The dead souls were believed to migrate to the Sun, the Moon, and the stars before attaining the state of Nirvana.

As astronomy developed, the concept of the existence of life on other worlds began to acquire some scientific bases. Most of the early Greek philosophers, both the materialists and the idealists, thought that our Earth was not the sole dwelling place of intelligent life. Considering the limitations of science at that time, these early philosophers displayed great originality and ingenuity. Thales of Miletus, the founder of the Ionian school of philosophy, taught that the stars and the Earth were made of the same material. Anaximander asserted that worlds are created and destroyed. Anaxagoras, one of the first proponents of the heliocentric theory, believed the moon to be inhabited. He also maintained that invisible "seeds of life," from which all living things originated, were dispersed throughout the universe.

In later eras, similar concepts of "panspermia" (ubiquitous life) were propounded by various scientists and philosophers. This idea was incorporated into Christianity soon after its inception.

The Epicurean school of materialist philosophy taught that many habitable worlds, similar to our Earth, existed in space. The Epicurean, Metrodoros, maintained: "To consider the Earth the only populated world in infinite space is as absurd as to assert that in an entire field sown with millet only one grain will grow." It is of interest that the proponents of this doctrine considered that not only the planets, but also other heavenly bodies in the vast reaches of space, were inhabited.

The Roman philosopher, Titus Lucretius Carus, was an ardent exponent of the concept of the plurality of worlds. In his famous poem, *On the Nature of Things,* he wrote: "Nature is not unique to the visible world; we must have faith that in other regions of space there exist other earths, inhabited by other peoples and other animals." Curiously enough, Lucretius did not understand the true nature of the stars, but conceived of them as luminous terrestrial vapors; therefore, his inhabited worlds were located on the periphery of the visible universe.

For fifteen hundred years after the birth of Jesus of Nazareth, Christian cosmology, influenced by the theories of Ptolemy, taught that the Earth was the

3

center of the universe. The concept of life on other worlds seemed to be incompatible with this philosophy. The extrication of cosmology from the Ptolemaic system began when the gifted Polish astronomer, Nicolaus Copernicus, placed man in his proper position in the solar system, downgrading the status of Earth to that of one planet among the many revolving about the Sun.

▽ Copernicus' achievement lay in his precise explanation, with a modest investment of hypothesis, of the motions of the planets. The Ptolemaic hypothesis that the Sun, Moon, and planets, embedded in crystal spheres, circled the Earth, encountered more and more difficulty with observations of the changing planetary, lunar, and solar motions as the centuries passed. A set of special motions, called epicycles, was a characteristic feature of Ptolemaic hypothesis. At the time of its

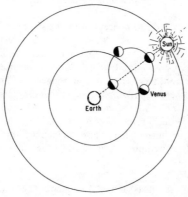

FIGURE 1–1. *Schematic illustration of the relative positions of the Earth, the Sun, and Venus in the Ptolemaic cosmology. To explain the motions of Venus, it was necessary to imagine the planet revolving about a point on a straight line between the Earth and the Sun. Note that the center of the bright side of Venus (towards the Sun) can never be seen by an observer on the Earth.*

invention, the heliocentric hypothesis of Copernicus merely explained the motions in a simpler way; at a later time, with Galileo's discovery that the planet Venus exhibits phases like those of the moon, the Copernican hypothesis was, in its gross features, demonstrated correct, and the Ptolemaic views overthrown. If any modern refutation of the Ptolemaic cosmology is needed, it is provided by space vehicles. The flights of Luna III, Mariner II, and Mariner IV were not accompanied by the tinkle of broken crystal spheres.

▽ The distinction between the Ptolemaic and the Copernican cosmologies is an interesting example of model-building, or hypothesis construction in science. Both the Ptolemaic and the Copernican views explained the motions of the planets. The heliocentric view of Copernicus was a simpler hypothesis. This in itself is not a demonstration of its validity. Nature may, after all, be complex. But if each view explains the planetary motions equally well, we certainly cannot be criticized if we think in terms of the simpler model. The Ptolemaic and Copernican pictures differed in another respect, however. According to Ptolemy, the Sun circled about the Earth, and inside the sphere of the Sun lay the sphere of Venus and Mercury. With such a geometry, it would be impossible for us ever to see the entire bright side of Venus [see Fig. 1–1]. According to Copernicus, however, both Venus and the Earth circled the Sun. Since Venus was sometimes beyond the Earth and the Sun, it would be possible for us to see its bright side [see Fig. 1–2]. Thus, when Galileo turned his telescope to Venus, and saw that its disk underwent phases from a "full Venus," corresponding to our full moon, to a "new Venus" (the dark side of Venus), corresponding to our new moon, it was clear that the Copernican hypothesis was vindicated. It does not follow that the Copernican view is completely valid in every respect; it is merely a model which conforms, with our desired degree of precision, to all the observations.

▽ In later years, Johannes Kepler showed that the paths of the planets about the sun were not circles, but ellipses. A prediction of the observed planetary motions on the basis of a law of gravitational interaction tested for the Moon was the

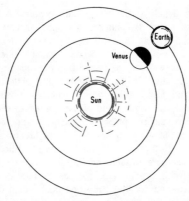

FIGURE 1–2. *Schematic illustration of the relative positions of the Earth, the Sun, and Venus in the Copernican cosmology. Note that the center of the bright side of Venus (towards the Sun) can sometimes be seen by an observer on the Earth.*

crowning achievement of Sir Isaac Newton, completing the goal of explaining in great detail the motions of the Sun, Moon, and planets from simple and largely testable starting points. △

The first telescopic observations by Galileo opened a new era in astronomy and dealt a mighty blow to the ideas of many of his contemporaries. It became evident that the planets were similar to the Earth in many respects. Galileo wrote in his *Sidereus Nuncius:*

I have been led to the opinion and conviction that the surface of the Moon is not smooth, uniform, and precisely spherical as a great number of philosophers believe it (and the other heavenly bodies) to be, but is uneven, rough, and full of cavities and prominences, being not unlike the face of the Earth, relieved by chains of mountains and deep valleys.

This evoked the following questions: If mountains and valleys exist on the Moon, then might not cities inhabited by intelligent beings also exist there? And is our Sun the only star accompanied by planets?

These bold ideas were advanced by the Italian philosopher, Giordano Bruno, who wrote: "Innumerable suns exist; innumerable earths revolve about these suns in a manner similar to the way the seven planets revolve around our sun. Living beings inhabit these worlds." The Roman Catholic clergy of his time denounced Bruno for his radical views. He was tried by a tribunal of the Inquisition and burned at the stake in Rome on February 17, 1600. Until the end of the seventeenth century, the Church violently opposed the new heliocentric theory. But in time, the Church adapted its philosophy to the new scientific concepts. Many present-day theologians accept the premise that intelligent beings may exist on other planets and do not find this view inconsistent with the fundamental tenets of their religions.

During the second half of the seventeenth century and into the eighteenth century, a number of scientists, philosophers, and writers (notably, Cyrano de Bergerac, Christianus Huygens, Bernard de Fontenelle, and Voltaire) published works dealing with life on other planets. Some of these publications were eloquent; some, especially those of Voltaire, contained profound ideas; but at the same time they were purely speculative. Brilliant scientists and philosophers such as Kant, Laplace, Herschel, and Lomonosov were advocates of the hypothesis of the plurality of habitable worlds. By the end of the eighteenth century, this hypothesis had gained almost universal acceptance by scientists and intellectuals. However, some were cautious about adopting the view that life existed on *every* planet. William Whewell, an English philosopher, in a book published in 1853, stated that perhaps not all planets were suitable habitats for life. He conjectured that the larger planets of the solar system were composed of "water, gases, and vapor" which would make them unfit for life. "In proportion to their distance from the sun, the inner planets would have large amounts of hot water on their surfaces." Whewell also argued against life existing on the Moon, and his view gradually gained acceptance.

Belief in the existence of extraterrestrial life continued to spread during the eighteenth and early nineteenth centuries. William Herschel, an eminent English astronomer, believed the sun to be inhabited. He thought that sun spots [Fig. 1–3] were apertures in a brilliant shell around the sun enabling us to see into its interior. Hypothetical solar beings inhabited this interior and could admire the stars through the openings in their roof. Even Sir Isaac Newton believed that the sun was inhabited.

In the latter half of the nineteenth century, a book written by Camille

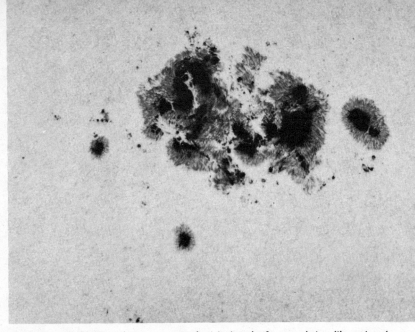

FIGURE 1–3. *Close-up of a sun-spot complex. Against the fine granulation, like grains of rice, of the visible disk of the Sun appear such dark sun-spots. They are much cooler than their surroundings, and are the sites of intense magnetic fields. Some early astronomers thought that sun-spots were windows to a cooler, more habitable region beneath the fiery exterior of the Sun. (Courtesy of Mt. Wilson and Palomar Observatories.)*

Flammarion, *On the Plurality of Habitable Worlds,* attained great popularity in France, and (through extensive translation) in many other countries. In this, as well as other publications, Flammarion contended that the planets were created purposefully for the formation of life. During a 20-year period, he published some 30 works, written in a florid style, which made a deep impression upon his contemporaries. Flammarion appealed more to the emotions of the reader than to his logic, but the appeal was often successful. Even today, reading his works is an evocative experience.

During the late nineteenth and early twentieth centuries various modifications of the panspermia hypothesis received wide circulation. According to this hypothesis, life in the universe exists eternally; living organisms never arise from nonliving matter, but are transmitted from one planet to another. At the turn of the century, the Swedish chemist, Svante Arrhenius, conjectured that microorganisms—spores or bacteria, probably adhering to small specks of dust—are propelled by the pressure of star light from one planet to another. If, by chance, they should land on some planet where conditions for life are favorable, these spores were thought to germinate and initiate the local evolution of life.

Although such transmission of life from planet to planet within a single planetary system cannot be completely discounted, the propagation of panspermia from one planetary system to another is today considered highly unlikely (see Chapter 15). The assumption that life is eternal seems inconsistent with current evidence on the evolution of stars and galaxies. This evidence, based on numerous observations, implies that the Galaxy at one time consisted purely of hydrogen or hydrogen and helium. Only as the Galaxy evolved were the heavier elements, necessary for the origin of life, formed (see Chapter 8). Finally, some calculations of the "red shift" of light from distant galaxies apparently indicate that 10 to 20 billion years ago the conditions in the universe were such that the existence of life would have been highly improbable (see Chapter 10). These observations seem to imply that life originates *de novo* in separate regions of the universe at such stages of the evolution of matter when conditions become favorable. The panspermia hypothesis therefore seems untenable as a fundamental concept.

Konstantin E. Tsiolkovskii, the Russian founder of astronautics, was an ardent believer in the plurality of worlds. He wrote,

> Is it possible that Europe is inhabited and other parts of the world are not? Is it possible for one island to be inhabited and other islands to be uninhabited? . . .

> All the phases of the development of life may be found on the various planets . . . Did man exist several thousand years ago and will he be extinct in several million years? . . . This entire process may be found on other planets . . .

While the first quotation seems to echo the view of the ancient philosophers, the second contains a new and important idea. Previous writers had depicted the civilizations on other planets as being socially and technologically similar to those of Earth. Tsiolkovskii, on the other hand, thought that extraterrestrial civilizations might exist at various developmental levels. We should note, however, that his point of view could not then (and cannot even now) be confirmed by direct evidence.

The development of the hypothesis of the plurality of worlds has often been linked to cosmogonic hypotheses—hypotheses concerning the creation or origin of the universe. The hypothesis of the English astronomer Sir James Jeans, which prevailed during the first third of the twentieth century, assumed that the planetary system of our sun was formed as a result of a rare cosmic cataclysm (perhaps the glancing collision of two stars). Life in the universe was an infrequent phenomenon; in our Galaxy (consisting of about 150 billion stars), it was considered highly improbable that more than one other star had a planetary system resembling ours. The failure of Jeans' hypothesis to explain the masses, motions, and composition of the planets, and the rapid development of astrophysics, has led to the present conclusions that there are a vast number of planetary systems within our Galaxy;

our solar system is the rule, not the exception, in a universe of stars. However, this theory, too, has not as yet been conclusively demonstrated [see Chapters 11–13].

Concepts about stellar and planetary cosmogony have had a considerable influence on the study of the origin of life. The age of a star and the time interval during which its luminosity is fairly constant (a condition necessary for the support of life on any accompanying planets) can now be determined. Stellar cosmogony also enables us to predict the future of our sun and hence the fate of life on Earth. Recent achievements in astrophysics have permitted a new scientific approach to the problem of the plurality of habitable worlds.

Today, the question is being approached from an entirely different direction—through molecular biology. It is now apparent that the origin of life can be explained, to a large extent, by studies in the field of chemistry. We are beginning to comprehend by what means and under what environmental circumstances those specific complex organic reactions leading to the origin of life can proceed. In recent years, chemists have made great strides in this direction. The outstanding advances in genetics and the clarification of the significance of deoxyribonucleic acid (DNA) and ribonucleic acid (RNA) have permitted a new understanding of the basis of life, and its beginnings. Now for the first time, problems of the origin of life have been subject to laboratory experimentation.

The concept of the plurality of habitable worlds entered a new phase with the first artificial Earth satellite hurled into orbit by the U.S.S.R. on October 4, 1957. The triumphal orbital flights of the Soviet cosmonauts Y. A. Gagarin, G. Titov, A. G. Nikolaev, V F. Byokovsky, P. R. Popovich, and V. Tereshkova, and the American astronauts, John Glenn, M. Scott Carpenter, L. Gordon Cooper, Walter Schirra, and their successors, were in one sense the culmination, and in another sense the bare beginnings, of a series of splendid successes in space technology. Today, many people, both scholars and laymen, are suddenly aware that they inhabit a small planet surrounded by boundless space. Astronomy is now taught in the schools, and students have a vague idea of the relative positions of the Earth and the other heavenly bodies. Some people may still be drawn to a kind of practical geocentrism; but the revolution in our awareness of our surroundings should not be underestimated. It *is* a revolution, one which marks the beginning of a new era in the history of mankind—an era of direct investigation and conquest of the cosmos.

The problem of life on other planets is no longer abstract. It has acquired practical meaning. Experimental methods are being designed for the direct investigation of our solar system. Special devices for the detection of extraterrestrial life will be landed on the surfaces of the planets and may provide a definitive answer to this age-old question. Astronauts will land on the Moon, Mars, and perhaps even on our mysterious and inhospitable neighbor, Venus. Then, at last, man will be able to seek and study extraterrestrial life by conventional biological methods.

There is enormous public interest in the possibility of extraterrestrial life. The primary purpose of this book is to acquaint the reader interested in life in the universe with our *current* state of knowledge. The word "current" is emphasized, because rapid progress is being made in the study of this problem. Other works devoted to this subject deal mainly with the question of life on other planets in our solar system. This book, however, includes, in addition to a study of our own solar system, a discussion of the possibility of life in other planetary systems, and of the problems of establishing contact with civilizations separated from us by interstellar distances.

The book is divided into three parts: Part I contains astronomical information necessary for an understanding of contemporary theories on the evolution of galaxies, stars, and planetary systems. Part II deals with the conditions necessary for the origin of life on a planet. We survey there the question of whether the conditions required for life exist on Mars, Venus, and other planets of the solar system and what direct evidence exists for life beyond the Earth. The contemporary variants of the panspermia hypothesis are also critically assessed. Part III contains an analysis of the possibility of intelligent life in other parts of the universe. Special attention is devoted to the problem of establishing contact with civilizations which may exist on the planets of distant stars.

The first two parts deal primarily with concrete results. In the third section, we are concerned with essentially speculative arguments; we have not as yet established contact with interstellar civilizations, nor do we know if we ever shall. It does not follow, however, that investigations of extraterrestrial intelligence are scientifically superfluous, or that they should be relegated to the realm of fantasy and science fiction. We have attempted to analyze rigorously the latest achievements of science and technology which may, in the future, give us an answer to this problem. The last section also illustrates the strength of man's intellect at its present level of development. Man, through his own activity, has already given real significance to and has in certain respects already changed the cosmos. What can we not expect in a few centuries?

2

Extraterrestrial life as a psychological projective test

"The Ethiopians make their gods black and snub-nosed; the Thracians say theirs have blue eyes and red hair. . . . Yes, and if oxen and horses or lions had hands, and could paint with their hands, and produce works of art as men do, horses would paint the forms of the gods like horses, and oxen like oxen, and make their bodies in the image of their several kinds."

Xenophanes

"If God did not exist, man would be obliged to invent him."

Voltaire

". . . are you so stupid as to think that just because we're alone here, there's nobody else in the room? Do you consider us so boring or so repulsive that of all the millions of beings, imaginary or otherwise, who are prowling around in space looking for a little company, there is not one who might possibly enjoy spending a moment with us? On the contrary, my dear—my house is full of guests . . ."

Jean Giraudoux, *The Madwoman of Chaillot*

▽ The possibility of life beyond the Earth evokes today strong and partisan emotions. There are some who want very much to believe that extraterrestrial life—particularly the intelligent variety—is common throughout the universe; and there are those who are committed to the view that extraterrestrial life is impossible, or so rare as to have neither practical nor philosophical interest. It seems to me appropriate that in this book more than passing attention be paid to such psychological predispositions.

One spring some years ago, the Department of Astronomy received a telephone call from the local District Attorney's office. There was in progress the criminal trial of a gentleman whom I shall call Helmut Winckler, a Nebraskan who claimed to have had personal contacts with inhabitants of the planet Saturn. The state desired an expert witness. With wry comments and professional asides, the message was conveyed to me. I agreed to serve as a surprise witness for the prosecution and was presented with a sheaf of publications written by or about the defendant, concerning his extraordinary adventures.

The following is my recollection of the statements made in these publications and subsequently verified by the defendant under oath:

Winckler was a salesman of agricultural implements in Nebraska; he was of German ancestry, but born in the United States. He had few intellectual pretensions, but had at least a grammar school education. Winckler was a trifle chubby, of florid complexion and robust countenance, and wore steel-rimmed glasses. He looked considerably younger than his sixty-odd years, was soft-spoken and polite on the witness stand. His accent was that of the rural midwest.

Winckler testified that one day while motoring along a back road in Nebraska, he had the remarkable good fortune to overtake a parked flying saucer. Naturally he stopped, as anyone would. To his surprise, he observed emerging from the saucer, several men and women of entirely human appearance, dressed in flowing robes and speaking mellifluously. The language which they were speaking so mellifluously was Hochdeutsch. Coincidentally, Winckler understood Hochdeutsch. The saucerians were delighted. Winckler was delighted.

The saucerians explained that they were from the planet Saturn, and had, for reasons of their own, selected Winckler as an "intermediary." They were to impart to him information of great value for the inhabitants of the planet Earth. It seems that the international political situation on Earth had reached serious proportions, a fact which concerned the Saturnians, an old, wise, and sympathetic race. They were here to save us from ourselves. Winckler never revealed why *he* had been selected. It appears that it was not because he knew Hochdeutsch. The Saturnians speak all human tongues.

13

Winckler accompanied the Saturnians into their saucer. His publications contain diagrams of the interior of the saucers, replete with esoteric and unintelligible descriptions of their method of propulsion. The interiors resemble those of the 1958 Buick.

The group then departed for the Arctic Circle, taking Winckler with them. On a subsequent saucer foray which Winckler made with the Saturnians, he was taken beneath the Bering Straits to inspect the Soviet Union's suboceanic missile emplacements. You may not have heard of them, but according to Winckler the government of the United States knows all about them.

In another of Winckler's flights, this time over the North Pole, the Saturnians were heard to remark that only a few months ago the axis of the Earth was tilting a dangerous six degrees. Winckler paled, but the Saturnians assured him that they had repaired the misalignment in short order.

When the court recessed, I queried Winckler about this delinquent behavior of the Earth's axis of rotation. I explained that even a very much smaller tilt would have been discovered immediately by astronomers who, each night, point their telescopes by assuming that they know precisely where the celestial poles are. Winckler's response was that he could hardly be held responsible for statements made by inhabitants of the planet Saturn. He was merely relaying information. But he left the distinct impression that the Saturnians knew quite a bit more about the subject than do bystanders in courtrooms.

On another expedition, the Saturnians took Winckler to that Mecca of the occult, the Great Pyramid of Gizeh in Egypt. They mingled with a group of tourists being guided *through* the interior of the pyramid. (I have a vivid mental image of this procession: Egyptian guide, two middle-aged ladies from Dubuque, some assorted French and German tourists, six Saturnians in flowing robes, and, bringing up the rear, Helmut Winckler in levis.) At a certain intersection of pathways, the tourists went in one direction, and Winckler and the Saturnians in the other. They were confronted with a blank wall. Appropriate pressures were applied to appropriate bricks, and the wall slid open, revealing a chamber within. The party entered, and the stone door slid silently shut behind them. In the room were (1) a small, one-man flying saucer, quite dusty with age; (2) a large and equally ancient wooden cross perhaps ten feet high; and (3) a toroid of thorns about eight inches in diameter. The Saturnians offhandedly explained that one of their number had attempted a mission to Earth some two thousand years ago. He had met with somewhat qualified success.

In extracting these marvels from Winckler, the Assistant District Attorney first displayed shock, then disbelief, and finally, righteous indignation. He shook his head and peered upwards—awaiting the thunderbolt which doubtless would terminate the proceedings. The courtroom was hushed. The jury was awed. Winckler was cool. From the tone of his voice, he might have been describing a reaper sale in Lincoln.

One of the principal pastimes of the Saturnians, while cavorting about the Earth, was their remote geological survey. They possessed instruments capable of determining, from quite remarkable altitudes, the location and distribution of mineral-bearing ores. They discovered untapped veins of gold, pristine platinum-bearing rocks, and uranium ores unknown to man. The locations of these finds were carefully kept from Winckler. One day, however, the Saturnians pointed out to Winckler the existence of a quartz mine—while flying over southern California. You may think that quartz is rather uninteresting, compared with gold, platinum, and uranium. But this was a rather special kind of quartz. It cured cancer.

Soon after landing, Winckler was selling quartz stock. I have the distinct impression that he sold half-interests in the mine—several dozen half-interests. Adding to his subsequent embarrassment was the fact that the mine was already owned by another gentleman and was actively producing quartz. It also transpired that by a perfectly remarkable coincidence, Winckler had visited this very mine several years earlier.

But none of these activities directly precipitated Winckler's indictment. His difficulties are traceable to his promotion of the healing properties of quartz among elderly and wealthy widows. Many ladies had lent him sizable sums to advance his venture. In the last months before his arrest, it was his practice to speak before large gatherings of flying saucer enthusiasts—some but by no means all of whom were also elderly, wealthy widows. They paid his transportation and living expenses, invited him to their homes, and accorded him the customary respect due prophets of new religions. The complaint leading to Winckler's arrest arose from a combination of money borrowed and not repaid, and affection promised and not delivered.

To give you the flavor of the courtroom proceedings, here is an approximation of the dialogue which preceded my appearance on the stand. After establishing that Winckler was married, back in Nebraska, the Assistant District Attorney pursued the following line of inquiry:

ASSISTANT DISTRICT ATTORNEY: Now, Mr. Winckler, you have several times told this court that it was not your custom to use words or gestures of affection in your dealings with Mrs. Brewster.

WINCKLER: Yeah, except when I would call her Lovey and Dear, like I do in my work.

ASSISTANT DISTRICT ATTORNEY: But you never expressed to Mrs. Brewster any deep feelings of love and affection?

WINCKLER: Yeah, that's right.

ASSISTANT DISTRICT ATTORNEY (hands clasped behind his back, eyes fixed on a point on the ceiling, and slowly pacing): Now, Mr. Winckler, did you, for example, ever convey to Mrs. Brewster sentiments such as these . . . ?

At this point, the Assistant District Attorney recited from memory some twenty lines of verse, dactylic trimeter in rhymed couplets, expressing very tragic sentiments.

WINCKLER: I never said nothing like that in my life.

ASSISTANT DISTRICT ATTORNEY: Your Honor, I would like to submit in evidence People's Exhibit Number 14.

The Assistant District Attorney passed a piece of paper to the judge. The judge read it and handed it to the Court Clerk. The clerk wrote in a large book and returned the paper to the Assistant District Attorney.

ASSISTANT DISTRICT ATTORNEY: Now, Mr. Winckler, would you care to examine the signature on the bottom of this card?

WINCKLER (polishing glasses, scrutinizing the paper): It *looks* like my signature.

ASSISTANT DISTRICT ATTORNEY: Mr. Winckler, do you now recall having sent this greeting card to Mrs. Brewster?

WINCKLER: Yeah, I guess so. But, see, it was this way. A guy come to my door a couple years ago. He was a disabled veteran and he was selling greeting cards. He sold me 200 cards, all kinds. I had these cards in a big box, and when it was her birthday, I just took one out and sent it. I didn't even read it.

ASSISTANT DISTRICT ATTORNEY: It's a wonder you didn't pick out a funeral condolence by mistake.

On the afternoon of the same day, I was called to the witness stand. I had been told that as a surprise witness, giving testimony in a specialized field, I would be subjected to no serious cross-examination. In this, the prosecution was mistaken.

The Assistant District Attorney inquired of my name and affiliation and established my academic credentials. He then invited me to discuss the likelihood of human beings inhabiting the planet Saturn.

I described the operation of the spectroscope and explained how it gives information on the chemical composition of distant objects. Astronomical spectroscopy of Saturn, I noted, shows its atmosphere to contain no oxygen, and large amounts of methane and ammonia, compounds which are poisonous to human beings.

I then outlined the way in which the temperatures of planets are measured with a thermocouple at the focus of a large telescope. The temperatures of those parts of Saturn which are accessible to our telescopes are several hundred degrees below zero Fahrenheit. Finally, I described how the surface gravity of a planet could be determined from its mass and radius, and mentioned that since the surface gravity on Saturn is some 17 percent greater than on Earth, any beings which evolved there would probably be squatter than we.

I summarized my testimony by saying that while these observations by no means exclude the possibility of some sort of life on Saturn, they provide quite convincing evidence that there are no human beings there. Indeed, I concluded, it would be most remarkable if four and a half billion years of independent biological evolution on the two planets had produced identical end results, even if their environments were not so dissimilar.

The defense attorney was then asked if he wished to cross-examine. Indicating that he might have a question or two, he approached the witness stand slowly, his voice gradually increasing in volume:

"Dr. Sagan, I don't mean to be disrespectful, but isn't it a fact that four or five hundred years ago, university scientists like yourself were maintaining that the Earth was . . . *flat?*"

The Assistant District Attorney leaped to his feet.

"Your Honor, I object!"

The judge inquired on what grounds he objected. Surely, on grounds of irrelevance, I thought. But no.

"Hearsay evidence."

The objection was sustained, and the defense attorney continued. The riposte and parry had not been lost on the judge, who was smiling faintly. But the jury maintained its glazed and somewhat haggard expression.

The defense attorney was puzzled by one part of my testimony. He understood, he thought, how astronomical spectroscopy worked, and how it was checked by laboratory comparison with the gas in question—for example, ammonia. But hadn't I been keeping an assumption from the jury? Weren't we tacitly assuming that the same physical laws apply on Saturn as on Earth?

Suddenly, in a proceeding for fraud in a criminal court, we had plunged into one of the basic questions of the philosophy of science. I explained that there are large numbers of spectral lines which are indicative of the presence of a compound, and that many of them exist both on Saturn and in the laboratory. The possibility of such a random coincidence would seem to be very small. I went on to describe how Newton had demonstrated that the same physical laws accounting for the gravitational attraction of objects on the Earth are responsible for the motion of the Moon. Glancing over to the jury, however, I had the distinct impression that the seed of doubt had been planted. I could imagine them thinking: After all, maybe the physical laws *are* different on Saturn. How does anyone know?

The defense then inquired about the temperature determination. What level in the atmosphere of Saturn did the temperatures which I quoted refer to? High in the atmosphere. How high? Well, possibly 10,000 miles above the surface —if any. Might the temperatures down at the surface—if any—be considerably warmer? Indeed they could, I replied; in fact, I had made a similar suggestion concerning the planet Jupiter. What temperature for the planet Earth would be derived by an extraterrestrial observer if he could only look at the top of our clouds? About $-60°$ or $-70°$ Fahrenheit. But we all know that that isn't the average temperature on the surface of the Earth, don't we? He had scored.

And now, doesn't the spectroscopic determination of composition also refer only to the very high atmosphere? And mightn't the chemical composition of the lower atmosphere near the surface be considerably different? In particular, mightn't it contain molecular oxygen, so that beings there could breathe as we do?

I replied in terms of chemical equilibrium. There is such an overabundance of hydrogen in the upper atmosphere of Saturn, I said, that it would instantly react with any of the oxygen around. Some estimate can be made of the abundance of hydrogen in the lower atmosphere; the body of Saturn is believed to be at least in part metallic hydrogen. I thought it highly unlikely that free molecular oxygen existed at the surface of Saturn. The defense attorney replied, "But these are indirect arguments, aren't they? You don't really *know* there's no oxygen on Saturn." I could only agree that the evidence, while convincing, was indirect. But astronomy is based on indirect evidence.

"Now, Dr. Sagan," he continued, "I have heard it said that fossil plants have been found in the arctic regions of the Earth, and that these fossil plants were of a tropical variety. Is this true? How could there be tropical plants at the pole?" I felt that I had completely lost the direction of the discussion. I explained the evidence for polar wandering garnered from studies of paleomagnetism. The present arctic regions of the Earth were once sub-tropical because the poles were once at a different geographical location.

"Now what I really want to know, Dr. Sagan, is this: At the time when the present poles of the Earth were in the tropics, were the present tropics at the poles? Or was it tropical all over?"

At this point the Assistant District Attorney somewhat resignedly got to his feet. "Your Honor, I must confess that I fail to see the relevance of this line of inquiry."

"I find that I must agree with the Assistant District Attorney," said the judge. "Perhaps the counsel for the defense could enlighten us."

"Well, Your Honor, it's not really relevant, but it's such an interesting topic that I thought, while we had Dr. Sagan on the stand, it might be fun to pursue it. I have no further questions."

I stepped down from the stand and resumed my seat in the audience. One local newspaper, the following day, printed in full the sequence of rhymed couplets that Winckler had sent to the unfortunate Mrs. Brewster, and then quoted me as saying that the temperatures on Saturn were several hundred degrees below zero Fahrenheit, and that this was too cold for love on any world.

The remaining topic of substantial interest—which was arranged by considerable side-of-mouth conversation between representatives of the prosecution and defense—was a motion picture film which Winckler had produced. It was shown in court, to the great delight of the jurors. It showed the landing of the Saturnians and their discussions and adventures with Winckler. Unfortunately, Winckler was unable to procure any Saturnians for the movie, and so had hired actors who were indistinguishable from Saturnians. In addition, Winckler had promised various leading roles in the movie to some of his lady friends, but at least in the case of Mrs. Brewster, this promise of stardom did not materialize.

Winckler was subsequently found guilty of fraud and sentenced to prison, despite the admirable efforts of his attorney. In my discussions with Winckler during recesses, I was unable to decide to what extent his escapades with the Saturnians were a conscious fraud, and to what extent he genuinely believed his account. But it was clear that many others found Winckler's adventures in ringing consonance with what they believed—or would like to believe.

Winckler's experience underlines the existence of an unfulfilled need in contemporary society. Almost any other of the many accounts of alleged contacts of human beings with the crews of flying saucers—accounts which regale the flying saucer societies—follow the same pattern and stress the same points. The extraterrestrials are human, with few even minor physical differences from local cosmetic standards. (I know of no case of Negro saucerians, or Oriental saucerians, reported in the United States; but there are very few flying saucer contact reports made in this country by Negroes or by Orientals.) The saucerians are wise and gentle and loving; concerned for our safety during this epoch of continuing international tensions, yet for some reason unwilling to intervene in force. They have long ago solved international disputes on their home planets. They have great gifts in the humanities—this is, of course, still an appropriate subject for them—but also immense technical abilities. In short, the saucerians are all-powerful, all-knowing, and concerned with the plight of mankind as a parent would be for his children. Yet they do not direct the course of the major events of the day, presumably on the grounds that mankind must work out its own destiny. I cannot help but conclude that the flying saucer societies represent a thinly disguised religion, and that the saucerians are the deities of the cult.

As science has progressed during the last few centuries, areas which were originally the exclusive province of religion have been increasingly preempted by science. We no longer hold that the Earth is stationary, or that it is at the center of the universe; nor that the world was made even approximately on October 23, 4004 B.C.; nor that it was made in seven days; nor that different species had separate creations; nor that the origin of the solar system and the origin of life are forever beyond the ken of man. Rather, the laboratory synthesis of life from materials which were abundant in the early environment of the Earth seems no more than a decade off. One result of these encroachments by science has been that there seems less and less for God to do. If he creates some hydrogen at the beginning of the universe, and establishes the physical laws, he can then retire. He is a *roi fainéant*. If God did not directly make life or man, it is hard to believe that he will intervene in our everyday lives, or answer our supplications.

Yet the temptation to believe in an omnipotent, omniscient, and loving God is especially great today. The pace of world events is out of the hands of the ordinary individual. We have no assurance that tomorrow will not find the world a radioactive pyre. Our destiny appears to be at the mercy of forces we little understand and only perilously control. If only there existed a god who was concerned with our plight, who would give some assurance of our survival; but who was explicable within the framework of contemporary science. . . . The saucer myths represent a neat compromise between the need to believe in a traditional paternal God and the contemporary pressures to accept the pronouncements of science.

While the saucerian contact cult is viable and widespread—at least, in the United States—it represents only a small fraction of the total number of saucer enthusiasts. There are large numbers of people who have, in all good conscience, observed unknown objects in the skies which they have called "unidentified flying objects"—UFO's—and which they believe to be of intelligent extraterrestrial origin. The diversity of these reports is as striking as the observations themselves.

UFO's have been described variously as rapidly moving or hovering; disk-shaped, cigar-shaped, or ball-shaped; moving silently or noisily; with fiery exhaust, with no exhaust whatever; accompanied by flashing lights, or uniformly glowing with a silvery cast. It is immediately clear that all UFO's do not share a common origin. Indeed, the use of a generic term such as "UFO's" or "flying saucers" has served to confuse the issue by implying a common origin.

As detailed by the American astronomer Donald H. Menzel of Harvard College Observatory, confirmed identifications of UFO's have been made with the following: unconventional aircraft; aircraft under uncommon weather conditions; aircraft with unusual external light patterns; meteorological and other high-altitude balloons; artificial earth satellites; flocks of birds; reflections of searchlights or headlights off clouds; reflection of sunlight from shiny surfaces; luminescent organisms, including one case of a firefly lodged between two adjacent panes of glass in an airplane cockpit window; optical mirages and looming; lenticular cloud formations; ball lightning; sundogs; meteors, including the green fireballs; planets, especially Venus; bright stars; and the Aurora Borealis. Radar detection of un-identified flying objects has also occurred occasionally. Many of these sightings have been explained in terms of radar reflection off temperature inversion layers in the atmosphere, and other sources of radar "angels."

Considering the difficulty in tracing out the visual and radar sightings—the visual sightings are often made by individuals with little experience in observing the skies—it is remarkable that all but a few percent of the reported UFO's have been identified as naturally occurring, if sometimes unusual, phenomena. It is remarkable that the professional astronomers, who are familiar with the skies and regularly scan them with sophisticated instrumentation, have never, to the best of my knowl-edge, photographed anything like the classical UFO. For example, in the Harvard Meteor Project, performed in New Mexico during the period 1954–1958, exten-sive photographic observations were made by Super-Schmidt cameras with a 60° field of view. In all a surface area of 7000 km² was observed to 80 km altitude for a total period of some 3000 hours. Visual and photographic observations were good down to magnitude +4. (The magnitude scale is defined in footnote 2 of the follow-ing chapter; a magnitude of +4 is close to the faintest object visible with the naked eye.) These observations by professional astronomers were made in a locale and period characterized by extensive reports of unidentified flying objects. No unex-plained objects were detected, despite the fact that rapidly moving objects were being sought in a study of meteors. Similar negative results have been obtained by large numbers of astronomers, and help to explain the general skepticism of the astronomical community towards flying saucer reports. There is no way to exclude the very occasional presence of unidentified objects in our skies, but the run-of-the-mill flying saucer observations (made in the United States on the average of about once a day) are certainly common astronomical objects and atmospheric phe-nomena—and perhaps some not so common—which have been misinterpreted by the observer.

Repeated sightings of UFO's, and the persistence of the United States Air

Force and members of the responsible scientific community in explaining the sightings away have suggested to some that a conspiracy exists to conceal from the public the true nature of the UFO's. But precisely because people desire so intensely that unidentified flying objects be of benign, intelligent, and extraterrestrial origin, honesty requires that in evaluating the observations, we accept only the most rigorous logic and the most convincing evidence.

There is also the opposite danger. Public interest in flying saucers, contact reports, and extraterrestrial life in general has proved a frequent source of embarrassment to many scientists, whose statements tend to be distorted, exaggerated, and otherwise perturbed by the bright light of popular concern. There is then a tendency to reject out of hand the possibility of extraterrestrial intelligence as baseless, improbable, or unscientific. There are also covert Ptolemaicists who find the prospects of extraterrestrial intelligence threatening.

A typical example of this other projective extreme can be found in the circumstances attending the first release of scientific results from the United States spacecraft Mariner IV, which encountered Mars on Bastille Day, 1965. Among the early announcements was the finding that Mars has no detectable magnetic field. The conclusion drawn (by no means a secure one, incidentally) was that Mars lacked mountains and volcanoes and could be considered geologically dead. Some segments of the press then reported that by failing to measure the Martian magnetic field, scientists had proved Mars lifeless—truly a marvel of twentieth century thought. The confusion between these two senses of the word "dead" was never noted or retracted, to the best of my knowledge, by the press.

The magnetometer results then set the stage for the popular interpretation of the Mariner IV photographs. First, despite the fact that a similar experiment directed at the Earth would be incapable of detecting life on our planet (see Chapter 18), since no life could be *seen* on Mars, the news media deduced a lifeless planet. Second, since no sign of recent bodies of water could be found on Mars— as expected—it was concluded that there was no life on Mars. Finally, the existence of craters on the Martian surface implied to many that Mars is lifeless. The syllogism seemed to go, "There are craters on the Moon. There is no life on the Moon. There are craters on Mars. Thus, there is no life on Mars."

Newspapers, magazines, television, and press releases are still replete with descriptions of how the "widely held" view of a lush, vegetated and canal-crossed Mars has now been abandoned because of the decisive findings of Mariner IV, and replaced by a lifeless, cratered Moon-like world. Even the often reliable New York *Times* displayed an editorial entitled "The Dead Planet," listing the supposed new findings about life on Mars. As we shall see in Chapters 19 and 20, these scientific conclusions drawn by public relations officers and by the news media do justice neither to the painstaking efforts of ground-based astronomy, nor to the exciting and significant findings of Mariner IV. This spacecraft was not designed to search for life on Mars. As the experimenters were careful to point out, the mission neither demonstrated nor precluded the possibility of life on Mars.

Why then were the communications media so quick to deduce a lifeless Mars?

I believe a partial answer can be found in the responses made to the Mariner IV findings by political leaders, by Mr. Billy Graham, and by other American divines— often sure barometers of common attitudes. They were unmistakably *relieved*. Finding life beyond the Earth—particularly intelligent life, although this is highly unlikely on Mars—wrenches at our secret hope that Man is the pinnacle of creation, a contention which no other species on our planet can now challenge. Even simple forms of extraterrestrial life may have abilities and adaptations denied to us. The discovery of life on some other world will, among many things, be for us a humbling experience.

The question of extraterrestrial life—and even more so, the question of extra-terrestrial intelligence—is then many things to many men. In assessing evidence for extraterrestrial life, and in evaluating statistical estimates of the likelihood of extraterrestrial intelligence, we may be at the mercy of our prejudices. At the present time, there is no unambiguous evidence for even simple varieties of extraterrestrial life, although the situation may change in the coming years. There are unconscious factors operating, in the present arguments of both proponents and opponents of extraterrestrial life.

I think Shklovskii and I can be described as cautious optimists on this question. In many places in the present book, we have made speculations, but I hope that we have labelled our speculations as such, and given the reader enough information to evaluate the basis for our speculations. In Part III, where we extrapolate from contemporary terrestrial technology to future extraterrestrial technologies, perhaps we have not been cautious enough, but I rather suspect that the opposite is the case. It is chastening to read nineteenth-century prog-nostications of the events of the middle twentieth century. Even their most grandiose extrapolations have proved a pale echo of our realities. It strained Jules Verne's imagination to picture giant passenger balloons transporting people through the air over thousands of miles in a period of only a week. He could not imagine contemporary jet transports, which cover the same distance in hours.

Whether we have been too optimistic or not optimistic enough, only the future will tell. △

THE UNIVERSE

In a universe whose size is beyond human imagining, where our world floats like a dust mote in the void of night, men have grown inconceivably lonely. We scan the time scale and the mechanisms of life itself for portents and signs of the invisible. As the only thinking mammals on the planet—perhaps the only thinking animals in the entire sidereal universe—the burden of consciousness has grown heavy upon us. We watch the stars, but the signs are uncertain. We uncover the bones of the past and seek for our origins. There is a path there, but it appears to wander. The vagaries of the road may have a meaning, however; it is thus we torture ourselves.

Loren Eiseley, *The Immense Journey* (1946)

3

The size and structure of the universe

What a wonderful and amazing Scheme have we here of the magnificent Vastness of the Universe! So many Suns, so many Earths . . . !

Christianus Huygens, *New Conjectures Concerning the Planetary Worlds, Their Inhabitants and Productions* (c. 1670)

And with an awful, dreadful list
Towards other galaxies unknown
Ponderously turns the Milky Way . . .

Boris Pasternak

▽ The great seventeenth-century religious philosopher and mathematician, Blaise Pascal, expressed a fear of the great spaces between the stars, and if some men have become more daring since his time, others have not become less afraid. △

The scale of space and time which we customarily observe on Earth, and which is part of our daily lives, is insignificant when compared with cosmic space and time. When, for the first time, we become aware of the vastness of our universe, we are awed and humbled.

But if astronomers spent all their time speculating about the immensity of the cosmos and the prodigious intervals of time necessary for the evolution of the stars, their accomplishments would be few. The primary concerns of the astronomer when studying the cosmos are physical and mathematical interpretations of observations, predictions of future observations, and the development and refinement of his instruments for such interpretation and prediction. To help him in the conceptualization of his problem, the astronomer may, consciously or unconsciously, visualize a small model representing the cosmic system under investigation. Using this method, he can arrive at an understanding of the relative dimensions of the system and an understanding of the time intervals involved.

I have spent a great deal of time in the study of the solar corona and the Galaxy. ▽ The solar corona is an extended halo of glowing gas which surrounds the Sun and which can be seen during a solar eclipse. The Galaxy is a system of stars, called the Milky Way, in which our Sun resides. The Galaxy is surrounded by a halo of gas called the Galactic corona [Fig. 3–1]. The sizes of the solar and Galactic coronae are, of course, very different. △ I have always visualized each of them as irregular, approximately spherical bodies with somewhat the same dimensions—about 10 centimeters (4 inches) across. Why 10 centimeters? This figure is entirely arbitrary; it is convenient and easily visualized. I have sketched the outlines of the objects of my reflections in my notebook, attempting to preserve the apparent scales of the phenomena. I am, of course, quite aware that the dimensions of the Galactic corona are at least 100 billion times greater than those of the solar corona. However, I could ignore this fact, since the absolute size was not important for an understanding of the problem at hand. When the actual dimensions of an object are of special significance, I use formal mathematics.

Until very recently the dimensions of the Earth were thought to be immense. Four and a half centuries ago it took Ferdinand Magellan and his men almost three years to circumnavigate the globe. Less than a hundred years ago, Phileas Fogg, the courageous hero of Jules Verne's novel, using the latest scientific achievements of his day, traveled *Around the World in 80 Days*. In 1961, our planet's first space

27

travelers, Gagarin and Titov, flew around the globe in 89 *minutes* in the cosmic ships "Vostok." ▽ Thus, the apparent size of the Earth has shrunk as vehicles of increasingly greater speed have been constructed. At the same time, △ the thoughts of men have almost involuntarily turned to the vast reaches of space in which our tiny planet is nearly lost.

There are nine known planets in our solar system. The Earth is situated relatively close to the Sun, although both Mercury and Venus are closer. The mean distance between the Sun and its most distant planet, Pluto, is forty times greater than the distance between the Earth and the Sun. At the present time we do not know if there are any planets further from the Sun than Pluto. We can only speculate that, if such planets do exist, they are relatively small in size and so have escaped detection.

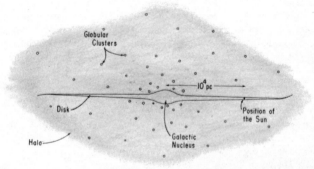

FIGURE 3–1. *Schematic illustration of our Galaxy. The Sun lies in a spiral arm in the disk, or Galactic plane, where the density of stars is relatively low compared with the nucleus. When we look above or below the plane of the Galaxy, we see only the stars in our local neighborhood, but when we look in along the disk, towards the Galactic nucleus, we see a broad, diffuse band of stars along the night sky, which we call the Milky Way. It is our Galaxy seen edge-on. Surrounding the Galaxy is a spherical cloud of hot gas called the halo, which is sparsely populated by stars, most of them in globular clusters.*

The diameter of the solar system is approximately 50 to 100 astronomical units, or 10 billion km.[1] This is an extremely large figure in our scale of distance, about a million times greater than the diameter of the Earth.

We can better visualize the relative sizes in our solar system by imagining a scale model: Let the Sun be represented by a billiard ball with a diameter of 7 cm. On this scale, Mercury, the planet closest to the Sun, would be at a distance of 280 cm, the Earth at a distance of 760 cm, Jupiter, the largest planet, approximately 40

[1] ▽An astronomical unit, abbreviated A.U., is the average distance from the Earth to the Sun, approximately 150 million km, or 93 million miles.

    A kilometer (km) is about 0.62 miles

    A meter (m) is 10^{-3} kilometers, or about 39 inches

    A centimeter (cm) $= 10^{-2}$ m $= 10^{-5}$ km, or about 0.4 inches

    A millimeter (mm) $= 0.1$ cm, or about 0.04 inches △

m, and Pluto, the most distant planet, would be nearly 300 m from the billiard ball. The diameter of the Earth would be slightly greater than 0.5 mm; the lunar diameter would be approximately 0.1 mm, and its orbit around the Earth would have a diameter of about 4 cm. The nearest star beyond the Sun, Proxima Centauri, would be at 2000 km, or about 1200 miles away—so far that the huge planetary distances shown on our scale would seem insignificant by comparison.

The kilometer, the centimeter, the mile, and all other units of measurement were adopted because of the practical requirements of man on Earth. They are obviously inadequate for gauging cosmic distances. The "light year" is used as a unit of measure for interstellar and intergalactic distances in science fiction—and sometimes in scientific literature. One light year is the distance traveled by light in one year, moving at a velocity of 300,000 km per second, ∇ or 186,000 miles per second. Since there are about 3×10^7 seconds in a year, a light year is about 2×10^5 miles per second $\times 3 \times 10^7$ seconds $= 6 \times 10^{12}$ miles, or six trillion miles. $\triangle$

The special unit of measure usually employed in scientific literature is the "parsec," defined as the distance from which the radius of the Earth's orbit subtends an angle of one second of arc. ∇ Apparent distances in the sky, as seen from Earth, are often expressed in angular measure. There are 360 degrees in a circle; each one is a degree of arc. Thus, a large imaginary circle, drawn above us in the sky and passing directly overhead, would encompass 180° from horizon to horizon. Each degree of arc contains 60 minutes of arc, and each minute of arc contains 60 seconds of arc. A second of arc is a very small unit of angular measure. $\triangle$ A one-kopeck coin would subtend an angle of one second of arc at a distance of 3 km. ∇ Or, for those readers with no kopecks handy, a second is the angle which a U.S. quarter dollar makes at a distance of 3¼ miles. $\triangle$ The full moon subtends an angle of half a degree. ∇ In order for the radius of the Earth's orbit—150,000,000 km—to subtend one second of arc, it must be at a great distance. That distance, 1 parsec, is 3.26 light years. $\triangle$

There are no known stars within one parsec of our solar system. Even Proxima Centauri, our nearest neighboring star, is 1.3 parsec (abbreviated "pc") away. In the scale used in our previous analogy to depict our solar system, we found the distance to the nearest star to be 2000 km. Our Sun and its planets are thoroughly isolated from the surrounding stellar systems.

The Sun is a modest member of an enormous collection of stars and dust which we call our "Galaxy" (from the Greek word *gala,* meaning milk). This mass of stars which, on a moonless night, resembles a broad swath of light crossing the sky, is called the Milky Way. It is estimated that there are more than 100 billion stars of various types and ages in the Milky Way. They are found, for the most part, within a gigantic disk with a diameter of approximately 100,000 light years, and with a thickness of some 1500 light years.

The Galaxy has an extremely complex structure. As a preliminary description, let us say that its shape is that of a flattened disk, or a large, rotating wheel. ∇ Figure 3–1 gives a schematic and idealized view of our Galaxy, as seen from a

FIGURE 3–2. *NGC 5364 in the constellation Virgo, a typical spiral galaxy seen face-on.* (*Courtesy of Mt. Wilson and Palomar Observatories.*)

million light years away. The thick, lens-shaped central region is called the *disk,* and contains the spiral arms which originate near the center and wind outward. They would be prominent if the Milky Way could be viewed from above or below, as in photographs of other galaxies [see Fig. 3–2]. The lens-shaped disk is surrounded by a roughly spherical halo, or galactic corona, which is composed most noticeably of hot gas. △

Stellar density in the Milky Way is not uniform. The brightest region, which has the densest aggregation of stars, is the Galactic nucleus, where, according to the latest data, there are approximately 2000 stars per cubic parsec. This is much greater than the average star density in the neighborhood of our own Sun. The stars also tend to form groups and clusters. The Pleiades is an example of a cluster visible to the naked eye [Fig. 3–3].

Certain types of stars are found in greater numbers in some parts of the Galaxy than in others. For example, giant, hot young stars occur mainly among the spiral arms near the Galactic plane. Older stars, of relatively small mass, appear more numerous in the Galactic center. The so-called globular clusters [Fig. 3–4] are found mostly in the center of the Galaxy, but out of the Galactic plane.

Our Sun is located well away from the center of the disk, in the Galactic suburbs. It lies about 30 light years from the Galactic plane, a distance which is

THE UNIVERSE

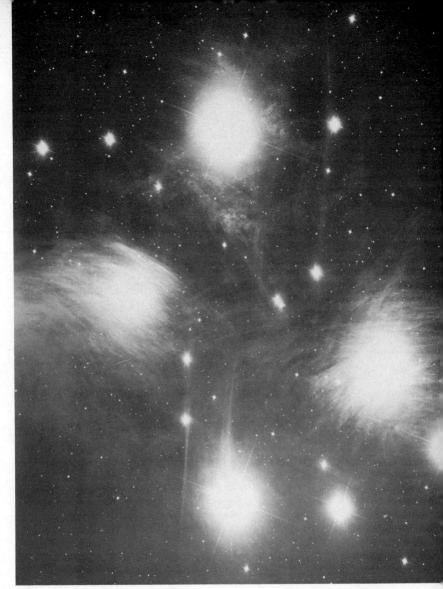

FIGURE 3–3. *The Pleiades, a nearby open, or "galactic" star cluster. The four luminescent spikes emanating from many of the bright stars in this picture are not intrinsic to the stars, but are due to diffraction effects in the reflecting telescope used to take this picture. (Courtesy of Mt. Wilson and Palomar Observatories.)*

FIGURE 3–4. *The globular star cluster M13 in the constellation Hercules. Some globular clusters are swarms of stars containing tens of thousands of individual members. Note that the density of stars in the center of M13 is so great that we are unable to resolve individual members. (Courtesy of Mt. Wilson and Palomar Observatories.)*

relatively small compared to the total thickness of the stellar disk. The distance from the Sun to the Galactic center is approximately 33,000 light years—10,000 pc.

The stars move in a very complicated way within the Galaxy. Primarily, they participate in the rotation of the Galaxy about its axis, which is perpendicular to the Galactic plane. This motion is different from the rotation of a solid body since different regions have different angular velocities. The Sun and the nearby stars in the solar neighborhood, a region several hundred light years across, rotate at about 250 km per second. A simple rule might be kept in mind: A velocity of 1 pc per million years is approximately equal to a velocity of 1 km per second. Other portions of the Galaxy may rotate at greater or lesser velocities. Our Sun takes some 200 million years to make a complete revolution. Since we estimate that our solar system has existed for about 5 billion years—from its birth from a cloud of gas and dust to its present state—we conclude that it has made some 25 revolutions about the axis of the Galaxy $\triangledown$ (5×10^9 yrs/2×10^8 yrs = 25). $\triangle$ We can therefore say that the age of the Sun is 25 Galactic years.

In addition to this motion about the Galactic center, the stars have their own peculiar chaotic motions. These velocities are considerably less—about 10 to 50 km per second—although different types of stars move at different speeds. The hot, massive stars have the smallest velocities (6 to 8 km per second); stars similar to our Sun have a velocity of about 20 km per second. The smaller the velocity, the more time a given star spends in the vicinity of the Galactic plane.

$\triangledown$ These stellar motions are determined in a variety of ways. For example, we can compare photographic plates taken of the heavens many years apart and see the changes which have occurred in the relative positions of the stars. These peculiar motions are recorded in angular measure—e.g., seconds of arc per century of observation. To convert angular velocities to real velocities—e.g., kilometers per second—it is necessary to know the actual distance of the star from the Earth.

$\triangledown$ The earliest, and still the most fundamental, astronomical distance determination involves triangulation, the same method used by surveyors to determine the distance to an inaccessible point. The astronomer observes the star of interest from two different, widely separated points, and notes the apparent motion of the star against a background of more distant objects. This effect can be demonstrated easily by holding a pencil a foot away from you and alternately opening and closing each eye. The pencil is seen to move relative to the background. The further away the pencil is from you, the less it seems to move as you wink your eyes. If your eyes were much further apart, the pencil could be seen to move as you wink, even when it was quite far away. Similarly, in astronomical observations, the greater the baseline between the two observations, the larger the measurable distances.

$\triangledown$ At first these observations were made at observatories in different parts of the world; then, observations were made at the same observatory, but six months apart, so the much larger baseline of the diameter of the Earth's orbit could be used. Since the Sun's own peculiar motion in relation to the neighboring stars is known, observations made many years apart can be utilized to give an even larger baseline, the distance the Sun has moved through its local neighborhood in the course of years.

▽ Another method used for determining velocities is the Doppler effect. For sound waves, the Doppler effect is familiar to us in the change of pitch of an approaching or receding automobile horn. An analogous Doppler effect exists for light waves where the frequency (or color) of the light changes according to the motion of the light source. A star moving away from us becomes redder; a star moving toward us becomes bluer. Astronomical spectroscopy provides a very precise method for measuring even minute changes in the frequency, or color, of light. Such observations of the Doppler effect are of particular significance in the study of the apparent recession of the galaxies from us [see Chapter 10]. △

On the scale model used earlier in this chapter, in which the Earth has a diameter of about 0.05 cm, the dimensions of our Galaxy would be approximately 60 million km. It is obvious that this scale cannot be used to illustrate the vast distances of the other galaxies in the universe. Another scale must therefore be set up to conceptualize galactic distances.

Imagine the Earth's orbit to be the size of the orbit of the electron in a hydrogen atom. ▽ In the simplest picture of this lightest atom, hydrogen is composed of a central proton, which has a positive electric charge, about which orbits an electron having a negative electric charge. The opposite sign of these charges—one positive, and the other negative—provides the electrical force holding the hydrogen atom together, since oppositely charged particles attract one another. △ The radius of this electron orbit is 0.53×10^{-8} cm. The nearest star would then be approximately 0.014 mm from the nucleus of the atom, the center of the Galaxy about 10 cm, and the diameter of our stellar system about 35 cm. The diameter of our Sun would be submicroscopic—about 4.6×10^{-11} cm.

It has already been stated that the stars are vast distances apart; for all practical purposes, they are isolated from each other. Hence, they almost never collide, although the motions of each of them is determined by the total gravitation of all the stars in the Galaxy. If we consider the Milky Way as a closed region filled with gas, with individual stars playing the role of molecules, this gas would be found to be extraordinarily rarefied. The average distance between the stars is ▽ 10^{19} cm. The diameter of the Sun is about 10^{11} cm. Thus, the average relative distance between the stars is 10^{19} cm$/10^{11}$ cm $= 10^8$, or △ almost 100 million times greater than the average diameter of the stars. Under ordinary conditions the average distance between molecules of air is only several tens of times greater than the dimensions of the molecules. The air would have to be made at least 10^{19} times less dense in order to attain the same relative degree of rarity as the stars in our Galaxy. ▽ A gas so rarefied would have only about one atom in every cubic centimeter. This is accidentally the average density of matter in interstellar space. So, by an interesting coincidence, the distances between the stars in interstellar space, relative to their diameters, are just about the same as the distances between the atoms and molecules in interstellar space, relative to *their* diameters.

Interstellar space is as empty as a cubical building, 60 miles long, 60 miles wide, and 60 miles high, containing a single grain of sand. △

However, in the center region of the Galaxy, where the star density is relatively greater, collisions do occur from time to time, one collision every million years or so. During the history of our Galaxy, which is thought to be at least 10 billion years old, a collision between stars has almost never occurred in normal regions of the Galaxy [see Chapter 12].

For several decades, astronomers have been studying other galaxies which resemble our own in varying degrees. This field of investigation is called "extragalactic astronomy." During the past two decades, great strides have been made in understanding the configuration of the metagalaxy (the system of galaxies external to our own). Although the general structure of the metagalaxy is becoming increasingly clear, many questions still remain unanswered. The vast distances separating us from these galaxies create problems which can be solved only by employing more powerful instruments of observation combined with more intensive theoretical investigation.

The galaxies closest to us are the Magellanic Clouds, so named because the explorer Magellan sighted them on his famous voyage around the globe. They are seen clearly in the evening sky of the Southern hemisphere as two large patches of light with almost the same surface brightness as the Milky Way. The distance to the Magellanic Clouds is only about 200 thousand light years—about two diameters of our Galaxy away. Another nearby galaxy is the Great Nebula in the constellation Andromeda [Fig. 3–5]. It is seen by the naked eye as a faint, luminous speck of the fifth magnitude.[2] Actually, this vast stellar system is almost three times larger than our own Galaxy, both in numbers or stars and in total mass. The Andromeda galaxy, called M31 by astronomers because it is number 31 in the catalogue of the eighteenth-century French astronomer Messier, is about 1.8 million light years away, or almost twenty times the diameter of our Galaxy. The Great Nebula has a clearly defined spiral structure and characteristics similar to those of our Galaxy. A small satellite galaxy with an elliptical form can be seen to one side of M31.

▽ In Figure 3–6 is seen a detailed photograph of the region of the galactic nucleus of M31. The bright white dots are foreground stars in our own Galaxy. The photograph does not resolve the individual stars in the nucleus of M31. Several dark lanes of gas and dust may be seen. In Figure 3–7, however, in a photograph of the periphery of M31, resolution into individual stars is accomplished. This is also true in Figure 3–8, a photograph of the companion galaxy NGC 205 [cf. Fig. 3–5]. Three other fairly typical spiral galaxies—one seen edge-on, the others approximately face-on—are presented in Figures 3–9, 3–10, and 3–11. These

[2] The amount of radiation from the stars is measured by stellar magnitude. The smaller the magnitude, the brighter the star. If a star is one magnitude *less* than another star, it is 2.512 times *brighter*. A difference of five magnitudes corresponds to a brightness ratio of 100. Stars weaker than the sixth magnitude cannot be seen with the naked eye. The brightest stars have negative magnitudes; e.g., Sirius has a magnitude of −1.6.

FIGURE 3–5. *The nearest spiral galaxy, M31, the Great Nebula in the constellation Andromeda. The numerous bright points which cover the picture are foreground stars in the solar neighborhood, within our own Galaxy. Also shown are two smaller companion galaxies, NGC 205, further from M31, and NGC 221, closer to M31. The dark dust lanes in M31 are readily visible.* (Courtesy of Mt. Wilson and Palomar Observatories.)

FIGURE 3–6. *Region of the galactic nucleus of the great galaxy M31. (Courtesy of Mt. Wilson and Palomar Observatories.)*

FIGURE 3–7. *The periphery of the great galaxy M31, showing resolution into individual stars. (Courtesy of Mt. Wilson and Palomar Observatories.)*

FIGURE 3–8. *The elliptical galaxy NGC 205, a companion to the great galaxy in Andromeda, M31. Note the resolution into individual stars in the outer portions of this galaxy. (Courtesy of Mt. Wilson and Palomar Observatories.)*

FIGURE 3–9. *The spiral galaxy M104 in the constellation Virgo. This galaxy is oriented so that we see it edge-on. Note the prominent dust lanes in the disk, and the luminous galactic nucleus. The object with diffraction spikes in the lower right is a foreground star in our own Galaxy. (Courtesy of Mt. Wilson and Palomar Observatories.)*

galaxies are too distant for us to resolve their individual stars. The bright nodules seen in such galaxies are either globular clusters or extensive glowing regions of hydrogen gas. Note the dark dust lanes in these photographs. △

The galaxies differ greatly from each other both in size and in shape. Besides the spiral systems, subdivided into groups a, b, and c, according to the development of the spiral structure, there are "elliptical" galaxies—for example, the small satellite galaxy of M31 mentioned above—and irregular galaxies such as the Magellanic Clouds.

A great many of these stellar systems can be observed with large telescopes. Only about 250 of them are brighter than the twelfth magnitude. There are, however, at least 50,000 galaxies brighter than the fifteenth magnitude. The faintest systems which can be photographed with the 200-inch reflecting telescope at Mt. Palomar have a magnitude of +24. Stellar systems of this magnitude may be billions of light years away. The light producing the image of a very remote galaxy on the photographic plate may have left the galaxy when the first cells were forming in the primitive oceans of the Earth.

▽ Even the light from our nearest neighboring spiral galaxy in Andromeda

Figure 3–10. *NGC 1300, a barred spiral galaxy in the constellation Eridanus, photographed at the McDonald Observatory.* (*Courtesy of Yerkes Observatory, University of Chicago.*)

(M31), which formed the image in Figure 3–6, left M31 during the Pleistocene epoch, when Megatherium, an eight-foot-tall ground sloth, roamed what is now the southwestern United States and when, somewhere east of the Atlantic, the first tool-using hominids were gradually emerging through slow evolutionary processes. The entire subject of extragalactic astronomy is based on light which left these remote galaxies in prehistoric times when man had not yet trod the Earth.

▽ Astronomers are not restricted to observations at visible wavelengths, where the eye is sensitive. Many other wavelengths exist, undetected by the unaided eye. Every object at any temperature above absolute zero ($-273°C$ or $-456°F$) radiates at all the wavelengths of the electromagnetic spectrum. This is called "thermal" emission, because it depends on no special emission mechanism—simply the heat of the object.

▽ In many respects, light has wave properties. The distance from crest to crest in light waves—as in water waves—is called the wavelength. The number of crests which pass a fixed point in a given time (say, one second) is the frequency of the wave, and can be measured in crests or cycles per second (cps). With a little thought we can convince ourselves that the wavelength, λ, and the frequency, ν, are related to the velocity of light, c, by $\lambda\nu = c$.

FIGURE 3–11. *The spiral galaxy NGC 7331 in the constellation Pegasus. Other galaxies may also be seen in this photograph. (Courtesy of Mt. Wilson and Palomar Observatories.)*

▽ Despite its general wave nature, light must also be considered composed of discrete packets of energy called quanta, or photons. The energy of a photon is proportional to its frequency, v. Thus, the higher frequency (shorter wavelength) photons are more energetic, and penetrate further into matter.

▽ The visible spectrum lies at wavelengths between 4×10^{-5} and 7×10^{-5} cm. Another unit of length used in discussions of light is the Ångstrom (abbreviated Å): $1 \text{ Å} = 10^{-8}$ cm. Thus, visible light lies between 4×10^{-5} cm $\times 10^8$ Å/cm = 4000 Å and 7×10^{-5} cm $\times 10^8$ Å/cm = 7000 Å, corresponding to deep violet and deep red, respectively. Wavelengths below 4000 Å are in the ultraviolet region of the spectrum; below about 100 Å, in the x-ray region; and below about 1 Å, in the gamma-ray region. Since the shorter wavelengths penetrate deeper into matter, x-rays are used in medical diagnosis. Wavelengths longer than 7000 Å are in the infrared region. When matter absorbs infrared light, its constituent atoms are induced to vibrate, a phenomenon which we call heat in a solid. For this reason, infrared radiation is also called heat radiation. Its wavelength is commonly expressed in units of microns (μ): $1\mu = 10^{-4}$ cm = 10^4 Å. Wavelengths longer than 1 mm are in the radio region of the spectrum. △

Among the galaxies there are some which radiate excessively large amounts of energy at radio frequencies. These are called "radio galaxies." The flux of radio radiation may many times exceed the flux of visible radiation. The classic example of such a galaxy is Cygnus A. In terms of visible radiation, this galaxy appears as two insignificant specks of light of the seventeenth magnitude [Fig. 3–12]. Actually, however, the absolute output of visible light is very great—about ten times that of our own Galaxy. It appears faint to us because it is some 600 million light years distant. The flux of radio radiation reaching us from Cygnus A in meter wavelengths is so great that it exceeds the flux of radio radiation from our Sun during a period of low sun-spot activity. But then, the Sun is very close—only 8 light minutes—as compared to 600 million light years for Cygnus A. The flux of the radiation is inversely proportional to the square of the distance.

In visible light, the spectra of the majority of the galaxies are similar to the spectrum of the Sun. ▽ Such a spectrum can be seen when sunlight, or any other kind of light, passes through a triangular glass prism. The different colors constituting sunlight travel at different speeds through the glass and are therefore bent different amounts in passing through it. The white light of the Sun is then spread out on the other side of the prism into a broad, rainbow-hued pattern of color. This spectrum can be either viewed with the naked eye or photographed. Figure 3–13 shows some examples of stellar spectra. Discrete dark absorption lines can be seen superposed on the background. Each line, at its own characteristic frequency, can be considered due to the absorption of sunlight (arising from deeper levels in the star) by atoms at cooler, higher parts of the stellar atmosphere.

▽ Each chemical element has its own set of frequencies where it characteristically absorbs radiation. Strong absorption lines in stellar spectra are often caused by such elements as hydrogen, helium, sodium, calcium, and potassium. The darkest of these absorption lines do not necessarily correspond to the most abundant elements, since some atoms have stronger absorption lines than others. Hydrogen and helium are principal constituents of almost all stars, while sodium, calcium, and potassium are present in relatively minor quantities. But the lines of calcium can nevertheless be stronger than the lines of helium. Comparison with laboratory measurements can allow for this effect. Therefore, the chemical composition of distant stars can be determined from the light which they radiate to us and the interpretations provided by modern physics.

▽ The spectra of galaxies also show dark absorption features, an understandable circumstance, since the visible radiation of these galaxies consists of the cumulative radiation of billions of stars more or less similar to our Sun and to the stars in the solar neighborhood. Information can thus be garnered about the composite chemical make-up of galaxies millions of light years away, an extraordinary achievement of the human mind. △

By measuring the displacement of the wavelengths in the spectrum of a light source relative to a laboratory standard, using the Doppler effect mentioned earlier, we can determine whether the light source is approaching us or moving away from us. If the light source is approaching, the wavelengths are decreased, and the spectral lines are displaced toward the blue end of the spectrum. If the light source

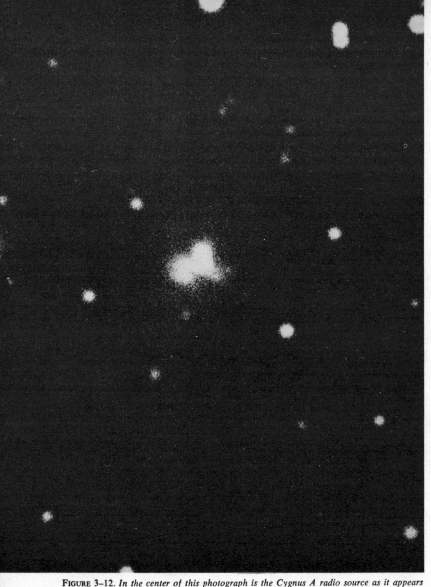

FIGURE 3–12. *In the center of this photograph is the Cygnus A radio source as it appears at optical frequencies. At radio frequencies, it is one of the brightest objects in the heavens. At visual frequencies, except for its double nature, it is a very unextraordinary object.* (*Courtesy of Mt. Wilson and Palomar Observatories.*)

is receding, the wavelengths are increased, and the lines shift toward the red end of the spectrum.

A very important discovery was made about the spectra of galaxies several decades ago ▽ by the American astronomer V. M. Slipher, of Lowell Observatory. △ The spectral lines of all the galaxies—except those very close to us—undergo a shift towards the red end of the spectrum. This phenomenon is called the "red shift," and as later found by the American astronomer Edwin Hubble of Mt. Wilson Observatory this shift increases with the increasing distances of the galaxies. The simplest explanation is that all galaxies are receding from us, and that the velocity of this "expansion" increases with the distance. The greater the distance, the faster

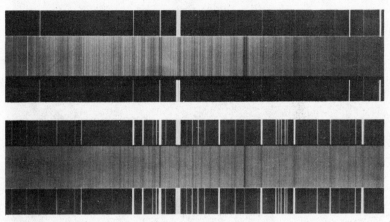

FIGURE 3–13. *Typical stellar spectra. In an ordinary photographic positive, the absorption lines of the individual chemical elements characteristically appear dark against a brighter background. In a negative, the absorption lines appear bright against a darker background. The wavelength of light ordinarily increases from left to right in such a spectrum. A spectrum in color of the complete visual spectrum would be purple on its left, and then progressively blue, green, yellow, orange, and red at the extreme right. (Courtesy of Yerkes Observatory.)*

the galaxy recedes. These velocities of recession become enormous. The velocity of the receding radio galaxy Cygnus A is almost 16,000 km/sec. A very weak radio galaxy, 3C–295, has a very great velocity of recession. Visually, it is of the twentieth magnitude. In 1961, its spectrum was obtained [see Fig. 3–14], and it appears that the ultraviolet spectral lines produced by (ionized) oxygen are displaced to the orange region of the spectrum. Therefore, by simple calculation, we find that the velocity of recession is 138,000 km/sec, or almost half the speed of light. This radio galaxy is five billion light years from us. ▽ More recently, even more distant objects have been detected by similar techniques. △ Astronomers are now investigating light which started its long journey through space when the Sun and the planets were forming.

THE SIZE AND STRUCTURE OF THE UNIVERSE   45

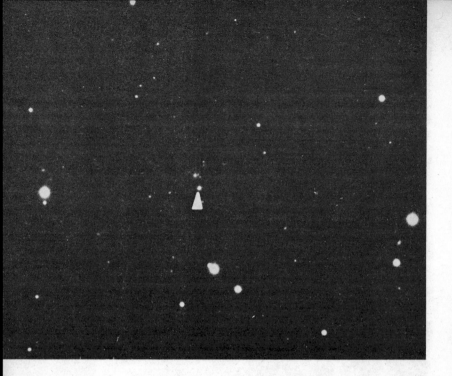

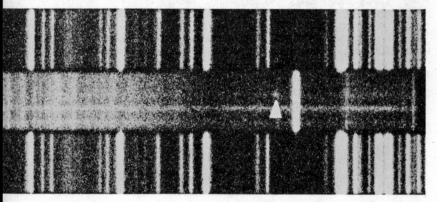

FIGURE 3–14. *At the top is a photograph of the object 3C 295 in the constellation Bootes. It is some 5 billion light years away, and a source of cosmic radio noise. The lower half of the picture shows negatives of three sets of spectra. The upper and lower spectra are obtained in the laboratory to establish wave-length standards. The middle spectrum is taken of 3C 295 through the terrestrial atmosphere. Most of the lines in the middle spectrum are due to atoms and molecules in the terrestrial atmosphere. The arrow, however, points to a spectral feature which is not present in spectra of the sky, and which is due to 3C 295. This is a line which has been very greatly red-shifted, and provides the best grounds for attributing immense distances to 3C 395. Because of the faintness of such features, great care must be taken in obtaining and interpreting such spectra. (Courtesy of Mt. Wilson and Palomar Observatories.)*

FIGURE 3–15. *A cluster of galaxies in the constellation Hercules. Spiral, elliptical, and irregular galaxies may be seen in various inclinations to our line of sight. Some of the galaxies are connected by luminescent bridges. The spiked objects, and many of the small, perfectly circular objects, are foreground stars in our own Galaxy. (Courtesy of Mt. Wilson and Palomar Observatories.)*

In addition to the over-all expansion of the universe, individual galaxies have their own irregular, disordered motions. These velocities are usually several hundred kilometers per second. Since the velocity of expansion increases by about 100 km/sec for each million parsecs, the irregular velocities exceed the velocity of recession for those galaxies which are within a million parsecs of the Milky Way. Therefore, their red shift cannot be detected. Some of the nearest galaxies are in fact approaching us.

The galaxies are not distributed uniformly in metagalactic space; they form separate groups and clusters of galaxies. Galaxies are found tens of times less often outside such clusters than inside them. A group of seventeen galaxies, including our own, make up the so-called "local group." The local group, in turn, is part of a larger cluster, the center of which is in that part of the sky where the constellation Virgo is located. This large cluster is thought to contain several thousand galaxies. ▽ Figure 3–15 shows a cluster of galaxies in the constellation Hercules. Elliptical, spiral, and irregular galaxies may all be seen. Some clusters may have as many as a thousand galaxies. △

Let us now consider the differences between clusters of stars and clusters of galaxies. The number of stars in a stellar cluster is much greater than the number of galaxies in a cluster of galaxies. The distances between the stars in a cluster are very large compared with the size of the stars themselves. The mean distances between the galaxies in a cluster of galaxies are only several times greater than the dimensions of the galaxies. If we think of all the galaxies in the sky as a gas in which the individual galaxies are represented by molecules, this medium would be very viscous and unlike an ordinary gas. (In many problems of metagalactic astronomy, it is often useful to treat the metagalactic medium as a continuum, possessing characteristics such as viscosity, electrical conductivity, etc.)

Now, let us turn back to our second model, in which the Earth's orbit is reduced to the dimensions of the first electron orbit of the hydrogen atom. On this scale, the distance to the Andromeda galaxy would be somewhat greater than 6 meters, the distance to the central part of the local system of galaxies in the constellation Virgo, about 120 meters, the distance to the radio galaxy Cygnus A, 2.5 km, and the distance to the radio galaxy 3C–295, about 25 km.

With this background, we have some conception of the scale and general structural characteristics of the universe as it exists today. The old picture of a static universe must be replaced by one of a dynamic universe filled with evolving cosmic objects. Everything is changing; stars appear, grow, and die; clouds of gas and dust and galaxies develop; everything is in motion. ▽ The universe is filled with planets, stars, galaxies, which, on the immense cosmic time scale, are evanescent, ephemeral entities, forming, flickering briefly, and then fading, lost forever in the infinite recesses of space and time. △

4

Fundamental properties
of the stars

I must be of the same Opinion with all the greatest Philosophers of our Age, that the Sun is of the same Nature with the fix'd Stars.

. . . May not every One of these Stars or Suns have as great a Retinue as our Sun, of Planets, with their Moons, to wait upon them? Nay, there's a manifest Reason why they should. For if we imagine ourselves placed at an equal Distance from the Sun and fix'd Stars we should then perceive no difference between them. For, as for all the Planets that we now see attend the Sun, we should not have the least glimpse of them, either because their Light would be too weak to affect us, or that all the Orbs in which they move would make up one lucid point with the Sun.

Christianus Huygens, *New Conjectures Concerning the Planetary Worlds, Their Inhabitants and Productions* (c. 1670)

With the invaluable aid of the spectroscope, astronomers have amassed a great deal of information about such fundamental properties of the stars as their masses, radii, chemical composition, the total amount of energy each radiates per second (called the luminosity, and designated by the letter L), and the temperature of their surface layers.

A star's surface temperature determines both its color and its spectrum; at 3,000–4,000 degrees Kelvin,[1] the color is reddish; at 6,000–7,000°K, yellowish; very hot stars—at temperatures above 10,000–12,000°K—are blue or white.

▽ The relation between color and temperature in stellar atmospheres is very similar to that observed with everyday materials. For example, as a bar of iron is heated, its color passes progressively from red, to yellow, until, finally, it becomes white hot. Similarly, the color of the star can be used to determine the temperature of its atmosphere. △

A standard non-visual method for measuring the color of a star is based on the determination of its "color index," which is equal to the difference between the photographic magnitude and the apparent (visual) magnitude. The usual photographic plate is especially sensitive to blue light; the eye, to yellow and green light. ▽ (In fact, the wavelength of maximum sensitivity of the eye is very close to the wavelength at which the Sun emits the most energy. This is, of course, no coincidence: Human eyes have evolved in landscapes bathed with solar radiation, and there is clearly an evolutionary advantage in high sensitivity to low levels of light. If there are organisms with sight on other planets, we may expect a similar connection between ocular sensitivity and the color of the local sun.) △ Thus, the photographic and the visual magnitudes are not identical. The visual magnitude is determined by means of photographic plates which have a sensitivity resembling that of the eye. The color index of red stars can reach +1.5 stellar magnitudes and even higher; with blue stars, the index is negative. A specific type of spectrum accompanies each star's color index. The relatively cold red stars have spectra with absorption features characteristic of the neutral atoms of metals and of certain very simple compounds, for example, CN, CH, and others.

▽ A neutral atom is one which has no net electrical charge. In the hydrogen atom, discussed previously, the positive electrical charge of the nuclear proton is exactly balanced by the negative electrical charge of the electron, so that, from a distance, the atom is electrically neutral. Similarly, the next atom in order of complexity, helium, is electrically neutral because its nucleus contains two positive

---

[1] For stellar temperatures, the difference between Kelvin degrees (K°) and Centigrade degrees (C°) can be neglected in an introductory discussion. Those readers who like their degrees Fahrenheit can multiply the number of K° by 1.8 to get F°.

protons, and two neutral neutrons, while the nucleus is surrounded by two electrons. If somehow—for example, by the collision of another atom, or by the absorption of light—helium is made to lose an electron, it is said to be "ionized." It would then have a net positive charge, since there would be more positively charged protons in the nucleus than negatively charged electrons outside the nucleus. The absorption properties of ionized atoms are different from the absorption properties of the same atoms when neutral. As the temperature of a star increases, the relative number of ionized atoms of a given sort will also increase, because of a rise in both the number of collisions and the number of absorptions. In addition, as the temperature increases, simple chemical compounds such as CN are dissociated, torn apart by collisions with their more rapidly moving neighbors, and by bombardment by high energy photons. △

As the surface temperature increases, the molecular spectral absorption features vanish, many lines of the neutral atoms diminish in intensity, and the lines of ionized helium appear. Stars with a surface temperature of approximately 6,000°K have lines of ionized calcium located at the end of the visible and the beginning of the ultraviolet part of the spectrum. Our sun has such a spectrum. Stars with a surface temperature of approximately 10,000°K have intense lines of hydrogen. Very hot stars with a surface temperature exceeding 20,000°K have lines chiefly of neutral or ionized helium, and the continuous spectrum is very intense in the ultraviolet regions.

The spectral sequence of the bulk of the stars (their classification according to their spectra) is denoted by the following, essentially arbitrary, sequence of letters: O, B, A, F, G, K, M. ▽ The time-honored mnemonic device for remembering this sequence of letters is the immortal phrase, "*O*h *B*e *A F*ine *G*irl, *K*iss *M*e." △ Each letter indicates a spectral class, O being the hottest star and M being the coldest. The measurements are so sensitive that it is possible to divide each class into 10 subclasses, for example, B1, B2, B3, and so forth. A star with a spectrum B9 is nearer the spectral class A1 than B1.

▽ Figures 4–1 to 4–4 illustrate this change in the spectral properties with spectral class. Each horizontal strip corresponds to the spectrum of an individual star in our Galaxy. Each star shown belongs to the "main sequence," a category to which most stars belong. The spectra are taken from the Morgan-Keenan-Kellman atlas, a collection of spectra named after the compilers, American astronomers then at Yerkes Observatory, University of Chicago. The names of the stars are shown on the left in each figure, and their spectral types arranged sequentially on the right. Each spectrum is a "negative"; that is, for purposes of presentation, the absorption lines are shown as bright features on a dark background, instead of as dark lines on a bright background, their usual observed configuration. At the top and bottom, individual spectral lines are identified according to laboratory comparisons. The atom causing the absorption, its state of ionization, and the wavelength at which it absorbs are shown. For example, He I 4009 refers to neutral helium absorption at a wavelength of 4009 Å; the background would appear blue in the vicinity of this line, if the photographs of Figures 4–1 to 4–4

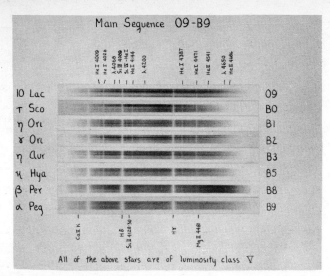

FIGURE 4–1. *Representative spectra of late O and early and late B stars of the main sequence. These spectra are reproduced from the Morgan-Keenan-Kellman Atlas. (Courtesy of Yerkes Observatory.)*

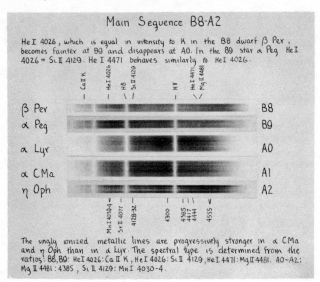

FIGURE 4–2. *Representative spectra of late B and early A stars of the main sequence. These spectra are reproduced from the Morgan-Keenan-Kellman Atlas. (Courtesy of Yerkes Observatory.)*

were in color. Helium II indicates singly ionized helium, that is, helium in which one electron has been lost. Si IV indicates silicon atoms from which three electrons have been lost. The names of the individual stars arrayed along the left-hand border of these figures also show a variety of nomenclature systems, the patrimony of a hoary astronomical classification convention in which each of many different workers compiles his own catalogue. △

▽ It had originally been intended by those who invented this stellar spectral type classification that the sequence of spectral types could be represented by letters in alphabetical sequence—A, B, C, D, etc. However, after the original assignment of letters to spectral types had been made, it was discovered that through errors in

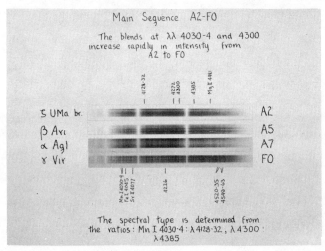

FIGURE 4–3. *Representative spectra of early and late A and early F stars of the main sequence. These spectra are reproduced from the Morgan-Keenan-Kellman Atlas. (Courtesy of Yerkes Observatory.)*

classification some letters had been assigned to nonexistent or insignificant spectral types while others had been assigned so that there was not a smooth transition between adjacent spectral types. A star of late O spectral type has a spectrum quite similar to a star of early B spectral type (see Figure 4–1). Thus, O had to be placed before B, B before A, and the entire astronomical alphabet almost randomly reassorted. It is an interesting commentary on human conservatism that this clerical error has been enshrined by repeated use, until there is now no hope of introducing another system. However, since the sequence of letters in the alphabet is also arbitrary, the astronomical nomenclature for spectral types is fundamentally not much more obscure than a true alphabetical system. △

The luminosity differs greatly from star to star and is often expressed in terms of the luminosity of the Sun. Our Sun has a luminosity of 4×10^{33} erg/sec.

▽ The basic metric system unit of mass is the gram. One gram equals approximately 0.035 ounce. An erg is the unit of energy expended in lifting 1 gm a distance of 10^{-3} cm on the Earth, obviously a very small quantity. It is very much in the range of interest of the flea. The output of a 100-watt bulb is 10^9 erg/sec. Thus, the Sun's output is the equivalent of four trillion trillion light bulbs, each putting out 100 watts. △

The vast majority of stars are "dwarfs" that are significantly less luminous than our Sun—as much as a thousand times less luminous. However the

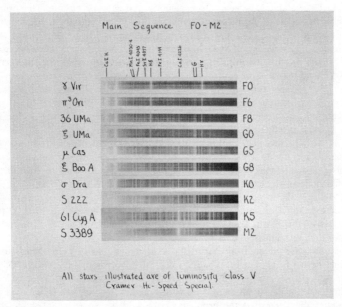

FIGURE 4–4. *Representative spectra of F, G, K, and early M stars of the main sequence. These spectra are reproduced from the Morgan-Keenan-Kellman Atlas. (Courtesy of Yerkes Observatory.)*

"supergiant" stars (relatively few in number) have luminosities which are from 10^4 to 10^6 times greater than that of our Sun.

▽ It is common, in astronomy, to refer to certain broad categories of stars both by their relative sizes and by their colors. The astronomical zoo is replete with "supergiants," "giants," "dwarfs," and "sub-dwarfs," but no individuals of ordinary stature, and a simple statement of solar evolution often sounds like an excursion into the world of the brothers Grimm. A typical star begins life auspiciously, as a bright yellow giant, and then metamorphoses, in early adolescence, into a yellow dwarf. After spending most of its life in this state, the yellow dwarf rapidly expands into a luminous red giant, jumps the Hertzsprung gap, and decays violently into a hot white dwarf. It ends its life, cooling inexorably, as a degenerate black dwarf. Few readers will recall the original title of this moderately depressing life history, but many will find it vaguely familiar. To understand the underlying causes of the varied careers of the stars, we must discuss further astronomical observations and their interpretations. △

The apparent magnitude of a star is a measure of its apparent brightness; that is, its brightness as it appears to us. The apparent magnitude is therefore dependent on both a star's intrinsic brightness and on its distance from us. Even a very brilliant star will appear inconspicuous if it is very distant. The ordinary bright stars, visible to the naked eye on an average night, have apparent magnitudes mostly between 1 and 4. (A star of the first magnitude is brighter than one of fourth magnitude.) △ Very bright stars have negative apparent magnitudes. Most stars have small positive magnitudes. The apparent magnitude of the Sun—much brighter than the stars, of course—is −26.8. However, if we moved the Sun to a distance of 10 parsecs (approximately 2 million times further than its actual distance), its apparent magnitude would be +5, and it would appear as a tiny point of light in the sky, barely visible to the naked eye. The faintest star which can be seen with the naked eye has a magnitude of +6.

If we take any star at the standard distance of 10 parsecs from the solar system, its magnitude is called "absolute." Stars of high intrinsic luminosity have negative absolute magnitudes—for example, −7 or −5; stars of low intrinsic luminosity have large positive magnitudes—for example, +10, +12, etc.

Stellar mass, in contrast to luminosity, varies within relatively narrow limits from star to star. The mass of our Sun is 2×10^{33} gm—more than 330,000 times the mass of the Earth. Few stars have masses as much as ten times greater or smaller than our Sun's.

Radii differ greatly from star to star. The dimensions of white dwarfs do not exceed those of the Earth. White dwarfs have an enormous average density, ranging to 10^4 and 10^5 gm/cm^3. ▽ By comparison, the density of water is only 1 gm/cm^3, and the density of an average rock is about 3 gm/cm^3. △ Other stars have such huge diameters that the orbit of Mars could be placed comfortably inside them. Such immense stars are sometimes called "bubbles." Since there is comparatively little variation in the masses of the stars, a star with a large radius will have a low average density. The density of the Sun is about 1.4 gm/cm^3, or slightly denser than water. In contrast, stellar "bubbles" are millions of times less dense than air.

Investigations during the last three decades have indicated that stars rotate about their axes. It is now clear that stars of different spectral classes rotate with different velocities. Chapter 13 will be devoted to this very important cosmogonical question.

Spectral analyses indicate that the chemical composition varies from star to star. The hot giant stars, concentrated in the Galactic plane, are relatively rich in heavy elements, for example, iron or silicon, while the stars in globular clusters [see

Fig. 3–4], quite far removed from the plane, have a heavy element content which is ten times smaller. This important fact is one starting point for contemporary theories on the evolution of stars and stellar systems.

The principal constituents of the stars are usually hydrogen and helium plasmas—ionized gas which is electrically neutral because the number of positive charges on the ions (e.g., He II) is just balanced by the number of free negative electrons, which are not bound by electrical forces to any atom. The remaining elements are present in the form of relatively insignificant impurities. ▽ The average

TABLE I. COSMIC ABUNDANCE OF THE ELEMENTS

Atom	Relative atomic weight	Relative cosmic abundance, atoms
Hydrogen	1.0	10,000,000.
Helium	4.0	1,400,000.
Lithium	6.9	0.003
Carbon	12.0	3,000.
Nitrogen	14.0	910.
Oxygen	16.0	6,800.
Neon	20.2	2,800.
Sodium	23.0	17.
Magnesium	24.3	290.
Aluminum	27.0	19.
Phosphorus	31.0	3.
Potassium	39.1	0.8
Argon	40.0	42.
Calcium	40.1	17.
Iron	55.8	80.

relative chemical composition of the outer layers of the stars is given in the accompanying table, which shows the relative abundance of other elements for every 10 million atoms of hydrogen. Also given is the weight of one atom of the elements listed, relative to hydrogen. The mass of a hydrogen atom is 1.66×10^{-24} gm. While the most abundant elements by far are hydrogen and helium, there is no obvious systematic dependence of abundance on atomic weight for the atoms displayed here. These abundance questions will arise again later, when we discuss the chemical reactions leading to the origin of life on Earth.

▽ Comparison of Table I with Figures 4–1 to 4–4 bears out the point that the most abundant atoms are not necessarily those most easily discerned by spectroscopy. △

Although the so-called heavy elements (those heavier than helium) are underabundant compared with hydrogen and helium, they play a very important role in the universe. The luminosity of a star depends on its opacity to the radiation generated in its interior. Many of the heavy elements tend to be quite opaque, so that small quantities of them may significantly influence the character of the light emitted from the stellar interior, and the subsequent evolution of the star.

The heavy elements have a decisive meaning for life in the universe. The role of carbon in the structure of living material is well known. Equally important for life on earth are nitrogen, oxygen, and phosphorus; and, for many life forms, iron, magnesium, sulfur, potassium, etc. Life is based upon the complex linkages of such

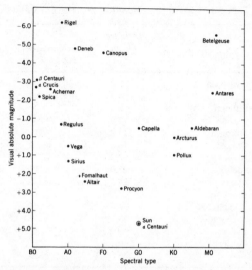

FIGURE 4–5. *The Hertzsprung-Russell diagram of the brightest stars in the sky taken from Bart J. Bok and Priscilla Bok,* The Milky Way, *third edition, Harvard University Press, Cambridge, Massachusetts, 1957. (Courtesy of Harvard University Press.)*

atoms. Thus, if there were no elements heavier than helium in the universe, there would be no life. Does this mean that stars which have a low content of heavy elements could not have habitable planets? We will consider this question later; here we merely stress the importance of the chemical composition of cosmic objects (stars, nebulae, planets) in assaying the possibilities of life in any particular region of space.

The following question can also be asked: Were the heavy elements always present? And if not, how were they formed? There is some evidence that in the distant past there were significantly smaller amounts of the heavier elements than there are today. Perhaps there were none at all, and the universe consisted solely of hydrogen and helium. The formation of these elements will be discussed in **Chapter 8.**

THE UNIVERSE

By spectroscopic methods astronomers have detected the presence of powerful magnetic fields in the atmospheres of certain stars. The intensity in individual cases can be as great as 10,000 gauss, that is, 20,000 times greater than the surface magnetic field of the Earth, which has a magnetic field strength of about half a gauss. We note that sun spots on our star have magnetic fields reaching an intensity of 3,000 to 4,000 gauss. Magnetic phenomena, as understood in recent years, play an important role in the physical processes which occur in the solar atmosphere. There is some basis for assuming that the same is true in other stellar atmospheres. At first glance it would appear that stellar magnetism is unrelated to the problem of the origin and development of life in the universe. However, the sequence of events which, when taken as a whole, leads to the origin of life is

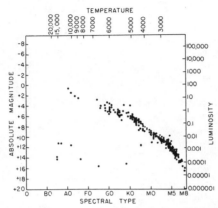

FIGURE 4–6. *The Hertzsprung-Russell diagram for stars with distances less than 10 pc from the Sun. Reproduced from Otto Struve, Beverly Lynds, and Helen Pillans,* Elementary Astronomy, *Oxford University Press, New York, 1959. (Courtesy of Oxford University Press.)*

unusually complex. When we consider theories of the origin of the planets in Chapter 13, we shall see that the magnetic effects of a star may play a critical role in the formation of planetary systems.

We have discussed the basic characteristics of the stars. Is there any connection among these properties? It appears that such a connection does indeed exist. It was independently discovered half a century ago by the Danish astronomer E. Hertzsprung and by the American astronomer Henry Norris Russell of Princeton University.

Figure 4–5 depicts a Hertzsprung–Russell diagram. The points represent the brightest stars in the night sky, the horizontal axis represents the spectral types of the stars, and the vertical axis represents the absolute magnitudes. We see that the majority of the stars are found within the limits of a relatively narrow band, going from the upper left-hand corner of the diagram to the lower right-hand corner. This is the so-called main sequence of the stars. ▽ There must be a fundamental reason that the stars are not strewn, more or less at random, throughout the Hertzsprung–Russell diagram. △ In the upper right-hand section we see some stars in a disordered array. Their spectral classes are G, K, and M, and their absolute magnitudes lie between +2 and −6. They are the "red giants," although there are yellow stars among them. Had we included stars which have smaller apparent luminosities we would have found in the lower left of the diagram a small number of stars with absolute magnitudes less than +10 and spectral classes within the limits B to F. These are very hot stars with low luminosity. But low luminosity with a high surface temperature can occur only when the radius of a star is quite small. Consequently, such stars are called "white dwarfs."

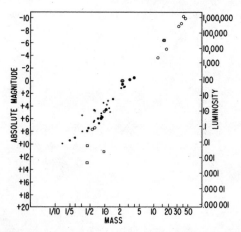

FIGURE 4–7. *The relation between mass and luminosity for a variety of stars. The squares which show deviations from the mass-luminosity relation of the bulk of the stars represent the white dwarfs.* From Otto Struve, **Stellar Evolution,** *Princeton University Press, Princeton, New Jersey, 1950. (Courtesy of Princeton University Press.)*

The number of points in the "spectrum-luminosity" or Hertzsprung–Russell diagram do not give an accurate representation of the relative number of stars in each spectral class within the Galaxy. The giant stars with high luminosity are represented in disproportionately large numbers because they can be seen from a very great distance. The dwarf stars are difficult to observe and are accordingly less equitably represented. We can obtain a more accurate idea of the relative numbers of stars in each spectral class if we consider only those which are found within 10 parsecs of our Sun (32.6 light years) [see Fig. 4–6]. Here we see that the lower right-hand side of the main sequence is very sharply defined, but there is an absence of giants. Within 10 parsecs, the overwhelming majority of stars are dimmer and colder than our Sun, ▽ a circumstance typical of other parts of the Galaxy as well △; these are the "red dwarfs," which lie in the lower right-hand part of the main sequence. Only eight stars in this diagram (of approximately 170 found within this area) are brighter than the Sun. Eight white dwarfs are represented. Since within a small radius of 10 parsecs we observe so many white dwarfs, we conclude that they are very numerous throughout the universe. Calculations show that there are at least several billion, and perhaps as many as ten billion white dwarfs in our Galaxy. There are approximately 150 billion stars of all types in the Milky Way. The number of white dwarfs is ten thousand times greater than the number of giants of high luminosity, which are represented in such great numbers in Figure 4–5. This example shows the important role in astronomy (as in other natural sciences) played by observational selection.

There are other categories of stars. In Figure 4–6 we see a number of stars situated a little lower than the main sequence. These are the "sub-dwarfs." Although there are relatively few sub-dwarfs near our Sun, they exist in vast numbers in the central regions of the Galaxy, and in the globular clusters. Rarely are sub-dwarfs found near the Galactic plane, but they are very numerous towards the Galactic center. They are apparently the most numerous type of star in the Galaxy. Sub-dwarfs differ from stars of the main sequence in their relatively low content of heavy elements. ▽ If an ordinary main sequence star were somehow to have its heavy element content suddenly decreased, its luminosity would increase, and it would move upward and to the left in the Hertzsprung–Russell diagram, entering the sub-dwarf region, but still lying below the main sequence. The low heavy element content causes less absorption of the radiation emitted from the depths of the star and therefore leads to higher luminosities. △

As we go along the main sequence from spectral classes O to M, the masses of the stars continuously decrease. For example, stars of type O have a mass which is several tens of times greater than the solar mass. Stars of class B have a mass approximately five times greater than that of the Sun, which is in spectral class G2. Most main sequence dwarfs are of spectral class M and have their masses approximately ten times less than the Sun's. Since mass and luminosity continuously change along the main sequence, there exists an empirical relationship between them [see Figure 4–7].

Soon after the "spectrum-luminosity" diagram was published, its intimate connection with the problem of the evolution of the stars was intuitively felt by astronomers. It was formerly believed that the stars evolved directly along the main sequence. According to these naïve concepts, the red giants were the first stars to be formed. As they condensed and shrank, their temperatures increased, and they entered the main sequence. Evolving along the main sequence, they became cooler and radiated less. The present terminology of astronomers still reflects these old concepts: the spectral classes O, B, A, and part of F are called the "early" types, and G, K, and M are called the "late" types. If the stars evolved directly along the main sequence, it would be necessary to conclude that they continuously lost a significant part of their original mass. Such concepts present insurmountable difficulties. The modern theory of stellar evolution, based on contemporary concepts of the source of stellar energy and on much observational material, was developed during the last decade. This theory, which successfully explains the "spectrum-luminosity" diagram, will be discussed in Chapter 6.

5

The interstellar medium

Nothing exists but atoms and the void.

Democritus

S ince contemporary theories propose that the stars were formed from a condensation of the interstellar medium, we must investigate the properties and
content of this material before discussing the evolution of the stars. This
subject will also be important when we consider the problem of contacting life in
other regions of the universe. The possibility of establishing communications
between the civilizations of different planetary systems depends, to a certain extent,
upon the characteristics of the matter which fills the intervening space.

The interstellar medium is composed largely of gas and dust. The mass ratio
of gas to dust in a typical volume of space is approximately 100:1. Observations
indicate that this material is distributed irregularly and unevenly throughout the
Galaxy. There are clouds which are much denser than the medium in general;
they appear to us as dark or luminous nebulae and are found mostly in the spiral
arms. Individual clouds may have velocities of 6 to 8 km/sec. In other regions of
the Galaxy, the density of the interstellar material is extremely low.

The dimensions of cosmic dust grains are from 10^{-4} to 10^{-5} cm, ∇ or about the
same size as the wavelength of visible light $\triangle$. These particles are responsible for
the absorption of light in interstellar space that prevents us from observing objects
in the Galactic plane at distances greater than 2,000 or 3,000 parsecs. Fortunately,
this cosmic dust and the interstellar gas associated with it are concentrated near the
Galactic plane in a layer only about 250 parsecs thick. Therefore, radiation
emitted by objects at a sufficiently large angle to the plane is not significantly
absorbed.

∇ Interstellar grains are built up by low-energy collisions among the atoms
and molecules of the interstellar medium. Very energetic collisions vaporize the
grains. It is believed that these energetic collisions occur just frequently enough to
limit the size of the grains to the range of 10^{-4} to 10^{-5} cm. Because the composition
of the grains should approximately parallel the composition of the interstellar gas,
the grains should be composed primarily of molecules of the atoms carbon,
nitrogen, oxygen, and hydrogen. By an interesting coincidence, the size range and
chemical composition of interstellar grains are therefore quite close to the size and
composition of terrestrial bacteria. The similarity in composition has an underlying
cause in the cosmic abundance of the elements; the similarity in size is a
coincidence only. $\triangle$

The presence of interstellar gas was discovered in the early part of the
twentieth century from the absorption lines of ionized calcium which occur in the
spectra of remote hot stars, but which are really due to calcium in the intervening
interstellar medium. The density of this gas is extremely low, approximately one
atom per cubic centimeter, on the average, in regions near the Galactic plane. In

air there are 2.7×10^{19} molecules per cubic centimeter. Even in the best vacuum which can be produced in the laboratory, the concentration of atoms is at least 10^{13} cm^{-3}. And yet we cannot consider interstellar space a vacuum. A vacuum is defined as a system in which the mean free path of the atoms or molecules ($\triangledown$ that is, the average distance that the particles move between collisions $\triangle$) exceeds the characteristic dimensions of the system. In interstellar space, the mean free path of the atoms is hundreds of times less than the distance between the stars. Therefore, we can rightly consider interstellar gas as a uniform, continuous medium, to which the laws of gas dynamics can be applied.

The chemical content of interstellar gas, revealed through spectroscopy, is similar to that of the external layers of stars on the main sequence. Atoms of hydrogen and helium predominate; metallic atoms are comparatively rare. The simplest molecular compounds (for example, CH, CN) are present in detectable amounts. It has been postulated that perhaps a significant part of the interstellar gas could be in the form of molecular hydrogen, H_2, but there are as yet no methods for determining the validity of this view.

The temperature of the interstellar gas depends upon its distance from a hot star. The ultraviolet radiation of hot stars of spectral class O5 will ionize nearly all the gas within a radius of approximately 100 parsecs. Such regions are called "H II" regions, and their temperatures can reach 10,000°K. (The temperature of a gas is defined by the velocities of the characteristic random motions of the particles.) Under these conditions, the medium emits radiation in the visible part of the spectrum at distinct frequencies, particularly at the frequencies characteristic of a red hydrogen line. When almost all of the interstellar material is far from the hot stars, the interstellar hydrogen is not ionized, and the temperature of the gas is as low as 100°K or lower. There are probably significant amounts of hydrogen molecules in such cold regions.

During the last decade, radio astronomy has proved very valuable in the study of interstellar gas. Investigations at a wavelength of 21 cm have been particularly fruitful. Why this wavelength? Several decades ago, it was theoretically predicted that neutral atoms of hydrogen under the conditions of interstellar space would radiate at a wavelength of 21 cm.

$\triangledown$ At ultraviolet, visible, infrared, and radio wavelengths, atoms emit or absorb radiation because their electrons change energy. In the case of the simplest atom, hydrogen, there are many possible electron orbits. An electron in an orbit far from the nucleus has more energy than an electron in an orbit closer to the nucleus. When the electron's orbit changes from large to small, this difference in energy is emitted as a light photon. The lowest-energy orbit of the hydrogen atom is called the "ground" state. Actually, it consists of two different orbits of very slightly differing energy. The nucleus of the hydrogen atom is a proton, which has a small associated magnetic field. This field can be pictured as having a direction in space perpendicular to the plane of the electron orbit. In this simplest picture of the hydrogen atom, the electron, moving about the hydrogen nucleus, has a magnetic field associated with it, since moving charged particles produce magnetic fields. The magnetic field produced by the electron revolution about the proton can also be pictured as perpendicular to the plane of the electron orbit; but whether the electron field and the proton field are in the same direction or in exactly opposite directions depends on the direction in which the electron revolves around the proton, clockwise or counterclockwise. These two different directions of revolution correspond to the two slightly different energies which make up the ground state of the hydrogen atom. △ According to the laws of quantum physics, occasional spontaneous transitions take place from the higher ground energy level to the lower ground energy level. When this occurs, a photon of low energy is emitted. Its frequency is proportional to the difference between the two energy levels. Since the difference is very small, the frequency of the radiation will be low. The corresponding wavelength is 21 cm.

Calculations indicate that such transitions between levels of hydrogen atoms occur rarely; on the average, one transition per atom every 11 million years! For other lines in the visible spectrum, the transitions occur perhaps once every 100 millionth of a second.

Since the interstellar atoms have different velocities as seen from Earth, then, due to the Doppler effect, not all the radiation emitted by hydrogen will be at 21 cm. Those moving towards the observer will emit at wavelengths somewhat shorter than 21 cm; those moving away, at longer wavelengths. As a result, there will be a spread of wavelengths around 21 cm. Thus, by measuring the width of the 21 cm line, it is possible to determine the state of motion of the interstellar gas in the Galaxy, and investigate Galactic rotation and the disordered motions and temperatures of individual clouds of interstellar matter. The approximate number of hydrogen atoms in interstellar space has also been determined.

These methods have been used to study other galaxies, for example, the Andromeda Galaxy, M31 [Figure 3–5]. As the techniques of radio astronomy are improved, we shall be able to study the motions and rotations of very remote galaxies. The investigation of interstellar hydrogen at the 21 cm wavelength has inaugurated a new era in astronomy.

▽ Recently, an additional interstellar radio absorption line has been discovered at a wavelength of 18 cm. This line is due to absorption by the molecular fragment OH, called the hydroxyl radical. That OH absorbs at 18 cm was first predicted by Shklovskii many years ago. It already appears that the distribution of OH in interstellar space is different from the distribution of H. As we shall see in Chapter 8, it is believed that oxygen, but not hydrogen, is synthesized in the deep interiors of hot stars. Thus, the difference in distribution of oxygen and hydrogen in interstellar space may provide some significant clues on the sites of element generation within the Galaxy. At the present time many aspects of the interstellar absorption and emission spectrum near 18 cm have been investigated, but they are not at all well understood. The spectral features seem to be localized preferentially near H II regions. The details of the spectrum have been very difficult to interpret, especially since the emission is strongly polarized and sometimes varies in strength over a period of months. Other interstellar lines besides H and OH have been predicted by Shklovskii and others. If they are discovered and their distributions mapped, it may be possible one day to draw maps of the relative abundances of various chemical elements through the Galaxy. △

Astronomers have obtained a number of indirect proofs of the presence of interstellar magnetic fields. These magnetic fields are associated with clouds of interstellar gas and move with them. Their intensity is approximately 10^{-5} gauss. The general direction of the lines of magnetic force coincides with the direction of the arms of the spiral structure of the Galaxy. We can say that the spiral arms themselves represent magnetic tubes of force of gigantic dimensions. If interstellar gas is found in a magnetic field, the 21 cm lines should be split into several components (which differ in polarization). Since the magnitude of the magnetic field is very small, the splitting will be slight. The width of the absorption line is also affected by the magnetic field. ▽ Confirmed observation of this magnetic splitting and broadening of interstellar radio lines should permit a more direct determination of interstellar magnetic field strengths. △

The primary cosmic rays which fill interstellar space are closely associated with the interstellar magnetic fields. Cosmic ray primaries are particles (protons, the nuclei of the heavier elements, and also electrons) which frequently have energies exceeding 1 erg per particle, and sometimes approach $10^6 - 10^7$ ergs/particle. ▽ (A hydrogen atom has a mass of 1.66×10^{-24} gm; for particles of such small mass to have such high energies, they must move exceedingly fast. The high energy cosmic ray primaries in fact have velocities very close to the velocity of light.) △ They move along the lines of force of the magnetic fields in spiral trajectories. Until recently, cosmic rays could be studied only in the immediate vicinity of the Earth's surface. Now, with radio astronomy, we can study cosmic radiation indirectly in the depths of the Milky Way and even beyond its limits, since the electrons of the cosmic rays radiate radio waves. Radio astronomy has placed the problem of the origin of cosmic radiation on a firm scientific foundation.

Until fairly recently, investigators working on the problem of the origin of life did not consider the question of ultra-high energy radiation. In my opinion, however, cosmic rays are an essential factor in evolution. The evolution of life on Earth might have been entirely different if the level of high energy radiation had been ten times greater than the present level. The rate of mutations would have increased greatly. Hence, a very important question arises: Does the level of cosmic radiation remain constant on all planets where life develops? (We are here concerned with periods of time covering many hundreds of millions of years.) Contemporary astrophysics and radio astronomy have answered this question, as we shall see in Chapter 7. ▽ This view of Shklovskii's is, in my opinion, not strongly supported by existing biological evidence. Some discussion of the causes of evolution and the role that radiation may have played in the development of life on Earth is made in Chapters 14 and 17. △

The mass of the interstellar gas in our Galaxy is approximately a billion times the mass of our Sun; yet it is no more than one percent of the total mass of the Galaxy. The remainder of the mass of the Galaxy is mostly in the form of stars.

In other galaxies, the relative content of the interstellar gas varies greatly. In elliptical galaxies [Figure 3–8] it is very small, approximately 10^{-4} or even less. In the irregular galaxies (for example, the Magellanic Clouds), interstellar gas makes up from 20 to 50 percent of the total mass of the galaxy. This circumstance is closely connected with the question of the evolution of the galaxies, a topic which we treat in Chapter 9.

6

The evolution
of the stars

But what comes after? What passes when all Creation is destroyed, when the gods are dead, and the chosen warriors, and the races of men? . . . Will there be gods again; will there be any earth or heaven?

The Ragnarok

O n a clear night, we can look up into the sky and see myriads of twinkling stars. These tiny pinpoints of light seem to move across the sky from the eastern to the western horizon, as the Earth rotates from west to east; but their relative positions are unchanged from night to night. Therefore, we can recognize certain random star groupings which suggest mythological or other images to us and call them "constellations." We know from ancient manuscripts and tablets that the constellations had much the same form many thousands of years ago as they do today—although, as is also the case with non-cosmic projective tests, they evoked different images. However, if stars were forming, evolving, and dying on a timescale of a few thousand years, the constellations of ancient times would have been very different from the present ones. Hence, we may conclude that the characteristic stellar evolutionary timescale must be at least ten thousand years—and may be much greater.

▽ Our Sun is a typical star in many respects. Its mass, radius, luminosity, and chemical composition are not extraordinary. Some stars are more massive than our Sun, others less. Some are larger in radius, others smaller. The brightest visible stars have an intrinsic luminosity much greater than our Sun's. But the nearest stars are intrinsically less bright. There are stars with a higher proportion of heavy elements than the Sun's, and others which appear to be composed primarily of hydrogen.

▽ Since the Sun is typical in so many of its characteristics, its age may also be expected to be typical. How can the Sun's age be determined? If we understood why the Sun radiates energy into space at such a prodigious rate, we could estimate its total fuel supply. This would give us a rough idea of its age and anticipated lifetime. We are therefore led to another fundamental question: Why does the Sun shine?

▽ Combustion is a familiar source of energy. If a substance such as coal—composed primarily of the element carbon—is heated in the presence of the oxygen in the atmosphere, a chemical reaction follows producing the gas carbon dioxide, CO_2, from C and O_2. Carbon and oxygen have such an affinity for each other at elevated temperatures that the reaction is violent, and much more heat is generated than is used in initiating the reaction. This released energy is observed as fire. Let us make the naïve but instructive hypothesis that the Sun shines because it is on fire. Let us assume the Sun's composition to be half coal and half oxygen, ignoring, for the moment, the spectroscopic evidence that the Sun is composed primarily of hydrogen, and contains little carbon and oxygen. The formation of one gram of carbon dioxide by the reaction $C + O_2 \rightarrow CO_2$ yields about 3.4×10^{11} ergs. Therefore, if all 2×10^{33} grams of the Sun were burnt, 3.4×10^{11} erg gm^{-1} × 2 × 10^{33} gms = 6.8 × 10^{44} ergs would be released. The Sun is radiating to space 4 × 10^{33} ergs sec^{-1}. This is the value of the solar luminosity. Therefore, the length of time the Sun could be radiating to space with our hypothetical combustion energy source at its present luminosity is (6.8 × 10^{44} ergs)/(4 × 10^{33} ergs sec^{-1}) = 1.7 × 10^{11} seconds. There are about 3.16 × 10^{7} seconds in a year; therefore, the lifetime of our burning Sun appears to be about 5400 years. If it were any older, it would be extinguished by now.

▽ Our conclusion is in reasonable agreement with the age of the Earth determined by Archbishop Ussher who, in the seventeenth century, added the lifetimes of various personages in the Bible, made appropriate interpolations and extrapolations, and concluded that the Earth was formed approximately 6000 years ago. We assume the Sun is on fire, and deduce that its lifetime is about 5400 years. This is an interesting example of the pitfalls of science. The methods are different, but the conclusions are roughly the same. (Presumably the Sun and the Earth are approximately coeval.) Some might be tempted to conclude that Biblical chronology and the coal-burning Sun hypothesis are both strengthened, and that an apocalyptic death of the Sun is imminent. However, there are other facts which are inconsistent with these views.

▽ For example, geologists find that the Earth is covered by sedimentary rock, layered down by the action of rivers and waterways. At the present sedimentation rate, tens of millions of years would be required to give the observed amount of sedimentary rock. Paleontologists find these sedimentary layers filled with fossils of organisms, now extinct, which once had world-wide distribution. Tens or hundreds of millions of years are necessary to explain the evolutionary origin of these creatures with present rates of evolution. The amount of salt in the ocean comes from alluvial erosion. From the present abundance of salt in the ocean and the present rate of erosion, it can be concluded that the salt took at least a hundred million years to accumulate.

▽ This kind of argument was common in written discussions of the ages of the Earth and the Sun late in the nineteenth century. Since that time, the discovery of radioactivity has placed the entire subject of the Earth's chronology on a firm basis. The isotopes of some elements, such as uranium, spontaneously and unpredictably emit charged particles from their nuclei and then weigh less; they have been transmuted to a different atom of lower atomic weight. When a uranium isotope completes its sequence of radioactive decays, it becomes a particular isotope of lead. The lead is stable, and decays no more. The characteristic time for, say, half a given lump of uranium to turn into lead can be determined; the time is unaffected by the local temperature, pressure, or other conditions. Therefore, by measuring the amounts of uranium and lead isotopes in a given sample of rock, we can derive the time elapsed since the piece of rock first formed, as well as its original chemical composition. In this way, it has been possible to conclude that the Earth assumed its present form some 4.5 × 10^{9} years ago. Analyses of meteorites—small chunks of stone and iron from the asteroid belt—show they were formed in the same epoch as Earth. Since it seems unlikely that the Earth or the asteroids were formed much before the Sun, we can conclude that the Sun is at least 4.5×10^9 years old. And, because the Sun is a typical star, the characteristic ages of many stars are therefore several billions of years.

▽ But what is the energy source which makes the Sun shine? We have seen that combusion is far too feeble. At the turn of the century, other explanations were proposed. Some thought that solar energy was supplied by the collision of large numbers of meteors with the Sun; others suggested that the Sun was slowly contracting, and that the slow increase of density in the solar interior was responsible for the observed solar luminosity. But the lifetimes computed with these assumptions were too small by factors of 100 or more. Obviously, some other energy source existed, but its nature could only be dimly surmised. In 1926, the British astrophysicist Sir Arthur Stanley Eddington mused, "Does energy issue freely from matter at 40,000,000° as steam issues from water at 100°?"

▽ It is curious that the same discovery of radioactivity which led to an accurate determination of the age of the Earth also resulted in an understanding of the solar luminosity. From the mass and composition of the Sun, it is possible to compute the pressure in its interior, since this pressure is determined by the weight of the overlying material. The gases near the Sun's center are found to have temperatures of ten million degrees or more. Advances made in nuclear physics in the 1930's proved that at such temperatures atoms collide with each other so vigorously that enormous quantities of energy are released, in an atomic analogy to the way heat is released during the molecular combustion of carbon. Eddington's question was answered affirmatively. Since the Sun is composed primarily of hydrogen, the thermonuclear reactions which occur in the solar interior involve the jamming together of four hydrogen nuclei, or protons, and the formation of one helium nucleus. The rate of such reactions is strongly dependent upon the temperature. The liberated energy slowly emerges from the interior of the Sun, and is finally transformed, near the surface, into radiation that is emitted into space. This is the only source of the Sun's power today.

▽ The energy released is about 6×10^{18} ergs for each gram of hydrogen converted into helium. Thus, the process is about ten million times more efficient than the burning of coal. This is also approximately the same factor of increased efficiency—if that is the word—of thermonuclear weapons over ordinary explosives such as TNT. A nuclear device weighing about a ton may provide an explosive energy of ten megatons—that is, of ten million tons of TNT. This common nomenclature for nuclear weapon firepower testifies to the 10^7 greater efficiency of thermonuclear processes over chemical processes.

▽ The same factor of 10^7 is the increase in the age of the Sun which we obtain by using thermonuclear rather than chemical energy sources. Instead of 5×10^3 years for the lifetime of the Sun, we obtain $5 \times 10^3 \times 10^7 = 5 \times 10^{10}$ years, or, comfortably, about ten times the age of the Earth. Thus, if the Sun should spend all of its hydrogen nuclear capital, it could shine with its present luminosity for another 45 billion years or so ($5 \times 10^{10} - 5 \times 10^9 = 4.5 \times 10^{10}$). However, there is a limit to the amount of hydrogen which the Sun can convert into helium before other complications occur. Recent calculations estimate that the Sun can be expected to shine at its present luminosity, on the main sequence, for about another 8 billion years. What happens after that, and the resulting consequences for the Earth will be discussed presently.

▽ It was once believed that all the stars in the heavens were formed at about the same time, several billions of years ago. But there are now a number of lines of evidence indicating that stars are being formed continuously, by condensation of the interstellar gas and dust. Even today, the mysterious processes of stellar origins are occurring in regions of the Galaxy difficult for us to observe, and by mechanisms we only incompletely understand.

▽ The problem of stellar evolution can be likened to the processes of human development. Imagine, in keeping with the ultimate subject matter of this book, that you are an intelligent extraterrestrial being—probably not a Martian—landed for the first time on Earth. You would most probably, quickly pass over other living creatures, from viruses to baleen whales, and come to focus your attention on human beings as the most important life form on the planet. Looking at a random sample of human beings, you would observe two sexes, a fairly wide range of colors, various physiognomic peculiarities, and a continuum of sizes, from about 50 cm to about 200 cm. The 50 cm human beings would be very rare. There would be a continuous distribution of sizes, with a peak around 170 cm. Occasionally, you would come upon locales—say, schoolyards—where there was a concentration of human beings in the 120 cm size range. You would be faced with the problem of explaining the origin of human beings. Is each size, sex, and color immutable? Do the little ones become big ones? Do the big ones become little ones? Do changes in sex or color occur? Frequently, or rarely? If you were only on the Earth for a period much shorter than the characteristic timescale for human development—say you were on the Earth for a week—any conclusion regarding human growth would have to be inferential, and not directly observed. You would also have to eliminate effects of observational selection, because the newly formed human beings would be the most difficult to observe. And even if you had formulated the correct hypothesis about human development, the methods of origin of individual human beings might still be obscure; in fact, the correct explanation might seem, on superficial grounds, highly unlikely. Our understanding of the life cycle of the stars is not dissimilar.

▽ We have been observing stars in detail for only a few hundred years. We have seen the lifetime of a star such as the Sun to be about 10^{10} years. Therefore, we have observed typical stars for only 10^{-8} of their life cycle. The comparable situation in the observation of human beings (characteristic lifetimes, 60 years) would be observations for $60 \times 10^{-8} = 6 \times 10^{-7}$ years $= 6 \times 10^{-7}$ years $\times 3 \times 10^{7}$ seconds year^{-1} = 18 seconds. It would be a very intelligent extraterrestrial indeed who could understand the human life cycle after 18 seconds of observation. The depth of our understanding of stellar evolution is therefore especially remarkable.

▽ We know that all stars, like all people, are not the same age, and that, as a star passes through its life cycle, it takes on the characteristics of many superficially different kinds of stars. Some stars are relatively young objects; others are much older than the Sun. The young stars are generally the very bright ones. Stars with large intrinsic luminosities burn their nuclear fuel very rapidly, and have corresponding short lifetimes. △

The groups of young stars are concentrated in the spiral arms of the Galaxy, those twisting tubes of magnetic force which contain most of the interstellar gas in the Milky Way. We recall that the Galactic magnetic field strengths are very weak, not exceeding 10^{-5} gauss. Magnetic forces, then, would not be strong enough to affect the motions of such dense and massive objects as the stars. Thus, we conclude that young stars are found only within the spiral arms, not because the Galactic magnetic field holds them there, but because they have only recently been formed out of the interstellar gas concentrated there. The older stars are found in great numbers in the Galactic nucleus, and in the halo of the Galaxy. Here, the gas density is very low. Some of these older stars have traveled far from their birthplaces over timescales of 10^8 or 10^9 years. Thus the distribution of old stars and young stars in the Galaxy is an important argument supporting the view that stars are formed from the interstellar medium.

▽ Let us now consider the evolution of the stars. Since the earliest stages of stellar evolution are still unknown, we will concern ourselves with the current theoretical picture of the evolution of interstellar gas masses. It is postulated that, under certain specific conditions, a cloud of interstellar gas and dust begins to condense. Perhaps this occurs by gravitational forces, each part of the interstellar cloud attracting all the other parts. The cloud may fragment into smaller clouds; the smaller clouds, into still smaller ones, until eventually a cloud of approximately stellar mass is formed. We may picture it as a relatively dense, opaque gas sphere. △

Strictly speaking, this sphere is not yet a star, since the temperatures in its central regions are not high enough for the occurrence of thermonuclear reactions. At these low temperatures, the gas pressures inside the sphere are not great enough to overcome the forces of gravitational attraction between individual grains and atoms. Hence, the sphere continues to contract. It is believed that protostars in this opaque, distended stage, can be seen, in gaseous nebulae, as small, dark splotches, called globules [see Figures 6–1 and 6–2]. There are reasons to believe that protostars are formed collectively. Subsequently, these groups of protostars evolve into stellar associations or clusters. It is highly probable that during this early stage of evolution aggregates of smaller masses are formed around the stars, and that these are gradually transformed into planets [see Chapters 11–13].

As a protostar contracts, its gravitational potential energy is being converted into heat and light. It takes tremendous amounts of energy to heat a stellar mass from temperatures near absolute zero to tens of millions of degrees. The remainder of the potential energy released during contraction is radiated into surrounding space. Since the dimensions of the contracting gas sphere are very large, the amount of energy radiated to space by each unit of surface area—say, one square

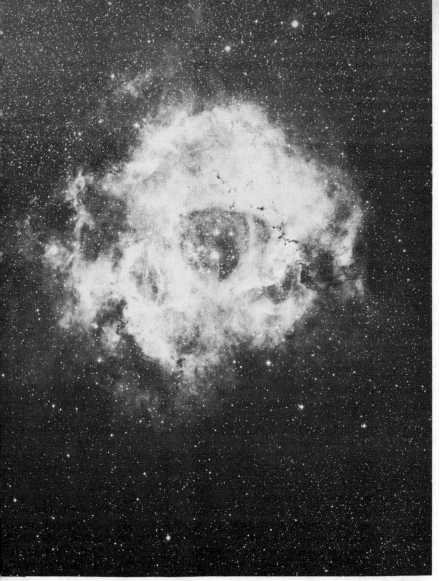

FIGURE 6–1. *The gas and dust nebula NGC 2237 in the constellation Monoceros. The dark splotches are thought to be great concentrations of absorbing dust. The small black globules may be cold stars in the earliest stages of formation. (Courtesy of Mt. Wilson and Palomar Observatories.)*

FIGURE 6–2. *An enlarged portion of the nebula NGC 2237, showing the absorbing clouds and globules more distinctly. (Courtesy of Mt. Wilson and Palomar Observatories.)*

centimeter—will be very small. The Stefan-Boltzmann law of physics shows that the amount of energy radiated by unit surface area is proportional to the fourth power of the temperature. Thus, if the temperature is doubled, the radiation per unit surface area is increased by $2^4 = 16$ times. The surface layers of such protostars may therefore be relatively cool, while the luminosity may be almost the same as for older evolved stars of similar mass, the larger surface area compensating for the lower temperatures. Such protostars, with low temperatures, but not necessarily low luminosities, therefore lie to the right of the main sequence in the spectrum-luminosity, or Hertzsprung-Russell, diagram described in Chapter 4; that is, they fall into the region of the red giants or red dwarfs, depending on the mass of the protostar.

As time passes, the protostar continues to contract. Its dimensions become smaller, and both its interior and surface temperatures increase. ▽ This earliest contraction phase of the protostar occurs relatively rapidly, on the cosmic timescale. The contraction time depends only on the initial density of the gas cloud. If the original gas cloud had a density of 10^4 atoms in every cubic centimeter, the collapse time would be about 5×10^5 years. If the original density is greater, the collapse time is smaller, because the attractive gravitational forces leading to collapse become more efficient as the density is increased. The interior temperatures of the protostar reach about 100,000°K at this point. Since this is not high enough to initiate thermonuclear reactions, a star has not yet formed. But the temperature is large enough to ionize the hydrogen and helium which are the predominant constituents of the protostar; that is, the temperatures become high enough so that electrons are stripped off atoms of hydrogen and helium by violent collisions. These ionized atoms are much more efficient absorbers of the radiation generated in the protostellar interior than are their neutral counterparts having a full complement of electrons. The increase in stellar opacity, in turn, raises the internal temperatures. Radiation which previously escaped to space is now trapped in the interior and causes it to heat still further. At this critical temperature, the atoms and ions in the interior of the star are moving fast enough to exert an upward pressure approximately balancing the weight of the overlying material. In this approximate equilibrium situation, the rate of contraction of the star declines.

▽ The star now goes into a stage of convection, in which there is mass exchange between the interior and the exterior. Having increased in luminosity during the collapse phase, the star now decreases in luminosity and approaches the main sequence, as shown in Figure 6–3. Here, we see a temperature-luminosity diagram such as was described in Chapter 4. The oblique, solid line represents the main sequence.

▽ The vertical axis represents the luminosity, in units of the solar luminosity, $L\odot$. For example, $L/L\odot = 10$ represents a luminosity ten times greater than the Sun's. The horizontal axis represents the temperature of the outer layers of the star, those which radiate directly to space. The temperatures are expressed in thousands of degrees Kelvin. The present position of the Sun is located at the point $L/L\odot = 1$, and a temperature of 6000°K, approximately. We see that the contraction phase in the early evolution of a star of solar mass begins at the very

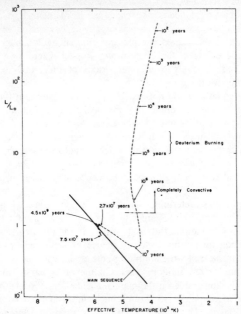

FIGURE 6–3. *A theoretical diagram of the evolutionary track of a star of solar mass, on its way toward the main sequence. The evolutionary track is shown as the dashed line beginning at very high luminosities and descending towards the inclined solid line which represents the main sequence. The point marked 4.5 × 10⁹ years represents the present position of the Sun. (Courtesy of Dr. A. G. W. Cameron and Dr. G. Ezer, Institute for Space Studies, New York.)*

high luminosity of $L/L\odot$ somewhat less than 1000. We see, however, that it is declining in luminosity very rapidly, and in a few million years it has approximately the present solar luminosity. In something like 100 million years, it has traversed the hook, shown by the dashed line, and entered onto the main sequence. △ The temperature in the stellar interior has now become sufficient for thermonuclear reactions to begin. The pressure of the gas in the interior regions balances the forces of gravitational attraction, and the gaseous sphere stops contracting. The protostar has become a star.

We may, in fact, be observing stars in the stage of vertical contraction towards the main sequence. A species called the T Tauri stars are found embedded in dark nebulae. ▽ Their luminosity changes, sometimes erratically, with time. There is some evidence that they are losing mass, and they are found in the appropriate part of the temperature-luminosity diagram. △

After the star terminates its contraction phase and enters the main sequence, its position in the temperature-luminosity diagram changes very little, over long periods of time. ▽ For example, our Sun has moved up and to the left along the main sequence only a very small amount (corresponding to an increase in luminosity of half a magnitude, or by about 20%) during the past 5×10^9 years. △ On the main sequence, the radiation is maintained by thermonuclear reactions in the interior and by the accompanying conversion of hydrogen into helium. Thus, the main sequence represents not an evolutionary track but the geometric locus of points in the Hertzsprung–Russell diagram on which stars of various masses radiate stably over long periods of time, due to thermonuclear reactions in their interiors.

All stars of equal mass do not occupy the same position in the Hertzsprung–Russell diagram, because of differences in chemical compositions. If a protostar has a relatively small amount of heavy elements, the star arrives on the main sequence at a lower position than if its heavy element content were high. We have already mentioned this theoretical result which explains the sequence of subdwarfs, having a heavy element content about ten times smaller than that of the main sequence stars, and lying below the main sequence appropriate to the majority of stars.

A star's initial mass determines its lifetime on the main sequence. If the mass is great, the interior temperatures are also very large, and the star becomes a very powerful source of radiation. But as a result, it rapidly depletes its supply of hydrogen fuel. Thus, for example, main sequence stars with masses 20 or 30 times greater than that of the Sun—the hot blue giants of spectral class O—remain on the main sequence only a few million years. On the other hand, stars with masses close to that of our Sun reside on the main sequence for 10 or 15 billion years. In Table II, we see a computed estimate of the main sequence lifetimes of stars in various spectral classes. The values of the masses, radii, and luminosities of these stars are also indicated in solar units—a mass of 10 means a mass ten times that of the Sun, or $10 \times 2 \times 10^{33}$ grams $= 2 \times 10^{34}$ grams, and so forth.

According to present estimates, the Galaxy is approximately 10 to 20 billion years old. In Table II, we see that the calculated period of time that stars later than K0 spend on the main sequence is much greater than the Galaxy's age. Therefore we conclude that none of these stars have left the main sequence.

The burning of hydrogen—its conversion into helium by thermonuclear reactions—occurs in stellar interiors, because both the high temperatures required to initiate such reactions and the convection necessary for supplying fresh hydrogen for future reactions are found only in this region. Since there is a finite amount of hydrogen in the core, the nuclear fuel will, sooner or later (depending on the star's mass) become entirely depleted. All the hydrogen in the star is not available for nuclear reactions, and eventually a star is left with a hot core composed almost entirely of the thermonuclear reaction product, helium.

What happens to a star when all, or almost all, of the hydrogen in its core is exhausted? The generation of nuclear energy in the central regions must cease. At this juncture the temperatures and the pressures will not be great enough to oppose the gravitational forces which originally contracted the star. The core will then begin to contract while—▽ because of the high temperatures of the interior △—the surface layers expand. The internal temperatures will then increase, while

TABLE II. PROPERTIES OF MAIN SEQUENCE STARS

Stellar spectral type	Mass in units of the Sun	Radius in units of the Sun	Luminosity in units of the Sun	Residence time on the main sequence in years
B0	17.0	9.0	30,000	8×10^6
B5	6.3	4.2	1,000	8×10^7
A0	3.2	2.8	100	4×10^8
A5	1.9	1.5	12	2×10^9
F0	1.5	1.25	4.8	4×10^9
F5	1.3	1.24	2.7	6×10^9
G0	1.02	1.02	1.2	1.1×10^{10}
G2 (the Sun)	1.00	1.00	1.0	1.3×10^{10}
G5	0.91	0.92	0.72	1.7×10^{10}
K0	0.74	0.74	0.35	2.8×10^{10}
K5	0.54	0.54	0.10	7.0×10^{10}

the surface temperatures decline. ▽ The increase in surface area of the star more than compensates for the decline in surface temperature; therefore, after the hydrogen in its core becomes depleted, the luminosity of the star will increase. If the star increases in luminosity and decreases in temperature, it must move off the main sequence upward and to the right in the Hertzsprung–Russell diagram. The star has now become a red giant. △

Meanwhile, back in the interior, a very dense, hot region is formed within the core, consisting of helium and small amounts of heavier elements. Nuclear reactions will not occur in this hot region, because the hydrogen there is exhausted. Such reactions *will* take place in a relatively thin layer on the periphery of the nucleus. As the star becomes a red giant, its luminosity is maintained by a thin shell of hydrogen "burning," which separates the helium-rich core from the hydrogen-rich envelope. If the heavy element content is smaller, the red giant will have a higher luminosity.

▽ Figure 6–4 shows a temperature-luminosity diagram giving the theoretically computed evolutionary tracks of stars of various masses. The figure is not as complicated as it appears at first sight. The vertical axis is the logarithm of the stellar luminosity, in units of the sun—that is, 0 indicates a luminosity $10^0 = 1$ times that of the sun, or just the solar luminosity; 2 denotes $10^2 = 100$ times the solar luminosity; -2 indicates 10^{-2}, or $1/100$ the solar luminosity, and so forth. The horizontal axis gives the logarithm of the effective surface temperature; hence a value of 3.0 means a temperature of $10^3 = 1000$ degrees; 4.0 indicates a temperature of $10^4 = 10,000°$; 5.0 indicates a temperature of $10^5 = 100,000°$, etc. The evolutionary tracks off the main sequence are shown for stars having 0.7 of a solar mass, 4 solar masses, and 15.6 solar masses. These stars leave the main sequence at the positions marked by H; that is, they are burning hydrogen in a shell source. We see that a star of 0.7 solar mass leaves the main sequence almost

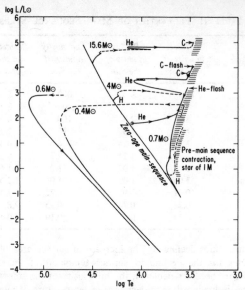

FIGURE 6-4. *Theoretically computed evolutionary tracks on the Hertzsprung-Russell diagram for stars of various masses.* After C. Hayashi, R. Hoshi, and D. Sugimoto, *Progress of Theoretical Physics, Suppl. 22, Kyoto* (1962).

vertically, while stars of larger solar masses leave more horizontally. As a result, the evolutionary tracks tend to "focus" the stars into the same red giant region of the diagram. △ The subsequent evolutionary history of these red giants, as indicated on the diagram, will be discussed presently.

It is important to compare the observed spectrum-luminosity diagrams for individual star clusters with the results of calculations such as those exhibited in Figure 6-4. Clusters of stars—for example, the Pleiades—are chosen because we can assume that such stellar aggregations are approximately coeval. ▽ If they had not been formed at about the same time, it would be difficult to understand their physical association. The faster-moving members of such stellar associations would escape; the cluster also tends to be disrupted by external gravitational perturbations. △ By comparing the spectrum-luminosity diagrams of older clusters with those of younger ones, it is possible to confirm the theoretical calculations of stellar evolution, and even to deduce the ages of individual star clusters. In Figures 6-5 and 6-6, we see spectrum-luminosity diagrams for two different stellar clusters. The horizontal axis is given in terms of color index $(B - V)$, a quantity closely related to the spectral type and temperature of the star, and defined at the beginning of Chapter 4. In Figure 6-5, each dot represents the color index and luminosity of an individual star in the galactic star cluster NGC 2254. (▽ NGC is

80

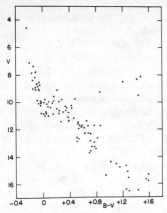

FIGURE 6–5. *Hertzsprung-Russell diagram of the very young galactic star cluster NGC 2254. Reproduced, with permission, from M. Walker,* Astrophysical Journal, *Suppl. 23 (1956).*

an abbreviation for New General Catalogue, a fairly indiscriminate collection of galaxies, gaseous nebulae, and star clusters. It *was* new, when first published, in 1888, but the name now seems less appropriate as the Catalogue has become musty with age. △) The diagram for NGC 2254 shows a heavy concentration of hot, massive stars situated in the upper left of the main sequence. (The color index 0.2 corresponds to a surface temperature of 20,000°K, that is, to a spectrum of

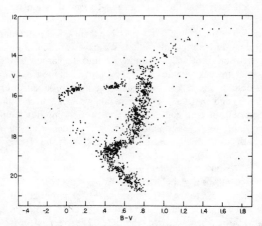

FIGURE 6–6. *Hertzsprung-Russell diagram of the highly evolved globular cluster M3. Reproduced, with permission, from H. L. Johnson and A. R. Sandage,* Astrophysical Journal 124, *379 (1956).*

type B.) ▽ The presence of such hot stars immediately tells us that NGC 2254 is a relatively young formation. △

The globular cluster M3 is an old object. (▽ It is called M3 after an entirely separate, and partially overlapping, catalogue compiled by a French gentleman-astronomer named Messier. △) The diagram of M3 contains almost no stars in the upper left segment of the main sequence. On the other hand, the red giant branch, extending to the right of the main sequence, is very populated. We note that in the diagram for NGC 2254, there are very few red giants. Thus, we conclude that the older clusters, such as M3, have a large number of stars which have already left the main sequence, while the young clusters, such as NGC 2254, contain only a few stars which have evolved this far.

In Figure 6–6, for M3, we see an almost horizontal branch of stars, gently sloping from the upper right to the middle left. There is no analogous branch in Figure 6–5, for NGC 2254. Is it possible that highly evolved stars travel through this horizontal branch? After the temperatures of the dense, contracting helium core of the red giant reach 1.0 to 1.5×10^8 °K, a new kind of thermonuclear reaction sets in. At these temperatures, helium nuclei are jammed together to form carbon nuclei, and additional radiation is released. As soon as this helium burning begins, the contraction of the core ceases. The temperature of the surface layers increases, and the star moves to the left in the spectrum-luminosity diagram. ▽ This feature can be seen in the theoretical evolutionary tracks [Figure 6–4], for example, for a star of 4 solar masses. Detailed computations show even more complicated tracks, and a single star may traverse sections of the horizontal branch many times during its lifetime. The sudden onset of helium burning is known as the "helium flash." The star of 0.7 solar masses, in Figure 6–4, can be observed to reverse its upward motion in the Hertzsprung–Russell diagram very rapidly, after the helium flash.

▽ After much of the helium in the core is exhausted, the situation is somewhat analogous to that after hydrogen depletion. We have carbon burning only near the center, and a shell source of helium burning around the carbon core of the star. In the star of 4 solar masses [Figure 6–4], the onset of carbon burning occurs very rapidly, and is described as a "carbon flash." The main products of carbon burning are oxygen, neon, and magnesium. In general, we can see that there will be a continual progression of core contractions, increases in interior temperatures, and the synthesis of more massive elements in the stellar interior, as the star wends its complicated path through the horizontal branch of the Hertzsprung–Russell diagram.

▽ Figure 6–7 shows the combined color-luminosity diagram for eleven clusters, one of which, M3, is a globular cluster. We see that the main sequence of the different clusters are bent to the right and upwards. The horizontal axis as before, is the color index, which is related to the spectrum and to the temperature of the star, the temperature increasing to the left. The vertical axis is the visual magnitude of the star, which is proportional to the logarithm of the stellar luminosity. These units are the same as for the previous diagrams, in which individual stars were shown for the clusters M3 and NGC 2254. The only

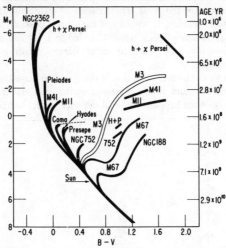

FIGURE 6–7. *Combined Hertzsprung-Russell diagrams for a variety of star clusters.* (*After A. R. Sandage.*)

difference between the figures is that in Figure 6–7 the absolute visual magnitude is used, to facilitate the comparison of different clusters. In Figures 6–5 and 6–6 only the apparent visual magnitudes have been displayed.

▽ We have seen that the most luminous stars on the main sequence—those toward the top of the Hertzsprung–Russell diagram—burn their nuclear fuel most quickly and are therefore the first stars in a given cluster to turn off toward the right in the spectrum-luminosity diagram and become red giants. With the passage of time, stars further down the main sequence will move off it into the red giant region. Therefore a simple examination of the turnoff point in the main sequence of any star cluster provides an estimate of its age. The ages of the clusters can also be plotted along the vertical axis on the right-hand side of Figure 6–7. We see, for example, that the cluster h and χ Persei has an age of a few million years, while M3 has an age of perhaps 6 billion years, and the galactic cluster M67 is even older. The Hertzsprung–Russell diagram of M67, showing the individual stars, is given in Figure 6–8. We see that the turnoff is at about apparent visual magnitude 12.5. The existence of the giant branch and the horizontal branch testify to its age. The age of the oldest cluster in the Galaxy, determined from its turnoff point, sets a lower limit to the age of the Galaxy. The Galaxy must certainly be older than the star clusters contained within it. In this way, an estimate of 10 to 20 billion years has been obtained for the age of the Galaxy. If the individual stars in globular or galactic clusters of other galaxies could be resolved and their magnitudes measured, we would be able to make some estimates of the lifetimes of other galaxies. Unfortunately, the other galaxies are too far away to permit such measurements. △

THE EVOLUTION OF THE STARS

This advancement in our understanding of the constitution and evolution of the stars has been one of the great achievements of astronomy during the second half of the twentieth century. It would not have been possible without investigations in the field of nuclear physics, which have led to a detailed comprehension of the nuclear reactions which take place in stellar interiors, or without the aid of high-speed electronic computers.

Let us consider the further evolution of the stars, the stage that comes after red giants. Helium, carbon, and similar burnings in the interiors of the stars cannot proceed indefinitely. What happens when all the nuclear fuel sources are exhausted?

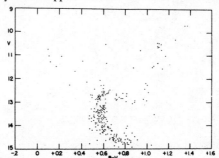

FIGURE 6–8. *Hertzsprung-Russell diagram for the very old galactic star cluster M67. Reproduced, with permission, from H. L. Johnson and A. R. Sandage,* Astrophysical Journal *121, 616 (1955).*

Direct observations and a number of theoretical considerations suggest that in the next stage of the stellar life cycle, a significant fraction of the mass of the star is shed. The outer layers may become separated from the star, and move further and further away, to form a planetary nebula, such as that shown in Figure 6–9.

The intense ultraviolet radiation of the central star, the "nucleus" of the planetary nebula, will ionize the neutral atoms in the nebula and cause them to fluoresce. In some tens of thousands of years, the nebula will dissipate, and only the small, hot, dense central star will remain. Gradually cooling, this star eventually becomes a white dwarf. Thus, the white dwarfs grow in the interiors of the red giants and appear after the external layers of the red giants are ejected. ∇ It is conjectured that in some cases, the shedding of the stellar envelope may occur, not by the formation of a planetary nebula, but by gradual mass ejection. Some examples are known of red giants which are gradually losing matter to space. △

That white dwarfs, of immense density, are a final stage in stellar evolution has been supported by direct observations. The older stellar clusters, for example the Hyades and Praesepe, contain many white dwarfs, while the younger clusters, for example the Pleiades, contain few.

As the white dwarfs gradually cool, they radiate less and less, changing into invisible "black" dwarfs. These stars are dead and cold, but have an enormous

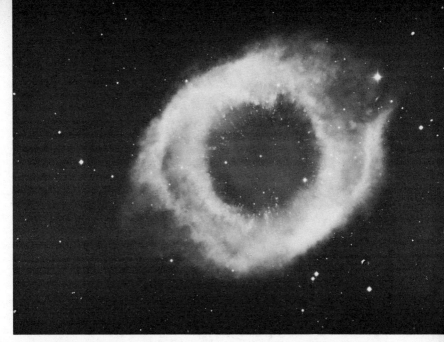

FIGURE 6–9. *The planetary nebula NGC 7293 in the constellation Aquarius. Note the fine lines radiating away from the central star, suggesting that this planetary nebula was formed in an explosion of titanic proportions. (Courtesy of Mt. Wilson and Palomar Observatories.)*

density, millions of times greater than water. Their dimensions are less than the dimensions of the Earth, but their masses are comparable with that of the Sun. The cooling process goes on for many billions of years. ▽ Such final evolutionary tracks in the Hertzsprung–Russell diagram can be seen in Figure 6–4, in the lower left of the diagram. The stars move downward and to the right, that is, towards lower temperatures and lower luminosities. The light from the star becomes feebler and feebler, and ultimately disappears. The star has died. △

We must emphasize again that the rate of stellar evolution is determined by the initial composition and initial stellar mass. Since our Galaxy has been in existence approximately 10 to 20 billion years, only those stars with masses exceeding a certain critical value will have gone through the entire evolutionary sequence towards the black dwarf. This critical mass seems to be only 10 or 20 percent greater than the mass of our Sun. ▽ That is, a star of 1.2 solar masses, formed 10 billion years ago, would now be well into the white dwarf evolutionary stage. △

Our Sun was formed about 5 billion years ago. It is believed that the Galaxy at that time was similar, in its basic characteristics, to its present form. For at least 4.5 billion years, our Sun has resided on the main sequence, stably radiating energy due to the thermonuclear reactions in its interior. How long will this stability continue? ▽ The evolution of the Sun can be seen in Figure 6–10. The vertical axis shows the luminosity and the radius of the Sun, in terms of their present values. The horizontal axis shows the age of the Sun in units of 10^{17} seconds. We recall that one year is about 3×10^7 seconds, so 10^{17} seconds is about 3×10^9 years. The two curves for the change in the luminosity and radius of the Sun as time progresses intersect at about 1.5×10^{17} seconds, or about 4.5×10^9 years, approximately the age of the Sun. We see that from the Sun's origin to the present, its luminosity has increased somewhat, while its radius has hardly increased at all. As time goes on, the luminosity of the Sun will begin to increase sharply. In another 6 billion years, when the age of the Sun is 3.5×10^{17} seconds, the luminosity will be increasing very rapidly indeed, and the radius will also begin to increase. The Sun will be well on its way to becoming a red giant. Several calculations have been performed, giving results similar to those of Figure 6–10. △

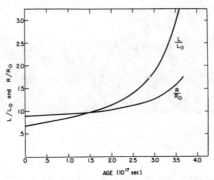

FIGURE 6–10. *Theoretical calculations of the variation of the luminosity, L, and the radius, R, of the Sun as a function of time. $L_\odot$ and $R_\odot$ refer to contemporary values. (Courtesy of Professor Fred Hoyle, Cambridge University.)*

The most recent calculations indicate that our Sun will become a red giant in approximately 8 billion years. The red giant stage will last for several hundred millions of years. Finally, by mass ejection or nova outburst, the gigantic Sun will discard its atmospheric envelope, and rapidly become a white dwarf.

▽ One result of the evolution of our Sun through the red giant phase will very likely be the reduction of our Earth to a bleak, charred cinder. The increase in luminosity of the Sun will cause the surface temperatures of the Earth and the other planets to increase. As the swollen, distended red Sun increases in size, the oceans of the Earth will boil away. The top of the terrestrial atmosphere will become exceedingly hot, and our atmosphere will evaporate away to space. Eventually the Sun will engulf the orbits of Mercury and Venus; its surface will approach the orbit of the Earth. Whether life of any sort will survive until that remote epoch, and whether terrestrial intelligence could conceivably be equal to the supreme challenges of those times, are questions worth pondering. △

THE UNIVERSE

7

Supernovae

If the radiance of a thousand suns were to burst into the sky that would be the splendor of the Mighty One.

Bhagavad Gita

In the previous chapter we discussed the evolution of a normal star from its origin as a condensing cloud of gas and dust to its old age as a super-dense, cold, black dwarf. All stars, however, do not pass through these normal stages of development. Certain stars, at definite periods during their evolution, explode, creating a brilliant display of cosmic pyrotechnics, called supernovae.

There is no cataclysm of individual stars which is larger or more magnificent than the supernova. After the explosion, the stellar luminosity may increase 100 million times; for a short period, one supernova may radiate more light than a billion stars. Cases are known where the brightness of a supernova surpasses the brightness of the entire galaxy which contains it.

▽ The spectra of supernovae show that, compared with ordinary stars, they contain a relatively small amount of hydrogen and a relatively large amount of helium, iron, and other heavy elements. Because it is thought that older evolved stars have transmuted their hydrogen into heavier elements, the spectra support the hypothesis that supernovae are one cause, more violent than most, of the death of a star. △

Supernovae occur infrequently. In large stellar systems such as the Milky Way, there is only about one explosion each century. As a result, astronomers are much more likely to observe such phenomena in the other galaxies. If we systematically search several hundred galaxies during a period of one year, it is highly probable that we will discover at least one supernova. This is a more expedient observational technique than waiting for an explosion to occur in our own Galaxy.

▽ The appearance of a supernova in the spiral galaxy NGC 4725 may be seen in Figure 7–1. The top photograph was taken on May 10, 1940, when the supernova exceeded in brightness all other regions of the spiral arms of this galaxy, except for the galactic nucleus; the bottom photograph was taken on January 2, 1941, when no supernova was evident. Figure 7–2 shows a less spectacular but more common variety of supernova; this occurred in the nearer galaxy M101. Here too, we have a "before" and "after" sequence, with the arrow indicating the supernova. △

Despite the infrequency of supernovae in the Milky Way, a number have been recorded in historical times. On July 4 (▽ sic! △), 1054, a "guest-star" appeared in the sky; it was duly reported by Chinese scholars. This star was so bright that it could be seen during the daylight hours. It surpassed Venus in luminosity; only the Moon and Sun were brighter. For several months this star was visible to the naked eye; then it gradually faded from view.

In compiling his catalogue of nebulae, Messier placed as first an object of unusual form which subsequently became known as the "Crab Nebula," or, more

FIGURE 7–1. *Top: Photograph of the galaxy NGC 4725 in the constellation Coma Berenices, taken on 10 May, 1940. A supernova explosion is indicated by the straight line. Bottom: The same galaxy photographed on 2 January, 1941. The great decline in intensity of the supernova is evident. (Courtesy of Mt. Wilson and Palomar Observatories.)*

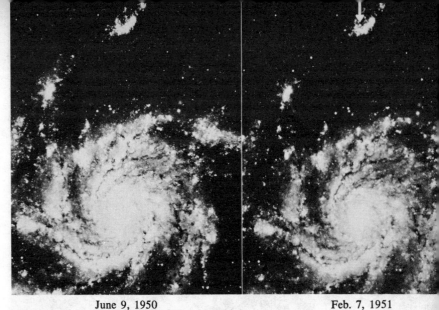

June 9, 1950   Feb. 7, 1951

FIGURE 7–2. *Two photographs of the type Sc galaxy NGC 5457 in the constellation Ursa Major. The supernova is observed in one of the extensive spiral arms of this galaxy, which is also known as Messier 101. (Courtesy of Mt. Wilson and Palomar Observatories.)*

familiarly, "The Crab." Figure 7–3 shows a photograph of the Crab taken through a filter which passed only red light. Systematic observations indicate that the Crab Nebula is slowly expanding, as if it were unraveling in the sky. Since it is more than 1000 parsecs from us, the very fact that we can detect this increase in dimensions means that its velocity of expansion is enormous. ▽ Since we can measure its apparent rate of expansion in angular units, and since we know its distance, we can compute its true velocity of expansion. △ It has been calculated that this velocity approaches 1000 km/sec; that is, more than 100 times the velocity of an artificial Earth satellite. In contrast, the velocity of the motion of normal gaseous nebulae is usually no greater than 20 to 30 km/sec. Only an explosion of titanic proportions could have caused the observed expansion.

The Crab is located in that region of the sky where the strange stellar "guest" was observed in 1054 A.D. The velocity of expansion indicates that approximately 900 years ago the whole cloud was contained within a very small volume. It can be concluded that this nebula is indeed the residue of the gigantic cosmic cataclysm observed in China during the time of the Sung Dynasty.

The Crab Nebula has played a particularly important role in astrophysics during the last decade. As one of the nearest supernova remnants, it is more easily

FIGURE 7–3. *Photograph of Messier 1, the Crab Nebula, in the constellation Taurus, taken in red light. These turbulent expanding gases are the remnants of a supernova which exploded in our own Galaxy in A.D. 1054. (Courtesy of Mt. Wilson and Palomar Observatories.)*

investigated than others. The remains of similar stellar explosions which have briefly flared from time to time in our Galaxy are scattered throughout the sky. All, with a few exceptions, are older than the Crab. The clouds of Figure 7–4, a filamentary nebula of supernova origin in the constellation Cygnus, are estimated to be several tens of thousands of years old.

How can we distinguish normal gas clouds, the diffuse nebulae such as M 20, the Trifid Nebula [shown in Figure 7–5], from a supernova? In 1949 it was discovered that the Crab Nebula is a very powerful source of radio radiation. ▽ There are several possible sources of radio radiation. Might there be a titanic radio broadcasting station in the Crab Nebula? This seems unlikely for several reasons. The signals from the Crab Nebula are not modulated and occasionally intelligible, as the emission from radio broadcasting stations sometimes is; nor is the emission confined to one frequency, or "station." Instead, the radiation is spread over a wide range of radio frequencies. It sounds very much like "static." Any hot object will emit electromagnetic radiation at all frequencies—gamma rays, x-rays, ultraviolet light, visible light, infrared radiation, and radio waves. However, in thermal radiation, the intensity at radio frequencies should be inversely proportional to the square of the wavelength. Instead, the intensity of radiation from the

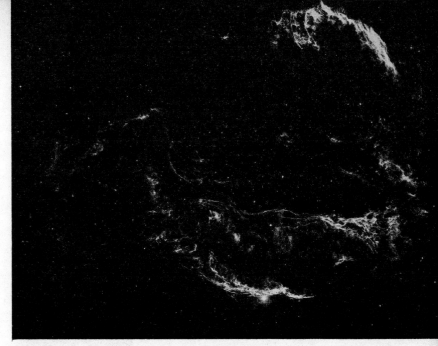

FIGURE 7–4. *A filamentary nebula in the constellation Cygnus, showing a region of strong radio emission. Photographed in red light. (Courtesy of Mt. Wilson and Palomar Observatories.)*

Crab is found to be more nearly the same at many frequencies. Hence, the emission must be non-thermal.

▽ Shklovskii was able to demonstrate that the non-thermal radio emission of the Crab Nebula can be explained as synchrotron radiation. This is radiation such as is observed in an electron synchrotron, a successor to the cyclotron. In the synchrotron, strong magnetic fields cause electrons to move at very high velocities, approaching the velocity of light. They are constrained to spiral along the magnetic lines of force. The acceleration of the electrons causes them to emit light; by adjusting the acceleration, the electrons can be made to emit light of any frequency desired, from the visible to the radio region. If we postulate appropriate magnetic fields in the Crab Nebula, the radio emission can be explained in a similar way. △ The radio radiation of the entire Galaxy can be explained in the same way. Normal nebulae such as M20 do not exhibit this intense radio emission.

▽ If the Crab Nebula is an explosion relic, with an envelope expanding at 1000 km every second, might there not have been much faster-moving particles which long ago escaped? If the radio emission is due to synchrotron radiation, then some of these fast-moving charged particles must also sometimes escape from the Crab. It is possible that supernovae are a source of cosmic rays [see Chapter 5]? △

FIGURE 7–5. *Messier 20, the Triffid Nebula, in the constellation Sagittarius. This is an excellent example of a cosmic projective test. The object to the right is the diffraction pattern of a nearby star. (Courtesy of Mt. Wilson and Palomar Observatories.)*

FIGURE 7–6. *A photograph in red light of the region of the intense radio source Cassio-peia A. Some faint wisps of nebular material can be seen. (Courtesy of Mt. Wilson and Palomar Observatories.)*

The total amount of cosmic rays emitted by the Crab Nebula can be estimated by using the theory of the synchrotron radiation of fast-moving electrons, the measured flux of radio radiation, and the known distance and dimensions of the Crab. Then, taking into consideration the estimated frequency of occurrence of supernovae in our Galaxy, we find that the total cosmic radiation emitted by supernovae is sufficient to account for the cosmic ray intensity observed on Earth. Thus, the evidence seems to indicate that supernovae are the main source of cosmic rays in our Galaxy. In addition, these explosions enrich interstellar space with the heavier elements. This is very significant both for the evolution of the stars and for the Galaxy as a whole, as we shall see in the next chapter.

The Crab possesses another remarkable characteristic. As I pointed out in 1953, its visual radiation—at least 95 percent of it—is also produced by high energy electrons as synchrotron emission. The energy of the electrons which radiate in visual wavelengths is one hundred times greater than the energy of the electrons which radiate in radio wavelengths. Their energy reaches 0.1 to 1 erg/electron. On the basis of my then new explanation of the optical radiation of the Crab Nebula, I predicted that this radiation would be polarized. Soviet and American observations have since confirmed this deduction. Subsequently, synchrotron optical radiation was detected from other objects, mainly the radio galaxies.

All supernova remnants, without exception, are powerful sources of radio radiation. One nebula found in the constellation Cassiopeia has a meter wavelength radiation flux which is ten times that of the Crab Nebula, although it is almost three times as far away. However, this supernova remnant is a very weak source of optical radiation [see Figure 7–6]. It has been calculated that the Cassiopeia explosion occurred approximately 300 years ago. The exploding star was not noticed at the time because it was embedded in dense clouds of interstellar dust.

The amount of radiation now emitted by supernovae which occurred even 10,000 years ago differs greatly from that now emitted by more recent explosions. The nebula in Cygnus [Figure 7–4] is a radio source ten times less powerful than the Crab.

The last observed supernova in the Milky Way—recorded by Johannes Kepler —took place in 1604, before the telescope had been invented, or spectral analysis discovered. Recent data concerning the course and mechanism of these explosions have been acquired solely from observations of other stellar systems.

These data indicate that supernovae fall into two categories, Types I and II. Supernovae of Type I are older stars, with masses only slightly greater than that of our Sun; the radiation from their explosion is very great, although the mass of the gaseous cloud does not exceed several tenths of the mass of the Sun; and they are found in the elliptical and spiral galaxies. Such supernovae have a certain characteristic time for their brightness to decline, after the explosion occurs. From an examination of the Chinese records of 1054, we can conclude that the Crab Nebula was a Type I supernova.

Type II supernovae take place only in the spiral galaxies. They are initially massive, hot, young stars, usually occurring in the spiral arms, where the process of star formation is localized. A number of stars of spectral class O probably end their existence spectacularly, in explosions of this type. The mass of the gases expelled exceeds by several times the mass of our Sun. The material therefore requires a significantly longer time for its dispersal than does the less massive supernovae of Type I. The powerful radio source in the constellation Cassiopeia [Figure 7–4] is a remnant of a Type II supernova.

There are several important hypotheses attempting to explain the causes of these titanic stellar explosions. In all probability, they are due to the catastrophic, sudden release of gravitational potential energy attending the collapse of the internal layers of a star. It has been postulated that the interior, remaining after the outburst, would be an object more dense than the white dwarfs.

There is no generally accepted hypothesis to enable us to predict when a supernova will occur. The question of whether our Sun will become a supernova is of some interest for the present generation of human beings on Earth and for all future generations. Such an explosion would entirely vaporize all the planets, with the possible exceptions of Jupiter and Saturn. However, there is little cause for worry. We can quite definitely state that, because of its small mass, the Sun will never become a supernova.

▽ It is possible that some day we will be able to determine which stars are about to become supernovae. All modern theories of supernovae require very high temperatures at the center of the star—hundreds of millions of degrees or more. At these high temperatures, electrons and positrons (positively charged electrons) are colliding with each other at fantastic rates. Such collisions often result in the complete conversion of matter (the electron-positron pair), into energy (e.g. gamma rays). But it also happens that electron-positron interaction produces much less familiar particles, a neutrino-antineutrino pair. A neutrino is an elementary particle, in some respects like the photon. It has no mass and travels at the speed of light. The reason it is so unfamiliar is that the neutrino effortlessly passes through matter. The bulk of neutrinos pass through the planet Earth as easily as light through window glass. Neutrinos have been discovered only by very patient searching for their rare interaction with matter. At a temperature of several hundreds of millions of degrees, a star should give off more energy as neutrinos than as photons. Neutrinos pass through the overlying bulk of the star into space. When neutrino telescopes become feasible, it will be possible to, in a sense, peer directly into the innermost cores of the red giants. Stars gradually evolving into supernovae will be detectable as sources of gradually increasing amounts of neutrinos, and we should be able to determine long in advance any potential supernovae in our stellar neighborhood. △

As previously stated, supernovae occur infrequently. But our Galaxy has existed for so long that there have probably been a fair number of these events since the formation of our solar system. Could a supernova have exploded relatively close to our planet during the Earth's history? To answer this question, we shall make the following simple calculations:

Let us assume that a supernova of Type II exploded somewhere in the Galaxy 100 years ago. An explosion of this type occurs only in a thin region near the Galactic plane, within a thickness, d, of some 100 parsecs. The Galactic orbit of the Sun is now (and has always been) within this thickness. Consider a spherical region of radius R which surrounds the Sun. Its volume will be $\frac{4}{3}\pi R^3$. If r is the characteristic size of the spiral arms of our Galaxy, and d the thickness of the region of the Galactic plane in which a supernova of Type II can occur, then the volume of the disc in which such supernovae can occur is $\pi r^2 d$ [see the sketch in Figure 7–7]. The ratio of the volumes of these two regions, of the sphere to the disc, will be $\frac{4}{3}\pi R^3 / \pi r^2 d$. The ratio of these volumes is also the probability that, when a chance supernova explosion occurs somewhere within the Galaxy, the Sun will be at a distance R or less from the explosion. ▽ We see from Figure 7–7 that R must always be less than or equal to d. Therefore, since $\frac{4}{3}\pi R^3$ is always less than $\pi r^2 d$, the probability that the Sun will be near any particular explosion is less than 1, as, of course, it should be, since a probability of 1 indicates a certainty of occurrence. △

If one supernova occurs, on the average, every T years, then a "nearby" explosion will occur once every

$$t = \frac{\pi r^2 d}{\frac{4}{3}\pi R^3} \, T = \frac{3r^2 d}{4R^3} \, T \text{ years.}$$

Let us now put numbers in our algebraic equation. Assuming that $r = 10,000$ parsecs, $d = 100$ parsecs, $R = 10$ parsecs, and $T = 100$ years, we find that $t = 750$ million years.

Thus, during the 4.5-billion-year history of the Earth, the Sun has several times been closer than 10 parsecs to a supernova explosion. If we believe our estimate for t to be reliable, then this has happened $(4.5 \times 10^9)/(7.5 \times 10^8) = 6$ times. It is possible that t may be smaller, because the Galactic orbit of the Sun will occasionally take it into regions where Type II supernovae occur more frequently. ▽ It might also be larger, if our estimate for the average period for recurrence of

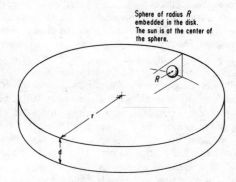

FIGURE 7–7. *Schematic diagram showing the Galaxy represented as a disk. Embedded in the disk is a small sphere with the Sun at its center. The radius of this sphere represents the distance from the Sun to a nearby supernova.*

a supernova, T, should be larger. But the conclusion that the Earth has several times been closer than 10 parsecs to a supernova during its lifetime seems rather firm. This simple geometrical argument is a good example of the power of elementary mathematical reasoning in physics and astrophysics. △

How would a nearby supernova explosion affect the Earth? If intelligent life were present, an unusually bright star would be seen in the heavens. It would be a million times brighter than Sirius (the brightest star in the sky); but 10,000 times less brilliant than the Sun. At night, the star would illuminate the countryside.

The flow of radiation in the ultraviolet region of the spectrum would be tens of times greater than the Sun's. Although this would give rise to significant ionization in the upper layers of the Earth's atmosphere, it would have no catastrophic biological consequences with our present oxygen atmosphere. ▽ The ozone in our atmosphere would absorb essentially all the ultraviolet radiation before it reached the Earth's surface. But in the Earth's earlier history [see Chapter 16], such an ultraviolet intensity increase may have had a more profound significance for living systems. △

A supernova occurring near the Earth would shine in the heavens for several months and then gradually fade. Around the star would form a nebula which, expanding rapidly at a velocity of several thousand km/sec, would cover a significant part of the sky in a few hundred years. Although the night sky would glow at the wavelengths of light characteristic for such nebulae, the fluorescence would be weak, hardly visible to the naked eye. In a thousand years, because of the gradual retarding influence of the interstellar medium, the velocity of expansion would decline. The expanding gas would reach our solar system in approximately 10,000 years. Then, during several tens of thousands of years, the Sun and its planets would be embedded inside a "radio nebula" of supernova origin.

What would happen on Earth? First, the density of primary cosmic rays would increase greatly, since radio nebulae are a source of such high-energy particles. However, cosmic rays are distributed irregularly within a radio nebula, so during one time interval—perhaps several centuries long—the intensity of cosmic radiation would be 100 times greater than at other intervals.

Such an increase in the flux of primary cosmic rays could conceivably have a serious effect on living organisms. The evolution of life on Earth is regulated by natural selection. Of the range of physical types available for a given organism, only a certain fraction is, by chance, best adapted to the environment, and reproduces its kind. ▽ The remainder eventually perish, because, for example, of competition or predation. The variety of types available for natural selection to act upon is determined by the mutation rate—that is, by the frequency of occurrence of inheritable biological changes.

▽ Mutations are caused by a variety of factors: the natural radioactivity of the soil, the waters, and the air; the cosmic ray flux; and a sizable remainder of causes, largely unknown, possibly random chemical changes in the hereditary material. All of the foregoing contribute to the "spontaneous" mutation rate and are regarded as "spontaneous" mutations. To some extent, the word "spontaneous" is a cover for our ignorance of the ultimate causes of such naturally occurring, inheritable changes. An increase in the background radiation intensity will cause an increase in the mutation rate. The majority of mutations are random, and hence deleterious. The genetic material is a finely tuned molecular instrument; a mutation is no more likely to improve its functioning than a watch is likely to work better after having been dropped from a tall building. The possibility exists, but it is unlikely. On the other hand, mutations provide the raw material on which natural selection acts. If there were no mutations, there would be no genetic inventory of possible adaptations to future environmental changes. If the mutation rate were extremely high, any characteristic selected would soon be mutated away. Thus, there is a most appropriate mutation rate for any organism. In fact, organisms exert control on their own mutation rates. There are specialized regions of the genetic material which can increase or decrease the general mutation rate, and even regions which control the mutation rate of specific characteristics. △

As a result, the biological response to an increase in the background radiation varies from organism to organism. Forms with a short reproductive cycle often require an increase of 100 to 1000 times in the background radiation for the mutation rate to double. Many long-lived forms, on the other hand, require an increase of only 3 to 10 times, for a doubling of the mutation rate.

At the present time, the average background ionizing radiation near the surface of the Earth is 0.12 roentgens per year. ▽ A roentgen is an arbitrary unit of radiation dose. △ Two-thirds of this background radiation comes from terrestrial sources, mainly from the radioactivity of the crust of the Earth. About 0.04 roentgens per year is due to primary cosmic radiation.

If the cosmic ray intensity were increased 30 times, the average radiation dose near the Earth's surface would increase by about 10 times—an increase which might have serious genetic consequences for long-lived organisms. Those organisms which are highly specialized in narrowly circumscribed environmental niches would be particularly vulnerable. For such forms, prolonged exposure to this increased dose for a period of tens of thousands of years could conceivably be catastrophic.

V. I. Krasovskii and I have suggested that the extinction of the dinosaurs at the end of the Cretaceous period in the history of the Earth, about one hundred million years ago, was caused by such an increase in the cosmic ray background. We postulated that in the epoch, the Sun was embedded in a radio nebula a distance of five to ten parsecs from a recently-exploded supernova. If the background cosmic ray intensity had increased by factors of tens or hundreds, then the increase in the dinosaur mutation rate may have caused their extinction. The lifetimes of such enormous beasts were almost certainly several centuries.

▽ One difficulty with this interesting suggestion is that it predicts the extinction of dinosaurs everywhere on the Earth during a relatively short period of time. The paleontological evidence, however, indicates that the timescale for the extinction of the dinosaurs was about 10^7 years. This is longer than the period of 10^4 years which the supernova hypothesis would suggest, unless a very long time were occupied in the reassortment by mating of deleterious recessive genes.

▽ There are in fact too many causes proposed for the extinction of the dinosaurs—not too few. One author has pointed out that the changing climatic conditions on the Earth in the middle Cretaceous period evidently eliminated a fern similar to contemporary plants which have laxative properties. In his view, the dinosaurs died of constipation.

▽ Nevertheless, there have undoubtedly been some biological effects of supernova explosions in the vicinity of the Earth during geological time, although perhaps not so spectacular as the extinction of the dinosaurs. △ At any rate, a prolonged increase in the background high-energy radiation dose would not necessarily be fatal to all living organisms. Perhaps such an exposure would be favorable for the evolution of certain life forms and the origin of some life-related substances during the early history of the Earth.

There is one other curious circumstance which may be related to supernovae. For a decade, an unexplained detail has remained in our picture of the distribution in the sky of cosmic radio noise. The intensity of the radio emission usually tends to concentrate towards the nucleus of the Milky Way, and in the Galactic plane containing the spiral arms. However, this rule does not apply to an intense tongue of radio emission extending across the sky almost perpendicular to the Milky Way. The tongue begins in a region removed from the Galactic center by approximately 30 degrees, and extends almost to the north Galactic pole, on the axis perpendicular to the Galactic plane. In Figure 7–8 we see a schematic diagram of

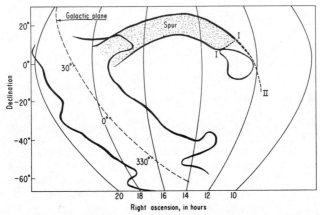

FIGURE 7–8. *Schematic diagram showing isophotes of the radio emission of the Milky Way galaxy. The region extending downward from the upper left corner is approximately in the Galactic plane. The "spur" is the shaded region extending out of the plane.*

the heavens, showing curves joining the regions of the sky where the radio brightness is the same. Such curves, called "isophotes," give a graphic representation of the distribution of the intensity of radio radiation in the sky. In this sketch, we can clearly see the concentration of intensity toward the plane of the Milky Way at Galactic latitude 0°. At the same time, it is apparent that to the left of the Galactic center the isophotes of radio radiation abruptly climb upwards. This is the unexplained tongue, or "spur."

A hypothesis of the English radio astronomer Hanbury Brown and his colleagues concerning the nature of this anomaly deserves special attention. They believe that it may be the radio envelope of a supernova which exploded very close to our solar system several tens of thousands of years ago. Since this envelope is at a distance of 30 to 40 parsecs and its linear dimensions cover 30 to 40 parsecs, it must occupy a vast part of the sky. This is shown in the diagram of Figure 7–9. However, Brown's hypothesis runs into difficulty. There are no optical traces of a supernova in this part of the heavens. Recently, in the southern part of the sky, another radio tongue was detected. The presence of two supernova remnants, both of which exploded near our Sun, during the last few tens of thousands of years seems highly improbable and suggests that these radio features have another

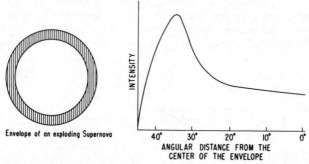

Envelope of an exploding Supernova

INTENSITY

ANGULAR DISTANCE FROM THE CENTER OF THE ENVELOPE

FIGURE 7–9. *Diagram illustrating a supernova explosion near the Sun.*

explanation. But if future investigations confirm the Brown hypothesis in spite of these difficulties, then in several thousand years the density of cosmic radiation in the solar system may increase by a factor of ten, as the radiation from the supernova reaches the Earth. Perhaps even the present cosmic ray intensity is abnormally higher than it was typically during the evolution of life on the Earth. We hope that a solution to this interesting problem in cosmic physics will soon be found.

8

The origin
of the elements

[Atoms] move in the void and catching each other up jostle together, and some recoil in any direction that may chance, and others become entangled with one another in various degrees according to the symmetry of their shapes and sizes and positions and order, and they remain together and thus the coming into being of composite things is effected.

Simplicius (sixth century A.D.)

I believe a leaf of grass is no less than the journeywork of the stars.

Walt Whitman, *Leaves of Grass*

▽ **W**hat is the origin of matter? Were the chemical elements made together, in the same epoch, or have they evolved through time, one from another? Fifty years ago, this question would have been scientifically meaningless. The origin of the elements! Yet today, we think we understand the basic processes involved. There has been a debate between proponents of evolutionary origin and proponents of independent creation which evokes some of the flavor of the debate which followed the publication, in 1859, of Charles Darwin's *Origin of Species*. But it now appears that the origin of the elements occurs mainly in the remote interiors of red giant stars. Not only can the observed cosmic abundance of the elements be explained by this hypothesis, but also, direct evidence exists for element-building in stars. The most striking example of such direct evidence is the discovery of the element technetium in the atmospheres of giant stars.

▽ Technetium is a very unstable element. Given a lump of the longest-lived kind of technetium, half of it would have decayed to other elements in about 200,000 years. If it had been produced in the early history of the solar system, there would now be none of it on the surface of the Earth, since its lifetime is so short. This expectation is confirmed. In fact, it is just the absence of naturally-occurring technetium on the Earth, and the fact that it can only be produced synthetically, in nuclear accelerators, which has led to its name. Of course 200,000 years is much shorter than the lifetime of the star. Thus, technetium must either be made near the surface of giant stars, or made in the interior and carried up towards the surface in times not much greater than 200,000 years.

▽ Technetium is only one of the hundred or so elements which are known. Each element can be characterized by its atomic number, which is simply the number of electrons surrounding the atomic nucleus [see Chapter 4]. The sum of the number of neutrons and protons in the atomic nucleus is called the atomic weight and is written as a superscript to the right of the chemical symbol; e.g., He^4. Since the atom is electrically neutral, the number of protons in the nucleus must equal the number of surrounding electrons. Therefore, the difference between the atomic weight and the atomic number equals the number of neutrons in the nucleus.

▽ Since the chemical properties are determined only by the number of electrons, a statement of the atomic number is equivalent to a specification of the element. Thus, atomic number 1 indicates hydrogen; atomic number 6 means carbon, etc. By changing the number of neutrons, but leaving the numbers of protons and electrons fixed, we produce different *isotopes* of the same chemical element. Thus, we find C^{12}, the most abundant naturally occurring form of carbon which contains six protons and six neutrons. There is also, however, a C^{13}, which contains seven neutrons, and a C^{14}, which contains eight neutrons. C^{13} and C^{14} are naturally radioactive—that is, they have a tendency to decay spontaneously to another isotope, either of carbon or of some other element, in times short, compared with the age of the solar system. The spontaneous decay of C^{14} is widely used in radioactive dating of organic matter. From analyses of the chemical material in the crust of the Earth and in meteorites, and from astronomical spectroscopy, it has been possible to determine the cosmic distribution of a great many of the isotopes of the known chemical elements. A table of the resulting cosmic distribution of the most stable isotopes of some familiar elements was given as Table I of Chapter 4, where we saw that hydrogen and helium were by far the most abundant elements in the universe. In Chapter 6, on stellar evolution, we have seen that reactions such as

$$4H^1 \longrightarrow He^4 + energy$$
$$3He^4 \longrightarrow C^{12} + energy$$
$$C^{12} + He^4 \rightarrow O^{16} + energy$$
$$O^{16} + He^4 \rightarrow Ne^{20} + energy$$
$$Ne^{20} + He^4 \rightarrow Mg^{24} + energy$$
$$Mg^{24} + He^4 \rightarrow Si^{28} + energy$$
$$Si^{28} + He^4 \rightarrow S^{32} + energy$$
$$S^{32} + He^4 \rightarrow Ar^{36} + energy$$
$$Ar^{36} + He^4 \rightarrow Ca^{40} + energy$$

are the successive sources of stellar energy for more and more highly evolved stars. These successive syntheses of elements of atomic weights which are multiples of four account for the high cosmic abundances of these familiar elements. The helium nuclei, symbolized by He^4, are also called alpha particles. The temperatures in the stellar interiors are, of course, so hot that all the atoms are ionized. Successive reactions with alpha particles construct elements of higher and higher atomic weight.

▽ Can this process continue indefinitely? The answer is no. After the formation of Fe^{56}, the most abundant isotope of iron, successive reactions with alpha particles produce elements which are naturally unstable, and spontaneously decay back into iron and other elements. Some other processes are needed to account for the synthesis of elements above atomic weight 56, and the interstitial elements whose atomic weights are not multiples of four. Nevertheless, the general form of the cosmic abundance of the elements can be understood from the four-proton reaction and the successive alpha processes alone.

▽ The general shape of the cosmic distribution of the elements shows a decline in abundance with increasing atomic weight. This is entirely expected, from the alpha processes, because the higher mass number elements have to wait their turn to be synthesized; the lower mass number isotopes must be made first. One of the principal exceptions to the smooth decline in cosmic abundance with increasing atomic weight is the case of the elements near iron. Because Fe^{56} is the highest mass number isotope which can be made by alpha processes, there tends to be a piling up of nuclear products near this isotope. △

We have noted in Chapter 6 that near the end of their evolutionary lifetimes, red giants discard, in one of a variety of ways, their outer gaseous envelopes, which then gradually diffuse into interstellar space. Thus, during the evolution of a star, some fraction of its mass returns into the interstellar medium from which it arose. Subsequent generations of stars, forming anew from the interstellar medium, will be composed in part from the debris of previous stellar generations. Since a major fraction of the mass of a star is not so ejected into interstellar space, but eventually ends up in the interior of a black dwarf, it is clear that, as time passes, the amount of matter in the interstellar medium declines.

▽ The sequence of nuclear reactions described above is appropriate for a star initially formed only of hydrogen. Alpha processes dominate its subsequent chemical evolution, and when it passes through the red giant stage, it will eject into the interstellar medium such newly formed isotopes as C^{12}, O^{16}, etc. Thus, if the galaxy had originally been composed only of hydrogen, the chemical composition of the interstellar medium would, in time, become gradually enriched with heavier elements. If, now, a second generation star is formed in the interstellar medium, it will have, in addition to hydrogen, smaller amounts of helium, C^{12}, O^{16}, and so forth. The presence of these isotopes, even in small amounts, during the hydrogen-burning phase on the main sequence, leads to nuclear reactions which are impossible in a star formed of pure hydrogen. Protons are added to C^{12}, and, after some intermediate reactions, successively produce C^{13}, C^{14}, and N^{15}. Ne^{20} successively forms Ne^{21}, Ne^{22}, and Na^{23}. In a similar way, the bulk of the interstitial isotopes can be synthesized.

▽ The synthesis of elements of higher mass number than iron is believed to occur by neutron capture. Neutrons are produced in stellar interiors by such reactions as:

$$Ne^{21} + He^4 \rightarrow Mg^{24} + \text{one neutron.}$$

Successive neutron capture is capable of synthesizing heavy elements up to Bi^{209}. Neutron capture by bismuth and heavier elements ordinarily does not lead to the synthesis of more complex elements, because the newly-synthesized elements are radioactive and spontaneously decay. But if the supply of neutrons were very great, the construction of the heavy elements could occur before they had a chance to decay spontaneously. Such a high neutron flux is believed to be available only during a supernova explosion. The existence of the elements gold and uranium on the Earth provides strong evidence that the material from which the Earth was formed once passed through a supernova. The influence of these two supernova products, gold and uranium, on the recent history of mankind is striking. Possibly, there are other planets in the Galaxy, formed in regions of the Galaxy where supernova explosions are few. Are their inhabitants happier for having no gold and uranium? △

If it is true that the elements beyond bismuth are constructed only in supernovae, then the abundance of such elements must tell us something about the rate at which supernovae occur. We saw in Chapter 7 that supernovae of Type II occur in young, massive stars. The rate of formation of such stars is strongly dependent on the density of the interstellar medium. There are some reasons for believing that this rate is proportional to the cube of the density. Thus, in the early history of the Milky Way, when the interstellar gas density was considerably greater than at present, and the rate of star formation was much higher, supernovae must have exploded at a much greater frequency than occurs today. Calculations suggest that when our Galaxy was less than one billion years old, the frequency of supernova outbursts was approximately 100 times greater than today. ∇ This corresponds to an interstellar density only a little less than 5 times greater than the present value, since the cube root of 100 is 4.7. The present rate of supernova explosion in our Galaxy is about one per century, and therefore, about 10^7 per billion years. If the rate in the first billion years was 100 times greater than this, then $\triangle$ we can conclude that since the birth of the Milky Way, approximately one billion supernovae have occurred. This number completely accounts for the observed content of elements heavier than bismuth in the Galaxy. ∇ Note, however, that this computation implicitly assumes that the mechanism of supernova outburst is not dependent upon the presence of heavy elements. $\triangle$

The oldest stars in our Galaxy are the sub-dwarfs, and those stars in globular clusters which have a mass of less than 1.2 times that of the Sun. More nearly than any other stars, we expect them to preserve, at least in their outer layers, the original distribution of the elements characteristic of the medium from which they were formed. And indeed, it is found that the content of heavy elements in such old stars is some tens of times less than that in the Sun. The fact that the stars of the main sequence are much richer in heavy elements than are the sub-dwarfs can thus be explained by the continuous enrichment of the interstellar medium by ejected stellar material.

∇ From spectroscopic observations of the Sun, it has become clear that our Sun is not a first generation star, and probably not even a second generation star— that is, many of the atoms which constitute the Sun have, in the past, been in the insides of other stars, stars now long since decayed into white dwarfs. And the atoms inside us—they too were cooked in the interiors of stars. Our bones are made of calcium formed by alpha processes in some red giant, billions of years ago. The same is true of the iron in our bloodstreams, the carbon, the nitrogen, and the oxygen which are constituents of all our tissues. Only the hydrogen which in our bodies is chemically bound to C, N, and O has any chance of having avoided stellar cookery. It is the most ancient of the elements, and if it was formed at all, it was formed eons ago, on the grandest imaginable scale, and by processes which even today, with our understanding of the synthesis of all the other elements, we cannot even dimly guess at.

∇ The atoms which, by spectroscopy, signal to us their presence in distant stars, are the same as their congeners here. The iron atom which we see in zeta Ursae

Majoris [Figure 4–3] is indistinguishable from the iron in the girders of a modern building. It is one of the triumphs of astronomical spectroscopy that we now know the universe to be constructed of just the same kinds of atoms as are present here on Earth.

▽ In the middle of the nineteenth century, the French philosopher Auguste Comte was seeking an example of a kind of knowledge which human beings would never achieve. Unfortunate man! He chose the chemical composition of the stars. Less than half a century later, astronomical spectroscopy was in full flourish. Negative prognostications are risky. Not only do we now know the chemical composition of the stars; we also understand how the elements were made. The iron atoms in zeta Ursae Majoris and in steel girders were made in precisely the same way. They have simply been put to different uses. △

9

The evolution
of the galaxies

We may also draw a very important additional conclusion from the gradual dissolution of the Milky Way: for the state into which the incessant action of the clustering power has brought it at present, is a kind of chronometer that may be used to measure the time of its past and future existence; and although we do not know the rate of going of this mysterious chronometer, it is nevertheless certain, that since the breaking up of the parts of the Milky Way affords a proof that it cannot last forever, it equally bears witness that its past duration cannot be admitted to be infinite.

William Herschel, *The Construction of the Heavens* (1811)

▽ W hen large telescopes and long exposure times are used to gather light from very distant sources out of the plane of the Milky Way, a point is eventually reached when one can see more distant galaxies than foreground stars. There may be more galaxies within reach of the 200-inch telescope on Mount Palomar than stars in our own Galaxy; in photographing objects fainter than about the eighteenth magnitude, we can obtain a view of the universe like that of Figure 3–15. Here, we see spiral galaxies with various degrees of winding of the spiral arms; we see them face-on, edge-on, and at all intermediate inclinations. We see the fuzzy, almost featureless elliptical galaxies, and a variety of misshapen, irregular galaxies. The situation is the same in every observable direction. (Due to heavy concentration of stars and dust in our own Galaxy, we cannot see galaxies on the other side of the Galactic nucleus.)

▽ The galaxies, however, are not uniformly distributed. There are occasional close groupings, such as Stefan's Quintet seen in Figure 9–1, in which clouds of gas connect individual galaxies. There are also looser associations of galaxies; our Galaxy, M31, M33, the Magellanic Clouds, and a handful of ellipticals and irregulars form an association of nearby galaxies called the "local group."

▽ Beyond the local group are other clusters of galaxies, some much richer than the local group. The nearest of these is the Virgo cluster, approximately 40 million light years distant. Beyond 60 million light years, the number of galaxies unexpectedly declines, and there are no rich clusters for much greater distances. This has led us to suspect that clusters of galaxies may in turn be grouped into vast superclusters. Is it possible that the superclusters in turn are aggregated into clusters of clusters of clusters? Is the universe arranged into an infinite regression of such clusterings, forming a grand and endless hierarchy?

▽ Since the chance juxtaposition of galaxies in an association of this sort is very unlikely, there must be some physical connection, probably gravitational, among the members of a given cluster of galaxies. In addition, since it is very difficult for galaxies to come together by random encounters, the existence of clusters of galaxies provides some clue to the origin of galaxies. Are galaxies, like stars, formed collectively, in great associations which only subsequently dissipate? △

It is postulated that some 10 or 20 billion years ago, a vast but diffuse cloud of gas existed at a very high temperature. The chemical composition of this cloud differed substantially from the present composition of the interstellar gas. It is possible that hydrogen was the only element present, perhaps as only its constituent fundamental particles, protons and electrons. ▽ The production of all the other elements would, in this view, have occurred at later times, in the interiors of

111

FIGURE 9–1. *A group of galaxies in the constellation Serpens, exhibiting gaseous connecting bridges. This group is known as Stefan's Quintet. (Courtesy of Mt. Wilson and Palomar Observatories.)*

stars. △ It is believed that the various regions of the cloud gravitationally attracted one another, resulting in a contraction of the cloud and an increase in its density, just as is postulated for the origin of stars. As the density increased, collisions among protons and electrons and the resulting emission of radiation would have occurred increasingly often. As the cloud cooled, the internal gas pressure was unable to support the overlying weight of material, and contraction proceeded at an even greater tempo.

Some mathematical calculations suggest that in such a condensation the cloud would inevitably fragment into smaller masses which many astronomers believe are the forerunners of clusters of galaxies. The potential energy of the original cloud, liberated during contraction, was transformed into the kinetic energy of motion of the individual gaseous fragments. Further contraction of the individual fragments led to a secondary decomposition into even smaller gas masses, each with high random velocities. These secondary masses are believed to have been the nascent forms of individual galaxies. Each of these newly formed protogalaxies, contracting again under the influence of their gravity, fragmented into still smaller masses, which later became the globular star clusters. ▽ The fourth level fragmentation of the globular clusters led, it is believed, to the individual stars of the first generation

112

—that is, to those composed entirely, or almost entirely, of hydrogen. One of the many remaining questions in this hypothetical hierarchy of condensations is this: Why do the forces which led to the preceding fragmentations not also fragment individual stars into smaller units? Why are the stars stable end products in the fragmentation hierarchy? △

During this remote era of fragmentations, the relative velocities of the individual condensations were quite high, and the protogalaxies must have had an approximately spherical shape. Evidence supporting this contention can be found in the spatial distribution of stars of the first or second generations, and in the spatial distributions of the very old globular clusters. These objects form an almost spherical system about the center of our Galaxy, their numbers increasing towards the Galactic center. Their numbers do not increase towards the Galactic plane. ▽ These old stars and globular clusters must have been formed at a time when the Galaxy had not yet condensed towards the present plane of the Milky Way. As the gas and dust then contracted towards this plane, those stars which had been formed earlier were left behind. Figure 9–2 outlines the early shape of the Milky Way.

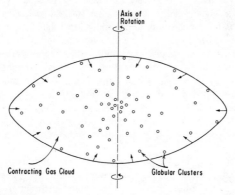

FIGURE 9–2. *Schematic representation of a galaxy in the process of formation. As the gas cloud collapses towards the nucleus, its velocity of rotation increases. Globular star clusters condense out of the contracting gas cloud preferentially in regions of high density.*

▽ It is easy in fact to understand why the early spherical or irregularly shaped galaxies settled down into a disc shape: △ Collisions of the individual gas particles in the protogalaxy, one with another, heated the cloud. The hot cloud then radiated into space, resulting in a loss of kinetic energy. The motions of the relatively cold particles were now dominated by the gravitational forces and settled down towards the Galactic plane. Consequently, stars that were formed at a later time were highly concentrated toward the disc.

▽ A protogalaxy that was rotating even very slightly when condensation began would have been rotating much faster as contraction proceeded, because of the conservation of angular momentum. The situation can be easily illustrated by taking a brick in each hand, and sitting on a piano stool with arms outstretched. Have someone spin you rapidly, then draw in your arms. The result is striking. Along the axis of rotation (with the piano stool, the legs are along the axis of rotation) contraction is easy, because there is no rotational force opposing it. Contraction in the plane perpendicular to the axis of rotation, however, is very difficult, since the centrifugal forces of rotation counteract the gravitational forces of contraction. Therefore, in the case of a protogalaxy, the net effect of gravitational attraction and rotational forces is a highly flattened rapidly rotating system, where material has contracted along the axis of rotation, but not perpendicular to it. The same circumstance explains why the planets in the solar system lie in a plane, why the satellite systems of the individual planets lie in a plane, and why the sun and all the planets are slightly flattened along their axes of rotation. △

We have outlined the present hypothesis on the origins of galaxies. ▽ All astronomers agree that many aspects of it still remain incomplete. Our present picture can be tested only by examining other galaxies. △ As noted in Chapter 3, there are large variations among different categories of galaxies. How may these differences be explained? ▽ Is there an evolution of galactic types similar to the evolution of stellar types? The character of a star, we remember, is determined primarily by its initial mass, composition, and present age. In the opinion of many astronomers, △ the characteristics of a galaxy are determined by its initial mass, its present age, and its initial velocity of rotation—that is, the rate of rotation of the protogalaxy. For example, if the initial galactic mass is relatively small, the average density of interstellar gas will be rather low, and star formation will proceed slowly. Indeed, the formation of the first generation stars in appreciable numbers may be delayed several billion years. The Magellanic Clouds may be examples of such a galaxy. These irregular galaxies have prominent hot, massive, young stars which, as shown by spectroscopic investigations, contain only small amounts of the heavy elements.

If the initial mass of the protogalaxy is large, but its rotational velocity relatively small, star formation may occur very rapidly. The interstellar medium should quickly condense into stars, and the density of the interstellar gas should soon become very low. Further star formation will occur in such galaxies only towards the galactic nucleus, where residual interstellar gas may be concentrated. Eventually, star formation ceases altogether, and the galaxies should be characterized by little gas and dust, and highly evolved stars. Elliptical galaxies [see, e.g., Figure 3–8] show such properties. If the protogalaxy is massive, and also rotates relatively rapidly, there is some expectation that spiral arms will form, and a spiral galaxy similar to our own evolve.

▽ The preceding is one scheme of galactic evolution, in which irregular galaxies, elliptical galaxies, and spiral galaxies have independent origins, and do not evolve one into another. The presentation of another scheme, such as the following by the American astronomer Allan Sandage of Mt. Wilson and Palomar Observatories, illustrates the range of uncertainty in our present knowledge of the evolution of the galaxies. Sandage points out that there is a close correspondence between the presence of dust in galaxies and the presence of the very bright young O and B stars. Thus, where dust is present, star formation must be occurring today. Such young stars are present in the irregular galaxies (Irr), the ordinary spiral galaxies (Sc) of type c, and the barred spiral galaxies (SBc) of type c. These and other spiral galaxies are illustrated in Figures 9–3 and 9–4. Moreover, whenever the spiral arms are tightly wound about the galactic nucleus, the bright blue stars cannot be seen, and dust is rare. Such galaxies are the Sa and Sb galaxies. It is reasonable to conclude that the dust in such galaxies has been depleted in previous processes of stellar formation, and that the origin of stars occurs infrequently, if at all, at the present time. If, then, the tight winding of the spiral arms is an index of a highly evolved galaxy, we may imagine the arms as winding up about the galactic nucleus as the galaxy turns. Galaxies of types Sa, SBa, S0, Sb, and all the elliptical galaxies, show no bright young stars, and an almost entire absence of dust. Finally, the integrated spectra of the billions of stars in such galaxies show characteristics of very highly evolved stars, such as the red giants. White dwarfs may exist in large numbers, but because of their low luminosity their contribution to integrated spectra of galaxies is probably negligible.

▽ The following picture of galactic evolution is suggested from these data: Protogalaxies are chaotic configurations of gas and dust, contracting from the intergalactic medium. As time progresses, there is a great initial flurry of star formation, and the galaxy is recognizable as an irregular. The galaxy then contracts towards its median plane and, by some processes not currently understood, forms open, loosely trailing spiral arms, in which dust is concentrated and star formation preferentially occurs. It may be that magnetic fields control the production of spiral arms, but the details of this process are, at the present time, very obscure. As successive generations of stars deplete the interstellar gas and dust, the density of the interstellar medium declines, the number of highly evolved stars increases, and the spiral arms wind closer and closer to the galactic nucleus. The galaxy evolves from Sc to Sb to Sa (or through the corresponding sequence for a barred spiral). Eventually, essentially all the gas and dust has been utilized in star formation, the spiral arms have entirely wound about the galactic nucleus, and the galaxy is characterized by old, evolved stars having disordered motions, and no longer restricted to the galactic plane. An S0, or elliptical galaxy, is produced. △

In still other discussions of galactic evolution the existence of spiral arms is associated with the presence of a galactic, magnetic field. The Soviet astrophysicist N. S. Kardashev, of the Sternberg Astronomical Institute, has proposed that the magnetic field of any galaxy has a metagalactic origin. As intergalactic gas contracted in the development of a protogalaxy the intergalactic magnetic field must also have been compressed, increased in strength, and then twisted by the rotation of the galaxy. Developing these ideas, the Australian astrophysicist, J. H. Piddington, has pointed out that the strength of a galactic magnetic field formed in this way depends on the angle between orientation of the metagalactic field and the axis of

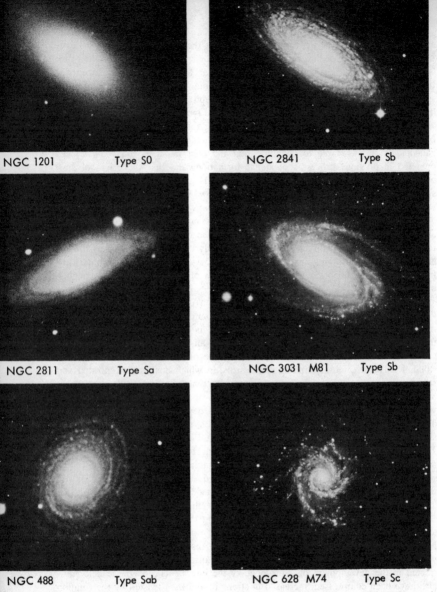

NGC 1201   Type S0

NGC 2841   Type Sb

NGC 2811   Type Sa

NGC 3031 M81   Type Sb

NGC 488   Type Sab

NGC 628 M74   Type Sc

FIGURE 9–3. *Some representative normal spiral galaxies. (Courtesy of Mt. Wilson and Palomar Observatories.)*

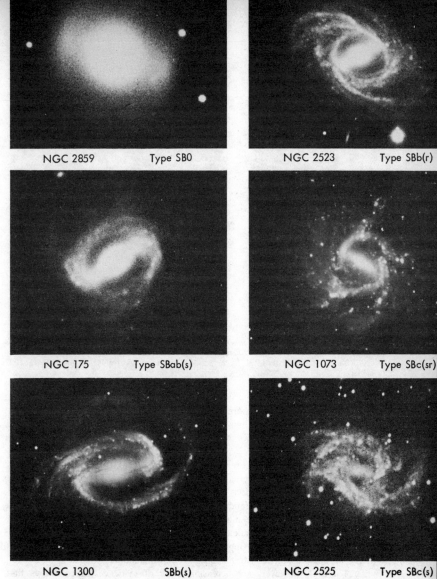

NGC 2859	Type SB0	NGC 2523	Type SBb(r)
NGC 175	Type SBab(s)	NGC 1073	Type SBc(sr)
NGC 1300	SBb(s)	NGC 2525	Type SBc(s)

FIGURE 9–4. *Some representative barred spiral galaxies. The "bar" is the broad band of stars and gas which connects the nucleus of the galaxy with the spiral arms. Compare with Figure 9–3, which exhibits no bars. (Courtesy of Mt. Wilson and Palomar Observatories.)*

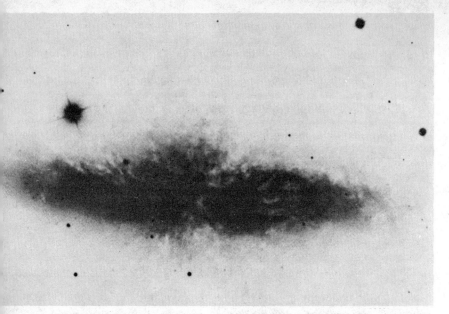

FIGURE 9–5a. *A photograph taken in blue light of the galaxy M82. This photograph is designed to bring out the overall distribution of stars, gas, and dust in this galaxy.* [*Reproduced, with permission, from C. R. Lynds and A. R. Sandage,* Astrophysical Journal *137, 1005 (1963).*]

rotation of the galaxy. For example, if this angle is small, the galactic magnetic field will be relatively weak. Even more recently, the Soviet astrophysicist S. B. Pikelner, also of the Sternberg Institute, has extended these views, and worked out an orderly theory which attempts to explain the multiple forms of the galaxies, and in particular their spiral structures.

Much more work, both observational and theoretical, is needed to resolve the conflicts among these hypotheses and to determine the validity of their common features. In addition to questions about the relationships among different galactic types, we do not fully understand such matters as the origin of spiral arms or the reason for the difference between normal and barred spirals. The important problem of the nature of the galactic nucleus is only beginning to be investigated, and the promising technique of analyzing the composite spectrum of an entire galaxy in terms of the spectra of its constituent stars is still in its infancy.

▽ There is, however, an increasing body of evidence which shows that, whatever the process, the evolution of galaxies is not a smooth one. Violent events occur in the nuclei of galaxies. We can sometimes detect such events by seeing the actual displacement of material. For example, in the galaxy M82, there is a jet of outward-moving interstellar matter leaving the galactic nucleus. The jet can be

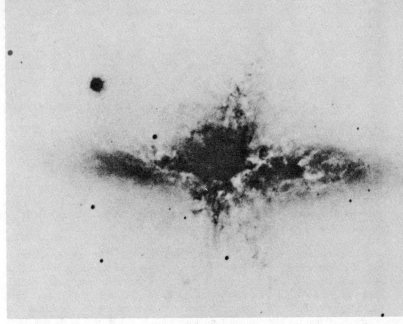

FIGURE 9–5b. *Photograph of M82, the same galaxy shown in Figure 9–5a, but here, observed in the light of hydrogen emission. The enormous quantity of material coursing upwards from the plane of the galaxy indicates the existence of a great explosion in M82. The turbulence throughout this galaxy, and the fainter plumes in other directions, suggest previous explosions. [Reproduced, with permission, from C. R. Lynds and A. R. Sandage, Astrophysical Journal 137, 1005 (1963).]*

observed in photographs of M82 taken in light emitted by hydrogen atoms in that galaxy [see Figure 9–5]. In the case of our own Galaxy, there is evidence from radio observations in the 21-cm line of neutral hydrogen that large amounts of gas are flowing out from the center of our Galaxy in the Galactic plane. The rate of outflow is so great that, had it been continuing for the last 10^{10} years, no gas would be left in the Galactic nucleus. Thus, either the gas in the nucleus of the Galaxy is being replenished from some source, such as the Galactic halo, or the outflow of gas is a temporary occurrence.

▽ Many galaxies are radio sources. The radio emission appears to be due to synchrotron radiation, in which energetic charged particles are constrained by relatively strong magnetic fields to move in restricted regions of space. The most energetic particles produce the most energetic, highest frequency radiation; but by the same token, they lose their energy fastest. If there is no source of replenishment for these high energy particles, the lifetime of effective radio frequency radiation of a galactic radio source can be computed. One can also compute the time for the material violently leaving a galactic nucleus to be dissipated. Both of these timescales turn out to be short, compared with the lifetime of a galaxy, and are characteristically between 10^4 and 10^7 years. There is reason to suspect that the events are correlated—that is, that the violent events leading to the expulsion of large amounts of matter from a galactic nucleus also provide the high energy particles which lead to synchrotron radiation.

▽ Now, within 300 megaparsecs (3×10^8 pc) of the Sun there are about 10^6 large galaxies more or less like our own, not including the dwarf galaxies. Of these million galaxies, some 300 are known radio sources. Let us set the average lifetime for radio emission by a radio source at 3×10^6 years. If the average lifetime of a galaxy is 10^{10} years, then an average outburst lasts approximately $3 \times 10^6 / 10^{10} = 3 \times 10^{-4}$ of the lifetime of the galaxy. Likewise, the fraction of nearby galaxies which are currently radio sources is $300 / 10^6 = 3 \times 10^{-4}$. Therefore, we can conclude that every galaxy is likely to be a source of radio emission at least once during its lifetime. These violent events are observed in elliptical, spiral, and irregular galaxies. We do not know whether they play a fundamental role, or are only a passing incident, in galactic evolution. △

In recent years, observations have been made of remarkable objects which may be radio galaxies in the initial stages of formation. Through the telescope, they resemble ordinary stars, ▽ and, for many years, were thought to be just that. A typical object of this sort might be of the seventeenth magnitude—entirely unpresuming. Since they are also intense radio sources, these objects have been called "quasi-stellar" radio sources or quasars. The name itself is a confession of ignorance. When we better understand what they are, it is very likely that there will be a change in nomenclature. △

In their visible spectra, intense lines due to hydrogen, oxygen, magnesium, and other elements are observed. These lines are strongly displaced toward the red end of the spectrum. This red-shift is almost certainly due to the Doppler effect; ▽ all other attempts to explain this wavelength displacement have met with apparently insuperable difficulties. △ Their velocities can be computed from the Doppler effect. These velocities are very great, and all in a direction away from our Galaxy. From these immense velocities of recession and Hubble's law [see Chapter 10], it is concluded that the quasi-stellar radio sources are many hundreds of millions of parsecs away. One of the most distant at the time of writing, 3C-9, may be about 3 billion parsecs distant. By scaling their apparent brightness by these immense distances, using the inverse square law, it is possible to reach the remarkable conclusion that their luminosity is about 100 times greater than the luminosity of the most intense galaxy otherwise known. It seems possible that the optical radiation, as well as the radio radiation, is produced by synchrotron emission.

The most astonishing characteristic of the quasi-stellar radio sources, however, is that their radiation at visible frequencies varies with time. Individual stars of a galaxy are known to be variable, ▽ but the variation in the light output of an entire galaxy over a period of years, or even months, is entirely unprecedented. Indeed, it seems at first impossible. How could the light output of millions of stars be synchronized? The fastest velocity at which information can be transmitted is the velocity of light. If a galactic nucleus is 3,000 light years across, it takes at least 3,000 years for information to travel from one end of the nucleus to the other. Only if the actual size of the quasi-stellar radio source is less than a light year across does there seem to be any hope of understanding the luminosity variations, if the quasars are the nuclei of distant galaxies. △

If the quasi-stellar radio sources are indeed the initial stages of galactic outbursts, then the timescale of this early phase could scarcely exceed several thousand years. The radio galaxies 3C-295 and Cygnus A are older than this. Particles traveling close to the speed of light, which arose in their initial outbursts, have left the limits of these galaxies and formed two symmetrical clouds about them, which are detected by their radio emission. 3C-295 is several tens of thousands of years old; Cygnus A, several hundred thousand years old; and such radio galaxies as Centaurus A, in still later stages of development.

What could cause these explosions? The Anglo-American astrophysicist Geoffrey Burbidge believes that a chain reaction of supernovae could be the initiating factor [see Chapter 7]. Other investigators, for example, the British astronomer Fred Hoyle of Cambridge University and I, believe that the explosion of an immense, unstable starlike body, with a mass at least millions of times that of the Sun has occurred.

▽ Could an object of this mass be stable? It was believed—at least until recently—that any star with a mass exceeding about 100 times the mass of the Sun would be unstable. In fact, the British astronomer Sir Arthur Stanley Eddington once suggested that the hypothetical inhabitants of a cloud-bound planet—say, Venus—could deduce the existence and mass range of stars partly from this fact, using only physics, and no astronomy. Consider objects of successively larger masses. A one-gram object just sits there. As the masses increase, so, of course, do the sizes of the objects. Eventually, their masses become so large that the effects of gravity become important, and their interiors become compressed, because of the high internal pressures. Eventually, still increasing the mass, we reach and surpass characteristic planetary masses. Soon, due to the release of gravitational potential energy, as we construct larger and larger masses, the surface temperatures of our objects become so great that they glow, and slowly radiate energy into space. By the time the masses reach about 10^{32} gm, Eddington reasoned, these objects would be bright enough to see (in the absence of clouds), and the stars would "turn on." We now know that at slightly larger masses, thermonuclear reactions in the interior would begin, and we certainly would have a star.

▽ As the mass of the star increases towards 10^{35} gm, a new phenomenon enters the picture: radiation pressure. In reflecting off a wall, or any other object, light exerts a pressure. Ordinarily, due to the small intensity of the light, the pressure exerted is very small and is not a common feature of our everyday lives.

As the intensity of the radiation increases, the pressure becomes more and more important. In a star with a mass of about 10^{35} gm, the radiation pressure exerted by the hot interior on the cooler exterior becomes enormous, and stars of much greater mass may be blown apart by radiation pressure. In addition to demonstrating the existence of stars to sophisticated inhabitants of cloud-bound planets, this argument also makes it seem unlikely that stars with masses many millions of times that of our Sun can exist.

▽ Nevertheless, the quasars must have some energy source. The quasar 3C-273 emits a total energy supply at all frequencies of about 10^{54} ergs per year. If we take its lifetime to be that of other radio sources—say, 10^5 years—then its total energy output during its lifetime is about 10^{59} ergs. There are only two general types of energy sources which might be capable of supplying this energy: nuclear and gravitational. The Sun, which is burning its nuclear fuel with an efficiency of about one percent, has a luminosity of 4×10^{33} ergs per second. Therefore, in its lifetime of 10^{10} years it will emit approximately 4×10^{33} erg sec$^{-1} \times 10^{10}$ years $\times 3 \times 10^7$ sec yr$^{-1} = 10^{51}$ ergs, approximately. A quasar, working on thermonuclear energy as does the Sun, would require a mass of 10^{59} ergs/10^{51} ergs sun$^{-1} = 10^8$ suns. If a quasar were capable of complete conversion of mass to energy, by the equation $E = mc^2$, its efficiency would be 100%, and its total mass would be only 10^6 suns.

▽ On the other hand, if the energy is supplied by the gravitational collapse of a large cloud, an even larger total mass of about 10^9 suns is required. Thus, whatever the energy source, the quasar must be extremely massive; yet because of the variation in the light output of the quasar, it seems unlikely that its total dimensions can be much larger than a few light months. The quasar must be an extremely massive object in a very small volume, that is, an object with an extraordinarily high density. Because of the difficulties which we have already alluded to in understanding the stability of such an object, some astronomers feel that quasars are not intrinsically starlike and do not run on nuclear energy, but rather, run on the energy of a vast gravitational collapse. The mass required, about 10^9 suns, is less than one percent of the total mass of a typical galaxy. A reasonable place for such a collapse to occur is in the nucleus of a galaxy, where, indeed, violent events have been directly observed [see Fig. 9–5b].

▽ Perhaps, during the formation of a galaxy, much of the matter which does not condense out into dust and stars falls into the galactic nucleus. Because the total mass of the collapsing matter is so large, the pressure of the underlying material—as in the case of red giant evolution—is insufficient to support the exterior layers, and the mass continues to collapse, converting more and more gravitational potential energy into kinetic energy. Eventually, so much kinetic energy is produced that the collapse rebounds, implosion becomes explosion, and we call it a quasar. After a quasar explosion, other material in the galaxy may continue to fall into the galactic nucleus, and a series of collapses and explosions of gradually diminishing amplitude may ensue. In the particular case of the galaxy

M82 [Fig. 9–5], there is some evidence for more than one explosion. A quasar would then be merely a more violent example of the kind of explosions which have previously been observed in the nearby galaxies.

▽ The study of quasars has generated another interesting speculation. As we shall see in the next chapter, when the density of matter is very great, a light ray passing near it is deviated from a rectilinear path. As the density becomes greater, so does the curvature of the path of the light ray. When the density reaches a certain critical value, different for different masses, the light ray has curved to such an extent that it might be considered to be in a circular orbit about the dense mass. At such a density, radiation emitted by the object is unable to escape to space. Instead, it is gravitationally bound to the object. For a given mass, the radius of an object which exhibits this behavior is called the Schwarzschild radius, after the German astronomer Karl Schwarzschild, of the University of Göttingen.

▽ Now, an object smaller than the Schwarzschild radius cannot be seen, but its gravitational influence can be felt. It has been postulated that the quasars are objects of immense density which are oscillating between two radii, one larger and the other smaller than the Schwarzschild radius. Since there is no way of communicating with or receiving information from an object with a radius smaller than the Schwarzschild radius, such an oscillating object might be described as periodically entering and leaving our universe. However, it has since been shown by the Indian-American astronomer Subrahmanyan Chandrasekhar of the University of Chicago that other instabilities are experienced by a collapsing object long before the Schwarzschild radius is reached. These instabilities tend to reverse the collapse and produce an explosion. Quasars may be exotic objects, but they are not so exotic that they are smaller than the Schwarzschild radius.

▽ A slightly less exotic source of energy for the quasars has been suggested by the American astrophysicist Lyman Spitzer, of Princeton University, by Thomas Gold, and by the Dutch-American physicist, L. Woltjer, of Columbia University, among others: they invoke frequent and violent collision of stars in the nuclei of galaxies. For example, at the center of the galaxy M31 there is a nucleus with a luminosity as bright as 10^8 suns; yet, its diameter is less than 5 pc. The average star density in this and other galactic nuclei is at least 10^5 to 10^6 stars per cubic parsec. The corresponding average distance between stars in such galactic nuclei is a few hundredths of a parsec or a few thousand astronomical units. If there are occasional galactic nuclei where the star density is substantially greater, and the average distance between stars is tens of astronomical units, then collisions among the stars will occur frequently enough to provide the observed energy outputs and deduced lifetimes of the quasars. In such galactic nuclei the average distance between the stars would be comparable to the distance between the Earth and Saturn. In the version of this theory due to Spitzer, a few percent of the mass of each star is driven off in each stellar collision. This gas cools, falls towards the center of the galactic nucleus and there condenses into further stars which again lose mass in collision. This stellar collision model of quasars invokes no new physical principles, but it does require star densities in galactic nuclei which have not yet been observed.

▽ In part because of the difficulties in accounting for the quasars if they are very distant, some astronomers have suggested that they are relatively nearby (tens of millions of parsecs); their intrinsic radio and optical brightness can then be much less. The red shift is still due to the Doppler effect in this view. But the huge recessional velocities are attributed, not to the expansion of the universe, but to a titanic explosion which is imagined to have occurred in our galactic vicinity—perhaps within our Galaxy itself—some tens or hundreds of millions of years ago. The energies for this explosion remain to be explained.

▽ The study of the quasars is just beginning, but there is little doubt that they represent a very significant episode in galactic evolution. △

The distribution of radio galaxies may not be irrelevant to the question of life in the universe. For example, in the giant stellar system Cygnus A, the level of hard, ionizing radiation is hundreds of thousands of times more intense than on the surface of the Earth. It is unlikely that higher life forms, when exposed to such radiation intensities, could exist for long. If radio galaxies such as Cygnus A are old, it is possible that galactic explosions in the nuclei of old stellar systems can destroy the life which evolved before the outburst. ▽ Events occurring in the galaxy's interior can destroy life on millions of planets throughout the entire galaxy. △ If a smaller explosion of this type occurred in the nucleus of our own Galaxy at some past time, it apparently did not constitute an insuperable hazard to the development of life on Earth. ▽ However, no one can predict the likelihood of an explosion in the center of our Galaxy at some future time. △

10

Cosmology

Who knows for certain? Who shall here declare it?
Whence was it born, whence came creation?
The gods are later than this world's formation;
Who then can know the origins of the world?

None knows whence creation arose;
And whether he has or has not made it;
He who surveys it from the lofty skies,
Only he knows—or perhaps he knows not.

The Rig Veda, X. 129

Human thought knows no bounds. Scientists have studied the origin of elements, stars, and galaxies, as we have discussed in the preceding chapters. But what is the origin of the initial cloud of gas from which the galaxies were formed?

In this chapter we come face to face with the most momentous question of contemporary natural science: the cosmological problem. Cosmology is defined as the study of the structure and development of the universe as a whole. It goes to the heart of profound problems, both scientific and philosophical. ▽ Is the universe finite or infinite? Is it eternal, or did it have a finite beginning in time? If it was created at an instant in time, how was this accomplished? If the universe is infinitely old, is there any sense in which it has a purpose? Are the physical laws fixed, or do they alter with time? What determines the physical laws? Does the universe have the same appearance at all places and times? What is its geometry? Why do the galaxies seem to be flying apart, one from another? Is there an over-all irreversible conversion of hydrogen to the heavy elements? The cosmologists grapple with many of these problems; eventually they may be solved.

▽ The sky is dark at night. This seemingly trivial observation has profound cosmological consequences. Why should it be dark at night? Because it isn't bright. Why isn't it bright? Because there are insufficient stars·close enough together to make the night sky appear bright. Consider the following geometrical argument. In Figure 10–1 we show our Galaxy, in the center of the figure, surrounded by two imaginary spherical shells of radii R_1 and R_2. The thickness, s, of each shell is much less than either R_1 or R_2. Consider the innermost shell. The inside surface has an area approximately equal to $4\pi R_1^2$. The outer surface of the innermost shell also has an area approximately equal to $4\pi R_1^2$, since the thickness is negligible. Therefore the volume of the spherical shell is $4\pi R_1^2 s$.

▽ Now, suppose that space is uniformly filled with galaxies. We represent the space density of galaxies by N, the number of galaxies in a unit volume of space—say, in a cubic megaparsec. A megaparsec is a million parsecs; a cubic megaparsec is, of course, a cube a million parsecs on a side. Let us call the average absolute luminosity per galaxy L. Thus, N, the number of galaxies per unit volume, times L, the luminosity per galaxy, is NL, the luminosity emitted by all the galaxies within a unit volume of space. The absolute luminosity of the innermost spherical shell is therefore $NL4\pi R_1^2 s$. By the same type of reasoning, the absolute luminosity of the outer shell, of radius R_2, is $NL4\pi R_2^2 s$, since we have assumed the thickness of the two shells, s, to be the same. Since R_2 is greater than R_1, the volume of the outer shell is larger than the volume of the inner shell. There are more galaxies in the outer shell, and therefore the outer shell has a greater intrinsic luminosity. But

127

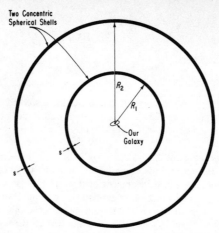

FIGURE 10–1. *Two concentric, spherical shells of equal thickness, seen in cross-section, surrounding our Galaxy. The distances from our Galaxy to these imaginary shells should be considered to be millions of parsecs, at least.*

the outer shell is further away! The light from a distant object is attenuated by the inverse square of its distance. Thus, while a distant spherical shell has a greater number of galaxies, proportional to R^2, than a nearby shell, the luminosity of each of those galaxies is reduced by the same factor R^2. Hence any spherical shell anywhere in the universe contributes the same *apparent* luminosity, as seen from the Earth.

▽ The argument is valid, of course, only insofar as our assumptions are valid; in particular, if the distribution of galaxies throughout the universe is constant, and if the luminosity per galaxy does not systematically change with distance from the Earth. If each spherical *shell* contributes an apparent luminosity £, ten spherical shells will contribute an apparent luminosity 10£, and so forth. Thus, if the universe is infinite, so that there are an infinite number of shells, the light of the night sky should be infinitely bright. However, observation does not confirm this prediction. This contradiction between prediction and observation is known as Olber's paradox.

▽ Actually, we should not expect the night sky to be infinitely bright, even if the universe is infinite in extent, because as we successively add more and more spherical shells, a point would eventually be reached at which nearby galaxies block the light from more distant galaxies. The largest amount of light that could reach the Earth would occur when, in whatever direction we looked, our line of sight intercepted a star. We would see a sky uniformly illuminated by an immense galactic population, with no spaces between stars. The sky would be radiating to the Earth at the surface temperature of an average star—say, 5,000°K. As an equivalent, we can imagine the Earth (and our solar system and Galaxy) being

128

placed inside an enormous oven at a temperature of 5,000°. The temperature of the Earth would soon also rise to 5,000°, and life would then be impossible. Thus, the existence of life on Earth must be due in part to the solution of Olber's paradox.

▽ Let us explore some attempted solutions to Olber's paradox. First, there is dust. Could there be enough dust and other absorbing material in intergalactic space for all the light from the most distant objects to be absorbed? This is equivalent to saying that the luminosity per galaxy, L, in the above expression is not the same for each spherical shell. But this does not solve Olber's paradox, since the dust grains would be heated by starlight, and as hot objects they would re-emit radiation. At equilibrium, they would be at the same temperatures as the stars.

▽ Alternatively, we might imagine that the space density of galaxies, N, declines with distance. As cited in Chapter 9, the galaxies are apparently distributed in a hierarchical manner; that is, the average density of galaxies in the universe does seem to decrease with distance from the Earth, if we take large enough distances. In detail, however, the hierarchical solution is not in accord with the observations.

▽ Perhaps we could add only a finite number of spherical shells and then stop. If we stop adding spherical shells soon enough, then there should be places in the sky as seen from Earth where no galaxies are visible. Thus, Olber's paradox can be solved if we postulate that the amount of matter in the universe is finite. We shall explore this possibility in more detail later in this chapter.

▽ Finally, we may solve Olber's paradox by assuming, instead of an end to space, a beginning of time. We recall that light travels with a finite propagation velocity, $c = 300,000$ km sec^{-1}. Thus, as we look to the most distant galaxies, we are seeing epochs further and further back into the past. If the universe began at a finite moment in time, eventually we would see at great distances to a point in space corresponding to the time of the origin of the universe. Beyond that, of course, there would be no galaxies. This is a possible solution of Olber's paradox, but to many people it is an uncomfortable one. An apocryphal story relating to the life of St. Augustine is relevant to this issue. Augustine was delivering an address on some of the same topics we are discussing in this chapter, but, of course, in the conceptual framework of his time—just as this chapter is in the conceptual framework of ours. A member of the audience objected: "Now see here, Augustine. You have told us that in the beginning God created heaven and Earth. You have also told us that God is immortal, with no beginning and no end. What, then, was God doing before he created heaven and Earth?" Augustine's riposte was: "He was creating Hell, for people who ask such questions."

▽ It is important to remember what infinity is; it is not merely a large number. There are not an infinite number of grains of sand on the beach, or an infinite number of hands of bridge. These are large but finite numbers. To illustrate how large numbers can be without coming even close to infinity, the 8-year-old nephew of the American mathematician, Edward Kasner, has called the number 10^{100} a *googol*. This can be written as a 1, followed by one hundred zeros, and is larger than the number of elementary particles in the known universe, that is, particles out to a distance of a few billion light years. A much larger number, still nowhere near infinity, is a *googolplex,* which is $10^{googol} = 10^{10^{100}}$. A googolplex is so large that simply writing down its number of zeros in ordinary decimal notation would occupy much more than a human lifetime. Yet a googolplex is not infinity. However, in this chapter, we are concerned with whether the universe is *infinitely* large, whether it contains an *infinite* amount of matter, whether it is *infinitely* old, and whether it has an *infinite* future life expectancy.

▽ As another example of large numbers, let us calculate the number of elementary particles—protons and electrons—in the observable universe. We have mentioned that our Sun has a mass of about 2×10^{33} gm. A hydrogen atom has a mass of 1.66×10^{-24} gm. If the Sun is made only of hydrogen—not a bad approximation—it contains 10^{57} hydrogen atoms. The number of electrons is about equal. There are about 10^{11} stars in our Galaxy. Therefore, the number of protons and electrons in our Galaxy is about 2×10^{68}. There are at least 10^9 other galaxies within range of the 200-inch telescope at Mt. Palomar, giving 2×10^{77} elementary particles. If we make a generous allowance for the amount of interstellar and intergalactic matter, and for the possibility of undiscovered galaxies out to a distance of some 10 billion light years, we find that the number of elementary particles in the observable universe is not more than about 10^{80}—a hundred million trillion times smaller than a googol.

▽ With 10^{11} stars in our Galaxy and 10^9 other galaxies, there are at least 10^{20} stars in the universe. Most of them, as we shall see in subsequent chapters, may be accompanied by solar systems. If there are 10^{20} solar systems in the universe, and the universe is 10^{10} years old—and if, further, solar systems have formed roughly uniformly in time—then one solar system is formed every 10^{-10} yr $= 3 \times 10^{-3}$ seconds. On the average, a million solar systems are formed in the universe each hour. △

▽ We will return to Olber's paradox presently. But first, we must consider the question of the over-all geometry of the universe. The simplest and most natural assumption is that the universe is three-dimensional and Euclidean; that is, the position of an object can be specified by three coordinates, and the familiar axioms of Euclidean geometry apply to the measurement of distance. While simplicity is of heuristic value, nothing compels the universe to be simple. However, what is difficult for one generation of scientists is simple for the next.

▽ In the first and second decades of this century, Albert Einstein proposed that we live in a four-dimensional universe in which time (or rather, the velocity of light multiplied by time, to make the units consistent) is on an equal footing with the ordinary spatial coordinates. Instead of talking about points in space, we must talk about events in a four-dimensional space-time continuum. This, at least, seems quite reasonable. Of course, we cannot picture four physical dimensions—length, width, height, and something else at right angles to the other three; but mathematically, four dimensions can be dealt with almost as simply as three. If the four-dimensional space-time continuum were flat, or Euclidean, calculations in it would be especially easy. For example, if the side of a square is of length a, the area of the square is a^2. A cube with a side of length a has a volume a^3. The corresponding four-dimensional object, all of whose sides have length a, is called a *tesseract*. It has an interior "capacity" of a^4. (There is, of course, no word in everyday parlance for the four-dimensional equivalent of the three-dimensional volume.)

▽ By comparing the area of a circle, πr^2, with the volume of a sphere, $\frac{4}{3}\pi r^3$, we immediately see that geometrical excursions into non-Euclidean four-space may be complicated. Einstein proposed that in the presence of matter space-time becomes curved, and non-Euclidean geometry must apply to the motion of material objects and of light. In the General Theory of Relativity, Einstein made specific numerical predictions of, for example, the deflection of starlight on passing near the Sun (easily visible, of course, only during a total solar eclipse) and of anomalies in the motion of Mercury, the planet nearest the Sun.

▽ These brilliant predictions have been partially confirmed by observation, and most physicists agree that space-time is curved. However, the observational difficulties in performing these checks, and the fact that some of them do not test the full General Theory of Relativity, permits some room for skepticism still. A new means of testing General Relativity has been suggested by the American physicist Irwin I. Shapiro, of the Massachusetts Institute of Technology. He recommends that radar signals be transmitted to Venus or Mercury when these planets are on the other side of the Sun from the Earth. Then, the radar pulse must pass near the Sun to reach the planet. According to General Relativity, the path of the radar pulse will be deflected towards the Sun, and Shapiro concludes that the resulting delay in the echo should be about 2×10^{-4} seconds. Such an extraordinarily short time can be measured by existing equipment, and this critical test of General Relativity will probably be performed in the near future.

▽ Having successfully predicted the behavior of space-time in the vicinity of a single material object such as the Sun, Einstein went on to consider the behavior of space-time in the universe as a whole. Assuming an approximately uniform distribution of galaxies, Einstein deduced, in his initial cosmological foray, a closed universe of "positive" curvature. Its three-dimensional analog would be a sphere. Consider a two-dimensional organism walking on the inside of a hollow sphere. He would find that while there were no obstacles in his path, the amount of two-dimensional space available for his peregrinations was limited. The reason, of course, is that the two-dimensional area of the sphere, $4\pi r^2$ (where r is the radius of the sphere), is cleverly rolled through a third dimension, so that there are no edges. In an analogous manner, Einstein imagined that the three ordinary physical dimensions are curved, so that if we were able to travel over immense distances, we might set out in what we think is a straight line, and without ever turning back or meeting a boundary, find ourselves returned to the point of origin. It would be possible to circumnavigate a closed universe.

▽ In the 1920's, when the universe was thought to be closed, and the radius of curvature modest by present standards, some astronomers turned their telescope in the exact opposite direction in the sky from our nearest spiral galaxy, M31 [see Figure 3–5]. There, sure enough, was another spiral galaxy of similar form, and the exciting possibility arose that this was M31 seen from the other side. In fact, beyond M31 there should be another spiral galaxy, our own. If light traveled infinitely fast, and if telescopes had infinite resolving power, astronomers might photograph the backs of their heads by pointing the telescope out into space. Perhaps fortunately, such observations are impossible.

▽ Einstein also found, with his early cosmological models, that unless he made some other assumption, static universes were impossible. It seemed that a closed universe tended to contract, due to the gravitational attraction of the matter contained within it. Models in which the universe expanded were also found. Since at that time no one believed the universe itself to undergo any net motion, Einstein introduced, to circumvent this difficulty, a new force of cosmical repulsion. It was so weak at small distances that no one could measure it, and so large at great distances that it propped up the universe, making it stable against contraction.

▽ But almost as soon as these model universes were formulated, astronomical observations made them obsolete. In the early 1920's, the American astronomer Edwin Hubble at Mt. Wilson Observatory was able to deduce the distance of these galaxies from the Earth. They turned out not to be solar systems of our own Galaxy in the process of formation, as had previously been thought, but independent galaxies like our own, or, as they were called in those days, "island universes." (The existence of more than one universe is impossible, by definition, so we now call them galaxies.) By successively using the so-called Cepheid variables, bright O and B stars, associations of bright O and B stars, and all the stars in the galaxy together, as absolute luminosity indicators, it was possible to compare absolute and apparent luminosities, and derive the distances of even fairly remote galaxies. At about the same time, V. M. Slipher discovered that the spectral lines of the galaxies which lie beyond our local group were shifted towards the red. Interrelating these observations, Hubble discovered that the red-shift and the distance of a given galaxy from the Earth were correlated; the further the galaxy, the greater the red-shift. The only interpretation of the red-shift which has stood the test of time is the Doppler effect, discussed in Chapter 3. It must then follow that except for the nearby galaxies, whose random motions obscure the effect, the further a galaxy is from us, the faster it moves away from us. This can be expressed by the equation $V = Hr$, where V is the velocity of recession, r is the distance to the galaxy, and H is the proportionality constant known as Hubble's constant, after the discoverer of this linear relation. Current estimates for Hubble's constant lie between 75 and 100 km sec^{-1} per megaparsec—that is, for every megaparsec in the distance of a galaxy, we must add an increment of about 100 km sec^{-1} to its recessional velocity.

▽ But what does this mean? Are all the galaxies fleeing from us? Why should they be fleeing *us?* Are we at the center of the universe? The bulk of the

132   THE UNIVERSE

astronomical evidence shows that there is nothing unique about our particular corner of the universe. First men discovered that the Earth was not at the center of the universe; instead of the Sun moving about the Earth, it was the other way around. Then it was found, from the distribution of the globular clusters, that our Sun was not at the center of the Galaxy, but was rather in an obscure position near the rim. Now, are we to find that our Galaxy, one of at least 10^9 others, happens to be in the center of the universe?

▽ Not if the universe as a whole is expanding. Let us use the following analogy. Imagine the universe is an unbaked raisin cake. (Worse analogies have been made.) Each raisin represents a galaxy. The cake is placed in an oven and, after a while, it rises. The volume of the cake has increased—that is, the "universe" has expanded—but, in addition, there has been an increase in distance from any raisin to any other raisin. If we were to stand on a raisin and view the other raisins, it would appear that all the other raisins were receding from us, and that the most distant raisins were moving away at the greatest speed. The same view would be obtained regardless of which raisin we stood on. In the same way, if our universe is expanding, something similar to Hubble's law should be seen by astronomers on any of the more than 10^9 galaxies.

▽ Very well then, the universe is expanding, and there is nothing special about our position in it. But it must follow that in the past the galaxies were closer together. △ If the velocity of expansion increases at a rate of 75 or 100 km sec^{-1} with each million parsecs, then by extrapolating into the past, we come to the following remarkable conclusion: Approximately 12 billion years ago, ▽ roughly, $1/H$, △ the entire universe was concentrated into an extremely small volume. Some scientists believe that, at that time, the density was in excess of 10^{14} or 10^{15} gm cm^{-3}; that is, the density of the universe exceeded the density of the atomic nucleus. The universe, in other words, was one gigantic, super-dense, nuclear "drop." For some reason, the drop became unstable and exploded. The results are now observed as the expanding universe. ▽ This cosmogony is known as the evolutionary, or "big bang" hypothesis.

▽ But it is not necessary to conclude that the universe was *created* when the galaxies were close together. Other models of the universe exist. At about the same time that the evidence for Hubble's law was accumulating, a new solution was found to the equations of general relativistic cosmology. It was discovered that open, hyperbolic universes and closed, pulsating universes were both possible. An open, hyperbolic universe is one in which the universe begins after taking an infinity to contract, then expands towards infinity, taking an infinite amount of time to reach it. Or, the universe could have been created at any moment in these infinities. In this view, the universe has a finite age, but an infinite future. The infinities here are true mathematical infinities, and not simply large numbers like googolplexes. If the hyperbolic model is correct, then at the present moment, the universe is on the expansion leg [see Figure 10–2].

▽ In the pulsating universe, the universe is always closed, in the same sense that a sphere is, but its radius of curvature varies periodically with time, as in

Figure 10–3. Here, the universe is infinitely old, and has an infinite future life expectancy. We are situated on one of the upward rises of the oscillation, as shown in Figure 10–3.

▽ Both models are consistent with general relativity. The distinction between them lies mainly in the value of the average density of the universe. If we were to take all the stellar and interstellar matter which we are certain exists in the universe and spread it uniformly in a sphere of radius some ten billion light years, we would have a density of matter of about 10^{-30} gm cm^{-3}. If this is the mean density of matter in the universe, the various parts of the universe do not exert a sufficient mutual gravitational attraction to counterbalance the high expansion velocities towards the periphery, and the universe will be hyperbolic. We are using words like

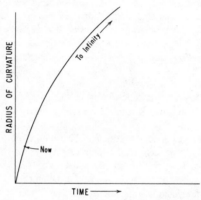

FIGURE 10–2. *Schematic representation of the change of the radius of curvature in an open, hyperbolic universe with time.*

"periphery" somewhat loosely, but having spent most of our lives as three-dimensional beings, we have no ready stores of four-dimensional experience to draw upon.

▽ If, on the other hand, there exists some tens of times more intergalactic matter, at present undiscovered, than catalogued matter, then the mean density of the universe would be about 10^{-29} gm cm^{-3}. At these densities, the gravitational self-attraction of the universe is sufficient to resist the expansion, and the pulsating model will more nearly describe the universe as a whole.

▽ Before we go on to discuss the possibility of observational tests of these two models, let us examine some of their implications. First, both of them admit the possibility of an infinitely old universe. Many people will not grant this possibility. They are willing to admit a universe which has an infinite life expectancy, but they feel much more comfortable in a universe which was formed at a finite point in time. In the pulsating model, there is no method of determining which oscillation we are presently immersed in, because at the cusps of the curves there is a definite possibility that all matter of the previous cycle, no matter how complex or elaborate its architecture, is ground down into elementary particles, and then—like the legendary phoenix—emerges from its own ashes. The pulsating universe also bears some curious resemblances to Hindu cosmology, particularly since the period per cycle is of the order of some tens of billions of years in both systems. It certainly appears possible, although there is no compelling scientific reason for the belief, that the universe began at an arbitrary point in the pulsation sequence—say, the point marked "P" in Figure 10–3.

▽ In the Soviet Union, the pulsating model encounters difficulties of another sort. In the Russian edition of the present work, Professor Shklovskii writes: "The simple repetition of cycles in essence excludes the development of the universe as a whole; it therefore seems philosophically inadmissible. Further, if the universe at some time exploded and began to expand, would it not be simpler to believe that this process occurred just once?"

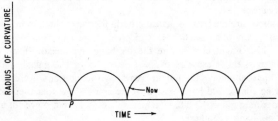

FIGURE 10–3. *Schematic representation of the change of the radius of curvature of a closed, pulsating universe with time.*

▽ In Marxist philosophy, the potentiality for self-improvement is axiomatic at all levels of study, and for all subject matters. In biology, for example, the development of Lysenkoism in the Soviet Union was in part a simple development of this precept of dialectical materialism. In modern versions of the theory of natural selection, organisms evolve one from another because the inherited characteristics of some are better fit to the environment than others; yet, the raw material for natural selection to operate upon is provided by mutation, which is essentially a random event. There is no purpose in the evolutionary process, and in an evolutionary sense organisms do not "learn" by experiences acquired during their lifetimes. Except for a few higher animals, and except for mutation, each organism starts out its life without benefit of the learning experiences of its forebears. But such a view is in apparent contradiction to the self-improvement precept of Marxist philosophy. The view that inheritable acquired characteristics are developed in particular organisms, when subjected to rigorous environments, was a position strongly maintained by Trofim Lysenko, a Soviet agronomist much in favor during the Stalin regime. This hypothesis, totally unsupported by careful experiment, has in recent years become unfashionable in the Soviet Union.

▽ An analogous involvement of dialectical materialism with cosmology is a recurrent theme in Soviet scientific literature, and is criticized in the following words by Shklovskii in the Russian edition of the present work: "The opinion that the theory of a finite universe is incompatible with the philosophy of dialectical materialism is in error. It is nonsense to connect this philosophy with any concrete property or characteristic of the universe. Dialectical materialism states that among the basic attributes of the universe are its objective reality and its knowability. Therefore, the laws of nature do not depend on the preconceived opinions of various individuals who do not comprehend the underlying spirit of dialectical materialism."

▽ A universe which grinds to ashes 50 to 100 billion years of galactic, stellar, planetary, biological, and cultural evolution is an uncomfortable one to live in, and not only for Marxists. Some religions, such as the Hindu, find no difficulties in the notion of a cyclical cosmos, but the pointlessness of such a universe is awesome. Fortunately, the determination of whether the universe is hyperbolic, pulsating, or in some other configuration is not restricted to philosophical skirmishes. There are always observations. △

Observations are the basic practical criteria for the evaluation of hypotheses in astronomy, as in any other science. It is of great interest to examine any observed phenomena which might corroborate the big-bang hypothesis. If we extrapolate back into the past the present recessional velocities of the galaxies, then, as we have seen, approximately 12 billion years ago conditions were certainly so unusual that no stars could have existed. If we could show that there are no stars with ages older than about 12 billion years, we would have a powerful argument in favor of the big-bang hypothesis.

As described in Chapter 6, studies of the main sequence turnoff point of certain globular clusters indicate that their constituent stars may be as much as 20 billion years old. However, these conclusions must be qualified. Purely theoretical considerations enter into the estimation of the ages of the stars from the turnoff point on the main sequence. Although these calculations are based on well-known principles of nuclear physics and seem to be valid for some stars, many uncertainties remain. Furthermore, the estimation of the age of the expanding universe itself is not entirely reliable. During the past decades, there have been several radical revisions of the intergalactic distance scale, and it is quite possible that errors of at least several tens of percents still exist. Thus, we can neither verify nor disprove the big-bang hypothesis on the basis of presently available information on the ages of globular clusters.

▽ Whether the universe is open and hyperbolic, or closed and pulsating, or satisfies some other cosmological model, can, in principle, be determined by other observations. One method is to search for deviations from Hubble's law. We recall that Hubble's law states that the velocity of recession of a galaxy is directly proportional to its distance. As we look to more and more distant galaxies, we are, of course, seeing them as they were in past epochs. If the rate of expansion of the universe is now accelerating, we should expect the observations of the most distant nebulae to show smaller velocities than those predicted by Hubble's law. Alternatively, if the velocity of expansion is now slowing down, we should expect the most distant galaxies, seen as they were billions of years ago, to be receding faster than predicted by the Hubble law. If very reliable estimates of the distance and velocity of the most remote galaxies could be obtained, then not only could changes in the rate of expansion of the universe be determined, but also a choice could be made among the various cosmological models. Unfortunately, the observations are very difficult to perform, and at the present time many more-or-less questionable assumptions must enter into the derivation of the distance scale. The distance to the furthest galaxies is determined by comparing their apparent magnitude with an assumed absolute magnitude typical of bright nearby galaxies. Such a calculation implicitly neglects the effects of galactic evolution, because a galaxy several billion light years away is being seen when it was several billion years younger. If such galaxies have ages of the order of 10 billion years, then we would be seeing them, say, when their ages were between 5 and 8 billion years, but not when they were less than 1 billion years old, when the most rapid evolution of stellar populations is believed to occur [see Chapter 6]. However, it is apparent that as we look to immensely distant galaxies, the effect of galactic aging will become increasingly important. Unfortunately, it is not even clear what effect differences in galactic evolution will have on the determination of the distance scale. Very early in the history of a galaxy, there should be few stars, and therefore it should appear less bright than a typical nearby mature galaxy. At a later time— perhaps during the first billion years of a galaxy's lifetime—a flurry of star formation is expected, and the average luminosity of the galaxy may be much higher than the local average. Because of such complications as aging and non-uniform rates of star formation, at the present time no unambiguous determination can be made by this method about whether the universe is open or closed, finite or infinite. Some astronomers hold that the evidence most nearly suggests a closed and finite universe, such as the oscillating model; others believe that the evidence is most consistent with an open and infinite universe, such as the hyperbolic model previously discussed.

The measurement of the angular distance between components of binary radio galaxies is another method of determining whether the universe is open or closed. It has recently been established that such duality among radio galaxies is very widespread. ▽ Figure 10–4 is a photograph of an extraordinary galaxy, NGC 5128 in the constellation Centaurus. It was once thought to be two galaxies, a spiral seen edge-on, and an elliptical, in collision. It now appears possible that this object is one more galaxy caught in the act of an explosion in its nucleus. This galaxy is also known to be an intense source of radio emission, and is more commonly known as Centaurus A. The radio emission comes predominantly from the periphery of the optical image of Figure 10–4. It is divided into two main components, one above, and the other below the dark and disrupted lanes of dust in the plane of the galaxy. △ The distance between the components of radio galaxies is characteristically about 100,000 pc. If this figure is constant throughout the

FIGURE 10–4. *The extraordinary galaxy NGC 5128 in the constellation Centaurus. As a source of intense radio emission, it is known as Centaurus A. (Courtesy of Mt. Wilson and Palomar Observatories.)*

universe, then in Euclidean space the apparent angle between the components will decrease as our distance from the radio galaxies increases. However, if space is closed, then, as we look to increasingly remote galaxies, this angle should decrease only to a definite limit. With a further increase in distance, the angle will begin to grow. No observations of this nature have as yet been carried out. They would have to be very numerous, in order to draw statistically significant conclusions from such difficult and delicate measurements.

▽ An alternative method for deciding between open and closed universes is to determine whether there exists in the universe some tens of times more matter than has been detected to date. But such an observational determination must await a theoretical prediction of the nature, temperature, and distribution of such matter. △ Weak magnetic fields are probably connected with the intergalactic medium. Their intensity could be tens or hundreds of times weaker than the intensity of interstellar magnetic fields. There is reason to believe that the intergalactic fields will rotate the polarization vector of radio radiation from the galaxies by an angle which increases with the distance to the source. (Recently, it was found that the radiation from the radio galaxies is indeed linearly polarized; the polarization is a few percent. These observations are consistent with the hypothesis that radio galaxies emit primarily because of synchrotron emission.) Although this may be a potential method for determining the density of intergalactic matter, it must be noted that this, too, is a very complex and delicate task.

▽ One further cosmological model should be mentioned, which differs in principle from the preceding evolutionary models. This is the "steady state" universe of the British astronomers Herman Bondi, Thomas Gold, and Fred Hoyle. The evolutionary models explicitly assume what is called the "cosmological principle," which states that the universe is so constructed that no observation made by any hypothetical observer anywhere in the universe can tell him where he is, in an absolute sense. The cosmological principle then predicts that the universe should look more-or-less the same to observers situated anywhere in space. An observer 10 billion light years away from us does not see fewer galaxies ahead of him than behind him because of the curvature of space; just as, for example, a two-dimensional inhabitant of the surface of a sphere finds no edge to his universe, even though its area is finite.

▽ In one formulation of the steady state theory, a "perfect cosmological principle" is introduced. It is assumed that the universe has the same over-all appearance not only to observers in all places, but also to observers at all times. That is, an observer cannot tell, in an absolute sense, what epoch he lives in by any observations made of his surroundings. Yet the galaxies are receding, and we would imagine that the average density of matter in any volume of space should decrease with time, so that an observational determination of the density of matter should give us an estimate of what cosmic time it is. To avoid this contradiction, proponents of the steady state hypothesis have postulated that matter is continually being created from nothing throughout space, at a rate which just exactly compensates the depletion of matter in a given volume by the recession of the galaxies. The hypothesis that matter is continually created at a low rate—so low that no present instruments could possibly detect it on Earth—certainly seems no more absurd than the hypothesis that all the matter in the universe was created from nothing, some 10 or 20 billion years ago. But there are other observational consequences of the steady state hypothesis.

▽ In the steady state models, the universe is infinitely old. Moreover, at no time is highly evolved matter—synthesized in the interiors of many generations of red giants—ground down again into a nuclear pulp, as occurs, for example, at the cusps of pulsation in some evolutionary models [see, for example, Figures 10–2 and 10–3]. Thus, *somewhere* in the universe, there should be immensely old—indeed, infinitely old—galaxies. It is difficult to predict what such galaxies would be like. Almost all the hydrogen should be depleted; the predominant nuclear species may have high atomic weights; and because all the stars are white dwarfs or black dwarfs, its intrinsic luminosity should be very low. We know of no such galaxies, but because of their low luminosity, they would be difficult to see unless, by chance, they were situated nearby. Intermediate stages in galactic evolution should also be seen. If they are being seen, we do not now know it.

▽ In the steady state theory, the reciprocal of the Hubble constant is *not* approximately the time since the galaxies were all very close together. Therefore, in the steady state theory, it would be possible to have in our Galaxy stellar ages which exceed the reciprocal of the Hubble constant. Such stars could not exist, of course, in the evolutionary cosmologies. There is some weak evidence that such very old stars may indeed exist in globular clusters of our Galaxy, as mentioned on page 82. Unfortunately, as we have seen, the uncertainties in both observation and theory do not permit a distinction between evolutionary and steady state cosmologies on these grounds.

▽ However, recent observations in radio astronomy now permit a tentative decision to be made between evolutionary and steady state cosmologies. △ Radio telescopes enable us to study radio galaxies which are separated from us by such vast distances that relativistic effects enter the interpretation of our observations. It has been found that the spatial density of radio galaxies which are several billions of light years distant from us is significantly greater than the spatial density of the relatively nearby radio galaxies. ("Nearby" is, of course, a purely relative term. For these purposes, a nearby galaxy is one which is as close as one billion light years.) This implies that in earlier epochs, the percentage of radio galaxies was significantly greater than at present. ▽ In itself, this circumstance is a contradiction of the perfect cosmological principle and is inconsistent with at least that formulation of steady state hypothesis. △

A possible cause for this non-uniform distribution of radio sources would be the presence of greater amounts of intergalactic gas in earlier times. The influx of this gas into the central regions of galaxies would have been much greater, leading to more explosions in galactic nuclei [see Chapter 9].

▽ An alternative explanation of the non-uniform distribution of radio galaxies at very large distances can be made in terms of the evolutionary cosmologies, in which we expect the galaxies to have been closer together in remote epochs than they are today. Since the distant galaxies are seen as they were in remote epochs, we would indeed expect the space density of radio galaxies to increase with distance.

▽ Finally, the deviations from Hubble's law shown by the motion of very remote galaxies also seem inconsistent with the steady state hypothesis. The evidence taken as a whole, then, appears to support the evolutionary cosmologies, although it cannot yet make a firm choice among them.

▽ We may now return to Olber's paradox. One reason that the sky is dark at night may be the absence of stars more than 20 billion years old. Then, no contribution to the light of the night sky could be made by objects more than 20 billion light years away. Another contemporary explanation of Olber's paradox arises from the recession of the galaxies. As a galaxy moves away from us, the Doppler effect decreases the energy of the light it emits towards Earth. This decrease is seen as a reddening of the light. As their speeds approach the velocity of light, the energy from more and more distant galaxies is increasingly diminished, so that ultimately a photon emitted in the visible region may be received on the Earth in the infrared, or indeed, in the microwave or radio region. Thus, as we look to distant galaxies, receding at velocities closer and closer to the velocity of light, the energy which we receive from them progressively declines, because of the Doppler effect, but also, of course, because of the law of the inverse square. No matter how sophisticated a radiation detection system we construct, we can always imagine a galaxy traveling so close to the speed of light that its energy output cannot be detected on Earth. Therefore, there is an effective cut-off to the distance of the furthest galaxy we can see. This cut-off is approximately 10 or 20 billion light years away.

▽ It may be asked if this explanation does not contradict the conservation of energy. Hypothetical inhabitants of a very distant, rapidly-receding galaxy measure a sizable radiation output directed towards the Earth. When a photon of visible light leaves that galaxy, the inhabitants measure it as a photon of visible light. Yet when that photon arrives at Earth, we find it reddened in frequency, and attribute to it a much smaller energy. Yet ultimately, our description and theirs of the energy output of the galaxy should tally. The solution to this conundrum is provided if we imagine some other observers, equally distant from the receding galaxy, but situated on the other side of it. These observers, if situated at rest with respect to us, will see the galaxy in question rushing towards them. The light emitted from the galaxy will now be shifted towards the violet, and the new set of observers will attribute to each photon more energy than is measured on the emitting galaxy. Thus, the deficit of radiation emitted backwards from the rapidly-moving galaxy is compensated by an enhancement of the energy of radiation emitted forwards. When the energy bookkeeping is completed, the energy remains conserved.

▽ In fact, however, there are no distant observers stationary with respect to us. The universe is expanding, and the cosmological principle requires that all observers arrive at something like the Hubble law. The energy degradation which the red-shift represents provides some of the energy for continued expansion of the universe, and no observers should now be witnessing a violet-shift.

▽ This consideration of the violet-shift is of some relevance when we consider that, in the pulsating universe, the universe would have been contracting some 20 billion years ago. △ This must have led to a significant increase in the short wave, "hard" radiation, due to the violet-shift of the radiation emitted by the converging galaxies. Eventually, the violet-shift would be so large that the likelihood of the origin and development of life in those times would be remote.

Thus, if the hypothesis of the pulsating universe is valid, and the epoch of the red-shift is ultimately to be replaced by the epoch of the violet-shift, we must come to the following conclusion: The origin and evolution of life in suitable regions of the universe are more probable during the times of the red-shift than during the times of the violet-shift ▽ because of the gradually increasing flux of ultraviolet light, x-rays, and gamma rays. △ Throughout the long period of expansion, life could negotiate the evolutionary journey from the lowest to the highest forms. But with the advent of the contracting phase, life would become increasingly difficult, and would eventually disappear, only to arise and develop again in the following epoch of expansion.

▽ While we do not yet know whether our universe must experience a contraction phase, we are on the verge of finding out: Does the universe expand forever, or are we trapped in a vast cycle of cosmic deaths and rebirths? △

11

Multiple star systems

Canst thou bind the chains of the Pleiades, or loose the bands of Orion?

Job, 38:31

▽ To pursue our inquiry into the nature and distribution of life in the universe, we must now contract our field of view from the grand cosmological panorama to the seemingly commonplace study of the individual stars. If the stars move in isolated splendor, unaccompanied by planetary systems, we can expect few occurrences of life in the reaches of cosmic space. In the next three chapters, we consider the observational and the theoretical evidence that beyond our solar system other planets circle other stars. △

In Chapters 3 and 4, we considered certain fundamental characteristics of the stars, their diameter, luminosity, color, age, and evolution. Here, we consider still another property—their multiplicity. Many stars ▽ (at least 30 percent; perhaps more than 50 percent) △ form double, triple, or multiple systems in which the individual stars revolve about each other. But the periods of revolution may vary from several hours to thousands of years, depending on their masses and separation. Figures 11–1 and 11–2 show the successive relative positions of the

1908   1915   1920

FIGURE 11–1. *Photograph of the visual binary star xi Ursae Majoris, in 1908, 1915, and 1920. The relative motion of the dimmer secondary about the brighter primary is evident. (Courtesy of Yerkes Observatory.)*

individual stars of the double star system xi Ursae Majoris. In many cases, the components of a multiple star system are so close together that they cannot be resolved into separate stars. ▽ The system then appears to the eye or the photographic plate as a single star. △ In such cases, the multiplicity can often be confirmed by spectral observations. Because of the orbital motions of the stars about each other, their velocities along the line of sight are unequal and time-variable. For example, at a given moment in their mutual orbital motion, one star may be approaching us, the other receding. ▽ Half an orbital period later, approach and recession will be reversed. △ These motions lead, through the Doppler effect, to a small wavelength displacement of the spectral lines of one star with respect to the corresponding lines of the other. Because of the orbital motions, the velocities along the line of sight will vary periodically, and hence the displacements of the spectral lines will also vary periodically. By systematically observing such spectral line displacements as they vary with time, not only can the multiplicity of the system be deduced, but the basic characteristics of the orbit can be reliably calculated, and some information about the masses of the individual components derived. Such close double stars are called *spectroscopic binaries*.

▽ The components of a multiple star system revolve about each other, usually in a common orbital plane, similar to that in which we find the Sun and the planets of our solar system. The orientation of these planes is more or less random, so that some stars will revolve about each other in the plane of the Galaxy; others in a plane perpendicular to that of the Galaxy; and most, at some intermediate angle. △ Thus, only rarely does the plane of the orbit of a double or multiple star system form a small angle with the line of sight. If it does, however, it is possible to

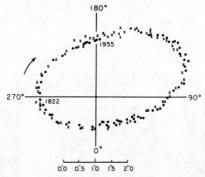

FIGURE 11–2. *The dots, circles, and crosses represent the apparent motion of the secondary of xi Ursae Majoris around the primary, in observations made between 1822 and 1955.* [*Reproduced from O. Struve, B. Lynds, and H. Pillans,* Elementary Astronomy (*Oxford University Press, New York, 1959*). *Courtesy of Oxford University Press.*]

observe an eclipse of one star by another. Since neither component can be seen separately, even by the most powerful telescopes, we observe only a periodic variation in the brightness of the double star system. At the beginning of the eclipse, the brightness declines; at its end, the star recovers its usual luminosity. (Often an eclipse lasts for several hours.) By plotting the brightness of the star against time (the so-called "brightness curve"), we can determine not only the basic parameters of the orbit, but also the diameters of the stars, and even information on the decline of the brightness of the stellar disks from their centers to their edges, ▽ or *limbs*. Since even the nearest star appears as a point of light to the most powerful telescope, such determinations of "limb-darkening" are all the more remarkable. △ A diagram of the orbit of the eclipsing variable star Algol, and the brightness curve which corresponds to it, are shown in Fig. 11–3. ▽ The Algol system, in the constellation Perseus, undergoes an eclipse approximately once every three days. When the bright component is partially eclipsed by the dimmer companion, the

146   THE UNIVERSE

over-all brightness of Algol falls by more than 50 percent. This variation in luminosity is readily detectable by the naked eye and is the reason that Algol was known in ancient times as "The Demon Star." △

In both spectroscopic binaries and eclipsing binaries, the component stars are situated very close to one another. In fact, sometimes their surfaces are in physical contact. ▽ Tidal forces then draw material from one star towards the other, in complex and beautiful patterns. The material being exchanged from star to star is itself luminous. From a hypothetical planet circling such a stellar system (and such planets are possible), an observer would see two suns in his sky, perhaps of different sizes, luminosities and colors, with a brilliant and luminous ribbon of light seemingly binding them together. △ Often such multiple star systems are immersed in extensive rarefied gaseous envelopes. Diagrams of two of these close pairs are shown in Figures 11–4 and 11–5. Unfortunately, these fascinating processes are not observed visually, even through the largest telescopes, and our understanding of them is acquired only from an analysis of the spectra and brightness of the stars.

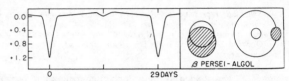

FIGURE 11–3. *Schematic representation of the light curve of an eclipsing binary star. On the left: The intensity and apparent magnitudes as plotted against time. The two major intensity minima correspond to the two configurations per orbit in which the stars eclipse each other. On the right: The relative configuration when the brighter star is eclipsed by the darker star, and the corresponding orbits.* [*Reproduced from O. Struve, B. Lynds, and H. Pillans,* Elementary Astronomy (*Oxford University Press, New York, 1959*). *Courtesy of Oxford University Press.*]

We know from Kepler's laws that the short periods of rotation belong to the very closest stars. The shortest known period, approximately 80 minutes long, belongs to the eclipsing variable WZ Sagittae.

▽ WZ Sagittae is the forty-eighth variable star discovered in the constellation Sagitta (which means "arrow," and which is to be distinguished from the nearby constellation Sagittarius, which means "archer"). The astronomical notation for variable stars in a given constellation is a tragic testimony to the deficiencies of the short-term view, and it will be profitable to tarry a moment and consider the vagaries of variable star notation. If a star which has already been named is discovered to be variable, it retains its original name. Thus, delta Cephei and Algol pose no problems. The first star in a given constellation which is recognized as a variable, and which has no proper, or Greek-letter name, is designated with the capital letter R; thus, R Sagittae. Subsequent discoveries are designated S, T, . . . , Z. This stratagem works as long as there are no more than nine new variable stars discovered per constellation. However, to the astronomers' surprise, more than nine such stars per constellation *were* discovered. Having exhausted the

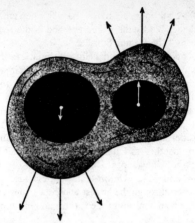

FIGURE 11–4. *Schematic representation of a close double star system, sharing a common gaseous envelope which circulates between them. The individual stars are distorted from a spherical configuration because of the mutual gravitational interaction and their rotation. [Reproduced from O. Struve, Stellar Evolution (Princeton University Press, Princeton, 1950). Courtesy of Princeton University Press.]*

letters R through Z, it was decided to use a double letter notation, beginning with RR, RS, RT, . . . , RZ; SS, ST, SU, . . . , SZ; and so on, until ZZ was reached, providing for the first 54 new variables discovered. But there are many stars in the skies, and as astronomical activities continued, variables beyond the ZZ's were discovered.

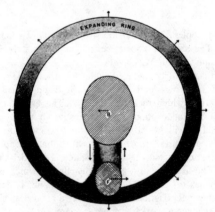

FIGURE 11–5. *Another example of an hypothesized circulating gaseous stream connecting close binary stars. [Reproduced from O. Struve, Stellar Evolution (Princeton University Press, Princeton, 1950). Courtesy of Princeton University Press.]*

▽ The next procedure was to begin with AA, and continue with AB, AC, . . . , AZ; BB, BC, BD, . . . , BZ, until QZ. Because of transcription problems, the letter J is omitted. This sequence stops at QZ, because the next logical doublet which has not previously been used would be RA. But since doublets beginning with R have been used earlier in the sequence, the designations RA, RB, . . . , were rejected.

▽ This elaborate tomfoolery accounts for the first 334 variable stars in a given constellation. A typical large constellation—Sagittarius, for example—may have 1700 identified variable stars. The letter notation obdurately assumed that the number of variable stars to be discovered was small. In fact, the number is very large, and the 1958 edition of the Soviet General Catalogue of Variable Stars lists 14,711 known variables in the Galaxy. To designate these, astronomers have finally taken to using the letter V to indicate a variable star, and follow it with a number, beginning with 335, to indicate its order in the discovery list; thus, V 678 Centauri. How much more sensible it would have been, had the first such variable star been designated V1, and the sequence continued *seriatum!* It is still possible, of course, to revise the notation, calling R, S, T, . . . 1, 2, 3, ..., etc., but the letter notation has jelled, and there seems little hope for a more rational system. Such notational anachronisms, while they need not concern us further here, do not aid the popularization of astronomy. △

It now seems very possible that all novae occur in close binary systems. During a nova explosion, the luminosity of the star increases greatly in a brief period of time, although the luminosity is still a thousand times less than that of a supernova. The mass of material expelled during each nova explosion is approximately 10^{-4} to 10^{-5} the mass of our Sun. Apparently the presence of a close stellar neighbor interferes with the normal evolution of a star, particularly when it enters the red giant stage. Then, as its radius greatly increases, instabilities arise which lead to repeated—sometimes periodic—explosions.

Often, the masses of the components of a binary star system are very similar. But it sometimes happens that the mass of one component is ten or more times the mass of the other. Their relative luminosities can vary widely. For example, the faint companion of Sirius is a white dwarf. ▽ It was the first white dwarf ever discovered, and its high mass for its small radius was first derived from its orbital motion. △

Certain components of multiple star systems have such a small size that their luminosity is insignificant. These components are impossible to observe visually, even through a large telescope. But if such underluminous components are at a great distance from the primary (the brighter and more massive star), their existence and properties can be deduced. The classic example of such a system is 61Cygni, ▽ which was investigated by the American astronomer K. A. Strand and the Soviet astronomer A. N. Deutsch. The primary has its own random, so-called "proper" motion against the background of a relatively fixed field of the stars. If the primary has a massive, underluminous companion, it will have, in addition to its proper motion, a smaller, periodic motion about the center of mass of the double star system. The resulting total motion, over a period of many years, is a wavy line such as that of Figure 11–6. Observations of such periodic motions require great patience, precision, and dedication. The further away such a perturbed primary is from us, the more difficult it is to see the periodic variations in the proper motion. It is therefore not surprising that of the several invisible companions found in this way all belong to primaries which are among the nearest stars.

▽ To obtain some idea of the frequency of multiple star systems and of dark companions, consider the 12 star systems closest to the Sun. They are listed in Table III, with their spectral type and their distance from the Sun, measured in light years. The multiplicity of names arises from the astronomer's insistence on using a

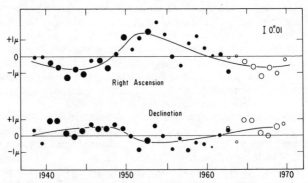

FIGURE 11–6. *The relative proper motion of Barnard's Star, as deduced by van de Kamp. Right ascension and declination are two common coordinates which are at right angles to each other, used in astronomy. The error bar in the upper right-hand corner illustrates a characteristic deviation of the actual observed points from this curve. While such observations are extremely difficult to perform, there seems little doubt about the reality of these curves. (Courtesy of Dr. Peter van de Kamp, Sproul Observatory.)*

multiplicity of catalogues. The symbol e in the spectral type column indicates stars which show emission lines; the symbol wd denotes a white dwarf. We note that the bulk of the nearest stars are M stars, of low luminosity. Of these dozen systems, at least four are multiple star systems, on the basis of visual and spectrographic evidence alone. One of them, alpha Centauri, is a triple system. The low-mass component, alpha Centauri C, is in orbit about the other two components. Since it is therefore sometimes slightly closer to the Sun than alpha Centauri A and B, it is the closest known star to the Sun, and is, accordingly, sometimes called Proxima Centauri.

▽ In addition, at least three of these twelve systems have dark companions with masses about one percent of the Sun's mass, or less. The first such companion, discovered by K. A. Strand in 1943, is associated with the 61 Cygni system, and has a mass about 0.8 percent that of the Sun. A companion having

150

about one percent of the solar mass was discovered in 1960 by the American astronomer, Sarah Lee Lippincott, of Sproul Observatory, for the star Lalande 21185. In 1964, Peter van de Kamp, also of Sproul Observatory, found an exceedingly interesting companion to Barnard's Star, the second nearest system, only six light years away. Barnard's Star is a faint red dwarf, discovered in 1916 and named after its discoverer; it has the largest proper motion of any known star. The results of 25 years' careful observations by van de Kamp are shown in Figure

TABLE III

THE NEAREST STARS

Number	Star system	Component	Spectral type	Distance from Sun (Light years)
0	The Sun		G 0	0
1	alpha Centauri	A	G 0	4.3
		B	K 5	4.3
		C	M 5e	4.3
2	Barnard's Star		M 5	6.0
3	Wolf 359		M 6e	7.7
4	Luyten 726–8	A	M 6e	7.9
		B	M 6e	7.9
5	Lalande 21185		M 2	8.2
6	Sirius	A	A 0	8.7
		B	wd	8.7
7	Ross 154		M 5e	9.3
8	Ross 248		M 6e	10.3
9	epsilon Eridani		K 2	10.8
10	Ross 128		M 5	10.9
11	61 Cygni	A	K 6	11.1
		B	M 0	11.1
12	Luyten 789–6		M 6	11.2

11–6. The dots are the observational points, and the solid line is the periodic curve which fits them. The dark companion inferred from these observations orbits Barnard's Star once every 24 years, and has a mass about 0.15 percent of the Sun. This is a mass only 50 percent greater than that of Jupiter, which orbits our Sun once every 11.9 years. The companions of Lalande 21185 and 61 Cygni are sufficiently massive that they may be shining dimly by their own light, and therefore may be classified as very subluminous stars, rather than as very massive planets. But the companion of Barnard's Star is almost certainly a planet. This as yet unnamed world is the first planet to be discovered since the American astronomer Clyde Tombaugh found Pluto in 1930. But it has the additional and unique distinction of being the first planetary companion, discovered with a fair degree of confidence, of another sun. Van de Kamp's planet may not be the only companion to Barnard's Star, but less massive planets would be much more difficult to detect. Similarly, there may be further planetary companions to Lalande 21185, to 61 Cygni, and indeed, to all the other stars listed in Table III. The more distant the star, the more difficult it is to detect such low-mass planets.

▽ The sample of stars presented in Table III is a very small fraction of the total number of stars in our Galaxy, but it is the only sample in which we can make even a preliminary search for dark companions. We will consider it typical of similar regions elsewhere in the Galaxy. Of these thirteen systems, including the Sun, at least two have planets—the Sun and Barnard's Star. But, from our vantage point, these are two of the three closest systems. These data suggest that at least 10 percent, and perhaps more than 50 percent, of the stars are accompanied by planetary systems. △

The difference between giant planets and dark companion stars is not absolute. Both consist mainly of hydrogen and helium. They are primarily gaseous spheres, held together by the force of gravity. If the mass of Jupiter were five times larger, the temperature in its central regions would increase, and it would begin to radiate, although feebly, in the visible part of the spectrum. Jupiter would then become a very dim red dwarf, with a surface temperature of approximately 1000 to 2000°K.

▽ To have a better idea of the distribution of planets throughout nearby space, we should like to extend the search for companions of Jovian mass and smaller to other star systems. This problem will be discussed in theoretical terms in the following two chapters. △ Here, we consider possible future astronomical techniques which may be used to extend our knowledge of planetary companions and nearby stars. We limit our discussion to the detection of large planets because if we cannot observe *them*, searches for the smaller, and perhaps more interesting, planets would be fruitless.

Let us assume that at a distance of 10 parsecs—about 33 light years—there is a star similar to the Sun. A large planet rotates about our hypothetical star at a distance of 5.2 astronomical units (A.U.), the same distance that Jupiter is from our Sun. Assume further that this planet has the same size and mass as Jupiter, and also that ▽ (lucky for us) △ this planet is in almost exactly the same orbital plane as is the Earth.

In principle, there are three methods which can be used to detect our planet. The first is by the periodic perturbations in the star's proper motion, ▽ just the technique used to discover van de Kamp's planet. △ The period of this perturbation would be equal to the period of revolution of the planet—in our case, 11.9 years. This periodic motion is again due to the fact that the star, influenced by the gravitational field of the planet, moves along an elliptical orbit about the center of gravity of the star-planet system. This orbital motion is superposed on the stellar proper motion. Since the mass of the star is about 1000 times the mass of the planet, the center of gravity of the system lies close to the star. △ Thus, the amplitude of the periodic motion would be very small.

Calculations carried out by the Russian-American astronomer Otto Struve indicate that the amplitude of this wave for a star 10 pc distant, superposed on the proper motion, would be smaller than 0.0005 seconds of arc per year. This is an extremely small angle [see Chapter 3], and lies far beyond the limits of accuracy of present astronomical techniques. However, if the mass were 10 to 20 times greater than the mass of Jupiter, such oscillations could be detected—although with some difficulty.

Another method of detecting the presence of such planets is by spectroscopy. The perturbations of the planetary companion produce periodic variations in the velocity of the star along the line of sight. It is easy to see that sometimes the star will be pulled slightly towards us, and at other times slightly away from us. The oscillation period of the radial velocities will again be equal to the period of revolution of the planet, but this effect is also very small. Otto Struve showed that the periodic variations in the radial velocity ▽ (that is, the velocity towards us or away from us) △ would not exceed about 10 meters per second. This is roughly 10^{-3} of the total radial velocity of an average star due to its proper motion. Through the Doppler effect, velocities of 10 meters per second correspond to a displacement of a spectral line by approximately 0.0001 Å. ▽ (We recall that 1 Å $= 10^{-8}$ cm, and that the wavelength of visible light falls between 4000 and 7000 Å.) △ Such small variations in wavelength cannot be measured at present, especially if we consider that spectral lines are not infinitely narrow, but have a finite width of the order of 0.1 Å.

A third method of detecting planetary systems about nearby stars is the photometric method—that is, the systematic measurement of the brightness of a star. We have assumed that the orbit of our hypothetical planet is in the orbital plane of the Earth ▽—a circumstance which will in fact occur only fortuitously. △ Hence, periodically each 11.9 years, the planet will be projected onto the disk of the star as it passes in front of it. Similar phenomena are observed in our solar system —for example, when the planets Venus and Mercury transit the disk of the Sun. Since the planet is dark, and not self-luminous, when it passes in front of the star, the brightness of the star (or more exactly, the flux of radiation from it) will appear slightly diminished, as measured on Earth. The phenomenon is quite analogous to that already described for eclipsing binaries [see Figure 11–3].

Calculations indicate that if a planet the size of Jupiter passed in front of a star similar to the Sun, the star's luminosity would decrease by about 0.01 stellar magnitudes. Such a small variation in the radiation flux can be recorded by existing photomultipliers. We must recall, however, that we are considering a very idealized case, in which such an eclipse actually occurs, as seen from the Earth. An inclination of the orbital plane of the hypothetical planet by only half a second of arc would cause the planet not to pass in front of the star at all, as seen from the Earth. ▽ Thus, while the method works in principle, it works in practice only if we are very lucky, because the planes of planetary orbits should have a random distribution. Only if we observe a large number of stars will we be fortunate enough to detect a planetary companion by such a method. △

These three methods for the discovery of extrasolar planetary systems are summarized in Figure 11–7.

▽ Many of the difficulties in implementing these methods are due to our unimaginative choice of the Earth as an observing station. △ The large telescopes on Earth cannot operate close to their theoretical capabilities because of atmospheric turbulence, or what the astronomer calls "poor seeing." Even a brilliant point source of light—for our purposes, a star—is smeared into a disk with a

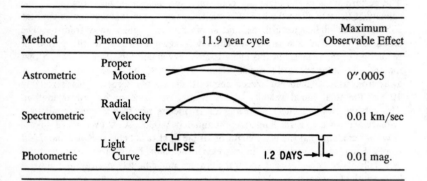

Method	Phenomenon	11.9 year cycle	Maximum Observable Effect
Astrometric	Proper Motion		0″.0005
Spectrometric	Radial Velocity		0.01 km/sec
Photometric	Light Curve	ECLIPSE 1.2 DAYS	0.01 mag.

FIGURE 11–7. *Schematic representation of the astrometric, spectrometric, and photometric methods of detecting extrasolar planetary systems about stars 10 parsecs distant.*

diameter of between 0.5 and 2 seconds of arc. If a planet were 1 A.U. from its primary, and the primary star itself were distant from us about 10 parsecs, then the angular distance between the planet and the star would be about 0.1 second of arc. Thus, no telescope on Earth, of whatever size, could separate the image of the planet from the smeared image of the star.

In the near future, there may nevertheless be a possibility of directly observing large planets associated with nearby stars. The required instrument is a large telescope in orbit about the Earth. ▽ Such Orbiting Astronomical Observatories are under intensive development by the National Aeronautics and Space Administration in the United States, although their primary scientific objectives are studies of stars and the interstellar medium in the presently inaccessible ultraviolet wavelengths. The Orbiting Astronomical Observatory of the United States space program is an unmanned satellite. Similar instruments may be under development in the Soviet Union, perhaps in conjunction with manned spaceflight. △

Although an orbiting observatory will be well above atmospheric turbulence, it will still not be possible to observe or photograph objects which have indefinitely small angular separations. A limit to our ability to resolve nearby objects is imposed by the wave nature of light itself. Due to diffraction in the objective lens or mirror of a telescope, the focal plane image of any star is a system of rings of definite width. The diffraction-limited resolution of any telescope is approximately equal to the ratio of the wavelength of the light to the diameter of the objective. For example, with blue light and an objective lens or mirror of diameter 1 meter (39 inches), two close stars will be distinguished if they are more than 0.1 second of arc apart. ▽ If they are any closer, their separate images will fuse, and an indistinct diffraction smear will result. △

The use of a special instrument called an interferometer may, however, permit us to measure light sources separted by so small an angular distance as 0.01 second of arc. ▽ If both the planet and the star had large and comparable intensities, interferometric observations could be carried out with telescopes on the Earth. But since the brightness of the planet is negligible, compared with the brightness of the primary star, light scattering and turbulence in the Earth's atmosphere would preclude such observations. △

Let us consider a Jovian planet 1 A.U. away from its star, which is of solar type, and about 10 parsecs from us. The apparent magnitude of this planet is assumed to be approximately +24. Even such a weak light source could probably be detected from an orbiting space observatory, using current astronomical techniques. However, it seems unlikely that the critical observations could be performed automatically, at least in the near future. Thus, an astronomer-astronaut is, ▽ in the context of this problem, △ required for the orbiting astronomical observatory. Perhaps some day a large and stationary observatory will be established on the Moon. It will then be possible to carry out extensive observations on many significant astronomical problems which are currently difficult or impossible to pursue because of obscuration by the Earth's atmosphere.

Although our direct evidence for extrasolar planetary systems is at the present time limited, it is entirely reasonable to regard stellar multiplicity and planetary systems as different aspects of the same phenomenon. According to the investigations of the Dutch-American astronomer G. P. Kuiper of the University of Arizona, the average distance between the components of a binary star system is approximately 20 A.U. This is close to the dimensions of our own solar system.

How do multiple star systems arise? In the past, theories have been proposed which attempted to explain the formation of binary stars by the separation of a single star into two components. The cause of this stellar fission was supposedly the rapid rotation of the star. Because of centrifugal forces, the surface of a rapidly-rotating star would cease to be spherical. Mathematical calculations indicate that under certain ideal conditions, a rapidly-rotating body takes on a characteristic pear-shaped form; as it rotates still faster, an instability is established and the star separates into two components, ▽ each of which is rotating more slowly than the parent star. △ However, this hypothesis does not adequately account for the observations. We therefore discount this model of binary star formation.

An alternative hypothesis, proposed, for example, by O. Y. Schmidt, of the Soviet Union, postulates entrapment; that is, under certain conditions, two stars moving independently in space are imagined to become gravitationally coupled during a random encounter, and form a double star system. Although such a process is possible mathematically (for example, in the accidental encounter of three independent stars), the probability of such an event is exceedingly small. In addition, the entrapment model is contradicted by observations. For example, it cannot explain why quadruple star systems are always found in the systematic two-by-two pattern of Figure 11–8.

FIGURE 11–8. *The invariable relative positions of a quadruple star system. In such systems, two binaries are always observed orbiting each other.*

The bulk of relevant astronomical information garnered during the last two decades indicates that the stars in multiple star systems are coeval, formed simultaneously out of the gas and dust of the interstellar medium. From such condensations, entire groups of stars, associations and clusters, are formed [see Chapter 6]. Multiple star systems seem to be formed in the same way. In many cases, the components of a multiple star system seem to be of the same age. Often, we see a system in which both components are hot stars of spectral class O, or are early B stars. ▽ In Table III, we find that the components of Luyten 726–8 are both of spectral type M6e; 61 Cygni A and B have similar spectral types. △ According to contemporary concepts of the evolution of stars, such components are of similar mass and were formed at the same time from the primordial nebula. They are now at the same stage of evolution. Sometimes, one component will be a hot, main sequence giant, and its companion will be a red, relatively cold supergiant. We can conclude that the masses of the two stars were initially different, and that the supergiant represents the more rapid evolution of the more massive component [see Chapter 6].

In recent years, an extraordinary occurrence relevant to binary star systems has been discovered. Massive, hot young stars have, as a rule, a relatively small random velocity, generally less than 10 km sec⁻¹, ▽ corresponding to a small proper motion. △ Such stars are concentrated towards the Galactic plane, ▽ since they have been formed recently, and travel slowly. △ The exceptions to this rule are of interest. A small number of hot, massive stars move at unusually high random velocities, sometimes approaching 100 km sec⁻¹. Such stars may have escaped from stellar associations. In Figure 11–9, the points depict three such rapidly moving hot stars. The straight dotted lines indicate the directions of their motion through the sky. These lines almost intersect in the region of the constellation Orion, where there is a large association of hot stars. Since their velocities and

156

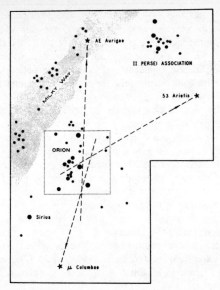

FIGURE 11–9. *Computed paths of the three best-known runaway stars. Note that they diverge from a comparatively small area in the constellation Orion.* (*Courtesy of Sky and Telescope, Cambridge, Massachusetts.*)

their distance to the Orion association are known, it is possible to compute backwards in time, and establish that these runaway stars left the Orion association some 2 to 5 million years ago.

Why are such stars ejected from their clusters? The Dutch astronomer Adriaan Blaauw has noted that these runaways are always single stars, an unusual circumstance, since multiplicity is particularly widespread among early type stars. According to Blaauw's hypothesis, the runaway stars were previously components of binary systems. The second components are postulated to be extremely massive hot stars of spectral class O, which became supernovae of Type II [see Chapter 7].

Consider now what would happen if the more massive component in a binary star system suddenly vanished, completely disappearing because of the supernova explosion. Gravitational forces could not hold the remaining star in its pre-explosion orbit, and it would fly off along a tangent to its original orbit, but with a velocity equal to its former orbital velocity. This "slingshot effect"—it is difficult to call it anything else—▽ is analogous to the situation in which a string, tied to a stone and whirled about the head, is suddenly cut. △

Now, the mass of the exploded star does not actually vanish without a trace; the supernova remnant is an expanding nebula which has a mass approximately equal to that of the original star [see Chapter 7]. If this nebula were inside the orbit of the surviving star, the gravitational forces would not be greatly altered, and the companion would not run away. If, however, the star were far inside the nebula, the nebula would have little gravitational effect. For the slingshot effect to work, it is necessary for most of the supernova remnant to leave the orbit of the surviving star during a time significantly less than the period of revolution. A binary star system with components quite far removed from one another—say, 10 to 20 A.U.—would have periods of revolution of the order of several years, and the condition for the slingshot effect would be satisfied. For sufficiently massive stars, the orbital velocities will be approximately 100 km sec^{-1}.

▽ The events we have been describing would be of considerable interest for the hypothetical inhabitants of a possible planet circling the runaway star. In earlier, more placid times, there would have been two brilliant suns in the sky, one near, the other further away. Some days would have no nights, because a star would be in the sky above each hemisphere. When both stars are above the same hemisphere, night must fall in the far hemisphere. The night would be extraordinary, because the stars in a stellar cluster, or association, are much more densely packed than in our region of the Galaxy.

▽ Suddenly, the farther star explodes. The biological consequences of a nearby supernova explosion are formidable indeed [see Chapter 7]. Unless an advanced technical civilization inhabited our hypothetical planet, all its inhabitants would be incinerated.

▽ For the purposes of this narrative, let us assume that our observers survive the supernova explosion. Shortly afterwards, the remaining star and its companion planets embark on an extraordinary interstellar voyage, moving about a parsec every 10,000 years. In less than a million years, the star would be well clear of the stellar association in which it was formed, and the nights, more frequent now, would exhibit a much more mundane celestial panoply.

▽ We must emphasize that the foregoing narrative is unrealistic in several respects. It is most unlikely for an advanced civilization to exist on such a planet, because the lifetime of the hot and massive local sun can itself only be a few million years old [see Chapter 6], not nearly enough time for the origin of life and the evolution of a technical civilization. We will return to the question of which stars are likely to hold indigenous planetary civilizations in Chapter 24. △

The presence of white dwarfs in multiple star systems—for example, in the system of Sirius (see Table III)—is explained by the fact that the more massive component has nearly completed its evolutionary history. However, it would be difficult to imagine a binary system which contained a hot, massive star of spectral class O, and also a red giant with a mass one and a half or two times that of the Sun. To leave the main sequence and become a red giant, a star of this mass would require 2 to 4 billion years (see Table I). A hot star of spectral type O, on the other hand, cannot remain on the main sequence for more than about 10 million years. Fortunately, binary systems similar to the one just described are entirely unknown.

Thus, the facts seem to indicate that the components of multiple star systems are formed simultaneously. If we can establish that the formation of planetary systems does not differ fundamentally from the formation of multiple star systems, then we shall be able to conclude that planets are coeval with their primary stars. The origin of planetary systems is the subject of the next two chapters.

12

Historical views on the origin of the solar system

But indeed all the whole Story of Comets and Planets, and the Production of the World, is founded upon such poor and trifling Grounds, that I have often wonder'd how an ingenious Man could spend all that pains in making such Fancies hang together. For my part, I shall be very well contented, and shall count I have done a great Matter, if I can but come to any Knowledge of the Nature of Things, as they now are, never troubling my self about their Beginning, or how they were made, knowing that to be out of the reach of human Knowledge, or even Conjecture.

Christianus Huygens, *New Conjectures Concerning the Planetary Worlds, Their Inhabitants and Productions* (c. 1670)

Upon a slight conjecture I have ventured on a dangerous journey, and I already behold the foothills of new lands. Those who have the courage to continue the search will set foot upon them.

Immanuel Kant, *Allgemeine Naturgeschichte und Theorie des Himmels* (1755)

From earliest times, the question of the origin and evolution of the Earth and the other planets in our solar system has challenged the keenest minds. Philosophers and scientists of the caliber of Kant and Laplace have wrestled with this problem; yet it still remains largely unresolved.

During the last decade, the theory of stellar evolution, sketched in Chapter 6, has gained widespread scientific acceptance. At first glance, it seems strange that astronomers should know more about the distant stars, which are in many cases difficult to observe, than about the relatively nearby planets. But the numbers of stars which astronomers can observe are vast, and stars are known that represent each stage of stellar evolution. We have been able to establish empirically, that the rate of evolution of a star depends on certain initial conditions—for example, on its mass. ▽ Given such observational hints, the theoretician's task has been simplified enormously. But no similar body of information on planetary evolution is currently available. △ If we should ever succeed in obtaining observations of numerous planetary systems in various stages of their development, then questions of planetary evolution may also be solved empirically.

Does it follow that we can say absolutely nothing about the origin of our solar system except that it was somehow formed, no later than 5 billion years ago? Such a stolid point of view is as reprehensible as unbounded speculation. Progress in stellar cosmogony has provided us with significant clues for planetary cosmogony. In addition to the observational evidence of the preceding chapter, there are today valid scientific arguments supporting the contention that many stars have planetary systems. ▽ We briefly consider in this chapter some earlier views on the origin of the solar system, and then proceed, in Chapter 13, to more current views.

▽ One of the earliest attempts to explain the origin of the world in scientific terms—insofar as science was, in those days, understood—was provided by Lucretius, in his "De Rerum Natura." Lucretius toyed with the idea that the universe was infinitely old, and that matter had always been in it. But he imagined a time before the origin of *things;* there was matter, but not in an organized form. The matter, naturally, was falling. Why? Because, as everyone knows, if you let go of an object, it falls. This was, of course, long before any connection was seen between the motion of falling bodies and the mass of the Earth. It was the nature of objects to fall; and in the beginning, matter fell. The motion was uniform, however, so one bit of matter could not jostle its neighbor. No forces were postulated between the particles. At this rate, the fall would continue forever, and the world would never begin.

▽ Lucretius therefore postulated the "Swerve." It was just the tiniest Swerve, barely adequate to produce collisions among the particles. Once there were

161

collisions, and the colliding particles adhered one to another, Lucretius could imagine the origin of the Earth through a random interaction of material particles. The origin of the First Swerve was never explained, to say nothing of the fact that, in Lucretius' view, we must still be falling today.

▽ In the light of modern knowledge, Lucretius' naïveté was very great, but he was hypothesizing in an information vacuum. He stressed *random* interactions because the laws of physics were almost entirely unknown. One key ingredient which Lucretius missed was the possibility of forces acting between objects not in material contact. Only after the theory of gravitation was developed by Newton could planetary cosmogony enter a stage of profitable speculation.

▽ Among the earliest Newtonian cosmogonies are those of Kant and Laplace. △ It will be apparent, in Chapter 13, that the essential premise of their remarkable hypothesis has withstood the test of time, and we can find their basic idea in all contemporary theories of planetary origins. The nebular hypothesis was first expressed by the German philosopher Immanuel Kant, and several decades later was formulated independently by the French mathematician Pierre Simon, Marquis de Laplace. Although it is called the Kant–Laplace hypothesis, these two brilliant scholars did not concur on a number of important questions. Kant, for example, assumed that first the Sun and then the planets were formed from an initially cold, dusty nebula. Laplace, on the other hand, believed that the planets formed somewhat before the Sun, from an initially hot, gaseous nebula in a state of rapid rotation. Despite these differences, both agreed on the central point of what is now called the Kant–Laplace nebular hypothesis, that the solar system arose from the condensation of a primordial nebula, a cloud of gas and dust.

In their view, the Sun and the planets were formed (roughly) at the same time, from the identical nebula. Contracting under the influence of gravitational forces, the cloud began to rotate more and more rapidly, owing to the conservation of angular momentum. As a result of the large centrifugal forces generated by this rapid rotation, matter was thrown out from the periphery of the contracting nebula, forming an equatorial belt of gas and dust. ▽ As the contraction continued, the nebula shed successive rings of matter. The rings were thought to have condensed at a later time, to form the planets. This view of the early development of the contracting nebula was considered supported by the observations, then being made for the first time, of spiral nebulae [see Figures 9–3 and 9–4]. We now know, of course, that these objects are in fact distant galaxies, not nearby protostars. △ The fundamental premises of the Kant–Laplace hypothesis are sketched in Figure 12–1.

In the middle of the nineteenth century, ▽ primarily through the work of the celebrated Scottish physicist James Clerk Maxwell, △ it became clear that the nebular hypothesis contained a fundamental difficulty. Our planetary system, which consists of the Sun, nine planets of assorted sizes, ▽ and miscellaneous debris, ▽ possesses one quite remarkable peculiarity: a singular distribution of angular momentum.

Angular momentum is one of the most important characteristics of every

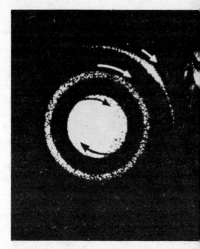

FIGURE 12-1. *Schematic representation of Laplace's nebular hypothesis. On the left is a rotating nebula of hot gas. On the right we see the nebula having contracted, increased its rotational velocity, and shed successive rings of gas. The rings were thought to condense into the planets, the dense central parts of the nebula forming the Sun.* (*Courtesy of Dr. Thornton Page, Wesleyan University.*)

mechanical system which is isolated from its environment. The Sun and its planetary accompaniment can be considered such an isolated system. Angular momentum in such a system is a reserve of rotational inertia, the tendency of a rotating body to resist braking. This rotational inertia arises from the orbital motion of the planets about the Sun, and from the rotation of the Sun and the planets on their respective axes. ▽ But the contribution from planetary rotation is negligible, compared to the contribution from planetary revolution and from solar rotation. The important point about angular momentum is that, like energy, it is a conserved quantity. In an isolated system, just as the total energy remains constant, so the total angular momentum remains constant. Since we can compute the angular momentum of the solar system at the present time, we can obtain some idea of the angular momentum of the solar system at the time of its formation—providing, again, that it is proper to consider the solar system as an isolated system. △

The orbital angular momentum of a planet is measured with respect to the center of gravity of the system, a point very close to the center of the Sun. It is defined as the product of the mass of the planet, m; its velocity of revolution about the Sun, v; and its distance, r, to the center of rotation—that is, to the Sun. In the case of a rotating, spherical, solid body, of uniform density the angular momentum with respect to an axis passing through its center is equal to $0.4 MVR$, where M is the mass of the body, V is its equatorial velocity, and R is its radius. ▽ Note that we are explicitly distinguishing revolution from rotation by lower case and capital letters, respectively. △

The total mass of all the planets is only about $\frac{1}{700}$ of the solar mass. On the other hand, the distance of the planets from the Sun is much greater than the radius of the Sun, and many of the planets have a velocity of revolution about the Sun which is greater than the velocity of rotation of the Sun itself. For example, the orbital velocity of the Earth is about 30 km sec^{-1}, while the velocity of rotation of the Sun at its equator is only about 2 km sec^{-1}. When we take these numbers into consideration, we find that 98 percent of the angular momentum of the solar system derives from the orbital motions of the planets, and only 2 percent from the rotation of the Sun on its axis. In Figure 12–2 we see the distribution of angular momentum among the Sun and planets.

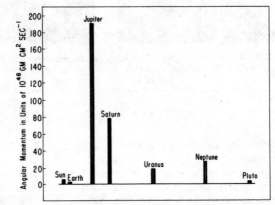

FIGURE 12–2. *Schematic representation of the distribution of angular momentum in the solar system. Despite its much larger mass, the Sun contains only a few percent of the total angular momentum of the solar system.*

In physics, masses are commonly expressed in grams, distances in centimeters, and time in seconds. ▽ Thus, the units of angular momentum, a product of mass, velocity, and distance, will be gm cm^2 sec^{-1}. △ Let us call the angular momentum of Jupiter, I. The mass of Jupiter is equal to $m = 2 \times 10^{30}$ gm (about 10^{-3} the mass of the Sun). The distance of Jupiter from the Sun, r, is 7.8×10^{13} cm (or 5.2 A.U.). The orbital velocity of Jupiter, v, is 1.3×10^6 cm sec^{-1} (13 km sec^{-1}). Therefore, the angular momentum of revolution is $I = mvr = 2 \times 10^{50}$ gm cm^2 sec^{-1}. ▽ On the other hand, the mass of the Sun is 2×10^{33} gm; its equatorial velocity is about 2×10^5 cm sec^{-1}; and its equatorial radius is about 7×10^{10} cm. The Sun is not quite a solid body; but for our purposes it will be sufficiently accurate to set the angular momentum of the Sun equal to $0.4\ MVR$. You can then easily convince yourself that the angular momentum of the rotating Sun is only about

1×10^{49} gm cm^2 sec^{-1}. Thus, Jupiter, having only 10^{-3} the mass of the Sun, has 20 times more angular momentum than the Sun. The actual figure, based on more exact calculations, is about 50 times more. △ From Figure 12–2, it is apparent that the terrestrial planets—Mercury, Venus, Earth, and Mars—have a combined total angular momentum which is some 380 times less than that of Jupiter. Thus, the lion's share of the angular momentum of the solar system is concentrated in the orbital motions of the giant planets Jupiter and Saturn.

This circumstance is entirely incomprehensible from the standpoint of the Kant–Laplace nebular hypothesis. In their view, the angular velocities of a given ring and of the contracting nebula should have been almost identical. When the ring separated from the nebula, it had approximately the same angular momentum per unit mass as the portion which continued to contract and form the Sun. But since the mass of the material destined to form the Sun was much greater than the mass of the protoplanetary ring, the angular momentum eventually residing in the Sun should have been much greater than that in the planets, if angular momentum were conserved. The Kant–Laplace hypothesis lacks any mechanism for the transfer of angular momentum from the protosun to the ring. ▽ Thus this otherwise promising theory floundered on the angular momentum difficulty. △

Other views replaced the nebular hypothesis. ▽ We will discuss here only one alternative—the collision hypothesis in the form enunciated by the English astronomer Sir James Jeans. It has both historical and philosophical interest. △ Jeans' hypothesis received wide acceptance during the first third of the present century, ▽ and is still treated warmly in obscure encyclopedias and some rural school textbooks in the United States. △ This theory is in all respects the complete antithesis of the nebular hypothesis. According to Kant and Laplace, the formation of the planetary system is a common process in stellar evolution. Jeans pictured the origin of our solar system as an exceedingly rare, perhaps even a unique, event.

Jeans believed that the original material from which the planets were formed was ejected by the Sun after the Sun had already reached its present form. The ejection was caused by the near collision of a passing star. The gravitational tidal forces of the interloper star drew out a filament of material from the surface layers of the Sun. The filament remained within the gravitational influence of the Sun as the interloper passed. After a period of time, the ejected material condensed and became the planets.

What can we say about this hypothesis? First of all, the initial event is exceedingly unlikely. As we mentioned in Chapter 3, the collisions of stars, and even their close mutual approach, are very rare phenomena in our Galaxy. Our Sun moves at a velocity of about 22 km sec^{-1} with respect to the nearest stars. Our closest neighbor—Proxima Centauri—is at a distance of 4.2 light years. It would take the Sun approximately 100,000 years, moving at the indicated velocity, to traverse this distance; ▽ and the Sun is, of course, not moving towards Proxima Centauri at all. △ It is not difficult to show that during its five-billion-year history, the Sun had only one chance in 10 billion of colliding with, or closely approaching, any other star. Similar probabilities apply to any other star. Since there are approximately 150 billion stars in our Galaxy, the total number of such close approaches throughout the entire Galaxy during the past 5 billion years would be approximately *ten*. (Near the center of the Galaxy, where the stellar density is tens of thousands of times greater than near the Sun, the probability of stellar collision would naturally be higher. ▽ But the bulk of the stars in the Milky Way are not in the Galactic nuclear region. △) Hence, if the hypothesis of Jeans were valid, the number of planetary systems formed in our Galaxy during 10 billion years could literally be counted on your fingers. ▽ (Actually, you might have to take off your shoes, and perhaps borrow someone else's toes, because *both* stars in the near collision would presumably have protoplanetary filaments expelled during the encounter. But the essential point is that Jeans' hypothesis makes our planets and the dark companions of nearby stars exceedingly, almost absurdly, improbable.) △

The number of further difficulties with Jeans' hypothesis is so great that we can consider such views completely refuted. It contains the same fatal inadequacy as the Kant–Laplace hypothesis: it does not explain why most of the angular momentum of the solar system is concentrated in the orbital motions of the planets. Mathematical calculations carried out by the Soviet astrophysicist N. N. Paruskii show that for all cases within the framework of Jeans' hypothesis, the planets would have very small, low-angular-momentum orbits.

Second, it does not follow that the stream of hot gas thrown off by the Sun would necessarily condense into planets. ▽ The reason is essentially this: since the putative filament initially had solar composition, it must have been composed primarily of hydrogen and helium (see Table I, Chapter 4). But hydrogen and helium are not even approximately the primary constituents of the terrestrial planets, and even in the outer planets like Jupiter and Saturn there seems to be less than the solar proportions of hydrogen and helium. This means that if the planets evolved from such a filament there must subsequently have been an escape of the lighter gases. If we add the cosmic proportions of hydrogen and helium to the present masses of the planets, we find that the filament must initially have had a mass of about 0.01 to 0.1 the mass of the Sun. The filament, then, could not have come from the ejection of *surface* material from the Sun; instead, it must have come from the solar interior. But the temperatures in the solar interior are so great—about 10^6 °K—that △ the filamentary material would not have condensed into planets. It would rather have been dissipated into interstellar space, as Lyman Spitzer, now at Princeton University, and other well-known astrophysicists, have shown. These difficulties, obvious by the late 1930's, provide an adequate basis for the rejection of the collision hypothesis.

▽ This last critique of Jeans' hypothesis is of considerable relevance to contemporary hypotheses. If the planets were formed initially from material of solar or cosmic composition, then the initial planetary mass must have been about 0.01 to 0.1 the present mass of the Sun. Since the total mass of the planets is now approximately 0.001 the mass of the Sun, we must imagine some means of dissipating most of this material. But for any condensation to have occurred, the planets must have been formed at relatively low temperatures, certainly temperatures below those of the interior of the Sun. We will return to these points later, in Chapters 13 and 16. △

The rejection of Jeans' views has led to a return, with various modifications, of the classical Kant–Laplace nebular hypothesis. At the time this hypothesis was initially formulated, astronomers knew virtually nothing about the nature of the stars and the galaxies; now, due to outstanding achievements in astrophysics, a vast amount of factual material has been collected. The Kant–Laplace hypothesis was originally based only on Newtonian mechanics, since at that time only mechanics had been mathematically well developed. Contemporary planetary cosmogony draws greatly on achievements in other areas of physics, particularly in magnetohydrodynamics. We shall see that magnetohydrodynamic considerations appear to eliminate the angular momentum difficulty in the nebular hypothesis.

13

Stellar rotation and the origin of the solar system

If then, Socrates, amid the many opinions about the gods and the generation of the universe, we are not able to give notions which are altogether and in every respect exact and consistent with one another, do not be surprised. Enough if we adduce probabilities . . .

Plato, *The Timaeus*

Who can number the clouds by wisdom
Or who can pour out the bottles of heaven,
When the dust runneth into a mass,
And the clods cleave fast together?

Job, 38:37

efore considering contemporary hypotheses on the origin of planetary systems, we must first discuss an important property of the stars—they rotate. In 1877, the English astronomer Captain W. de W. Abney, who is now all but forgotten, proposed that spectrographic observations could be used to determine how fast the stars rotate. If a star is rotating rapidly enough about its axis, and if the axis makes a large enough angle with the line of sight, then part of the surface of the star will be moving away from the observer, and part of it will be moving towards the observer. ▽ The side that moves away from the observer will be red-shifted by the Doppler effect; the side which moves towards the observer will be blue-shifted. These red- and blue-shifts apply equally to all the lines in the stellar spectrum. As a result, since the lines are shifted both to shorter and to longer wavelengths all spectral lines observed in the stellar atmosphere should be broadened. The more rapidly the star is rotating, the broader will be the lines. The only exception is the relatively rare case of a rapidly-rotating star which we see pole-on. If the axis of rotation is in the line of sight, no part of the star will be moving towards us or away from us, and therefore, despite the rapid rotation, there will be no Doppler broadening of the line from our vantage point. △

Abney's brilliant idea was not appreciated at the time, because astronomical spectroscopy was then in an embryonic state. Also, even early observations indicated that there could be both broad and narrow lines in the spectrum of the same star. Several decades passed before astronomers could distinguish among the several possible sources of line-broadening in stellar spectra. We now know that there can be a variety of causes for line-broadening ▽ —for example, strong electric or magnetic fields, local turbulence, or high temperatures and pressures— △ that have nothing to do with stellar rotation. In particular, we now know that lines belonging to the more abundant chemical elements can, under the physical conditions in stellar atmospheres, exhibit line-broadening independent of the rotation of the stars.

In 1928, the Russian-American astronomer Otto Struve and the Soviet astronomer G. A. Shajn solved this problem. Figure 13–1 shows schematically spectra of three hot stars, J Hercules, eta Ursae Majoris, and HR 2142. The three most intense lines which we observe in these spectra arise from transitions in neutral hydrogen and in neutral helium. A comparison of the upper and middle spectra shows that the hydrogen lines (Hγ) appear about equally broad in both, while the helium lines are noticeably broader and more diffuse in the middle than in the upper spectrum. In the bottom spectrogram, all the lines are very broad and diffuse, to such an extent that they are almost invisible; ▽ they must be examined closely on the original photographic plate in order to determine their widths. △

Interpretation of these spectra is simple. In the upper spectrogram, the rotational velocity relative to the line of sight is almost zero; that is, either the star is rotating very slowly, or, fortuitously, its axis is almost along the line of sight. The width of the hydrogen line can be explained by reasons having nothing to do with the stellar rotation. ▽ In the middle spectrogram, the hydrogen line is not noticeably broader, but it is already so broad that it is difficult for it to be influenced by stellar rotation. The helium lines, however, △ indicate a rotational velocity of approximately 210 km sec⁻¹. In the bottom spectrum, the rotational velocity is so great—approxi-

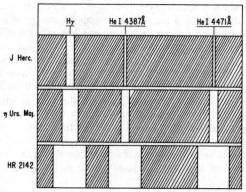

FIGURE 13–1. *Line-broadening in the spectrum of three stars, showing the effects of increasing equatorial rotational velocity. (Schematic drawing after photographic spectra of Struve and Shajn.)*

mately 450 km sec⁻¹—that all the lines, even the hydrogen line Hγ, are greatly broadened and appear washed out.

At the present time, the rotational velocities of a large number of stars are under investigation. The data in hand indicate that the rotational velocities differ greatly from star to star, and— ▽ a point first appreciated by Otto Struve △ — there is some relation between rotational velocity and spectral type. The hot, massive stars rotate very rapidly; the yellow and red main sequence dwarfs barely rotate at all. The velocity of the Sun at its equator is only about 2 km sec⁻¹. In Table IV, data on the velocities of rotation of stars of various spectral types is presented. Careful spectroscopic observations have shown, as is reflected in Table IV, that near spectral class F2, the velocity of rotation abruptly and characteristically decreases. The surface temperature of an F2 star is about 7000°K, ▽ about 1000 K° hotter than that of the Sun. △ What is the origin of this F2 discontinuity? ▽ Why do stellar rotational velocities decrease at all, as we go towards later spectral types?

▽ In itself, there is nothing strange about a variation of rotational velocity with spectral type. △ Other fundamental characteristics of the stars—for example, their luminosity and their surface temperature—vary uniformly from early type stars to late type stars. ▽ A tentative answer to the problem of the F2 discontinuity has been presented by Struve, and can be most easily grasped in the following terms: △ Let us imagine all the planets of the solar system somehow incorporated into the Sun. Since, in an isolated system, angular momentum must be conserved, such an imaginary fusion of the planets and the Sun would cause the latter to rotate much more rapidly. ▽ Since the planets represent only a small fraction of the total mass of the Sun, this fusion would change the mass of the Sun by a negligible amount.

TABLE IV

RELATION BETWEEN ROTATIONAL VELOCITY AND SPECTRAL TYPE

Stellar equatorial rotational velocity (in km sec⁻¹)	Percent of stars of a given spectral type with rotational velocities in the ranges given at left					
	Oe, Be	O,B	A	F0–F2	F5–F8	G, K, M
0–50	0	21	22	30	80	100
50–100	0	51	24	50	20	0
100–150	0	20	22	15	0	0
150–200	1	6	22	4	0	0
200–250	3	2	9	1	0	0
250–300	18	0	1	0	0	0
300–500	78	0	0	0	0	0

On the other hand, the planets contain so much angular momentum that △ the Sun would, under these circumstances, be forced to rotate some 50 times faster than it does at present—since its angular momentum would have to increase from its present 2 percent to the entire 100 percent of the total angular momentum of the solar system. The Sun would then be rotating with an equatorial velocity of about 100 km sec⁻¹. But this is exactly a typical velocity for stars which are more massive and hotter than spectral type F2. Thus, it is at least a reasonable hypothesis that the velocity of the Sun is small because somehow angular momentum has been transferred from the Sun to the planets.

▽ What, then, of all the other stars with spectral type later than F2? If our hypothesis is correct, we expect that they are rotating slowly because they too have transferred angular momentum to their planetary systems. Consider the implications of this result. We are in fact concluding that almost all stars of spectral type later than F2 are accompanied by planetary systems. But 93 percent of the main sequence stars in the sky are later than F2. The bulk of the remaining stars are giants, supergiants, white dwarfs, and dark companions. All but possibly the dark companions have gone through a main sequence evolutionary phase. Thus, from the widths of lines on spectral plates, we have reached the remarkable conclusion that the Galaxy is populated with planets! △ Since this conclusion is obviously of very great importance, we must convince ourselves that stars cannot lose angular momentum by other means—for example, by transferring it to the interstellar gas. In other words, we must prove that a rotating star with no planets is an isolated system, that it satisfies the law of conservation of angular momentum. How can we demonstrate this?

Let us consider first the case of the red giants. A great many of the giants are characterized by relatively rapid equatorial rotation. For example, the star xi Geminorum is of spectral type F5, and has a rotational velocity of 73 km sec^{-1}. This typical red giant (actually, it should be called a yellow giant) is a very old star; according to contemporary theories of stellar evolution [see Chapter 6], when it was on the main sequence, its spectral type was A [see the evolutionary tracks of Figure 6–3]. ∇ We can compare the present radius of xi Geminorum with the radius of a typical main sequence A star. △ When xi Geminorum was a main sequence star, its radius must have been about one-half its present radius. If it has conserved angular momentum during its evolution to the red giant stage, its equatorial velocity as a main sequence A star must have been 146 km sec^{-1}. We see from Table IV that this is a typical rotational velocity for main sequence stars of spectral type A. Thus, we can conclude that the angular momentum of xi Geminorum has been conserved during its evolution off the main sequence.

Now let us consider another example. ∇ There is a class of stars which resemble their prototype, T Tauri, the third variable star discovered in the constellation Taurus, the Bull. △ T Tauri stars belong to spectral type G, and have fairly high rotational velocities, up to 100 km sec^{-1}. They are believed to be very young—still in the stage of gravitational contraction [see Chapter 6]—and have not yet entered into the main sequence. Such stars are characteristically found to the right and a little above the main sequence, in the spectrum-luminosity diagram [see Figure 6–2]. As time progresses, their radii decrease. It appears that several millon years hence, when their contraction ends, T Tauri stars enter the main sequence at about spectral type A. In the course of such contraction, their radii decrease by a factor of approximately 2. Therefore, if they conserve angular momentum during contraction, their main sequence equatorial rotational velocity should be about 200 km sec^{-1}. We again see from Table IV that this is a typical equatorial rotational velocity for main sequence stars of spectral type A. Thus, in both early and late stages of stellar evolution, angular momentum seems to be conserved.

Nevertheless, we must emphasize that the results of these examples are based on contemporary theories of stellar evolution. The consistencies which we have found cannot serve as a *rigorous* proof of the conservation of angular momentum in stellar evolution. In fact, we shall see presently that there is at least a possibility that angular momentum may be lost independently of the existence of a planetary system.

The Swedish physicist Hannes Alfvén of the Royal Institute of Technology, Stockholm, first considered the problem of angular momentum transfer from stars to planets. He showed that a magnetic field could provide the mechanism for angular momentum transfer. Alfvén's view is incorporated in the theory of the origin of the solar system propounded by the English astrophysicist Fred Hoyle of Cambridge University. We believe that Hoyle's hypothesis is the most promising of those currently proposed, and we therefore will consider its basic tenets in some detail.

Following a now classic tradition, Hoyle pictures the planets formed from a cold nebula of gas and dust. Initially, the nebular density was very low. Individual regions of the cloud moved at varying velocities with respect to each other. By analogy with gaseous nebulae, Hoyle assumes that these velocities were about 1 km sec^{-1}.

As a result of such motions, the initial nebula must have possessed a small, but definite angular momentum. Moreover, the cloud must have had interstellar dimensions, being several light years across. Thus, if, in the process of condensation from interstellar to solar dimensions, angular momentum were conserved, the final equatorial velocity of the newly-formed star would have been almost equal to the speed of light. Such is not the case, as we have seen. Therefore, we must assume that more than 99 percent of the initial angular momentum was lost by the nebula during star formation. Such an angular momentum loss can, according to Hoyle, be explained by interstellar magnetic fields. ▽ The cloud and the interstellar medium initially share the same magnetic field, and we can imagine magnetic lines of force joining the contracting nebula with the material of the interstellar medium. As the nebula rotates more rapidly, because of its contraction, the lines of force cause an increased rotation of the interstellar medium external to the nebula, △ and thereby initiate an angular momentum transfer from the nebula to the surrounding interstellar medium. The lines of force act as bent strings. But, for a reason which we shall not discuss here, such transfer of angular momentum can occur only while the density of the nebula is low. When the density of the nebula ▽ increasing because of contraction △ reaches a certain value, angular momentum transfer from the cloud to the interstellar medium ceases.

▽ (The collective motion of charged particles in magnetic fields is a new branch of physics called magnetohydrodynamics. The hypothesis that solar rotation was braked because of angular momentum transfer along magnetic lines of force is an example of the application of magnetohydrodynamics to astronomy. Since magnetic fields are widespread in the universe, and since ionized atoms influenced by magnetic fields are commonplace, magnetohydrodynamics also has many other astronomical applications.) △

This theory has wide implications. As calculations carried out by Hoyle indicate, the remaining angular momentum, if it were concentrated only in the condensing star, would correspond to an equatorial rotational velocity of several hundred kilometers per second. As we have seen, relatively hot stars have rotational velocities of just this order. The theory does not yet account for the slow rotation of the relatively colder stars such as the Sun. We must assume that such stars lose angular momentum after contraction of the initial nebula to relatively small dimensions—say, to the dimensions of the solar system.

Therefore, two main problems remain with us: Why do stars of spectral type later than F2 lose nearly all of their rotational angular momentum? Why is this process of angular momentum loss inoperative in hotter stars?

To approach these questions, we note that as a nebula contracts, it rotates more and more rapidly about its axis. Let us call the contracting nebula a protostar. With the initial rotational velocities assumed by Hoyle, by the time a protostar of mass equal to that of our Sun contracts to a radius of 40 solar radii (about 0.2 A.U.), it will, according to Hoyle, be rotating so rapidly that the

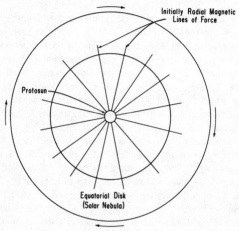

FIGURE 13–2. *An early stage in the evolution of the solar system, according to Hoyle. The contracting Sun has shed an equatorial disk of gas and dust which is connected to the Sun by magnetic lines of force.*

centrifugal force at the equator will just balance the force of gravity. Therefore a state of instability arises, and material is shed by the protostar to form an equatorial disk.

So far, the theory corresponds to the classical view of Laplace. The central problem in the Laplace hypothesis, we recall, concerns the transfer of angular momentum from the protostar to the disk which later condenses into the planets. Today we expect to find magnetic fields in condensing protostars. When the equatorial disk of gas is separated from the protostar, magnetic lines of force are likely to exist, connecting it to the protostar [Fig. 13–2]. The contracting protostar soon rotates more rapidly than the disk, and the lines of force connecting them, initially straight lines, now become twisted [Fig. 13–3]. As a result, the rotation of the protostar is effectively braked, and the disk is slowly forced outward from the protostar. In time, the width of the disk will increase due to internal friction, and part of this material should condense into the planets. In this way, the planets are the repository for the major fraction of the initial nebular angular momentum lost by the protostar.

Why does this process occur only in protostars destined to have main sequence spectral type later than F2? ▽ The protostar and the disk are, we recall, connected by magnetic lines of force which are initially radial, as in Figure 13–2. As the protostar continues to contract and rotate more rapidly, the magnetic lines of force tend to be wound around its periphery [Fig. 13–3]. The angular momentum is transferred through the lines of force to the disk, which also rotates more rapidly,

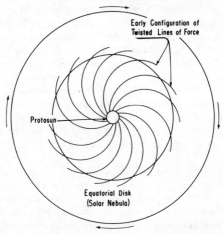

Early Configuration of
Twisted Lines of Force

Protosun

Equatorial Disk
(Solar Nebula)

FIGURE 13–3. *A somewhat later stage in the early evolution of the solar system, according to Hoyle. Angular momentum is being transferred from the rapidly rotating protosun to the equatorial disk by the magnetic lines of force.*

thus preventing very high rotational velocities in the protostar. It is clear that the more massive the disk, the more difficult it will be for the disk to be accelerated by the winding magnetic lines of force. △ The mass of the disk is, however, not very large. Therefore, there will not be very much winding of the magnetic lines of force about the disk. These twisted lines of force are attached to the outer layers of the protostar, which are characterized by turbulent and disordered mass motion.

These outer, turbulent layers are believed to originate in the following way: The temperatures in stellar interiors are, of course, much greater than those of the radiating surfaces of stars. Hydrogen which is ionized in the hot interior becomes a neutral gas in the outer layers of the star. ▽ The transition from the ionized region to the neutral region is fairly abrupt, and leads to mechanical instability and the establishment of a turbulent zone composed primarily of neutral hydrogen in the outer reaches of stellar atmospheres. △ With a deep hydrogen convection zone, such as is found in cool stars, the magnetic lines of force, acting as if they were glued to the moving gas, can become embedded quite deeply in a protostellar atmosphere. However, in a hot protostar, hydrogen will remain ionized until quite close to the surface, and the hydrogen convection zone will be small or absent. In this case, the lines of force of the magnetic field will not penetrate deeply into the star but will wind themselves about the superficial layers. ▽ The mass of the shallow hydrogen convection zone of a hot protostar will be very small, and the winding lines of force will, according to Hoyle, be unable to transfer significant angular momentum to the more massive protoplanetary disk. △

Hoyle thus explains the abrupt decline in stellar rotational velocities near spectral type F2 in terms of the dependence of hydrogen ionization on temperature. In stars of spectral type F0, where the temperature of the surface layers is only about 1000° greater than for stars of spectral type F2, the convection zone begins so close to the surface of the star that magnetic lines of force are only slightly submerged in the stellar atmosphere. ▽ In this case, the angular rotation of the protostar will not be magnetically braked, and a main sequence star of relatively high rotational velocity will result. Note, however, that a protostar destined to be a main sequence star of F0 spectral type may shed a protoplanetary disk during the process of its formation. We have not excluded the possibility that such a disk formed around hot stars also condenses into planets. Hoyle's arguments support the view that all late type stars have transferred angular momentum to protoplanetary disks, but for all we know the condensation of such disks into planets may not be easy.

▽ Current thinking about the condensation processes is focused on two mechanisms. The first, a gravitational process, has been suggested by G. P. Kuiper. Here, the local density of the nebula is imagined to be so large that the mutual gravitational attraction of contiguous matter leads to further condensation, until objects of planetary mass are formed. The initial density of the nebula must be large enough that the tidal forces of the Sun do not pull the early condensations apart. The familiar ocean tides on Earth occur in part because the Sun and Moon pull more strongly on the oceans—slightly closer to them—than on the underlying land. The mutual gravitational attraction between the oceans and the Earth is, however, much greater than the dissipative tidal forces, so the oceans do not fly away into space each day. But unless the density of the solar nebula were rather large, condensations would not hold together gravitationally, and, in the absence of other influences, tidal instability would prevent the formation of the planets. This argument is originally due to the Scottish physicist James Clerk Maxwell.

▽ The second mechanism, suggested by the American cosmochemist Harold C. Urey of the University of California and others, is based on weak chemical bonds between colliding bits of matter. In effect, the condensates in the primitive nebula are imagined to be sticky. The view is not so very different from that of Lucretius.

▽ It is clear that if the nebula had very high temperatures, gases would boil off, condensates would evaporate, and the continued formation of planets would be difficult. It is generally believed that condensation occurred at low temperatures,

176

perhaps as low as a few tens of degrees above absolute zero. Yet, as the Sun contracted towards the main sequence, its luminosity was very high [see Figure 6–2]. This apparent inconsistency between theories of solar and of planetary origins can possibly be resolved if we imagine a significant absorption of solar radiation by dust in the inner parts of the solar nebula, so that very little solar heating of the bulk of the nebula occurred; or alternatively that most of the planetary condensation was complete before the luminosity of the protosun became very great.

▽ One possible difficulty with the gravitational condensation mechanism is that the nebular densities required lead to very large nebular masses. The condensing protoplanets must then have been much more massive than they are today, and some process of dissipation of the bulk of their mass must be imagined. If there was an intense flux of charged particles emitted by the sun in those early times, such escape may have taken place. In the chemical accretion mechanism, much lower densities are adequate, and the dissipation difficulty is avoided. ▽ The problem of the escape of the light gases during the early history of the solar system is a pivotal one. Regardless of the temperatures at the top of the protoplanetary atmospheres, dissipation encounters very serious problems which were first pointed out by Shklovskii. △

The chemical content of the planets is clearly different from that of the Sun. If we added hydrogen and helium to the masses of the planets until these elements were present in cosmic proportions, the total mass of all the planets would be roughly ten times as great as it is at present—that is, the planets would comprise a few percent of the solar mass, a mass comparable to that of the invisible companion stars discussed in Chapter 11. Conceivably, the low-mass components of binary star systems were formed by processes similar to those which led to the formation of the planets. The difference may be that when the planets were formed the excess hydrogen and helium evaporated into interstellar space, while when the dark companion stars were formed the lighter elements remained gravitationally bound.

We now consider a more serious objection to Hoyle's theory. The existence of stellar magnetic fields raises the possibility that angular momentum may be lost even if planets are not formed. It is known that the Sun emits streams of charged particles ▽ —the so-called solar wind, which arises from the solar atmosphere and pervades interplanetary space. △ Individual clouds of hot, ionized gas are ejected from the vicinity of sunspots [Figure 1–3] at velocities of several hundred, or even several thousand, kilometers per second. This ionized material is an excellent conductor of electricity. It therefore moves along the magnetic lines of force of the solar magnetic field. At great distances from the Sun these magnetic lines of force have an almost radial direction, ▽ like pins in a pincushion. △ Moving along the lines of force, the ionized clouds of the solar wind can be ejected some tens of solar radii from the surface of the Sun.

The magnetic lines of force rotate about the axis of the Sun with the same speed of rotation as do the surface layers. We can imagine the lines of force as a rigid wire framework fastened to a rotating sphere. Thus, the clouds of gas ejected from the Sun will increase their angular momentum as they move outward along the lines of force, ▽ because, we recall, the angular momentum of revolution is proportional to the distance from the Sun. △ If the clouds can break loose from the lines of force at great distances, where the magnetic fields are weak, then significant quantities of angular momentum could be lost into interstellar space. ▽ Similar ideas have been expressed by the French astrophysicist Evry Schatzmann of the Paris Observatory. △ Assume, for example, that gas clouds escape characteristically at a distance of 30 solar radii from the surface of the Sun. Then, in order to lose nearly all its initial angular momentum, the Sun need eject only about 0.1% of its mass. Such a relatively small mass loss during billions of years of solar evolution is entirely possible. At the present time, the rotational velocity of the Sun is not being braked by the loss of angular momentum through the ejection of ionized gas clouds, because the mass loss due to the solar wind is too small. But is it possible that, perhaps in the past, the mass loss was greater.

Thus, while the slow rotation of stars of spectral type later than F2 strongly suggests that planetary systems are associated with these stars, the evidence is not conclusive. There is an alternative and still admissible hypothesis—the loss of angular momentum to the interstellar medium—which does not connect planetary rotation with stellar rotation.

▽ In addition to the hypotheses we have mentioned, other views of planetary cosmogony have been propounded in recent years. △ For example, the Soviet scientist O. Y. Schmidt did not believe that the Sun ever possessed a cloud of gas and dust which later formed the planets. ▽ Schmidt pictured the Sun as capturing an interstellar cloud of gas, dust, and larger, accreted objects some time after its formation. △ However, the capture process is highly improbable. In addition, investigations of the last decade indicate, as we have seen, that the processes of star formation and of planet formation are closely interrelated.

Recently, the English astronomer W. H. McCrea of the University of Sussex has proposed a cosmogonic hypothesis of a purely mechanical character, which does not take electromagnetic phenomena into account. Although McCrea's hypothesis explains why the angular momentum must be concentrated in the orbital motions of the planets, it does not explain the abrupt decline in stellar rotational velocity near spectral type F2. ▽ The advantage of the magnetic braking hypothesis is that it explains these two observations which otherwise are unconnected. △

Before the problem of the origin of planetary systems is definitively solved, much more work in theoretical physics and observational astronomy must be performed. But a beginning has been made, and the contours of a well structured theory have emerged.

"Sometimes I ask myself, 'Where will it ever end?'"

11

LIFE IN THE UNIVERSE

A Man that is of Copernicus' Opinion, that this Earth of ours is a Planet, carry'd round and enlighten'd by the Sun, like the rest of the Planets, cannot but sometimes think, that it's not improbable that the rest of the Planets have their Dress and Furniture, and perhaps their Inhabitants too as well as this Earth of ours.

. . . But perhaps they'll say, it does not become us to be so curious and inquisitive in these Things which the Supreme Creator seems to have kept for his own Knowledge: For since he has not been pleased to make any farther Discovery or Revelation of them, it seems little better than presumption to make any inquiry into that which he has thought fit to hide. But these Gentlemen must be told, that they take too much upon themselves when they pretend to appoint how far and no farther Men shall go in their Searches, and to set bounds to other Mens Industry; as if they knew the Marks that God has placed to Knowledge: or as if Men were able to pass those Marks. If our Forefathers had been at this rate scrupulous, we might have been ignorant still of the Magnitude and Figure of the Earth, or that there was such a place as America.

Christianus Huygens, *New Conjectures Concerning the Planetary Worlds, Their Inhabitants and Productions* (c. 1670)

14

On the definition of life

. . . For any living thing that has reached its normal development and which is unmutilated, and whose mode of generation is not spontaneous, the most natural act is the production of another like itself, an animal producing an animal, a plant a plant, in order that, as far as its nature allows, it may partake in the eternal and divine. That is the goal towards which all things strive, that for the sake of which they do whatsoever their nature renders possible . . . Since then no living thing is able to partake in what is eternal and divine by uninterrupted continuance (for nothing perishable can forever remain one and the same), it tries to achieve that end in the only way possible to it, and success is possible in varying degrees; so it remains not indeed as the selfsame individual but continues its existence in something *like* itself—not numerically but specifically one . . .

Aristotle, *De Anima*

. . . Ultimately life can be unequivocally explained in physicochemical terms. . . . We eat, drink, and reproduce not because mankind has reached an agreement that this is desirable, but because, machine-like, we are compelled to do so.

Jacques Loeb, *The Mechanistic Conception of Life*, 1912

. . . if "dead" matter has reared up this curious landscape of fiddling crickets, song sparrows, and wondering men, it must be plain even to the most devoted materialist that the matter of which he speaks contains amazing, if not dreadful powers, and may not impossibly be, as Hardy has suggested, "but one mask of many worn by the Great Face behind."

Loren Eiseley, *The Immense Journey*, 1946

Τhe problem of his own beginnings has intrigued man since remotest antiquity. Of more recent origin—and of perhaps even greater fascination—is the question of life on other worlds beyond the Earth. It is our immense good fortune to be alive at the first moment in history when these tantalizing issues can be approached with rigor and in detail. To hold in our hands the keys to these ancient riddles is a triumph of the highest order; it heralds an age of exploration and discovery unsurpassed in the history of mankind.

▽ The questions of extraterrestrial life and the origin of life are intertwined. But before we can approach either question, we must have some general understanding of the nature of living systems. Here, we face a fundamental handicap: our knowledge of biology is restricted to essentially one example. The inner workings of terrestrial organisms—from microbes to men—are so similar in their biochemical details as to make it highly likely that all organisms on the Earth have evolved from a single instance of the origin of life. This hypothesis is supported by a variety of observations. All organisms are composed of one or more cells. The organization and functioning of these cells show enormous similarities. In the biochemistry of the photosynthetic and respiratory apparatus; in the detailed reproductive behavior of cells; in the ubiquity of the molecule DNA as the genetic material; in the details of the breaking down of foodstuffs to extract energy; in the asymmetry of the constituent molecules; even in the microstructure of membranes and flagellae, and in the molecular basis of animal colors, the same materials, the same methods have been used over and over again in the extremely diverse aggregate of plants and animals which we describe collectively as "life on Earth."

▽ Thus, we see immediately one reason why the discovery and characterization of extraterrestrial life has a pervasive appeal to the biologist. He might then be able to separate what is necessary from what is contingent. He might begin to learn which characteristics terrestrial living systems have because *any* living system must have them; and which characteristics are historical accidents, the results of arbitrary and random concatenations of events which might elsewhere have developed along different lines and produced different kinds of living systems. In other sciences, it is possible to test Earthbound insights elsewhere in the universe. Indeed, this is one reason why physics and chemistry are, in a sense, "universal" sciences. But for all we know, biology is literally mundane and provincial, and we may be familiar with but one special case in a universe of diverse biologies.

▽ Because we have only one example, the question of the definition of life is beset with difficulties. Remembering that our conclusions may lack the generality we desire, let us try to find what life on Earth is all about. Is life merely a particularly subtle organization of matter, or is there something more to it? Any child can tell the difference between a live puppy, a dead puppy, and a toy puppy. Exactly what is this distinction?

▽ In primitive times, when very little was understood about the nature of living systems, the most routine biological activities, such as the germination of a seed or the flowering of a plant, were attributed to divine intervention. In the early years of the Industrial Revolution, when advances in celestial mechanics gave something close to a complete understanding of the positions and motions of the heavenly bodies, the concept arose that living systems may be nothing more than a particularly intricate kind of clockwork. But when early investigations failed to unveil the clockwork, a kind of ghostly mainspring was invented—the "vital force." The vital force was a rebellion from mechanistic biology, an explanation of all that mechanism could not explain, or for which mechanisms could not be found. It also appealed to those who felt debased by the implication that they were "nothing more" than a collection of atoms, that their urges and supposed free wills arose merely from the interaction of an enormously large number of molecules, in a way which, although too complex to use predictively, was, in principle, determined.

▽ But today, we find no evidence for a vital force; indeed, the concept is very poorly defined, a kind of universal catch-all for anything we cannot explain. The opposite tack—that all living systems are made of atoms and nothing else—has proved a particularly useful idea. An entire new science of molecular biology has made startling progress and achieved fundamental insights starting from this assumption. And there is nothing debasing in the thought that we are made of atoms alone. We are thereby related to the rest of the universe; and if we are made of the same stuff, more or less, as everything else, then elsewhere there may be things rather like us. We are a tribute to the subtlety of matter. As the distinguished American physicist Richard P. Feynman of the California Institute of Technology has put it to a lecture audience:

> If a piece of steel or a piece of salt, consisting of atoms one next to the other, can have such interesting properties; if water—which is nothing but these little blobs, mile upon mile of the same thing over the Earth—can form waves and foam, make rushing noises and strange patterns as it runs over cement; if all of this, all the life of a stream of water, can be nothing but a pile of atoms, *how much more is possible?* If instead of arranging the atoms in some definite pattern, again and again repeated, on and on, or even forming little lumps of complexity like the odor of violets, we make an arrangement which is *always* different from place to place, with different kinds of atoms arranged in many ways, continually changing, not repeating, how much more marvelously is it possible that [matter] might behave? Is it possible that that "thing" walking back and forth in front of you, talking to you, is a great glob of these atoms in a very complex arrangement . . . ? When we say we are a pile of atoms, we do not mean we are *merely* a pile of atoms, because a pile of atoms which is not repeated from one to the other might well have the possibilities which you see before you in the mirror.

▽ Let us consider an animal—any animal—in as general a way as we can. (We could just as well consider a plant, but animals are more fun.) What does it do? Mostly, it does nothing. It waits in a hole, lies in the grass, floats downstream, or rocks on the porch. Occasionally it does something interesting: it acquires a fragment of organic matter produced by some other organism, and incorporates it —not quite all of it, because some passes right through the animal virtually unchanged. But the ingested material per se is not utilized; it is broken down further, chemically rearranged, built up into molecules that the animal needs, and then used.

▽ Eating is so common that we tend to forget what an extraordinary process it is. We eat corn flakes, and yet, we do not *become* corn flakes. The corn flakes are changed into *us*. In Feynman's splendid phrase, "Today's brains are yesterday's mashed potatoes."

▽ How did such an effortless ability for molecular transmutation ever develop? And if the animal is an adult, why must it eat at all? It has reached its optimum mass; why must it go to all that trouble to seek, process, and utilize food? There seem to be two general reasons. First, the animal eats in order to acquire energy, so it can carry out other biological processes—e.g., moving, breathing, or further eating. Second, it eats so that it has a source of materials for repair. The chemical bonds which hold together the molecules composing the animal tend to break. If unchecked, molecules would dissociate, cellular systems would dissipate, and the organism would die. The relatively short periods of time which most familiar animals can survive without eating testify to the essential instability of higher living systems. Some organisms, when faced with a food shortage, or other environmental embarrassments, can simply shut up shop and wait until conditions improve; but most higher organisms need constant alimentary reassurance.

▽ Of the other obvious activities of animals, most are either accessory to eating or unessential. Respiration is a device to extract the maximum amount of energy from food; motility tends to insure the acquisition of food; excretion is a method of removing unmetabolizable food; irritability—the response of the organism to external stimuli—and the ability to learn increase the probability that the animal does not end its days in the gullet of some other animal: they are also properties of some electronic computing machines which no one is willing to call "alive," quite yet.

▽ The remaining characteristic, which does seem essential for living systems and which all animals share, is reproduction. It is true that a narrow definition of a living system as a self-reproducing one would seem to exclude mules; but despite superficial appearances, even they reproduce at a colossal rate, or at least their constituent cells do.

▽ If we observe the reproductive habits of animals, we are struck by several facts. Reproduction of the whole animal occurs relatively rarely. The animals are exceptionally strongly motivated to reproduce themselves, even though there is no obvious material benefit which thereby accrues to them. Organisms tend to reproduce their own kind, so that reproduction occurs only within a species.

Reproduction is far from identical, especially in higher animals, where fertilization is accompanied by a random reassortment of the parental genetic factors in establishing the characteristics of the new animal. There is generally an age when most animals are no longer capable of reproduction. Finally, we observe that most animals die a natural death soon after this age is reached.

▽ Can it be that reproduction is in some sense the "point" of biological activity? We can imagine an organism which carries out metabolism and all the other functions ordinarily ascribed to living systems in elementary biology textbooks; which has very efficient repair mechanisms, so that it easily survives the vicissitudes of its environment; and which has no reproductive organs and never reproduces. We can imagine such an organism, but we never find one. Why not? Because there is no way for such an organism to arise. The only mechanism which we know for the production of biological complexity is evolution by natural selection, the differential survival of the organisms which, by chance, are best adapted to their environments. But natural selection can occur only if the well-adapted organisms reproduce themselves. Thus, the development of complexity in living systems is intimately connected with their self-replication.

▽ The paleontological record shows clearly the gradual development of biological complexity during the history of the Earth. A billion years ago, there was, apparently, nothing more complex than one-celled protozoa and their colonies. Yet today you are a walking collection of about 10^{14} cells, coordinated in origin and function. Each of your cells bears strong family resemblances in size, function, and chemistry to contemporary protozoa. The principle of evolution by natural selection permits us to understand how this increase in complexity has occurred. It is not that complexity per se has survival value, but rather that a solution to an environmental crisis which involves many molecules is often qualitatively superior to a solution which involves only a few molecules. For example, the image-forming eye of the vertebrates is a qualitatively superior light receptor than the pigmented eye-spots of the protozoa; but a protozoan cannot construct an eye, because an eye is constructed of more molecules than there are in the entire protozoan. In an environment where the ability to detect swiftly-moving predators or prey is at a premium, organisms with efficient visual receptors will preferentially survive. Efficiency and complexity are here coupled. We expect that in time and through natural selection, large living systems of extraordinary complexity will develop, adapted in detail to their environments.

▽ The enormous complexity of even a simple, single-celled organism is illustrated in Figure 14–1, a photograph of part of an algal cell, taken with an electron microscope. The magnification is 25,000 times. At the periphery can be seen the cell wall, which separates the alga from its environment. Towards the upper left-hand corner is the cell nucleus, which contains the genetic material. Between the nucleus and the cell wall is the cytoplasm of the cell, which contains elaborate apparatus for photosynthesis, respiration, and enzyme production and operation, among many other functions. (The enzymes are largely proteins, composed of sequences of amino acids.) The cell is no sack of enzymes and other

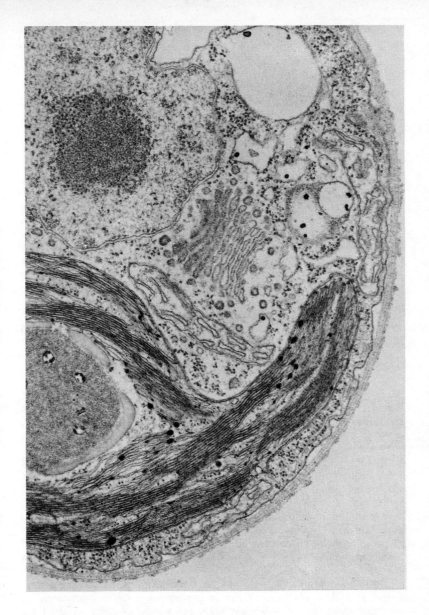

FIGURE 14–1. *An electron micrograph of a portion of an algal cell, a simple plant. The magnification is 25,000 times. (Courtesy of Dr. G. E. Palade, Cytology Laboratory, The Rockefeller Institute for Medical Research, New York.)*

chemicals. It has a detailed, functional architecture of great sophistication and complexity. Such a "simple" cell is clearly well along in the evolutionary process, and when we speak of the origin of life, we must be speaking of the origin of a much simpler entity.

▽ If we now follow the evolution of biological complexity backwards in time, we can imagine self-replicating and mutating entities even simpler than a cell, yet still capable of subsequent steps up the evolutionary ladder. Since the universe is primarily composed of very simple non-self-replicating molecules, we must eventually come face to face with the problem of the origin of the first self-replicating system, the subject of the next chapters. However, for the moment, let us probe a little deeper into our hypothetical animal.

▽ It reproduces. How does it reproduce? Think of the enormous number of characteristics which familiar animals have. There is the gross anatomy, the overall architecture of the organism. Then, there is the physiology, the dynamic functioning and articulation of the different parts of the organism in carrying out its functions. It has inherited behavior patterns—how to build a nest, how to bury a bone. It has ten trillion or so cells, each one of which is itself an extraordinarily complex structure. At the present time, we are making only the first fumbling steps towards assembling a cell from scratch. Yet the information to construct the entire organism is somehow contained in the genetic material, because, with striking regularity, animals look like their parents.

▽ The problem of heredity is really two problems: How is the genetic information transmitted from generation to generation? And how is this information translated into action, in the development of the new organism? These two questions can be phrased another way: What is the genetic "code"? And how, in the developing organism, is the code "read"?

▽ The most significant aspects of life are often not the most obvious. The most abundant organic molecule on Earth is cellulose; yet we are not constructed of cellulose, and we have great difficulty metabolizing it. Understandably, we might feel that its significance has been overrated. A tree, if its opinion could be polled, would probably disagree. The phylum with the largest number of identified species is the arthropods; in this sense, life on Earth is mostly beetles. Yet we would feel, with justified annoyance, that a biological survey party from some other planet that spent all its time on Earth studying the beetles had overlooked some items of importance. Similarly, it is possible to be misled when we examine the chemical composition of a typical cell—say, a bacterium—whose molecular census might be as follows: lipids, 30 million molecules; phospholipids, 20 million molecules; proteins, 5 million molecules; polysaccharides, 1 million molecules; ribonucleic acid (RNA), 40 thousand molecules; deoxyribonucleic acid (DNA), 1 molecule. If biochemists were to concentrate all their attention on the lipids, they would also be missing the point.

▽ In experiments with peas and other flowering plants, the Moravian monk Gregor Mendel, in 1865, derived certain empirical rules for the transmission of hereditary characteristics, subsequently known as Mendel's laws. At about the same time, the nucleic acids were isolated, and the chromosomes discovered. Yet the connection among Mendel's empirical laws, the microscopic behavior of the chromosomes, and the chemistry of the nucleic acids was not demonstrated until the 1950's; indeed, some aspects of the connection—especially between chromosomes and nucleic acids—remain obscure today.

▽ The chromosomes are small threadlike bodies in the cell nucleus which undergo an intricate ritual of duplication and segregation during the reproduction of a cell. In the first decade of the twentieth century, it was realized that the chromosomal choreography was exactly the process required by Mendelian genetics to account for the transmission of heredity characteristics. Thus, the original basis for the belief that the chromosomes are the genetic material was their behavior during reproduction and had nothing to do with their chemical composition. The fact that chromosomes are composed, to a significant degree, of nucleic acids has in turn supported the view that the nucleic acids are involved in heredity. Many more powerful demonstrations of this thesis are now available, including the observation that the DNA of a virus, injected into a bacterial cell, can change the entire function of the cell, converting it from a factory for making more bacteria to a factory for making more viruses.

▽ The genetic material of all known organisms on Earth is composed largely of DNA and RNA. These nucleic acids have coded into their structure the information which is reproductively transmitted from generation to generation. In addition, they have the capability for self-replication and mutation. DNA serves as a kind of molecular blueprint which controls metabolism, produces a replica of itself for the next generation to follow, and, through the centuries, gradually changes, or mutates, occasioning new forms of life.

▽ The structure and function of DNA have been elucidated chiefly by the American molecular biologist James D. Watson of Harvard University, and the British molecular biologist Francis H. C. Crick of Cambridge University. DNA is a long molecule, comprising two molecular strands wound about each other in a coil or helix; a short section of a DNA molecule is shown schematically in Figure 14–2 and as a molecular model in Figure 14–3. During cell division, the strands separate, and each synthesizes a copy of the other, yielding two molecules of DNA where originally there was only one. This is the primary molecular reproductive event. The building blocks for this synthesis are called nucleoside phosphates. Much of the activity of the cell is devoted to constructing these building blocks from yet simpler molecules acquired from ingested food and joining them together to form nucleic acids. The nucleoside phosphates are each composed of a sugar, a base, and some phosphates. A given nucleic acid molecule is generally composed of four kinds of nucleoside phosphates. Their sequencing along the chain is a kind of four-letter code that determines which sequences of amino acids, and therefore which proteins, a cell will make.

▽ In Figure 14–2 the two helical strands can be seen running vertically in opposite directions on the right- and left-hand sides of the Figure. As the detailed inset shows, the strands are connected by pairs of bases chosen from the four bases,

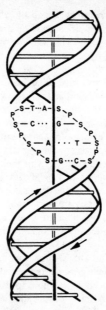

FIGURE 14–2. *Schematic diagram of a short segment of a DNA molecule. The two complementary strands are composed of alternating sugars and phosphates. The strands are joined by bases, either in the combination adenine-thymine or in the combination guanine-cytosine. The vertical axis in this drawing is for orientation only, and does not correspond to any feature of the DNA molecule.*

adenine (A), cytosine (C), guanine (G), and thymine (T). The strands themselves are made of sugars (S) and phosphates (P). Thus, a nucleoside is a combination of a base and a sugar, such as AS, while ASP is an example of a nucleoside phosphate. (A nucleoside phosphate with only one phosphorous group is called a nucleotide.) The sequence of bases—for example, the bases TCAG along the left-hand strand of the inset—specifies the genetic code by determining which proteins the cell will construct. Proteins, in turn, are long chains of amino acids. Recent evidence indicates that three nucleoside phosphates in the nucleic acid are required to specify each amino acid in the protein. The transcription sequence is this: DNA makes RNA; several kinds of RNA together make proteins, in particular, enzymes; and enzymes, by controlling the rates and varieties of chemical reactions in the cell, govern its metabolism. In this way, the nucleic acids actively control the form and functions of all cells. For several of these steps, protein intermediation is required.

▽ Exact replication—the production of two identical DNA molecules from one—occurs because only certain combinations of bases can fit across the two strands. During DNA replication, the strands of the helix separate. The bases

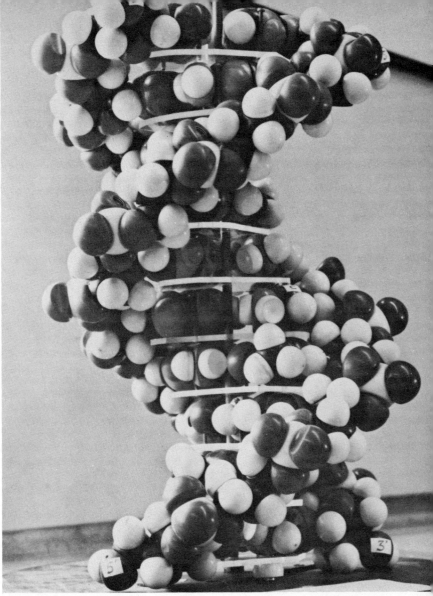

FIGURE 14–3. *A model of a short segment of a DNA molecule, in which atoms are represented by spheres and sections of spheres. Different varieties of atoms are represented by different colors. In Figure 14–2, letters such as S or A stood for molecules containing a dozen or more atoms. In this Figure, each atom is represented directly. Actual DNA molecules may be thousands of times longer than the short segments displayed in Figures 14–2 and 14–3. The complexity of the nucleic acid molecules is evident. (Courtesy of Professor Paul Doty, Department of Biological Sciences, Harvard University.)*

exposed to the cell medium determine which nucleoside phosphates from the medium can combine with the separated strands. For example, suppose an adenine-containing nucleoside phosphate is sitting bound in one strand. A variety of other nucleoside phosphates are available in the medium and occasionally come close enough for chemical bonding to occur. If a guanine-containing nucleoside phosphate is added, DNA synthesis will not proceed, because the guanine-adenine combination will be too large for the space available between the strands. An adenine-cytosine combination will not combine properly, nor will an adenine-adenine combination. Only an adenine-thymine combination fits between the strands. Elsewhere, a thymine-cytosine combination will be too small for the DNA double helix, and not reach between strands. The replication of DNA occurs in large part because thymine (T) will bind only with adenine (A), and guanine (G) only with cytosine (C). Thus, once the sequence of bases along one strand is specified, the sequence along the other strand is determined [see Figure 14–2]. For example, if a section of one strand of a DNA molecule had the sequence of bases T C A G A G T G A C C G A T A T T C, we could immediately decide that the sequence of bases along the other strand must be A G T C T C A C T G G C T A T A A G.

▽ The replication of nucleic acids is usually identical, but not always. Under the influence of external factors such as radiation, or by purely random molecular motions, changes in the structure of the nucleic acids may occur. For example, one base in a strand may be deleted, or may be substituted by another base; or the sequence of bases may be inverted in a short linear sequence. Since the sequence of bases is now changed, the proteins which this nucleic acid molecule now constructs will be different. In general, the changed sequence of bases will yield a "nonsense" portion of the protein it has coded; that is, the altered portion of the protein will serve no useful function.

▽ Some aspects of evolution and the genetic code can, perhaps, be illustrated by a parable. Once upon a time there was an ancient and stable empire, whose capital was connected with its many provinces by a system of royal roads. Day-to-day government in the provinces was the responsibility of the satraps, usually imperial appointees of local origin. The satraps excelled in executing the imperial commands; but their personal initiative was limited. They had a certain repertoire of responses to crisis situations; these responses survived repeated testing in previous generations, and generally functioned well. From time to time, a message from the emperor would arrive concerning some major issue, such as next year's agricultural quotas, or the retraining of industrial workers. These messages were obeyed instantly and literally; their wisdom was legendary. But in those days, the imperial messages were invariably phrased in a foreign tongue. The parlance of the capital was not the dialect of the provinces. The messenger, billeted at the imperial court, knew only the language of the capital. The burden of translation therefore fell to the satrap, who maintained for this purpose a group of bilingual viziers.

▽ The emperor, a member of a venerable and illustrious family, was permanently sequestered in the remote and inaccessible capital, insulated from the stresses of provincial life. The emperor was a conservative, in the best and worst senses. It was his firm belief that, with very minor changes, the imperial methods and mandates of his predecessor emperors were precisely valid in his day. Therefore, it was his practice to consult the ancient almanac and read the hoary mandates of his imperial forebears. At propitious moments, identical mandates were dispatched to the provinces. The times were stable, and external threats were few. The empire prospered.

▽ Yet there was a certain anxiety which the emperor's courtiers shared. It concerned a dark secret which had, from time to time, concerned imperial households through ages past, back to the founding of that august family: the emperor was afflicted with a hereditary mumble. Not all the time, you understand; mostly, the emperor was lucid and assured, his commands confidently transformed into provincial action. But on rare occasions, the mumble would come upon him. At these times, he could not be understood at all. The emperor would say, "Mumble, mumble!" The courtiers would repeat, "Mumble, mumble," and nod their heads sagely. The imperial courier, his message in hand, would mount his steed and race along the royal highway to the provinces. "Mumble, mumble!" he would say to the satraps. The satraps would turn to their translators. "Mumble, mumble," they translated, in the dialect of the provinces. "Mumble, mumble," the satrap would say to the workers and soldiers, his duty discharged. But the workers and soldiers knew nothing of "mumble, mumble." They continued to await an intelligible imperial command. And soon a lucid message was on its way with another courier. All would be put right, and only a little time lost.

▽ But the bad moments, the courtiers knew, were when the emperor's mumble *seemed* lucid. Oh, sometimes he would say, "Doubled be must quota potato the," and the workers might either reconstruct his meaning, or be idle. However, he did other things. He might insert a "not" into a decree, where none was intended, or substitute one noun for another. This invariably led to disaster. No courtier, no courier, no satrap ever questioned the imperial command. The word of an absolute autocrat is law, as the case of Lieutenant Kijé, the subject of a composition by Prokofiev, attests. So occasionally there was serious trouble in the provinces.

▽ One day it came to pass that a desperate crisis of external origin arose in the provinces. Its nature need not concern us here; the emperor never heard of it. He was very quick with mandates for the provinces and very loath to receive news from the provinces. The crisis was beyond the capabilities of the satraps; it was not encompassed in their repertoire of responses. At this moment, by chance—for the emperor knew nothing of the crisis—an imperial mumble was dispatched to the provinces. It was of the apparently lucid variety, and led to activities by the workers. Fortuitously, miraculously, the misapprehended mumble solved the crisis. Of all the possible mumbles—and of these there were many—the emperor had spoken by chance the right mumble at the right moment. The empire was saved.

▽ This is no way to run an empire, you are saying. Yet, in a sense, this is how living systems function. Very crudely—for the analogy is inexact—the capital is the nucleus, and the provinces the cytoplasm of a cell. The cloistered emperor with his almanac is the nuclear DNA; the courier and his message, RNA, coded in the nucleus and passing into the cytoplasm. The satraps and their viziers are the ribosomes and adapter RNA, which serve as a kind of molecular scaffolding, organizing cytoplasmic amino acids into the sequence specified by the messenger RNA. Translation is necessary, because the messenger RNA carries in the base sequence of its nucleotides the information on the amino acid sequence of the proteins to be constructed. The workers and soldiers are the enzymes. The feedback from cytoplasm to nucleus is apparently insignificant. An accidental disruption of the DNA base sequence almost invariably has a deleterious effect on the functioning of the assembled proteins. But very rarely, a mutation has a salutary effect. Biological evolution is based upon the fortuitous emergence of such random beneficial mutations. Clearly for each organism which is better adapted because of a beneficial mutation there are millions which perish because of a deleterious mutation. Natural selection works only because (1) enormous numbers of organisms are involved, and (2) the beneficial mutations are preferentially reproduced. But evolution by hereditary mumble is a slow process.

▽ From breeding experiments, primarily with the common fruit fly, *Drosophila melanogaster* (literally, the "black-bellied dew-lover"), it was found by Thomas Hunt Morgan and his students at Columbia University, in the second decade of the twentieth century, that the hereditary characteristics, or genes, were arranged in linear order along the chromosomes, with each gene controlling one or more traits of the organism. The common organisms all have more than one chromosome, and in sexual reproduction the chromosomes of the parents are randomly reassorted, thereby giving the offspring a chance for a previously untried physical constitution. The number of possible reassortments is so large that it provides a natural explanation for the fact that, except for identical twins, no two individuals are alike.

▽ *D. melanogaster* and other insects have, fortunately for us, a set of giant chromosomes in their salivary glands. These chromosomes [see Figure 14–4] are naturally banded, and the bands have a 1-to-1 correlation with the genes deduced from breeding studies. Since all cells in the fly arise from the same fertilized egg, we expect the chromosomes of the salivary glands to be structurally identical with the chromosomes of the reproductive cells. When a gene is absent, a band is absent; when it appears doubled, we see a doubled band, etc. This has provided a strong observational confirmation of the fact that the genes are strung in linear order along the chromosome, and that each gene does control at least one hereditary characteristic.

▽ Some salivary gland chromosomes show an occasional enlarged, bulbous region [see Figure 14–4]. It now appears that these puffs are the sites of active genes, where the genetic material is coding a particular sequence of nucleoside phosphates in messenger RNA. The puffs are found to be associated with high concentrations of RNA. The messenger RNA then presumably detaches itself from the DNA of the chromosome puff and migrates to the cytoplasm of the cell, where it directs protein synthesis. While such conclusions have been deduced for only a

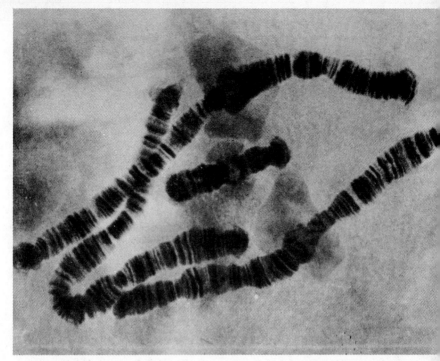

FIGURE 14–4. *A photograph, magnified some 700 times, of the four chromosomes in the salivary gland of the midge* Chironoumus. *The sequence of bands corresponds closely to the sequence of genes in the genetic material of the organism. The enlarged regions may be sites of active production of messenger RNA.* (*Courtesy of Professor W. Beermann, Max Planck Institut für Biologie, Tübingen.*)

small variety of organisms, there is every reason to believe that the same process occurs for all the organisms on the Earth.

▽ While there is a very vague correlation between the number of chromosomes and our estimate of the evolutionary complexity of the organism (for example, *Drosophila* has four chromosome pairs; human beings have 23), this correlation is far from a general rule. The particular plants which contain the largest number of chromosomes per organism are far from being the dominant species on the planet. What counts is not the number of chromosomes or the amount of genetic material, but rather its information content.

▽ A typical *Drosophila melanogaster* chromosome may be about 1 micron (= 10^{-4} cm) long. From *Drosophila* breeding experiments, it has been possible to determine, without ever looking at its chemistry, that a given chromosome of *D. melanogaster* contains at least 1000 genes. If we divide one micron into a thousand equal parts, we find that each gene is about 10 Å long (1 Å = 10^{-8} cm). Since there may be many genes which control traits not readily discernible to the geneticist, we would expect the width of the gene along the chromosome to be somewhat less than 10 Å.

▽ In the DNA structure we find that the distance between adjacent nucleoside phosphates along the same polynucleotide strand is 3.4 Å. A substitution in one of these nucleoside phosphates changes the meaning of the triplet code of which it is a part and will thereby alter one amino acid in the protein which this nucleic acid codes. For example, some hereditary diseases in human beings are known to result from just such a substitution of one amino acid. Therefore, the smallest genetically significant unit of the hereditary material is about 3.4 Å long.

▽ Is it really possible that the sequence of nucleoside phosphates along the DNA chain can contain enough information to construct an entire organism? A human being? The mass of DNA in one set of human chromosomes is about 4×10^{-12} grams. One pair of nucleoside phosphates (on opposite strands of the double helix) has a mass of the order of 10^{-21} grams. Therefore, there seem to be some 4×10^{9} pairs of nucleoside phosphates per chromosome set, according to this calculation by the American geneticist, H. J. Muller, of Indiana University.

▽ In each of the 4×10^{9} positions available for a nucleoside phosphate, only four combinations of nucleoside phosphates are possible. On a given strand, the base may be T, C, A, or G. The base on the complementary strand must then be A, G, T, or C, respectively. The number of possibilities for one slot along the DNA molecule is four. The number of possible combinations for two consecutive slots is $4 \times 4 = 16$; for three slots, $4^3 = 64$, etc. Thus, for 4×10^{9} slots, there are $4^{4 \times 10^{9}}$ or $10^{2.4 \times 10^{9}}$ possible varieties of human chromosomes. This is, of course, an enormous number vastly larger than the number of elementary particles in the detectable universe, which as we saw in Chapter 11, is about 10^{80}. It is vastly larger, also, than a googol; but much smaller than a googolplex.

▽ This number is a measure of our improbability. If you threw 4×10^{9} nucleoside phosphate pairs up in the air, and they came down by twos in random order, there would be only once chance in $10^{2.4 \times 10^{9}}$ of reassembling one of your chromosomes. You could perform this imaginary exercise of reassembling DNA molecules randomly, once a second, for the lifetime of the Galaxy, and come nowhere near constructing one of your own or anyone else's chromosomes.

▽ But if our DNA is *this* improbable, how could it have come into being at all? Our improbability is extracted from the environment by natural selection. Our nucleic acids are *not* constructed randomly. The vast majority of base combinations has never been tried. Each combination is built upon pre-existing ones. The sequences of nucleoside phosphates which work are carried over from generation to generation, unchanged for millions of years. In fact, the similarity of base sequences between the DNAs of two different organisms can now be used as an index of evolutionary kinship. In this way, it has been possible to show, for those who have wondered, that man and monkey are more closely related than man and mouse.

196

▽ The information contained in a single human sperm cell is equivalent to that of 133 volumes, each of the size and fineness of print of *Webster's Unabridged Dictionary*. Yet we now can understand how this information could have come into being through natural selection. We understand how natural selection can extract order from chaos, if there are self-replicating and mutating systems in a non-static environment. But we are again faced with the question of the origin of the first such system.

▽ The origin of life on Earth seems intimately tied to the prebiological origin of proteins and nucleic acids. We do not know that proteins and nucleic acids must be intimately involved in living systems on other planets, although some evidence supporting this view will be presented in Chapter 18. But if we are to design for the detection of extraterrestrial life equipment which is not hopelessly parochial in outlook, we must have some general approach to living systems. △ We may well encounter phenomena on other planets which, while possessing all the essential attributes of life on Earth—perhaps even intelligence—exist in different forms, and function according to different principles. It would be useful to have a purely operational definition of life which is not confined to familiar terrestrial chemistry. ▽ We conclude the chapter by returning to this question. △

Some interesting preliminary ideas on the subject have been formulated, in terms of cybernetics, by the Soviet mathematician A. A. Liapunov. Cybernetics, ▽ a term coined by the American mathematician Norbert Weiner, △ is concerned with the study of control processes and the construction of control systems. ▽ Cybernetics developed at the same time that the first large electronic computing machines were constructed. △ Liapunov believes that control, in its broadest sense, is the most universal property of life, independent of form.

▽ Because of the necessity for evolution by natural selection in order to develop living systems of any complexity, one possibly useful definition of life is this: a living system is any self-reproducing and mutating system which reproduces its mutations, and which exercises some degree of environmental control. This definition is much narrower than that of Liapunov. △

Another definition of life, supported by the Soviet biochemist A. I. Oparin of the A. N. Bach Institute, is expressed in terms of complexity and a highly regulated metabolic system for material exchange with the environment. Metabolism, of course, is an essential attribute of life. But in the context of origins, does life lead to metabolism, or does metabolism lead to life? No entirely satisfactory answer has been found to date. It should be noted that simple forms of material interchange (which are not highly regulated, and thus not metabolic processes) can be observed in non-living systems—for example, in liquid solutions.

In Liapunov's view, living systems have the following special characteristic: through definitely prescribed channels, the transmission of small quantities of energy or material containing a large volume of information is responsible for the subsequent control of vast amounts of energy and materials. (An obvious example is the control by the genetic material in man of the form, development, and chemical processes of the much larger individual.) Liapunov points out that heredity, irritability, and so forth can be described in cybernetic terms as information storage, feedback, communication channeling, etc.

All biological materials are dependent upon their mass, chemical composition, energy state, electric and magnetic properties, and so forth. Generally speaking, these properties will change over a period of time. But a small fraction of the materials will remain relatively stable. These substances maintain their stability despite changes which occur in the external environment. Liapunov calls such reactions, in which the substance survives changes in the external environment, *maintaining reactions*. Maintaining reactions underlie all biological processes. Indeed, life is characterized by its adaptation to the external environment.

In the language of cybernetics, maintaining reactions can be outlined as follows: the sensing material receives information about the external environment in the form of coded signals. This information is reprocessed and sent in the form of new signals through defined channels, or networks. This new information brings about an internal reorganization of the system which contributes to the preservation of its integrity. The mechanism which reprocesses the information is called the control system. It consists of a vast number of input and output elements, connected by channels through which the signals are transmitted. The information can be stored in a recall or memory system, which may consist of separate elements, each of which can be in one of several stable states. The particular state of the element varies, under the influence of the input signals. When a number of such elements are in certain specified states, information is, in effect, recorded in the form of a text of finite length, using an alphabet with a finite number of characters. ▽ These processes underlie contemporary electronic computing machines and are, in a number of respects, strongly analogous to biological memory systems. △

The control system directs the maintaining reactions of the organism or computing machine and their response to the external environment. The response occurs by collecting information about the external stimuli, analyzing it into its component parts, and comparing it with information which is already recorded in the memory. The greater the amount of information previously stored, the more adaptable the control system. An important property of the maintaining reaction is its speed of response. If the reactions are slow, the survival of the system is jeopardized. Thus, a large information storage capacity is required for the memory bank, and the information must be stored in an exact and stable manner.

Liapunov suggests that individual molecules, consisting of sufficiently large numbers of atoms, can conceivably act as stable physical information carriers. Such molecules are quantum systems. In order to reach another information state, they must be raised to another energy level, sufficiently distant from the original state that few transitions will occur due to random thermal motion.

The energy supply for the maintaining reactions must not run down. Nevertheless, such systems will constantly lose heat and energy because of their activity. According to the laws of thermodynamics, the energy levels in a closed system—one completely isolated from its environment—must eventually reach equilibrium. If a living system were closed, any loss of energy would endanger its stability. Thus, a stable state will not be maintained unless energy is obtained from the external environment, and the living system becomes an open system.

An important thermodynamic characteristic of any such system is its entropy. Entropy may be defined as a measure of the unavailability of energy in a thermodynamic system; ▽ or, alternatively, as a measure of the disorder of a system. In any closed system, no process can occur in which the entropy decreases; that is, the disorder of any closed system will increase as time goes on. In an infinite amount of time, disorder should be complete, and the atoms randomly distributed, in the absence of other influences. If a living system is represented as a closed system, its entropy would continuously increase. The burgeoning disorder would, in time, bring all biological processes to a halt. Consequently, a living organism must systematically lose entropy, to maintain internal order. This is possible only at the expense of the external environment. The organism must extract energy from, and increase the entropy of, the external environment, so that its own entropy may be continuously decreased, and its structural and functional integrity maintained. As we pointed out earlier, this is one reason why cells metabolize. △

Older definitions of life, which identified life with metabolism, were inadequate. Such definitions, in our opinion, are entirely worthless. Liapunov characterizes life as a highly stable material system which uses information coded by molecular states for the production of maintaining reactions.

The actual organization of living systems into subcellular organelles, cells, organs, organisms, populations, species, and so forth is analogous to a hierarchy of control systems. Each structural unit is controlled by its own semiautonomous control system, which acts upon all those units subordinate to it, and in turn is acted upon by those control systems which are above it in the hierarchy.

There is a distinction between the control systems within an individual organism and those acting upon an ensemble of organisms (for example, populations, species, and so forth). In the former case, the control system consists of units acting directly down through the hierarchy. Liapunov calls this the structural method of control. In the latter case, we have a large number of more or less independent statistically equal systems which interact by chance meetings. Liapunov calls this the statistical method of control. Those systems of higher rank order—for example, the species—are significantly more stable than any given individual constituent (here, an individual organism). But this greater stability of the higher system is possible only if the constituent parts are replaceable; that is, if reproduction occurs.

For the newly synthesized constituent part to partake of its measure of stability, it must contain a pre-formed supply of information, stored in its memory bank, which guarantees its maintaining reactions. It is quite inconceivable that this information supply could arise spontaneously within the constituent itself. Thus, a new constituent must obtain this store of information necessary for its functions from other constituents—most reasonably from other similar constituents which we may refer to as the previous generation. Thus, reproduction is seen to be in large measure information replication.

The transmission of information from generation to generation occurs in a background of interference which can partially alter its character. ▽ If such an alteration of the hereditary information cache is itself replicated identically—that is, if the altered information is transmitted to succeeding generations—then such an alteration can be called a "mutation." △ Such mutations change the control system, modifying the maintaining reactions, and thereby changing the character of the interaction of the system with its environment; they can radically alter the efficiency with which a given individual copes with its environment.

▽ It is possible therefore to describe living systems from a cybernetic point of view. At the moment, this is perhaps no more than a useful analogy. It has provided an insight, but not yet any new information. △ It is possible that in the future a synthesis of such a cybernetic approach with molecular biology will lead to a complete understanding of the nature of life, an understanding which we do not yet have, as Liapunov himself is fully aware. These ideas, and the related viewpoint of the Soviet physicist Kolmogorov—discussed in Chapter 35—may ultimately prove to be of great significance in the analysis of the problem of the origin of life on Earth and the probable widespread distribution of life in the universe.

15

The origin of life: Historical views and panspermia

But now to carry the Search farther, let us see by what Steps we must rise to the attaining some knowledge in the deeper Secrets concerning the State and Furniture of these new Earths. And, first, how likely is it that they may be stock'd with Plants and Animals as well as we? I suppose no Body will deny but that there's somewhat more of Contrivance, somewhat more wonderful in the Production and Growth of Plants and Animals, than in Lifeless Heaps of inanimate Bodies, be they never so much larger; as Mountains, Rocks, or Seas are. For the Finger of God, and the Wisdom of Divine Providence, is in them much more clearly manifested than in the other. One of Democritus's or [Des] Carte's Scholars may venture perhaps to give some tolerable Explication of the Appearances in Heaven and Earth, allow him but his Atoms and Motion; but when he comes to Plants and Animals, he'll find himself non-plus'd, and give you no likely account of their Production. For every Thing in them is so exactly adapted to some Design, every part of them so fitted to its proper Use, that they manifest an Infinite Wisdom, and exquisite Knowledge in the Laws of Nature and Geometry, as, to omit those Wonders in Generation, we shall by and by show; and make it an Absurdity even to think of their being thus happily jumbled together by a chance Motion of I don't know what little Particles.

Christianus Huygens, *New Conjectures Concerning the Planetary Worlds, Their Inhabitants and Productions* (c. 1670)

[May one] doubt whether, in cheese and timber, worms are generated, or, if beetles and wasps, in cow-dung, or if butterflies, locusts, shellfish, snails, eels, and such life be procreated of putrefied matter, which is to receive the form of that creature to which it is by formative power disposed[?] To question this is to question reason, sense, and experience. If he doubts this, let him go to Egypt, and there he will find the fields swarming with mice begot of the mud of the Nylus, to the great calamity of the inhabitants.

A seventeenth century opinion quoted by L. L. Woodruff, *The Evolution of Earth and Man* (1929)

Nothing seems now more contrary to reason, than that chance and nastiness should give a being to uniformity, regularity, and beauty . . . and create living animals . . . This, however, was the opinion not only of the ignorant and illiterate, but of the most learned grave philosophers of preceding ages; and would probably still have been taught and believed had not microscopes discovered the manner how all these things are generated . . .

Henry Baker, *The Microscope Made Easy* (1742)

▽ In an earlier and simpler age, life was believed to arise spontaneously, from nothing. It was a commonplace observation. Not quite from nothing, perhaps; but mice from the mud of the Nile, maggots from putrefying meat, lice from sweat, and fireflies from conflagrations—as the most elementary observation seemed to show. The question of the origin of life was trivial—life was arising all the time, at least for lower animals.

▽ Since higher animals arose from the reproduction of their own kind, the question of *their* ultimate origin was more difficult. The dominant view, found in Genesis 1, in the Hesiodic *Theogony,* and in the Sumerian creation myths, invokes a separate creation of each species by divine fiat. There were early murmurings against these beliefs, for if lower organisms arise spontaneously, might not the earliest self-reproducing higher organisms have developed in some way from simpler predecessors? The pre-Socratic philosopher Anaximander postulated that life arose in the sea, and that man developed from something like a fish. A view similar to Darwinian natural selection was expressed by Empedocles. Is it possible that higher organisms, so marvelously adapted to their environments, arose through some natural process from simpler organisms? In Book II of his *Physics,* Aristotle restated Empedocles' opinion in the following characteristic phrases:

> Wherever, then, all the parts came to be just what they would have been if they had come to be for an end, such things survived, being organized spontaneously in a fitting way; whereas those which grew otherwise perished, and continued to perish . . .

This passage is quoted by Darwin on the first page of *The Origin of Species,* apparently without his being aware that Aristotle then went on to criticize the Empedoclean hypothesis:

> Yet it is impossible that this should be the true view, for . . . all . . . natural things either invariably or normally come about in a given way: but of not one of the results of chance or spontaneity is this true. . . .

What is bothering Aristotle? He seems to be saying that a random but useful change in the characteristics of an organism cannot be maintained, because there is no way for the characteristic to become established among many organisms. The children of one-armed men are generally born with two arms. The possibility is overlooked that random variations in the genetic material may be reproduced, and adaptive characteristics thereby become established in an entire population.

▽ After the time of Lucretius, who echoed Empedocles' views, the combined authority of Aristotle and the medieval Church was so great that spontaneous origins of lower animals were accepted as tenets of faith. But when the Italian

Renaissance flowered across Europe, the confidence in hoary antiquity and traditional explanations became eroded: "Anyone who in discussion relies upon authority uses, not his understanding, but rather his memory . . . ," wrote Leonardo da Vinci. Experimental verification of hypothesis became widely accepted. Thus, in 1665, an Italian physician, Francesco Redi, put the hypothesis of spontaneous generation to an experimental test. When putrefying meat is covered with fine gauze, Redi found, maggots never develop. He discovered that maggots were the larval forms of flies, which deposited their eggs on the meat. When the meat was covered by gauze, the flies were unable to lay their eggs, and no maggots developed.

▽ About a decade after Redi was disproving spontaneous generation at the level of the house fly, a Dutchman, Antony van Leeuwenhoek, was discovering microorganisms, and thereby, through no fault of his own, extending the debate on spontaneous generation for another two centuries. Leeuwenhoek found that apparently pure water, but especially water which contained organic impurities such as hay infusions, abounded with microorganisms. His charming account of these discoveries follows:

> On April 24th, 1676, observing this water by chance, I saw therein with great wonder unbelievably very many small animalcules of various sorts; among others, some that were three to four times as long as broad. Their entire thickness was, in my judgment, not much thicker than one of the little hairs that cover the body of a louse. These creatures had very short, thin legs in front of the head (although I can recognize no head, I speak of the head for the reason that this part always went forward during movement). . . Close to the hindmost part lay a clear globule; and I judged that the very hindmost part was slightly cleft. These animalcules are very cute while moving about, oftentimes tumbling all over.

▽ From where did these "animalcules" come? Leeuwenhoek himself believed that tiny seeds, or germs, of the animalcules were present everywhere, and, upon gaining access to nutrient media such as hay infusions, proceeded to grow. Since the germs can arise from the microorganisms themselves, there is no necessity to invoke spontaneous generation. Yet many learned men were unable to accept the extraneous origin of microorganisms, especially when a variety of experiments seemed to show that organic solutions, whether covered or uncovered, boiled or not boiled, always developed "animalcules." It was not until 1861, two years after the publication of Darwin's *The Origin of Species,* that this problem was finally put to rest. Louis Pasteur, in his *Memoir on the Organized Bodies which exist in the Atmosphere,* demonstrated rigorously that the air does contain "germs," as Leeuwenhoek thought; that introduction of these germs into a sterile medium invariably leads to the appearance of microorganisms; and that sterile organic media exposed to air, but not to germs, never develop microbial cultures.

▽ (It is a curious fact that shortly after utilizing sterile techniques in solving one problem in the origin of life, Pasteur applied them to an experimental question on extraterrestrial life. In 1864 a large meteorite of a type now known as a carbonaceous chondrite fell near Orgeuil, France. Pasteur caused a special drill to be constructed, which, he hoped, would remove samples from the interior of the meteorite without contaminating them with microorganisms from outside. Using sterile techniques, Pasteur inoculated an organic medium to search for growth of any indigenous microorganisms which the meteorite interior might contain. The results were negative, and have relevance today: Pasteur extracted his sample shortly after the fall of the meteorite, and was, of course, a very careful experimentalist. In Chapter 23, we will return to more recent studies of possible living forms in the Orgueil and other meteorites.)

▽ Thus, by the 1860's, it was no longer possible to hold that contemporary organisms, no matter how simple, spontaneously arise from non-living precursors. By this time, Darwin had provided an intellectual framework in which the development of complex organisms from simpler ones by natural selection could be understood. Yet the problem of the origin of the first organism remained. No one felt the difficulty of this problem more keenly than Darwin himself: "It is mere rubbish, thinking at present of the origin of life," Darwin wrote in a letter to Hooker in 1863. "One might as well think of the origin of matter." In this, Darwin was correct. As we have seen in Chapters 7 and 8, we *are* today thinking of the origin of matter, with some success; and serious scientific studies of the origin of matter and of the origin of life have occurred contemporaneously. But at the end of the nineteenth century there was no experimental approach to the origin of a living organism from inanimate matter. The problem seemed impossibly difficult.

▽ In this intellectual climate, the Swedish chemist Svante Arrhenius in 1907 proposed the panspermia hypothesis. Arrhenius suggested that terrestrial life did not originate on Earth. He imagined that simple living forms may have drifted from world to world, propelled by radiation pressure through interstellar space. An extraterrestrial origin of life at least postponed the difficulties inherent in the origin of life, much as studies of stellar nucleogenesis ignore the problem of the origin of hydrogen. There may be no problem of the ultimate origin of matter; the universe may be infinitely old, and may always have had matter in it. By the same token, if panspermia is even a relatively inefficient method of populating a planet, in sufficient time the descendants of one organism might populate a static universe. △

Let us first consider the philosophical tractability of the panspermia hypothesis. What objection, in principle, could there be to spores making this magnificent cosmic journey from planet to planet, and from star system to star system, and then, by chance falling on a planet where conditions were suitable, reviving and initiating life? The idea is not inconsistent with materialist philosophy. Indeed, is it *necessary* to assume that life on Earth should arise locally, from non-living matter? And starting from the assumption that there are a multiplicity of populated worlds, is it not completely logical to investigate the possibility that organisms are exchanged between planets? Only by an interdisciplinary approach, through astronomy, biology, and allied sciences, is it possible either to confirm or forever lay to rest the panspermia hypothesis.

Sagan recently attempted a careful analysis of this problem. ▽ Arrhenius supposed that terrestrial microorganisms were sometimes wafted into the stratosphere by winds in the terrestrial atmosphere. There is some evidence, from balloon studies, that microorganisms can be found at great heights, well into the stratosphere. Arrhenius postulated that occasionally such organisms will be entirely ejected from the Earth by electrical forces. Such a mechanism works in principle, but in practice we do not know with what efficiency microorganisms are ejected—if they are ejected at all. This is one motivation for obtaining high-altitude microbiological profiles of the terrestrial atmosphere and exosphere.

▽ Let us assume, with Arrhenius, that such electrostatic ejection of microorganisms from the upper terrestrial atmosphere occasionally occurs. What will be the fate of such a microorganism? For notational convenience, let us call this microorganism a "bug," in full awareness that it will be much smaller than any ordinary insect usually called a bug. The fate of an ejected bug depends upon the ratio p/g, where p is the magnitude of the force due to radiation pressure, which tends to drive the microorganism away from the sun; and g is the magnitude of the gravitational force due to the Sun, which tends to drag the bug into the Sun. In the absence of other forces, if $p/g = 1$, the bug just sits in interplanetary space; if p/g is less than 1, it falls into the Sun; and if p/g is greater than 1, it leaves the solar system. Since p and g are both inversely proportional to the square of the distance, r, of the microorganism from the Sun, p/g is independent of r. But the value of the *net* force, $p - g$, varies inversely as the square of r.

▽ For a model bug, something like terrestrial microorganisms, only a narrow size range has p/g greater than 1 and can escape. These bugs must be approximately 0.2μ to 0.6μ in radius, assuming them spherical; their diameter must therefore be comparable to the wavelength of visible light [1 micron $(\mu) = 10^4$ Å $= 10^{-4}$ cm]. Any bugs seeding the Earth—to initiate life in primitive times, for example—would have to be outside this size range. Bugs leaving the solar system would have to fall within this size range. A characteristic dimension for an ordinary terrestrial microorganism is several tens of microns; but bacterial and fungal spores and many viruses have dimensions between 0.2 and 0.6μ.

▽ Since the force due to radiation pressure continues to act as an organism recedes from the sun, its velocity continues to increase, and it soon reaches very considerable speeds Thus, a bug in this size range starting in the vicinity of the Earth would reach the orbit of Mars in weeks, the orbit of Jupiter in months, the orbit of Neptune in years, and the distance to the nearest star in a few tens of thousands of years. If the bug made no collisions in its interstellar peregrination, it could transit the Galaxy in a few hundred million years. But Shklovskii has pointed out that over these distances, the bug will almost certainly not move in a straight line. △ The bug would tend to move in the same manner as a particle of interstellar dust (which it resembles in size, mass, and composition), that is, in an irregular, random manner. Having traveled the distance of several tens of light years, it may suddenly change direction upon collision, or even merge with another interstellar dust particle. Thus, the bug would tend to make a random "walk" through the Galaxy, similar to the Brownian motion of small particles in solution. ▽ Because of the resulting erratic path, which crosses back upon itself and retraces steps already taken, the transit time of a bug between any two places in the Galaxy is correspondingly much longer than if the bug traveled in a straight line and made no collisions. △ In order to traverse a distance of about 1000 light years (approximately $\frac{1}{30}$ our distance from the Galactic center), the bugs would require several hundred million years. To cross the entire Galaxy, they would require 10^{11} years, a time interval some 10 times greater than the estimated age of the Galaxy. ▽ Thus, if the Earth were seeded several billions of years ago—as would be required, to match the evolutionary timescale—that initial bug must have been ejected from a star no more than about 6000 light years away, *provided* that deflecting particles of interstellar dust were as common then as now. However, since, as we have seen in Chapter 5, the interstellar dust particles arise by collisions among themselves and with the interstellar gas, it is possible that some billions of years ago the interstellar dust density was much less than it is today; the Earth could then have been seeded by a bug arising on a planetary system more distant than 6000 light years from the Earth.

▽ But such discussions of transit times neglect a very serious question: Do the bugs survive the environmental hazards of the trip? First, the microorganism would be at a very low temperature and high vacuum for most of the trip. It was known even in Arrhenius' day that at least some spores can be immersed in liquid air (temperature $-196°C$) for long periods of time, without its affecting their ability to germinate subsequently; and we know today that some microorganisms survive extended laboratory exposures to high vacuum. In such experiments, the vacuums do not nearly approach those found in interstellar space, where the density of atoms is about 1 atom cm^{-3}; nor, for obvious reasons, do they approach the 10^9 or 10^{10} year transit times of which we have been speaking. Although a slow boiling-away of molecules that comprise the bug might occur over such immense journeys, let us assume, for the purpose of argument, that the bugs can survive tolerably well the high vacuum and low temperatures on interplanetary and interstellar space. △

Another hazard for wandering panspermia is the H II regions of hot, ionized interstellar gas surrounding early type stars. These regions encompass hundreds of light years and are extremely hot. ▽ But there is some question whether the densities of H II regions are great enough for the temperatures to affect the bugs. △

What about radiation? The bugs are exposed, among other varieties, to solar ultraviolet radiation and to cosmic rays. ▽ If we assume the bug to have the radiation sensitivity of the most resistant known microorganism, solar ultraviolet radiation at wavelengths short of 3000 Å would kill the putative panspermia at the moment of their departure—within a day of their ejection from Earth into interplanetary space. In the extremely unlikely case that the ejected microorganism has an infinite tolerance to ultraviolet radiation, then x-rays and protons of solar origin would kill the bugs before the orbit of Neptune is reached.

▽ We should emphasize that, at least for ejection from this solar system, the radiation hazards cannot be avoided by providing a protective shielding for the bug. With a shielding thick enough to be useful for radiation protection, the bug would be too large to be ejected by solar radiation pressure. Similarly, we cannot save the panspermia hypothesis by imagining interstitial spores locked within the fissures of some interplanetary dust particles or meteors and thereby shielded from the harmful radiation.

▽ The same arguments apply for an unprotected spore smaller than 0.2μ entering our solar system, instead of leaving it. It would accumulate a lethal dose of radiation while entering the solar system. But bugs ejected from planets at great distances from a star—for example, at the position of Uranus or Neptune in our own solar system—would run negligible radiation risks. Therefore, the possibility of ejection from or arrival on such worlds cannot be dismissed on grounds of radiation sensitivity.

▽ If panspermia tarry too long, they will be killed by another sort of radiation. We saw in Chapter 7 that the primary cosmic ray flux in the vicinity of the Earth was about 0.04 roentgens (R) per year; in interstellar space, the cosmic ray flux is essentially the same. The most radiation-resistant microorganisms known are not destroyed until they have accumulated doses of 10^6 or 10^7 R. On this basis, it would seem that in $4 \times 10^6/4 \times 10^{-2} = 10^8$ years, the laggard panspermia would be killed by cosmic rays. Actually, the problem is somewhat more complex. When a cosmic ray primary (usually a high energy proton) enters a microorganism, it produces its damaging effect partially by direct ionization of the internal structure of the organism. However, another part of the damage done is by cosmic ray secondaries—less energetic particles that are created in the deceleration of the primary. For a single microorganism floating in space most of the cosmic ray secondaries should emerge harmlessly from the organism into the surrounding space. Because of their small sizes microorganisms should accordingly be more resistant to cosmic rays than larger organisms whose tissues absorb the cosmic ray secondaries. If cosmic rays have always been as intense as they are in the vicinity of the earth today, they may restrict interstellar travel by panspermia over distances more than a few thousand light years, but the exact restriction depends on the largely unknown contribution of secondaries.

▽ Let us now turn to stars other than the Sun. In general, the hotter a star is, the greater is the value of p/g, but also the shorter is its main sequence lifetime— the period during which life can reasonably be expected to develop on the star's planets. Let us assume that the donor planet (the planet ejecting panspermia) was populated for at least a few hundred million years, either for the indigenous origin of life on that planet (in which case the estimate is very generous), or for the proliferation of a spore arriving earlier, from another donor world. We then find that only main sequence stars between spectral types A0 and G5 can eject panspermia. Most of the stars in the Galaxy are cooler than the Sun. Only a few percent lie between spectral types A0 and G5; therefore, only a few percent could hold donor planets for the panspermia hypothesis. For these spectral types, the hotter stars can eject a larger range of sizes of microorganisms; but at the same time, they almost certainly present a much more serious radiation hazard. Stars much cooler than the Sun can eject no panspermia at all. We can conclude that the only reasonable donors are the outer planets of stars in the range of spectral types A0 to

G5; these stars are capable of ejecting microorganisms in a size range between 0.1μ and 3.0μ.

▽ Acceptor planets must clearly be different from donor planets. In our solar system, bugs in the size range between 0.2 and 0.6μ are ejected; accordingly, bugs in this size range can never enter the solar system. The hotter the star, the greater the size range of bugs which are deflected away from that solar system by radiation pressure. Thus, the most likely acceptor planets are those circling cool M dwarfs and the outer planets of G and K stars. The most likely locales in the solar system to search for interstellar panspermia, then, are the moons of the outer planets, especially Triton, the inner satellite of Neptune. Larger panspermia—say, in the 1.0μ size range—might be found elsewhere, if they could survive the radiation of the voyage. It has been suggested by the American geneticist Joshua Lederberg, of Stanford University, that the Moon, which is unlikely to have any indigenous life forms, might be a useful place to search for interstellar panspermia.

▽ Another area of difficulty for the panspermia hypothesis, one which we have not yet touched upon, is geometry. The spaces between the stars are immense. A bug randomly "walking" its way across the Galaxy actually has a very small chance of accidental encounter with a possible acceptor planet. In order for the Earth to have received one microorganism from a stellar source in the first billion years of Earth history, each one of, say, 10^{11} assumed planets in the Galaxy must have ejected about one ton of microorganisms into interstellar space during that period. △ Of course these values could be modified. For example, if there are only 10^8 populated planets, then each of them would have to release 1000 tons of spores every billion years. ▽ Because we do not know the present rate of ejection of microorganisms from planets, especially by electrostatic mechanisms, we cannot assess the plausibility of these values; however, they seem quite high. Studies of the microorganism population of the upper atmosphere of the Earth would be very useful in such considerations; but the over-all prognosis for the panspermia hypothesis is not favorable. The restriction on possible donor and acceptor planets, the radiation hazards during transit, and the geometrical difficulty provide almost insuperable obstacles.

▽ Another sort of planetary seeding should be mentioned, at least in passing. We have so far discussed radiation pressure as a conceivable mechanism for interstellar transport of living things. Thomas Gold of Cornell University has pointed out another possibility. Let us assume, for the moment, that the Galaxy is populated here and there by advanced technical civilizations. Since many such civilizations probably are far in advance of our own, interstellar space flight may have been discovered and exploited [see Chapters 32 and 33]. Suppose, Gold says, that an expedition from such a civilization—a survey party, for example—lands on a previously uninhabited but nevertheless clement planet. Unless the most rigorous precautions are taken, they will contaminate the planet. Their ship, their air, and they themselves are populated with diverse microorganisms. In fact, the prevention of accidental contamination of Mars by the first unmanned space ships destined to land there is a very serious problem [see Chapter 19]. Gold, however, imagines such planetary contamination in a more vivid way. He pictures the visitors having a picnic on the virgin planet, and leaving their refuse behind. In this view, some microbial resident of a primordial cookie crumb may be the ancestor of us all.

▽ While this garbage theory of the origin of life understandably lacks appeal, we should not exclude it altogether. Perhaps a race of advanced extraterrestrials would be scrupulously careful not to contaminate a previously unpopulated planet; but perhaps not. There is also the complementary possibility that such an advanced civilization may intentionally initiate life on uninhabited planets, for any of a variety of reasons: to prepare the planet for subsequent colonization, with, of course, a very long timescale in mind; to distribute the genetic material of the home planet, so that in case of a disaster, the evolutionary patrimony is not irretrievably lost; or perhaps merely as an experiment in laboratory biology, with a somewhat grander laboratory than those to which we are accustomed. If there is intelligent life in the universe, then it is difficult to exclude such possibilities; but it is also difficult to say very much more about them. If we put away such last resorts—at best, they temporize with the real issues—we must finally come to grips with the problem of an indigenous origin of life. This is the topic of our next two chapters. △

16

The physical setting
for the origin of life

Looking back through the prodigious vista of the past, I find no record of the commencement of life, and therefore I am devoid of any means of forming a definite conclusion as to the conditions of its appearance. Belief, in the scientific sense of the word, is a serious matter, and needs strong foundations. To say, therefore, in the admitted absence of evidence, that I have any belief as to the mode in which existing forms of life originated, would be using words in a wrong sense. But expectation is permissible where belief is not; and if it were given to me to look beyond the abyss of geologically recorded time to the still more remote period when the Earth was passing through physical and chemical conditions which it can no more see again than a man can recall his infancy, I should expect to be a witness of the evolution of living protoplasm from not-living matter.

T. H. Huxley, *Biogenesis and Abiogenesis* (1870)

▽ Imagine the solar system viewed from afar: four planets, as the American science writer Isaac Asimov has said, and debris. The four are, of course, Jupiter, Saturn, Uranus, and Neptune. They are large bodies, far from the Sun—easy objects for a small telescope somewhat outside our solar system. The spectra of these outer, or Jovian, planets shows hydrogen, methane, and ammonia in their atmospheres; helium and water are expected. Such spectra are very common in the universe, because of the high cosmic abundance of hydrogen [Chapter 4]. But as we move closer to the sun, some of the debris becomes discernible. The apparent surface features and atmospheric composition of Venus, Earth, and Mars are soon detected. To the best of our present knowledge, the atmospheres of Venus, Mars, and perhaps of Mercury as well, are composed primarily of nitrogen and carbon dioxide. But there is something strange about the Earth. There is oxygen in our atmosphere.

▽ As rust and fire attest, oxygen is a reactive gas. It combines with other molecules rapidly at high temperatures, more slowly at low temperatures, to form new chemical compounds. Sometimes energy must be supplied in order for oxygen to react. Sometimes a catalyst, perhaps water, speeds the rate of reaction. But reaction with oxygen is inexorable, and, in the inorganic world, irreversible—a one-way street—as long as the oxygen lasts. When a material combines with oxygen, it is said to be "oxidized." Thus, water is an oxidized form of hydrogen. Materials with a large hydrogen content are said to be "reduced." Thus, water can also be described as a reduced form of oxygen. The atmospheres of the Jovian planets are reducing; the atmosphere of the Earth is oxidizing.

▽ Organic matter—matter of either biological or abiological origin which contains carbon—has a high hydrogen content. It and we who are made of it are characteristically reduced. Yet we live in an oxygen atmosphere. The complete oxidation of organic substances produces carbon dioxide, water, and nitrogen. Such indiscriminate oxidation is clearly debilitating, destroying the material of which we are made. Consequently living organisms on the Earth use a variety of mechanisms, some of them very sophisticated, to avoid contact with oxygen altogether, to shunt the oxidation to non-injurious molecular reactions, or to repair the oxidation damage which has occurred. In a very real sense, we Earthly organisms are living in a poison gas. But more startling yet, some of us are breathing it. Our ancestors have evolved systems for *utilizing* oxygen to the point where our accommodation to the poison has given us a great subsidiary advantage. Combination of metabolic products derived from the breakdown of food with molecular oxygen permits our food to be oxidized completely, to carbon dioxide and water.

▽ It appears that a great selective advantage was conferred upon organisms which evolved mechanisms to cope with the presence of free molecular oxygen in the atmosphere. Not only did they avoid indiscriminate oxidation of their own material and consequent degeneration; they also evolved the capability of *selective* oxidation of foodstuffs, which enables much more energy to be extracted from the food. For example, two organisms, an anaerobe which does not utilize molecular oxygen, and an aerobe, which does, may each ingest the same quantity of sugar, but the aerobe may extract ten times more energy from it.

▽ Because of the metabolic efficiency of aerobes, it has been suggested that organisms on planets which lack oxygen may not be very advanced. But this is an unimaginative conclusion. There may be more energetic foodstuffs available elsewhere; or the organisms there may eat at a faster rate than do organisms here; or their metabolic processes may be correspondingly slower. It is premature to infer that every planet populated with higher organisms must have an oxygen atmosphere.

▽ If oxygen utilization provides a significant metabolic advantage, why are there on Earth today the obligate anaerobes, organisms which are poisoned by molecular oxygen? These organisms, none of them more advanced than worms, live in the relatively few environments on Earth where molecular oxygen is absent— some soils and oceanic mud, for example. It is possible that many obligate anaerobes are degenerate, evolved from predecessor organisms which were capable of utilizing molecular oxygen. A species living many generations in an oxygen-depleted environment would have no selection pressure to improve, or even maintain, its oxygen-utilization apparatus. A mutation which cripples this apparatus would not be deleterious in an oxygen-poor environment. Given enough time, such a mutation is bound to occur, and the facultative anaerobe—one which can take its oxygen or leave it—would have evolved into an obligate anaerobe. But might some of the obligate anaerobes be descended entirely from anaerobic ancestors? Might they be relics of an earlier epoch when anaerobic conditions were more common than they are today?

▽ Interestingly, the metabolism of sugar by many anaerobes is identical in its early phases with the sugar metabolism of aerobes. (Both organisms take hexose —any 6-carbon sugar, like glucose—and convert it to a hexose phosphate. The hexose phosphate is transformed into hexose diphosphate; the diphosphate is split into two molecules of glyceraldehyde phosphate, etc.) Each step is catalyzed by at least one enzyme. In animal tissue, in yeast, and in many bacteria, 10 of the first 14 steps in the metabolism of hexose sugars are identical. This is another illustration of the essential biochemical similarities of diverse terrestrial organisms; it can most simply be explained by the supposition that all organisms now living on Earth had a common ancestor. After these common first steps in the breakdown of sugar, the metabolic pathways of various organisms diverge. The anaerobes carry the energy extraction process only a few steps further and are content. The energy is locked in the phosphorous bonds of a molecule called adenosine triphosphate (ATP), a ubiquitous molecule in terrestrial living systems which serves as a kind of common energy currency. When energy is extracted from food, it is put into the energy-rich bonds of ATP; when energy is needed to drive a reaction, the energy is extracted from the energy-rich bonds of ATP. (The letter T here stands for "tri," and not for thymidine, as it did in our discussion of DNA in Chapter 14.)

▽ On the other hand, aerobic organisms carry the metabolic pathway many steps further, utilizing molecular oxygen to extract all the chemical energy available in sugar, and to store it in ATP for future use. How curious that the anaerobic metabolic steps are common to both aerobes and anaerobes! Up to the point at which the molecule pyruvic acid is made, the pathways are common; after that, they are strikingly divergent. This circumstance suggested to the versatile Anglo-Indian scientist J. B. S. Haldane, in 1927, that the common ancestor of contemporary terrestrial organisms was an anaerobe, and that aerobic metabolism was a more recent elaboration. Haldane went further: he proposed that early organisms were anaerobic because the primitive atmosphere of the Earth lacked molecular oxygen, and was instead rich in reduced compounds. Haldane felt that the pre-biological synthesis of hydrogen-rich organic molecules would be much easier to understand in a reducing environment.

▽ At the time, it was a radical suggestion. Prevailing views on the chemical composition of the primitive terrestrial atmosphere leaned heavily towards N_2 and CO_2, neither of which are reduced. The fact that the universe is mostly hydrogen was not known until 1929, and the existence of methane and ammonia in the atmospheres of the Jovian planets was discovered only in 1934. A few years later, a book entitled *The Origin of Life* was published in the Soviet Union by the Russian biochemist A. I. Oparin. Drawing heavily upon the astronomical evidence then available, Oparin independently suggested that the primitive atmosphere of the Earth had been reducing. More than a decade earlier, Oparin had drawn the same conclusion, in an article for a Communist Party periodical, from the supposed abiological synthesis of petroleum. Incidentally, whether petroleum is produced entirely biologically, partly biologically, or entirely abiologically is still undecided.

▽ The idea, promulgated by Haldane and Oparin, of a reducing primordial environment of the Earth is the touchstone to later experiments on the origin of life, which form the subject of our next chapter. We have seen previously, in Chapter 4, that from cosmic abundances, a "typical" planetary atmosphere should be composed of hydrogen, helium, methane, ammonia, and water. The atmospheres of the Jovian planets—Jupiter, Saturn, Uranus, and Neptune—have, we believe, just this composition. The Earth, and the other planets of terrestrial type—Mercury, Venus, and Mars—should have begun their careers with similar atmospheres; at least in the case of the Earth, there is independent supporting evidence. Why did the terrestrial planets lose their primitive atmospheres, while the Jovian planets retained theirs?

▽ The outermost region of any planetary atmosphere is called its exosphere. It is from the exosphere that molecules escape into interplanetary space. Suppose we take an object—any object, of any mass—a great distance away from the Earth and then let it fall. In the absence of air resistance, there is a certain velocity with which it impacts the Earth. Reversing the process, if a mass—again, any mass—is projected upwards from the surface of the Earth with this same velocity, it will reach very great distances. There is a critical velocity, called the escape velocity, beyond which the ejected mass will continue to travel indefinitely—that is, when it is moving so rapidly that terrestrial gravity cannot quite drag it back. For the Earth, it is 11.2 km sec^{-1}, or about 7 miles per second, and is the velocity with which a space vehicle must be ejected, if it is to escape from the Earth and go someplace else.

▽ The same ideas which apply to Gemini capsules and Voskhods apply to atoms and molecules. If they are traveling fast enough in an upward direction, they can escape from the Earth—unless some other molecule is in the way. An oxygen molecule in the air just in front of you, moving upward with a velocity of 11.2 km sec^{-1}, will not escape from the Earth. It is in fact quite unlikely it will even escape from the room. Even if you direct that rapidly-moving oxygen molecule out into the open air, the situation is not much improved. As soon as it gets started on its hopeful journey outward, it collides with another molecule—probably a stolid, slow-moving, type—jostles its neighboring molecules some, and then slows down to a more pedestrian molecular velocity. It is only in the exosphere that a molecule moving outward with escape velocity has a good chance of escaping; there the density of the atmosphere is so low that the probability of collision with another molecule on the outward voyage is small. But since the molecular population of the exosphere is small (by definition, as we have just seen), the amount of mass escaping from a planetary exosphere tends to be relatively small.

▽ Low-mass molecules escape much more easily than high-mass molecules. Why? Because at a given exosphere temperature, all molecules tend to have the same energy. (This is not quite true, because the fastest-moving molecules have already escaped, but their place is soon taken by molecules from below.) Now a massive molecule moving slowly may have the same energy as a faster-moving molecule with a smaller mass. There is a distribution of molecular velocities. Most are moving with some average speed; a few are moving very slowly; a very few are moving very rapidly. Of those few moving very rapidly, some, by chance, are also moving outward. They escape.

▽ Thus, in any planetary atmosphere, hydrogen, the lightest molecule, will escape preferentially. The loss of hydrogen is replenished, to some extent, by outgassing from the interior, especially in earlier times; and by the solar proton wind—ionized hydrogen atoms blown outwards from the solar atmosphere. In the case of the terrestrial planets, the exosphere temperatures are relatively high, and the force of gravity is relatively low. Both circumstances tend to enhance the escape of gases from their exospheres. The rate of escape of hydrogen is today much larger than the rate of replenishment from outgassing or from the solar wind.

▽ The Jovian planets, by contrast, have such large gravitational forces and such low exosphere temperatures (since they are far from the sun) that even hydrogen, the lightest gas, never escapes. A characteristic time required for a significant fraction of the hydrogen in the terrestrial exosphere to escape is something like 1000 years. The corresponding number for the exosphere of Jupiter is a googol years or so. Heavier gases, of course, move more sluggishly, and have greater difficulty escaping. Significant amounts of helium also escape from the terrestrial exosphere, but molecules as massive as atomic oxygen are too heavy and do not escape from the Earth. Mars, with its lower gravity, may conceivably have permitted the escape of substantial amounts of atomic oxygen during the age of the solar system, a fact of some significance in assessing the possibility that conditions on Mars were more Earthlike in earlier times. In the case of Mercury, its low gravity and high exosphere temperature (because of its proximity to the Sun) suggest that all molecules less massive than argon (atomic weight 40) have escaped during the last 5×10^9 years.

▽ We should emphasize that it is the exosphere temperature, and not the surface temperature, which determines the rate of escape. On the Earth, surface temperatures are about 300°K, which is much too low to permit escape of substantial amounts of hydrogen. But since the exosphere temperature is characteristically 1600°K, and sometimes, during solar activity, goes above 2000°K, hydrogen escapes. Thus, we see that if the terrestrial planets and the Jovian planets started out their careers with extensive reducing atmospheres, the terrestrial planets would have lost their hydrogen by escape into interplanetary space, while the Jovian planets would have retained theirs, in good agreement with observation.

▽ But there is another wrinkle to this problem. As first noted by D. H. Menzel, of Harvard University, and Henry Norris Russell, of Princeton University, the Earth is deficient in such noble gases as neon, argon, krypton, and xenon. From astronomical spectroscopy and from analyses of meteorites—the only samples of extraterrestrial matter that we can get our hands on at present—we know that the noble gases are generally more abundant—relative, say, to silicon— almost everywhere else in the universe. Thus, if the Earth started out with cosmic composition, some process has depleted the noble gases. The depletion has been greatest for the lighter noble gases, such as neon and argon and less marked for the heavier noble gases, krypton and xenon. The noble gases are particularly important in studies of the evolution of a cosmic object, because with only a few exceptions they do not form chemical compounds; also, they remain gaseous down to very low temperatures. Since they do not combine chemically and do not freeze out, they must have been removed when they were gases. The preferential removal of the low atomic weight noble gases might suggest exospheric escape; but we have just seen that the escape of significant quantities of any gas heavier than helium would not occur, given the present gravity and exosphere temperature of the Earth.

▽ If we want to explain the noble gas depletion by molecular escape, we must therefore assume that the temperature of the primitive exosphere was greater, or that the force of gravity on the primitive Earth was less than at present. In Chapter 6 [see Figure 6–3], we discussed the early evolution of the sun and saw that as it was contracting approximately vertically, towards the main sequence, in the spectrum- luminosity diagram, its brightness was much greater than it is today.

▽ With present values of the acceleration of gravity on Earth, exosphere temperatures as high as 100,000°K were required for escape of noble gases, temperatures some scores of times larger than contemporary values. The same theory of exospheric escape shows that the escape timescale must have been extremely short, a few thousand years. The exosphere temperature is determined by the absorption in the upper atmosphere of ultraviolet photons from the Sun through the conversion of photon energy into the motion of the absorbing molecules, that is, into heat. While the exosphere temperature does depend on the particular molecular species in the upper atmosphere, very crudely the exosphere temperature is proportional to the intensity of absorbed ultraviolet sunlight. Thus, the depletion of noble gases can be understood if for a period of some thousands of years the Sun had a luminosity some scores of times greater than its present luminosity.

▽ From Figure 6–3, we see that such luminosities and such timescales are consistent with present models of early solar evolution. This rough numerical coincidence lends some credence to the view that the present underabundance of noble gases on the Earth is due to atmospheric escape from a hot primitive exosphere. The approximate numerical agreement makes the argument more persuasive than a purely qualitative argument would have been. However, there are other factors which must be examined—such as the rate of arrival of material from the lower atmosphere at the escape level—before this theory can be accepted.

▽ Alternatively, suppose that the Earth was still in the process of formation at the time the Sun reached the main sequence. The gravity at the surface of an object of the mass of the Earth, but greatly distended, can be much less than the present value—in fact, sufficiently less to explain the escape of the noble gases without invoking exosphere temperatures in excess of present values.

▽ But now, if a large fraction of the Earth's initial complement of a gas as heavy as xenon or krypton escaped into space, then essentially all of the lighter gases—methane, ammonia, water, hydrogen, and helium—must also have been wiped off the Earth. Yet we have an atmosphere today. Where did it come from? The solar wind is an entirely inadequate source. Our present atmosphere must then have arisen from outgassing—from volcanoes and fumeroles, bubbles of gas, penetrating to the surface and unable to escape from the now completed Earth.

▽ There is other geological evidence—from the composition of the Earth's surface and from the rate of outgassing observed today—to support this conclusion: the present atmosphere of the Earth is not the same as the gaseous envelope which surrounded the Earth during its formation. The initial atmosphere was lost; our present atmosphere is of secondary origin. What was the chemical composition of this secondary atmosphere, formed after the Earth reached its present size and the Sun reached the main sequence?

▽ The materials outgassed must have been trapped in the interior of the Earth during formation. Thus, their composition would be typical of the solar nebula in the vicinity of the Earth. Hydrogen was in excess; the other atoms were reduced. Material could have been trapped in two ways: by occlusion and by precipitation.

In occlusion, a gas bubble is physically trapped—for example, inside a rock; in precipitation, a chemical compound is formed which drops out of the atmosphere as a solid or a liquid, and cannot escape to space. Then, during the end of the formation process, the temperature of the Earth began to increase. The aggregation process itself provided one source of heat. Material of all sizes, from dust grains to asteroids, was plummeting down, colliding, and providing the material for the accreting Earth. These collisions released heat—possibly enough to melt the surface. Another source of heat was radioactivity. There are reasons, both from the study of meteorites and from theories of the origins of the elements, for believing that radioactive isotopes now long extinct (due to radioactive decay) were then present in great numbers. Their decay produced heat, and this again contributed to the temperatures required to cause outgassing. Whether the Earth was ever completely molten is today largely unknown, despite intensive geophysical and geochemical attacks on the problem.

▽ If the Earth's secondary atmosphere was also reducing, how do we explain the transition from a reducing to the present oxidizing atmosphere? Here, we recall the discussion of preferential molecular escape of lighter gases, especially hydrogen. In the upper atmosphere of the primitive Earth, hydrogen-rich molecules—in particular, water, methane, and ammonia—were being photodissociated by ultraviolet light. Just as a sufficiently energetic photon can ionize an atom, separating an electron from the nucleus, so can a less energetic photon break a molecule into pieces—water, for example, into the components OH and H. After absorption of another ultraviolet photon, the OH may be further separated into O and H. These hydrogen atoms escape to space; the oxygen atoms cannot. The net result is the preferential escape of hydrogen, and the oxidation of the atmosphere remaining behind. Methane tends to be converted to carbon dioxide, ammonia to molecular nitrogen. If the process continues long enough, free oxygen will form. We do not know whether water vapor photodissociation and the subsequent escape of hydrogen is adequate to account for the oxygen now in our atmosphere and chemically combined in the crust. Some calculations suggest that the process is adequate to account for the present oxygen; others suggest that it is not. Certainly, today, the oxygen content of our atmosphere is determined by green plant photosynthesis—a sophisticated sort of photodissociation of water, where visible photons are employed by the plants, instead of the ultraviolet photons which are effective in the upper atmosphere. Conceivably, there was an oxygen atmosphere before green plant photosynthesis was rampant on Earth; but it is possible also that no free oxygen was produced until green plants flourished.

▽ The date of the transition between the secondary reducing atmosphere of the Earth and the present oxidizing atmosphere is therefore difficult to establish. From Figure 6–3 of Chapter 6, we note that after reaching the main sequence, the sun had a distinctly smaller luminosity several billion years ago, than it has today. Thus, the temperature of the Earth should have been lower. The geological record shows signs that algae inhabited the Earth some 2.7 billion years ago [Figure 16–1]. More recently a number of workers have found phytane (a fragment of the

Dentate structure   Collenia structure   Fragmental limestone

FIGURE 16–1. *Algal limestones found in the Rhodesian Shield of Africa. These structures exhibit the characteristic features of limestone secreted by calcareous algae. It is unlikely, though still possible, that these patterns were produced abiologically. If they are of biological origin, as many scientists believe, they are among the oldest signs of life on the Earth. These limestones were found embedded in rocks dated about 2.7 billion years old. [Reproduced from a paper by A. M. MacGregor, in the* Trans. Geol. Soc. South Africa 43:9 (1940); *by permission of the Geological Society of South Africa.*]

chlorophyll molecule) and other signs of ancient biological activity in Minnesota sediments dated again at about 2.7 billion years. The temperatures on the surface of the Earth 2.7 billion years ago, must therefore have been above the freezing point of water. Yet at that time, the solar luminosity was so low that the average temperature on the Earth's surface should have been about 20 or 30 Centigrade degrees below present values—that is, well below the freezing point of water— unless there is some other factor which we have not yet taken into account.

▽ If we were to calculate the temperature of the Earth today from the albedo (or reflectivity) of the Earth, the solar luminosity, and the distance of the Earth from the sun, we would conclude that temperatures on the Earth were about 20° below zero Centigrade. Such a calculation neglects the effect of the atmosphere. Carbon dioxide and water in the terrestrial atmosphere are transparent in the visible, as everyday experience attests; however, they tend to be quite opaque at infrared wavelengths. Thus, sunlight passes unimpeded through water vapor and carbon dioxide in our atmosphere and heats the ground. But when the ground tries to radiate back to space in the infrared, it finds its efforts hampered by atmospheric absorption by CO_2 and H_2O. These molecules play the same role as the glass in a greenhouse, which is also transparent in the visible and opaque in the infrared. The effect is known as the "greenhouse effect." The temperatures inside a greenhouse and on the Earth are larger than we would expect if infrared radiation escaped from them unimpeded. It seems reasonable, then, to explain the additional 20 or 30 degree temperature increase 2.7 billion years ago by a slightly extended atmospheric greenhouse effect. But what molecules must we use?

▽ The carbon dioxide abundance in the Earth's atmosphere is believed, for reasons of chemical equilibrium, to be roughly constant throughout geological time. The water vapor abundance depends on the surface temperature. To increase the amount of water vapor, we must increase the surface temperature. But it is exactly an increase in surface temperature that we are trying to explain.

Therefore, some other molecule is needed—one which is not present in significant amounts in the present atmosphere. The reduced gases methane and ammonia are ideal for this purpose. They are such efficient infrared absorbers that even relatively small quantities could explain the required temperature increase. But if this argument is correct, it must follow that the atmosphere was at least slightly reducing as recently as 2 or 3 billion years ago. Is there any geological evidence to support this conclusion?

▽ There are minerals known which change their chemical composition when the oxygen or hydrogen concentration of their environment varies. The appearance of the minerals limonite, hematite and calcite in geological sediments between 2 and 2.5 billion years old shows that large amounts of free hydrogen were not available in that epoch. In very old South African sediments, an extremely rare mineral, uraninite, can be found. With a few exceptions, it is not found in recent sediments, because uraninite is a reduced uranium mineral, UO_2. In the presence of even small amounts of molecular oxygen, it is oxidized to U_3O_8, the form of uranium oxide found, for example, in pitchblende. The geological evidence suggests that the uraninite minerals were formed between 2 and 3 billion years ago.

▽ Thus it appears that between two and three billion years ago, the atmosphere was not very reducing, nor was it even slightly oxidizing. To avoid very low temperatures, we must postulate small amounts of methane and ammonia. This is still consistent with neutral or slightly reducing conditions. From several lines of evidence, it appears that green plant photosynthesis and oxygen reduction were fairly extensive. To avoid the accumulation of large amounts of free oxygen in that epoch, we must postulate that the photosynthetic oxygen produced was used in oxidizing the reduced constituents of the atmosphere and of the Earth's surface. Only later could free molecular oxygen form. Unfortunately, there is not yet enough geological evidence to determine when substantial quantities of free oxygen were first formed. The large insects, evolved in Carboniferous times some 500 million years ago, may have demanded large amounts of oxygen for their metabolism. Thus, the transition to an oxidizing atmosphere probably occurred between 2 and 0.5 billion years ago. As we go backward to earlier epochs, the atmosphere was progressively more and more reducing.

▽ We are now in a position to reconstruct something of the timescale of the origin of life. The Earth was formed some 4.5×10^9 years ago. While the Earth may never have been completely molten, its surface seems to have been quite hot during the process of formation. The origin of the Earth antedates the origin of life on the Earth. It is likely that several hundred million years after the Earth's formation surface temperatures were largely below the boiling point of water, and some atmosphere and ocean had been outgassed from the interior. The atmosphere was reducing, and the stage was set for the origin of life. By 2.7 billion years ago, the atmosphere was not yet oxidizing, but life had come into being and evolved to the stage of complexity of algae. Figures 16–2 through 16–7 give some idea of the kind of small plant and microorganism remains which are found in 2-billion-year-old sediments. They come from the Canadian Shield and were discovered by the

American paleobotanist Elso Barghoorn, of Harvard University, through whose courtesy they appear here in color. Not surprisingly, some of these microfossils correspond to no known variety of organism. More recently Barghoorn, has found fossil evidence of 3.1-billion-year-old bacteria.

▽ Since bacteria and especially algae are very complex living systems, enormously more advanced than the first living systems, the origin of life must be dated considerably before 3.1 billion years ago. As a guess, we may put the origin of life at $4.0 \pm 0.5 \times 10^9$ years ago. If the origin of life was easy, in a sense which we will define in the next chapter, then a date for it of about 4 billion years ago may be close to the truth. If we imagine one billion years from that date spent in the evolution of the first cell from simpler living systems, and two billion years for the elaboration of this single-cell design, we will come to a point about one billion years ago, shortly before the fossil record begins in earnest, when great varieties of multicellular organisms were emerging. Perhaps the great diversification of animals at the beginning of the Precambrian Epoch, some 600 million years ago, was due to the evolution of biological mechanisms for utilizing the large amounts of free oxygen newly available through plant photosynthesis, as the American geophysicist Lloyd V. Berkner has suggested.

▽ The times required for establishing the basic chemical patterns and structural organization of terrestrial life were probably much longer than the time required for the elaboration of such variations on the same theme as microbes, maple trees, mantises, and men.

17

Chemical syntheses
and early evolution
of life

. . . It is often said that all the conditions for the first production of a living organism are now present, which could ever have been present. But if (and oh! what a big if!) we could conceive in some warm little pond, with all sorts of ammonia and phosphoric salts, light, heat, electricity, etc., present, that a proteine compound was chemically formed ready to undergo still more complex changes, at the present day such matter would be instantly devoured or absorbed, which would not have been the case before living creatures were formed.

Charles Darwin (1871)

A hen is only an egg's way of making another egg.

Samuel Butler, *Life and Habit* (1877)

▽ Four and one half billion years ago the Earth was lifeless. Nowhere—not in the primitive atmosphere, not in the early oceans, nor in the newly forming crust—could even the simplest, most unassuming microorganism be found. Two billion years later, the Earth was fairly teeming with one-celled organisms of appreciable complexity. As we have seen in the previous chapter, the origin of the first living systems must have occurred within about a billion years of the formation of the Earth. How? Was it a vastly improbable event which, to our good fortune, occurred by chance in this small corner of the universe, and not elsewhere? Or, starting from the physics and chemistry of the primitive terrestrial environment, was the origin of life a likely event, given only a billion years of random molecular interactions?

▽ It is true that in enough time, almost any random concatenation of molecules, no matter how complex, will occur. But would the appropriate concatenation of molecules—nucleic acids and proteins, for example—occur in the time available? For example, suppose the probability for the origin of the first self-replicating system in the primitive environment in any given year was 10^{-6}. Then the probability that the origin of life occurs in any given century in that era would have been $10^{-6} \times 10^2 = 10^{-4}$, a small number. But in 10^9 years, the probability becomes very close to one, and we may talk of the origin of life as a "forced event"—that is, as a highly probable outcome of the chemical interactions on the primeval Earth.

▽ Suppose, instead, that the probability of the spontaneous origin of life in any given year on the primitive Earth were 10^{-12}. Then the probability of living systems arising, even over 10^9 years, would be $10^{-12} \times 10^9 = 10^{-3}$, a very small number. In this case, we would conclude that the origin of life was a highly improbable event in the time available in the early history of the Earth, and that life is here at all only through an extraordinary stroke of luck. We do not know what these probabilities really are, but they may be determinable by experimental investigation. If the probability of the origin of life turns out to be high, we can conclude that the origin of life is a likely event on many planets; if the probability turns out to be low, we must conclude that, except for such possibilities as panspermia or intentional colonization, the universe is sparsely populated.

▽ Several decades ago, it was fashionable to think that the probabilities were very low. In his book *Human Destiny,* le Compte de Noüy computed the probability that a sequence of amino acids arranged in random order would duplicate any given protein. We have performed a similar calculation in computing our own improbability, in Chapter 14. If the protein under consideration is 100 amino acids long, and any amino acid slot may be filled by any one of 20

227

biologically common amino acids, then the chance of random assembly of the given protein is one in 20^{100}, about 10^{130}, or more than a googol. Le Compte de Noüy concluded that such an event is so vastly improbable that it could not have occurred at all. He concluded that the origin of life required divine intervention.

▽ But there are other possibilities. We have seen in Chapter 14 that natural selection serves as a kind of probability sieve, extracting those structures and functions which improve the adaptability of the organism to the environment. But what of the origin of the first proteins, or the first nucleic acids? Must they have been *random* assemblies of their respective building blocks, the amino acids and the nucleoside phosphates? Or might it be that the molecules which spontaneously arose in the primitive environment are the ones which were later utilized in the origin of life?

▽ Contemporary organisms tend to be about 90 percent water, and human beings are no exception. Water is by far the most common molecule on the surface of the Earth. Evidently, life has used the building blocks available. However, sand (SiO_2) is also very abundant, yet relatively few organisms use it; those which do, use it structurally, and not biochemically or metabolically. The nucleic acids are made exclusively of carbon, nitrogen, oxygen, hydrogen, and phosphorus. The first four atoms are among the most abundant in the universe, as we have seen in Chapter 4; but phosphorus is rather rare. The proteins are made of carbon, nitrogen, oxygen, hydrogen, and sulphur. Again, sulphur is relatively rare. We can conclude that living systems have utilized, wherever possible, those atoms and simple molecules in greatest abundance. However, what is most available and what is most useful are often not identical. Thus, some common atoms or molecules have not been incorporated into living systems, while other uncommon ones have been selectively extracted from the environment.

▽ By chance, certain of the abundant molecules, notably water, seem peculiarly well suited for incorporation into living systems. In a book called *The Fitness of the Environment,* published in 1913, Lawrence J. Henderson, a biochemist at Harvard University, discussed at some length the salutary properties of water. For the origin and development of life, we need a liquid medium (or at the very worst, a very dense gaseous medium), in which molecular interactions can take place. For biological stability, the medium should remain liquid over a wide temperature range, and its temperature should vary only sluggishly when it is heated or cooled. In addition, Henderson felt that it would be useful if the liquid could dissolve salts, and participate in an acid-base chemistry. All these properties are shared by water; in several cases, water possesses them to a greater degree than any other common molecule. Henderson was struck by the apparent preadaptation of water for its biological role, and he felt that the coincidence was worth exploring. Others have used Henderson's arguments to conclude that the origin of life occurred by design. Henderson also discussed the "fitness" of carbon, oxygen, and other atoms and molecules for the fundamental roles they play in contemporary biochemistry.

▽ This question of the fitness of the environment provides some perspective on the problems inherent in extrapolation from a single example. We are talking and walking aggregates of carbon-based organic compounds in a liquid water solvent system. Might we be biased in our judgment that living systems must be carbon-based and aqueous? The American chemist George Pimentel, of the University of California at Berkeley, has argued that the fitness of water and carbon may be illusory, the product of our limited biochemical imaginations and the historical uniformity of terrestrial biochemistry. Some hydrocarbon solutions have wide liquid ranges and adequate temperature stabilities. The ability to dissolve salts or to participate in acid-base chemistry is not a prerequisite for molecular complexity, and many other alternatives can be imagined. At low temperatures, there are silicon compounds which have high stability, and can generate as much complexity as carbon compounds. At room temperature, however, they are not nearly so stable as comparable carbon compounds. In the presence of liquid water, many of them tend to dissociate. On the other hand, they are much more stable in ultraviolet light than many carbon compounds. Thus, silicon-based biochemistries may be appropriate in low-temperature, non-aqueous environments with high ultraviolet fluxes. Pimentel has pointed out that there are many known chemical reactions which proceed at biologically respectable rates at very low temperatures. At room temperature, however, the reactions occur so rapidly that we see only the products of the reaction, and tend to lose sight of the reactions themselves. Thus, while chemical reactions proceed much more slowly as the temperature declines, there do exist chemical reactions which proceed reasonably fast at low temperatures. Analogous statements may be made about high temperatures. We are just beginning to explore alternative biochemistries, and it is quite premature to conclude that ours is the only, or even the best of all possible, biochemistries.

▽ Our high water content has suggested to many biologists that life on Earth arose in the oceans. In fact, there is a rough correspondence between the content of such elements as calcium and potassium in sea water and in blood and tissues. This is our first hint that living systems tend to incorporate the primitive environment, so that their *milieu intérieur* would tend to resemble the familiar surroundings of the early history of life, a possibility first glimpsed by the nineteenth-century French physiologist Claude Bernard.

▽ Prior to 1953, several attempts were made to simulate the primitive environment of the Earth and synthesize organic molecules. The results were generally discouraging. In many of the earlier experiments, the over-all conditions were not reducing. For example, mixtures of H_2O, CO_2, and N_2 might be used and then irradiated with high-energy electrons. Only very simple organic molecules, such as formaldehyde, were produced, and even these, in very low yield.

▽ But in 1953, a major advance was made at the University of Chicago. Having convinced himself that the solar system arose under reducing conditions, the American chemist Harold C. Urey turned his attention to the problem of the origin of life. Urey's collaborator, Stanley L. Miller, prepared a mixture of methane, ammonia, water, and hydrogen as a simulated primitive atmosphere. The idea was to supply energy to such a mixture, and determine whether organic molecules were produced in detectable yield. Of the energy sources which seemed to be available in primitive times, and which are capable of driving organic synthetic reactions, solar ultraviolet radiation was the obvious choice. However, ultraviolet light is rather difficult to work with, as ordinary laboratory glassware is opaque to it. (This is why it is hard to acquire a sunburn through a window.) Accordingly, Urey and Miller used an electric discharge: high-energy electrons were passed between two electrodes through the simulated primitive atmosphere. Such a flow of electrons is an adequate lightning simulation. If there was water on the primitive Earth, clouds can be expected; and if there were clouds, electrical discharges between the clouds and the ground—that is, lightning—must have occurred. In the experiment, the gas was circulated so that after being sparked it was carried through a water bath, and the organic products produced in the gas dissolved in the liquid, where further reactions were possible. After a week of sparking, the liquid turned a deep brown. Clearly, new molecules were being produced from methane, ammonia, water, and hydrogen. But which ones? Were they organic?

▽ To analyze the composition of their mixture, Miller and Urey used an analytic technique called paper chromatography, which, with minor variations, has been used extensively in subsequent experimental work on the origin of life. If you dip a piece of white blotting paper in a bottle of black ink, the ink will move up the blotter a certain distance, and then stop, because of the molecular interactions between the ink and the paper. The ink is drawn up through the capillaries of the porous paper a certain distance and no further. If you perform such an experiment, you will observe that the black ink has separated into its constituent green and magenta pigments, and that the green and magenta pigments, being attracted in different degrees by the paper, have moved different distances up the blotter. This is a simple example of paper chromatography. In ordinary laboratory use, an unknown sample is spotted at the corner of a large piece of chromatography paper, which is similar to ordinary filter paper. The paper is then placed in an organic solvent, which seeps along the paper, carrying the unknown sample with it a certain characteristic distance. The paper is then turned at right angles and dipped into another solvent, which carries the unknown in a direction perpendicular to the first. The procedure is usually adequate to separate a large number of unknown samples into discrete spots on the chromatogram. Using the same paper and the same solvents, different organic molecules in the unknown will be carried to certain characteristic positions on the page. If these spots are colored, either intrinsically, as for ink, or extrinsically, by a spray, the position of the spots may be determined, and the composition of the unknown ascertained. Photographic emulsions are very sensitive to electrons emitted during radioactive decay. Thus, when the expected yield is very low, atoms of one of the original reactants—say, methane—may be labeled with a radioactive isotope—for example, radioactive carbon^{14} in place of the ordinary C^{12}. Carbon^{14} is subject to radioactive decay, giving off an electron from its nucleus (a neutron has been transformed into a proton and an electron), and the electron escapes from the molecule. This electron is capable of exposing a grain on a photographic emulsion. Consequently, newly synthesized compounds, whose atoms are so labeled, can be detected even in very small amounts by placing the paper chromatogram against an x-ray film and then developing the film. The newly-formed labeled molecules, in effect, take pictures of themselves.

▽ Figure 17–1 is an example of a developed autoradiogram negative. The brightest spot in the middle of the other spots is due to the molecule adenine, labeled with C^{14}. The adenine had been mixed with the sugar ribose and phosphoric acid, and irradiated with ultraviolet light for eighteen hours. The products were then run in two solvent systems, and the resulting two-dimensional chromatogram was placed against film with the result shown in the figure. Each of the spots, other than adenine, corresponds to an organic molecule synthesized in this experiment. Many of the molecules shown in this figure have not been identified as yet. This chromatogram was obtained with the assistance of Mrs. Elinore Green in my laboratory at the Smithsonian Astrophysical Observatory.

▽ Using ordinary paper chromatography, with a color stain, Miller and Urey found that they had produced, in high yield, large numbers of amino acids, the building blocks of the proteins. In addition, other organic molecules were produced, most of which are also involved in contemporary biological processes, although some, like urea, are involved mostly as end products. About 85 percent of the products produced in this experiment remain unidentified to this day. Some of these unknown products are believed to be sugars; others were long, tarlike polymers, responsible for the deep brown color which the aqueous solution acquired after a week of sparking.

▽ The original work of Miller and Urey has also been confirmed by the American geochemist Philip H. Abelson, of the Carnegie Institution of Washington. Using electric discharges in a wide variety of gas mixtures, Abelson found that as long as the net conditions were reducing, it was possible to replace CH_4 by CO_2, or NH_3 by N_2, and still produce the amino acids and the other products obtained by Miller and Urey. However, as soon as the net conditions become oxidizing, the organic synthesis effectively turns off. This is strong confirmatory evidence that for the large-scale prebiological synthesis of organic molecules, reducing conditions are required.

▽ Subsequently, in 1959 the German chemists W. Groth and H. von Weyssenhoff, at the University of Bonn, showed that ultraviolet irradiation at wavelengths where the gas mixture absorbed gave results similar to those of Miller and Urey. Ultraviolet light is fairly efficient in producing organic molecules from a mixture of ethane, ammonia, water, and hydrogen. The quantum yield is a quantity which expresses the number of organic molecules of a given type produced for every photon of ultraviolet light absorbed by the gas. Groth and von Weyssenhoff found characteristic ultraviolet quantum yields of about 10^{-5} to 10^{-6}; that is, it took between 100,000 and 1,000,000 photons to produce one organic molecule of a given type—amino acids, for example. Similar quantum yields have been found in later work, which we will discuss presently, on the ultraviolet synthesis of nucleic acid precursors.

▽ If we know the quantum yield, we can, in principle, compute the total

FIGURE 17–1. *An example of a two-dimensional autoradiographic chromatogram. The brightest spot corresponds to a labeled molecule used as a starting point in the experiment; the other spots, many of them unidentified, correspond to new organic molecules synthesized in the experiment.*

amount of organic matter formed while the Earth retained its reducing atmosphere. A typical mass for a simple molecule synthesized under primitive conditions is 10^{-22} gm. With a quantum yield of 10^{-5}, we have $10^{-5} \times 10^{-22} = 10^{-27}$ gm of organic matter produced per photon absorbed. A typical value of the ultraviolet photon flux at the top of the Earth's atmosphere in primitive times is 3×10^{14} photons cm^{-2} sec^{-1}. That is, every square centimeter of the Earth received 3×10^{14} ultraviolet photons per second. Since each photon produced 10^{-27} gm of organic matter, the total solar ultraviolet flux each second produced $10^{-27} \times 3 \times 10^{14} = 3 \times 10^{-13}$ gm over each square centimeter. If the primitive reducing atmosphere lasted 3×10^{8} years (about 10^{16} seconds), then $3 \times 10^{-13} \times 10^{16} = 3 \times 10^{3}$ gm of organic matter must have been produced by ultraviolet radiation during that time over each square centimeter of the Earth's surface. This is three kilograms per square centimeter, a sizable amount. The average depth of the present oceans is about 3 km, or 3×10^{5} cm. Since water has a density of 1 gm cm^{-3}, there are 3×10^{5} gm of water in a column one square centimeter in cross-section and 3 km high. Thus, if all the primitive Earth's organic matter were dissolved in the present oceans, we would have an aqueous solution which is $3 \times 10^{3}/3 \times 10^{5} = 10^{-2}$, or a one percent solution of organic matter. This is just about the consistency of a thin consommé, and confirms the expectation expressed by J. B. S. Haldane, in his earliest papers on the origin of life, that living systems arose in a "hot, dilute soup."

▽ Since the trail-blazing experiments of Urey and Miller, a large number of other, more complex organic molecules have been produced in a similar way. So far, the soup has been garnished according to the following recipe: start with methane, ammonia, water, and hydrogen, and see which simple molecules are produced in liquid water (for example, amino acids), or in the gas when liquid water is absent (for example, aldehydes and hydrogen cyanide). Then take these molecules, mix them together, and supply more energy. Take the products of this second step and use them as the reactants for the third step. Continue until the molecule you are looking for is made. A variety of energy sources have been used: high-energy protons and electrons, ultraviolet light, x-rays, gamma rays, and heat. Some of these energy sources—particularly electrons and ultraviolet radiation—are reasonable simulations for the primitive environment of the Earth; others are not. In some experiments, unrealistically high concentrations of organic matter have been used, as if the primitive seas had been composed of 50 percent organic matter, instead of perhaps one percent or less.

▽ The simulations are at best inexact. For example, pure reactants are used, whereas the primitive environment was not chemically pure. It is, of course, impossible for us to know the detailed chemical and physical conditions over the entire surface of the Earth, some 4×10^{9} years ago. Thus, the chemical reactions which occur in these studies cannot exactly simulate those which occurred on the early Earth.

▽ As another example, the energy source used to make the molecule of interest also tends to destroy it. Short wavelength ultraviolet light, for instance, will dissociate amino acids. To avoid such destruction, the experimenters have removed the product molecules from the energy source. This is one reason for circulating the gas through a liquid medium, in the Miller–Urey experiment. In experiments with ultraviolet light or heat, the energy source may simply be turned off after the desired products are synthesized. The primitive environment of the Earth was not as accommodating as the organic chemists, who, understandably enough, want to analyze their product before it is destroyed.

▽ A flash of lightning occurs and is finished; molecules synthesized by the flash are unlikely to be struck by a later lightning bolt. But with ultraviolet light, the synthesized molecules are generally even more liable to dissociation by ultraviolet light than are the precursor molecules. Was ultraviolet light, then, a useless energy source in primitive times, because the synthesized molecules were destroyed before they had any chance to react further and form molecules of biological interest? Not if the origin of life occurred in the oceans. A few tens of meters of pure liquid water will absorb essentially all the ultraviolet light incident on the surface of the waters in primitive times. As the content of organic matter in the waters increased, the organic molecules on the top of the ocean shielded organic molecules a few centimeters below from the dissociating effects of ultraviolet light. Because the primitive atmosphere was reducing, no ultraviolet-absorbing ozone could form. For this reason, I believe that light in the approximate wavelength range 2400–2900 Å penetrated to the surface of the waters in primitive times. As the transition to an oxygen atmosphere occurred, ozone was slowly produced by interactions of oxygen atoms and molecules, and eventually enough ozone was formed to establish a kind of molecular blanket at an altitude of about 40 km, which today protects us from the harmful effects of ultraviolet light. It seems likely that in primitive times the ultraviolet absorbing blanket was the top of the ocean, not the top of the atmosphere.

▽ We can now picture the primitive Earth between 4 and 4.5 billion years ago. There is a reducing atmosphere and bodies of water, both outgassed from the interior. Major tectonic changes are occurring; the continents are being formed; due to gravitational accretion and radioactivity, the Earth may have been, at least at certain times and places, much warmer than it is today. During storms, lightning bolts traverse the atmosphere; during the day, some ultraviolet light from the sun penetrates through the atmosphere and is absorbed in the ocean. The atmosphere is composed of methane, ammonia, water, and very small amounts of hydrogen. Soon, the ammonia will become dissolved in the oceans, where it forms ammonium hydroxide (NH_4OH), which will tend to make the oceans alkaline. The atmosphere may have also contained fairly large amounts of the relatively unreactive gases nitrogen and helium. Due to chemical interactions, the atmosphere has small amounts of aldehydes and hydrogen cyanide in it; dissolved in the oceans are amino acids. In such a setting, what else must occur?

▽ The next stages in prebiological organic synthesis, beyond the Miller–Urey experiments, have been performed in the United States in the 1960's, primarily in the laboratories of the Spanish-American chemist, John Oró, at the University of

Houston; the Ceylonese-American chemist, Cyril Ponnamperuma, at the Ames Research Center of the National Aeronautics and Space Administration; the American chemist, Melvin Calvin, at the University of California, Berkeley; and the American chemist, Sidney W. Fox, of the University of Miami.

▽ In experiments designed to simulate primitive conditions, these workers have succeeded in producing the 5-carbon sugars ribose and deoxyribose; the 6-carbon sugar glucose; the bases of the nucleic acids, adenine, guanine, and uracil; and polypeptides—long chains of amino acids which, at least in some gross chemical properties, resemble proteins.

▽ More recently, Ponnamperuma and I have produced nucleoside phosphates, the building blocks of the nucleic acids, under simulated primitive conditions. The rationale for these experiments is as follows: In the absence of ozone on the primitive Earth, it appears that ultraviolet light was penetrating the atmosphere and reaching the surface of the waters in the 2400–2900 Å region. This is a wavelength range in which ultraviolet light is deleterious to contemporary organisms. (Germicidal lamps emit ultraviolet light at these wavelengths.) Such ultraviolet damage occurs because certain molecular groups of contemporary organisms preferentially absorb at these wavelengths. The chief absorbers are the nucleic acid bases which preferentially absorb at about 2600 Å. In the environment of the primitive Earth, 2600 Å is just in the middle of the ultraviolet wavelength "window" transmitted by the atmosphere. Thus, by a curious coincidence, ultraviolet light was available at just the wavelengths at which the bases absorb. After ascertaining that the bases and the sugars ribose and deoxyribose are produced in simulated primitive Earth environments, we wondered what would happen in the presence of phosphorus. The early oceans should have had phosphates and other phosphorus compounds dissolved in them in small amounts. Thus, in one set of experiments, we prepared a dilute solution of the base adenine, the sugar ribose, and a phosphorous compound such as phosphoric acid in some experiments, or the more complex ethyl metaphosphate in others. The adenine was labelled with C^{14}, and the products were analyzed by autoradiographic paper chromatography. One of the compounds produced in highest yield was adenosine triphosphate, ATP. A molecular model of this molecule appears as Figure 17–2. It is a combination of adenine, ribose, and three phosphates, and can be written, in the notation of Chapter 14, as A-S-P-P-P. The possible primordial synthesis of ATP is significant in two respects.

▽ We have mentioned [Chapter 14] that ATP is ubiquitous in contemporary cells, where it serves as a kind of common energy currency. Today, ATP is made directly by plants in photosynthesis and is synthesized by animals and many microbes from food. But this experiment suggests that in primitive times, ATP may have been made "free," produced abiologically and raining down on primitive organisms like manna from heaven. The quantum yields in ATP production are so high that, if primitive synthesis was about as efficient as in our experiments, every square centimeter of the primitive oceans could have supported, essentially indefinitely, a population of 20,000 bacteria, each with contemporary generation

FIGURE 17-2. *A molecular model of the molecule, adenosine triphosphate (ATP). Different atoms are represented by different shaped and colored components. The ring of six wedge-shaped atoms on the left represents the adenine molecule. The "tail" of dark molecules on the right is the triphosphate group, and between them is the ribose sugar.*

times and energy requirements, using as sole energy source the ultraviolet-synthesized ATP. Thus, the elaborate metabolic machinery which today is devoted to generating ATP may have been unnecessary at the dawn of life.

▽ The other significance of ATP is that it is a precursor in the synthesis of nucleic acids in contemporary cells. One of the most exciting recent developments in biochemistry has been the laboratory synthesis of RNA by the Spanish-American biochemist Severo Ochoa, at New York University, and of a kind of DNA by the American biochemist Arthur Kornberg, now at Stanford University Medical School, with their respective collaborators. In each case, the experimenters took nucleoside phosphates, some inorganic substances such as magnesium, and an enzyme of biological origin. For the RNA synthesis, the enzyme is called polynucleotide phosphorylase; for the DNA synthesis, it is called DNA polymerase. Imagine a dilute solution of nucleoside triphosphates, magnesium, and, say, DNA polymerase. Drop into it a small amount of preexisting DNA. In a short time, Kornberg found, there will be synthesized larger quantities of a molecule which, in a great many respects, resembles the original "primer" DNA. A similar situation holds for the RNA. Now, imagine the experiment done again, but without the primer. What happens? Nothing happens, for a while. But soon, it is evident that there has been a slow synthesis of a nucleic acid, even in the absence of a primer. Such spontaneous polymerizations can occur both for RNA and for DNA. The synthesized DNA may be of a very simple and repetitive type (e.g., A T A T A T A T . . .), but it appears to be DNA nevertheless.

▽ To better simulate primitive conditions, imagine that we perform the same experiment, this time with neither the primer nor the enzyme. Now nothing perceptible happens. Why not? What is the function of the enzyme? These enzymes are catalysts which increase the rate, but not the direction, of a chemical reaction. This means that in the absence of DNA polymerase, appropriate nucleoside triphosphates will spontaneously join together, or polymerize, but on a much longer timescale than occurs in the presence of the enzyme. We do not now know what the rate of spontaneous polymerization of nucleoside triphosphates is, in the absence of the appropriate enzyme. Suppose it takes 1000 years. Clearly, such an experiment is not practicable to perform in the laboratory without the enzyme. In fact, the enzyme provides us with the laboratory tool we need. We can trade the enzyme for geological time.

▽ If the spontaneous polymerization of nucleoside triphosphates into nucleic acids takes much more than, say, 10^8 years, we can conclude that primitive nucleic acids did not arise by spontaneous polymerization of nucleoside phosphates. But if nucleic acids do polymerize spontaneously—in intervals short compared with geological time, if long compared with a human lifetime—we can circumvent an otherwise embarrassing problem: As we have mentioned in Chapter 14, proteins are made in contemporary biological systems only by nucleic acids. An enzyme such as DNA polymerase is a protein. So we need nucleic acids to make proteins, and proteins to make nucleic acids. One way onto this biological treadmill is the spontaneous synthesis of nucleic acids in the absence of proteins.

▽ Both some DNA and some RNA precursor nucleoside triphosphates have now been produced under simulated primitive conditions. We can imagine the origin of primitive nucleic acids by the spontaneous polymerization of ultraviolet-synthesized nucleoside triphosphates in a primeval body of water which contained some mineral catalyst such as magnesium. Once the first nucleic acid molecule is synthesized, subsequent syntheses would use it as a primer. A step towards exact nucleic acid self-replication—as occurs in contemporary biological systems—would have occurred on the ancient Earth. After the production of the first polynucleotide, subsequent generations of polynucleotides will mutate, either through interaction with light and with other molecules or "spontaneously." Some nucleoside triphosphates will be removed; others will be substituted for the deletions; in still other cases, short sequences of nucleoside triphosphates will be inverted. Eventually, we can anticipate that the primeval sea would be fairly full of a variety of self-replicating nucleic acids.

▽ If we now have understood in a general way the origin of the first self-replicating, mutating system, have we not also understood the origin of life? No, not quite. There is no way for these primitive nucleic acids to control their immediate environment in a way which enhances their continued replication. In contemporary cells, as we have seen in Chapter 14, there is an elaborate apparatus involving messenger RNA, adapter RNA, ribosomes, and a diversity of specialized enzymes all required for the nucleic acids to control the chemistry of the cell. We cannot imagine these complex and specific accessory molecules to have arisen spontaneously in the primitive environment. The apparatus for the transcription of the genetic code must itself have evolved slowly, through billions of years of evolution.

The major remaining problem in laboratory investigation of the origin of life is the origin of the genetic code. Perhaps nucleic acids are themselves weakly catalytic. Perhaps polynucleotides have a weak ability to order amino acids in a singlet code, rather than the contemporary triplet code. Since primitive nucleic acids would have been composed of four or so kinds of nucleoside triphosphates, this would mean that primitive proteins contained only about four amino acids. Yet the active site—the place on contemporary proteins where most of the catalytic effect occurs—often contains no more than four different kinds of amino acids. We should note that even very weak catalytic abilities will, through many generations, confer significant and perhaps decisive selective advantages on their owners.

▽ Much work has been done on the production of polypeptides from amino acids in simulated primitive environments. A wide range of combinations of amino acids are produced, more recently in aqueous solution. It is possible that the most prevalent varieties of these polypeptides have weak catalytic abilities useful for promoting further syntheses. But since, to the best of our knowledge, polypeptides are non-self-replicating, their spontaneous synthesis in the primitive environment cannot provide the answer to the fundamental questions of the origin of life.

▽ It is conceivable that the first self-replicating molecular system which was capable of evolution was not a nucleic acid, not RNA or DNA, but rather some molecule now biologically extinct, long since replaced by the more efficient self-replicating system involving the nucleic acids. But no evidence for such a molecule has been suggested, and few people support this view. On other planets, other molecules besides nucleic acids may be fundamental for self-replication, but terrestrial life, our only present example of life, seems oriented around nucleic acids and proteins.

▽ Once the problem of the interaction between primitive nucleic acids and primitive polypeptides is solved, it will be possible to state fairly that life has been synthesized in the laboratory. Not, of course, anything familiar, like an aardvark or an axolotl; merely a molecular system capable of self-replication, mutation, replication of its mutations, and some degree of environmental control. If we understand how such a molecular system came into being, we will have begun to understand the long evolutionary chain from the gases and waters of the primitive Earth to the origin of man.

▽ The laboratory synthesis of life, at least in the sense of a molecular system *capable* of evolution by natural selection, may be proved in a decade; some say it has already been accomplished. But if this is all there is to the origin of life, some may object, would not a race of self-replicating robots be alive? Certainly. If we can imagine an environment littered with mechanical arms and legs, transistors, cryogenic apparatus, and whatever other parts we require for a versatile robot, even today a robot can be developed which will use these parts to construct another identical robot. It would need an inheritable set of instructions on how to construct other robots. To be capable of evolution, a random or accidental change in the instructions would have to be incorporated in the next generation. This is, of course, analogous to the biological modus operandi, and such an analog could be

238   LIFE IN THE UNIVERSE

constructed mechanically. As time went on, provided the supply of spare parts did not run out, we would have a great increase in the number and diversity of robots.

▽ Now imagine that the supply of a particular building block—say, an arm—becomes exhausted. All the arms littering the landscape have already been used for robots. What happens? Robot reproduction will then grind to a halt, unless there is a mutation to rework, say, mechanical legs, which are still available, into the much-needed arms. In time, even the supply of legs will be exhausted. If a mutation were developed to make legs from another commodity in abundant supply—say, scrap automobile engines—and then the legs converted into arms, the robots with such an adaptation would, of course, preferentially reproduce. In time, perhaps, we would have an adaptation in which the robots would directly mine iron ore, convert the ore into scrap automobile engines, the automobile engines into legs, and the legs into arms. The most efficient sequence would be directly from ore to arm, but the robots are trapped by their history. Steps can be added only one at a time.

▽ The robots would then have developed a reaction chain analogous to the enzyme-intermediated reaction chains of contemporary biological systems. It was first suggested by the American geneticist Norman Horowitz, of the California Institute of Technology, that the origin of biochemical reaction chains occurred in a way similar to our fanciful robot analogy—that chemical building blocks, organic molecules, were made essentially "free," in the primitive environment, and then utilized by the first living systems. As the number of these living systems increased, the demand for certain critical molecular building blocks exceeded the supply. Those organisms which could use another common and previously untapped molecule and convert it into the desired building block clearly had a distinct selective advantage over their neighbors unable to effect such a transformation. As each required molecule becomes progressively depleted, another step in a long reaction chain must be added. The Horowitz hypothesis provides a neat and elegant understanding of the origin of complex biological reaction chains.

▽ If we imagine an ocean full of a variety of nucleic acids, each organizing its own short but useful reaction chain, utilizing ATP made by solar ultraviolet light at no cost to the organisms, we can see that we are well along towards the development of biological complexity. If, by chance, an aggregation of such nucleic acids were localized together, the interaction between them might be advantageous to both. Several methods are known by which such physical association might be managed. Figure 17–3 shows a number of "coacervates." In experiments which may possibly simulate conditions in the primitive oceans, the Dutch chemist H. G. Bungenburg de Jong found, in the 1930's, that there often is a spontaneous synthesis of objects in the $1-100\mu$ size range which are rich in colloidal organic matter on the inside, and clearly separated from the external environment on the outside. In some of these experiments, nucleic acids were concentrated in the interior of the co-acervate. △

A. I. Oparin believes that these coacervate droplets were, in essence, the first

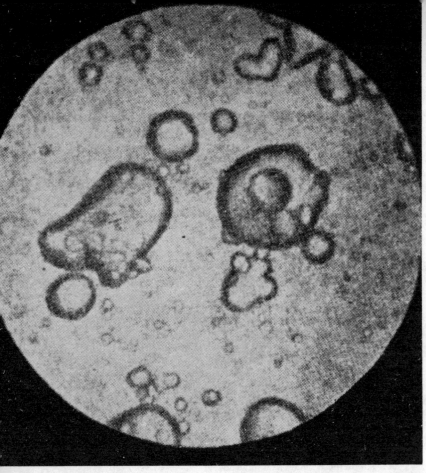

FIGURE 17–3. *Examples of coacervate systems with three components: gelatin, gum arabic, and RNA. (Taken from a publication by Prof. A. I. Oparin.)*

forms of life on Earth. They have a number of interesting properties. In particular, they can adsorb into their structure various simple organic molecules from the surrounding medium. Oparin believes that this is an elementary form of metabolism, an all-important property of life. He also states that the coacervate undergoes a process analogous to natural selection, which he describes in the following words:

> The coacervate droplets which were formed in the waters of the Earth found themselves immersed in a solution containing various organic materials and inorganic salts. These substances were adsorbed by the droplet, and entered into

LIFE IN THE UNIVERSE

chemical interactions with it. Thus, organic synthesis occurred. But in parallel was the process of decomposition. The rate of each of these processes, and of other processes, depended on the internal organization of the individual coacervate droplet. For a relatively long period of time, only those droplets could survive which possessed sufficient dynamic stability so that their rate of synthesis exceeded their rate of decomposition. If the rate of decomposition exceeded the rate of synthesis, those particles disappeared; such "poorly" organized particles played no role in the further development of living material.

We find it difficult to agree with Oparin that these coacervate droplets were the first forms of life on Earth. While the analogy between material exchange and metabolism is interesting, it hardly proves that coacervates were primitive living organisms. A fundamental property of living systems is self-replication, including the presence of a genetic code which transfers properties from generation to generation. Coacervates have no mechanism of inheritance. Oparin's hypothesis does not explain the transition from non-living to living systems.

▽ A possibly more relevant model of pre-cellular molecular enclaves are the microspheres of Sidney W. Fox [Figure 17–4]. The microspheres are made by heating and cooling synthetic polypeptides. The microspheres are far less complex than the superbly architectured bacterial cells [see Figure 14–1] which they resemble superficially; however, microspheres have considerably more stability than do the coacervates. They therefore provide some reason to believe that local enclaves of organic matter in the primitive oceans may have been common. We do not know in detail how such an enclave may have evolved into the contemporary cell, with its elaborate reproductive choreography. One promising possibility is that simple free-living organisms aggregated together into a loose cooperative arrangement, which slowly evolved into a smoothly interacting whole. It has recently been found that such cytoplasmic organelles as the chloroplasts (controlling photosynthesis), the mitochondria (controlling respiration), and the small bodies at the base of flagellae [see Chapter 14] all have their own DNA, different from that of the cell nucleus—suggesting their independent origins. The evolution of the cell clearly requires a long period of natural selection. But as we have seen in Chapter 16, the geological and paleontological evidence suggests about a billion years between the origin of life and the origin of the first cells.

▽ A characteristic property of molecules used in biological systems is that they tend to be asymmetric. What does molecular asymmetry mean? Suppose we were constructing gloves. We have material for the palm and the back of the hand, for the thumb, and for the four fingers. There are two ways of putting this material together. We can make a right-handed glove or a left-handed glove; the two kinds are not equivalent, as is evident when you try to put a right-hand glove on your left hand. Similarly, organic molecules, which fill three dimensions, are constructed in a variety of asymmetric and non-equivalent ways. Molecular asymmetry can be detected by optical rotation. If a beam of plane-polarized light is passed through a solution containing an asymmetric molecule, the plane of polarization will be rotated. If the plane of polarization is rotated towards the right, the molecule is

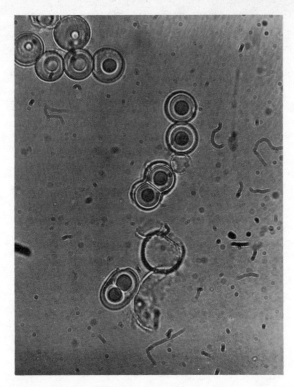

FIGURE 17–4. *Examples of microspheres of synthetic polypeptides produced by Prof. S. W. Fox and Dr. S. Yuyama, University of Miami. The twin aspect of some of these microspheres resembles cells in the process of division; however the microspheres do not always tend spontaneously to division. These twin forms were generally produced by pressing down on single microspheres with a microscope slide cover glass.* (*Courtesy of Prof. Fox.*)

said to have right-hand asymmetry, or to be "dextro-rotary" (abbreviated D). If the plane of polarization is rotated towards the left, the molecule is said to have left-hand asymmetry, or to be "levo-rotary" (abbreviated L). In either case, we say that the molecule is optically "active." Optical activity is therefore a measure of molecular asymmetry. No optical rotation at all can occur if the molecules in the solution are symmetric, or if there are equal numbers of levo-rotary and dextro-rotary molecules. A pair of molecules composed of just the same atoms but having opposite symmetries, like a left-hand and a right-hand glove, are known as "stereoisomers." A mixture of equal numbers of levo-rotary and dextro-rotary stereoisomers is known as a "racemic" mixture.

▽ In 1848, Louis Pasteur investigated the difference between tartaric acid, a dextro-rotary molecule, and racemic acid, a molecule which has the same apparent structure as tartaric acid—that is, the same atoms put together in the same way—but which is not optically active. In a brilliant series of experiments, Pasteur found that racemic acid was a mixture of the dextro-rotary tartaric acid and a previously unknown levo-rotary tartaric acid, which rotated the plane of polarization towards the left. Pasteur was able to separate microscopically the levo-rotary from the dextro-rotary crystals of racemic acid, and show that the two parts rotated the planes of polarization in opposite directions.

▽ We might expect that molecules used in living systems are racemic, that there are as many dextro-rotary as levo-rotary isomers. This is not the case. The molecules of living systems are characteristically optically active. In nature, we find only the D form of glucose. The cell walls of bacteria contain only the D isomer of amino acids, and the enzymes inside bacteria are made up only of the L amino acids. Why is optical activity such a common property of biological molecules? The enzymes in intermediate metabolism have a high degree of specificity; they catalyze only one set of reactants and no other. In fact, they often are able to distinguish between two stereoisomers, metabolizing, for example, D tartaric acid and not L tartaric acid. This has suggested that the enzymes work by forming a three-dimensional structure with the reactants in a kind of lock and key arrangement that brings the reactants together; then the enzyme goes in search of more reactants. Substantial evidence in support of this lock-and-key model of enzyme activity has appeared in recent years.

▽ For an organism to have enzymes which make one set of reactions work and not another, it must have a high degree of steric selectivity—that is, the enzyme must somehow be capable of distinguishing among various three-dimensional configurations of similar molecules. The American biochemist Lubert Stryor, of Stanford University, has pointed out that such steric selectivity for enzyme action will, in time, demand that a distinction be made among stereoisomers. We expect that a biochemistry without stereoisomerism is a primitive one, at best. Thus, the search for optical activity will be an important tool in any explorations for extraterrestrial life. If on Mars, for example, we find racemic mixtures of organic compounds, we will be tempted to conclude that biological evolution has not proceeded very far. If we find optical activity, it will be much more exciting, particularly if stereoisomers are found there which are different from the ones found here.

▽ But how did optical activity arise? In the experiments performed by Miller, Urey, and their successors, the synthesized organic molecules form a racemic mixture. Are there any mechanisms for abiological generation of asymmetric molecules? It is known that photochemical reactions involving polarized light can yield optically active products from racemic precursors; or a catalyst which is optically active, such as a quartz crystal, may yield optically active products; or finally, there may be a spontaneous reaction in the absence of optically active factors which nevertheless produces an optically active product. But none of these mechanisms can explain the origin of optical activity in biochemistry, because in the large each stereoisomer of a pair should be produced in equal amounts. The amount of left-hand polarized light striking the surface of the Earth is balanced by right-hand polarized light; the amount of left-asymmetric quartz equals the amount of right-asymmetric quartz; and the extent of spontaneous synthesis of levo-rotary compounds should be exactly balanced by the rate of synthesis of dextro-rotary compounds. It seems highly probable that the organic molecules synthesized on the primitive Earth at the time of the origin of life were not on the average optically active.

▽ Conceivably, optical activity in biochemistry is the result of natural selection. As enzyme systems and biochemical reaction chains developed, the three-dimensional specificity of the lock-and-key arrangement of enzymes and reactants must have improved. After a time, enzymes must have been capable of distinguishing levo-rotary from dextro-rotary stereoisomers. Let us imagine two organisms, one of which synthesizes L amino acids, and one of which synthesizes D amino acids, both from simpler precursors. Suppose, now, that for a reason entirely unconnected with amino acid stereoisomerism, the L amino acid synthesizer was slightly better adapted to its environment than the D amino acid synthesizer. After some generations have passed, the L amino acid synthesizers should dominate the biological landscape; after a while, the D amino acid synthesizers may become extinct. The descendants of this organism will continue to synthesize L amino acids, not because L amino acids have any intrinsic merit over D amino acids, but rather because L amino acids have been woven early into the fabric of life. If the prevalence of L amino acids in contemporary enzyme systems is such an historical accident, then the chance of finding D amino acids in any extraterrestrial enzymes should be 1 in 2. If, on the other hand, the investigations of extraterrestrial life forms show that L amino acids are predominant everywhere else, we will be forced to revise our beliefs on the origin of optical activity.

▽ We have, in this chapter, been discussing some of the chemical problems in the origin of life. Much of what we have said is speculative, for the fundamental reason that none of us was on the Earth at the time life arose. The best we can do, for the moment, is to invent a likely story and maximize its plausibility by laboratory investigation. But only by investigating living systems elsewhere will we be able to check our story with some rigor. Are extraterrestrial forms composed primarily of carbon, hydrogen, nitrogen, oxygen, phosphorus, and sulphur? How do they reproduce? Is the genetic material composed of nucleic acids? Are proteins their molecular catalysts? Are they arranged into cells? Are their molecules dextro-rotary or levo-rotary? Or racemic? We are on the threshold of these discoveries.

▽ The later evolution of life, by natural selection in response to the challenges of the environment, is increasingly well-documented in the fossil record. There is a general trend, as time progresses, towards enhanced complexity. Yet there is no reason to suspect any urge or desire towards complexity by the evolving organisms. We have seen that those mutants in the primitive environment which led to improved survival and replication of nucleic acids prospered; other molecular systems perished in enormous numbers. There is, accordingly, a sense in which the evolution of the cell, and all subsequent evolution up to man, may be viewed as a device for maintaining the continued survival of the nucleic acids. There is a sense in which our instincts and desires, our loves and hates, our breathing, eating, sleeping and dying exist because they help ensure the continued existence of the molecules of our genetic material; a sense in which we are fundamentally ambulatory repositories for our nucleic acids. Whether we like it or not this is at least in part what human beings are for; because of our intelligence we are more than this—but it is an open question how much more. △

18

Is there life
on Earth?

We approach now the only planet in which man is certainly known to exist, and which ought to have an interest for us superior to any which we have yet seen, for it is our own. We are voyagers on it through space, it has been said, as passengers on a ship, and many of us have never thought of any part of the vessel but the cabin where we are quartered. Some curious passengers (these are the geographers) have visited the steerage, and some (the geologists) have looked under the hatches, and yet it remains true that those in one part of our vessel know little, even now, of their fellow-voyagers in another. How much less, then, do most of us know of the ship itself, for we were all born on it, and have never once been off it to view it from the outside!

Samuel Pierpont Langley, *The New Astronomy* (1891)

∇ The origin of life seems to be an incidental adjunct to the early development of a planetary surface. We have seen that only very general conditions—a reducing atmosphere of approximately cosmic abundance, and bodies of liquid water—are required for the large-scale production of complex organic molecules. Judging from the history of the Earth, if such conditions prevail for only a few hundred million years, the origin of life seems to be probable. For all we know, much shorter periods of time are adequate. $\triangle$

It is believed that during the early days of the formation of our solar system, many of the physical and chemical conditions on the terrestrial planets (Mercury, Venus, Earth, and Mars) were similar. These planets, it is assumed, were all formed from the same solar nebula of gas and dust, and their early chemical compositions were very nearly identical. Thus, we would expect that the conditions which brought about the origin of life on Earth would also have been present on the other terrestrial planets.

∇ However, there are other factors to consider besides a common initial environment. If the surface temperatures are too high, common organic molecules will be thermally dissociated as fast as they are produced; and no liquid medium will be available as a solvent for early chemical interactions, and as a shield against primitive ultraviolet radiation. If surface temperatures are too low, familiar chemical reactions will proceed at insignificant rates; and any liquid medium will freeze and hence be unavailable. The freezing point of water can be lowered by adding salts to the solution. Thus, a reasonable range for liquid water as the medium for a living system, and for a reasonable stability and rate of reaction of familiar organic chemicals is between $-50°C$ and $+100°C$. Since the temperatures on the bright side of Mercury, for example, are much higher than this, there is some basis for a provisional exclusion of life there.

∇ Another factor is the temperature of the exosphere, the level from which molecules escape to space. If the exosphere temperature is very high, then the rate of escape of a planetary atmosphere would be very high. Its reducing atmosphere would be retained for a very short period of time, and there would be an inadequate period available for the origin of life. We have already discussed this point in Chapter 15, in connection with panspermia developing on possible planets of other stars. Mercury, again, has such a low mass and high exosphere temperature that any primitive reducing atmosphere which it may once have had departed into space very early in its history. In low-temperature environments, more exotic biochemistries may be possible. Liquid ammonia or hydrocarbon solutions may replace water as a solvent sysem, and silicon compounds might replace carbon compounds as structural biochemicals.

▽ Our knowledge of planetary environments permits us provisionally to exclude Mercury and the surface of the Moon as possible abodes of life; probably, also, Venus, the asteroids, and most of the other moons in the solar system. But in applying such a priori negative judgments, we must be very careful that we are not deceived by terrestrial analogy. On other worlds there may be chemistries and living systems which we cannot even imagine. The best approach is observational, not deductive.

▽ How easy would it be to detect, from a remote observation platform, living systems on the Earth? The mass of the Earth is 6×10^{27} gm; the mass of the atmosphere is 5×10^{21} gm. Yet the mass of biological material on the surface of the Earth is only a few times 10^{17} gm, according to the best recent estimates; less than 0.01 percent of the mass of the *air,* and some 10^{-8} percent of the mass of the Earth. Thus, for all our feelings of self-importance, we are only a kind of biological rust, clinging to the surface of our small planet, and weighing far less than the invisible air which surrounds us. Yet we have tamed and reworked the surface of our planet, altered its character, and are in the process of leaving it for distant parts. Are our activities, obvious to us, noticeable from a distant vantage point? Would our presence be detected? △

To appreciate the situation in which the Earthbound astronomer finds himself, let us imagine that we are Martian astronomers in a Martian observatory. Our equipment includes the most modern astronomical instruments currently available on Earth. From our splendidly equipped observatory, let us ask the question: Is there life on Earth?

The planet Earth, as seen in the Martian sky, would appear as a very bright star, only slightly less brilliant than Venus appears from the Earth. Just as we can see the planet Venus going through phases like those of the Moon, so could the hypothetical Martian astronomer observe the phases of the Earth. ▽ Since the Earth would appear in the Martian sky, at a greater angle from the Sun than Venus does in ours, it would be easier to observe the Earth from Mars than Venus from the Earth. The Earth would appear as a morning or evening "star," low in the Martian sky. Because of the phases, it would be impossible to see a place on the Earth near the middle of the day, local time, except when the Earth was a great distance from Mars, on the other side of the Sun. △

Could the engineering works of men be observed from a Martian observatory? Dams, reservoirs, cities—would they be detectable? ▽ Because of the turbulence in the Earth's atmosphere, even the largest of our telescopes, the 200-inch Hale reflector at Mt. Palomar, California, is capable of photographing detail no smaller than about 300 km across on Mars. The Martian atmosphere is much thinner than Earth's, and it is possible that resolution by an observatory on Mars would be less limited by the Martian atmosphere. The smallest feature on Earth visible from Mars might be only kilometers across.

▽ The Earth has by now been photographed many times from space. A systematic program for photography of the Earth has been undertaken in the United States in the Tiros and Nimbus series of satellites, to chart cloud formation,

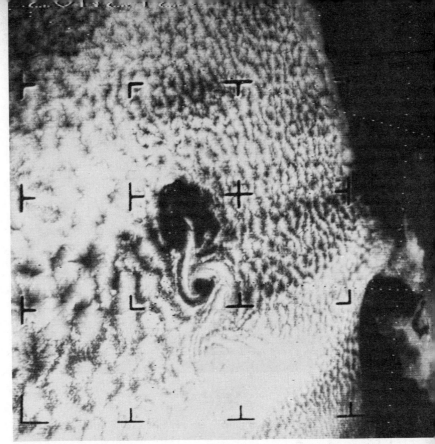

FIGURE 18–1. Nimbus 1 photograph of a cloud eddy pattern over Guadalupe and Baja California, 14 September, 1964. (Courtesy of Goddard Space Flight Center, NASA.)

movement, and dissipation, in an attempt to improve weather prediction. While the cameras on such satellites are not designed for life-detection, we may use them for such purposes. Photographs of the Earth taken from Tiros and Nimbus satellites sometimes show cloud covers as patterned and provocative as that of Figure 18–1. When there are breaks in the clouds, views of the Earth's surface, such as those in Figures 18–2 and 18–3, can be obtained. Figure 18–2 shows the eastern seaboard of the United States from Chesapeake Bay to Cape Cod. Figure 18–3 shows the southern tip of India and the island of Ceylon. The regions depicted in these photographs are among the most heavily populated and densely vegetated areas of the Earth; yet even close inspection shows no sign of life at all. New York appears deserted; India and Ceylon appear barren. These conclusions

FIGURE 18–2. *Tiros 7 photograph of the eastern seaboard of the United States, 23 June, 1963. (Courtesy of Goddard Space Flight Center, NASA.)*

have been repeated hundreds of times in close investigation of Tiros photographs of populated regions of the Earth: when the resolution is no better than a few kilometers, there is no sign of life on Earth.

▽ Altogether, there have been several hundred thousand photographs taken and examined in the Tiros series. On some of these photographs, objects as small as 2000 feet across are discernible. Yet in all of these photographs, only one— Figure 18–4—shows any clear sign of life on Earth. This is a photograph taken by Tiros 2 of the forest near the Canadian logging town of Cochrane, Ontario, on 4 April, 1961. In the upper left part of the picture, several wide parallel stripes can be seen; and at right angles to them, another set. Swaths one mile across had been cut through the Canadian forest by the loggers. The swaths were separated by about two miles. After the swaths had been made, snow fell, enhancing the contrast between the trees still standing and the treeless swaths. But even here, on this one-in-a-million photograph, do we have unambiguous signs of life, from the vantage point of Mars? Can the Martians imagine no geological process which could make such a pattern? Even here, with resolutions better than

LIFE IN THE UNIVERSE

FIGURE 18-3. *Tiros 5 photograph of southern India and Ceylon, 6 March, 1963.* (*Courtesy of Goddard Space Flight Center, NASA.*)

the Martians could reasonably have, there is no rigorous proof of life on Earth.

▽ My colleagues and I have made a study of the higher resolution photographs available from the Nimbus satellite. With resolutions of a few tenths of a kilometer, we have discovered a recently completed highway in Tennessee, perhaps a jet contrail in the Davis Straits, the wake of a ship in the Red Sea, but also a very straight feature off the northern coast of Morocco which had all the apparent signs of intelligent design, but was, in fact, a natural peninsula. At a few tenths of a

IS THERE LIFE ON EARTH?   251

FIGURE 18-4. *Tiros 2 photograph of the region of Cochrane, Ontario, Canada, taken on 4 April, 1961. (Courtesy of Goddard Space Flight Center, NASA.)*

kilometer resolution the signs of intelligent life on Earth can be detected but not unambiguously. Convincing photographic evidence of intelligent life on Earth requires resolution of 10 meters or better. △

Could the night-time illumination of the largest cities of the Earth—New York, Moscow, Tokyo, Paris, London, Chicago—be detected? Let us assume that the artificial illumination from one of our largest cities is, on the average, ten times greater than the illumination it receives from the full moon, and is confined to a region 10 km square. Then there is a bare possibility that the Martian astronomer observing the night hemisphere of the Earth could see a tiny speck of light, of about 16th magnitude. In reality, however, due to the scattering of sunlight from the illuminated hemisphere of the Earth, the Martian astronomer would be at best only marginally able to detect such a weak signal. ▽ Another factor which tends to make our largest cities invisible from above is smog. It seems that whenever a city becomes large enough so that its night-time illumination might be observable from Mars, the city also generates enough industrial pollution, even at night, so that the city becomes invisible. The American astronaut M. Scott Carpenter was able to observe mountain trails and smoke from chimneys when over Tibet; but when orbiting over Southern California, he could find no sign of the city of Los Angeles. △

Nuclear explosions which unfortunately sometimes occur on the planet Earth could be seen from Mars as short-lived, very bright flashes of light. Nevertheless, since nuclear weapons tests occur only infrequently, and since the resulting flash is itself visible for only a brief moment, it is highly improbable that such explosions would be detected from Mars. If a special program were initiated for synoptic observations of the Earth, perhaps nuclear explosions could be observed reliably. However, it seems unlikely that the civilized Martian astronomer could deduce from these short-lived flashes of light that life—to say nothing of intelligent life—existed on Earth. Even we who live on Earth can hardly consider these barbarous experiments, which could lead to the destruction of life on our beautiful world, as manifestations of intelligence!

With an optical telescope, an astronomer on Mars might be able to detect seasonal color variations over a vast area of the Earth's surface. ▽ There are major seasonal color and brightness changes in deciduous forests, and in areas with cultivated crops, such as the Ukraine, or the American Midwest. △ With these observations in hand, a wide range of explanations could be imagined. ▽ Perhaps there are crystals in some regions of the Earth whose color depends on temperature, or whose darkness depends upon humidity. Or perhaps they are due to life of some sort on Earth. △ But it seems unlikely that the Martian astronomer could *reliably* conclude that the seasonal color variations are of biological origin.

If the Earth were regularly observed over a period of several decades, major transformations of the surface might be noticed—for example, the systematic destruction of the forests. But could the Martian astronomer draw definitive conclusions from these observations? ▽ Similar major and systematic "secular" variations can be observed on the surface of Mars, as we shall see in Chapter 20. △ In themselves, such variations are very interesting, but certainly cannot be considered irrefutable proof of the presence of life. A number of such variations have been reported for the moon (although they were on a smaller scale), but the surface of the moon is almost certainly devoid of life.

▽ Extensive spectroscopic measurements of the Earth could be made from a Martian observatory. In a search for life, spectral bands in the infrared, which are due to absorption by surface organic matter, might be sought. But unfortunately, such bands at 3.5μ and longer wavelengths must, for existing equipment, be seen in reflected light to be detected. The light transmitted from the Earth to Mars in wavelengths longer than 3.5μ is mostly infrared energy radiated from the Earth, and not sunlight reflected from it. The Martian astronomer would find it difficult to detect spectroscopic signs of surface organic matter.

▽ Some minor atmospheric constituents which are of biological origin, such as CH_4 and N_2O, might be identified. Methane is a highly reduced gas, and must be continually produced in the Earth's atmosphere, so that the total amount is not depleted by oxidation. The methane in the Earth's atmosphere is produced primarily by methane bacteria, which convert organic compounds into CO_2 and CH_4. The methane bacteria live in mud at the bottoms of ponds, where there is much organic matter and the conditions are anaerobic. Hence, CH_4 is often called "marsh gas." Similar bacteria also live in the rumens of cows and other ungulates. Accordingly, one of the major sources of methane in the terrestrial atmosphere is bovine flatulence. The identification of methane in the Earth's atmosphere from a Martian vantage point would thus be a very significant observation, if only the Martian astronomer knew how to interpret it. But it seems unlikely that the appropriate interpretation would be forthcoming.

▽ What about methane in the atmospheres of the Jovian planets? The Soviet astronomer G. A. Tikhov proposed that methane on Jupiter has the same source as methane on Earth, leading to the conclusion that there must be at least Jovian bacteria, if not Jovian cows. Since we have seen [Chapters 4 and 16] that methane is a constituent of primordial planetary atmospheres, we need not take this suggestion very seriously. It does, however, emphasize the difficulties in connecting the presence of a simple molecule with biological activity. △

Nearly all of the free oxygen in the Earth's atmosphere is a product of plant photosynthesis. The main source of oxygen is not the higher plants, but rather marine plankton, which fill the oceans. ▽ The crust of the Earth is underoxidized —that is, it is capable of further chemical reaction with atmospheric oxygen. △ If it were not for the continuous production of oxygen by biological activity, it would vanish from the atmosphere within a relatively brief span of years. If the amount of free oxygen in a planetary atmosphere is so small that it can be detected only at the very limits of instrumental sensitivity, then its presence might be explained by abiological hypotheses. But such a vast amount of oxygen as is present in the Earth's atmosphere can be explained only in terms of extensive biological activity. ▽ Yet we can make two reservations here. It is conceivable that an extensive oxygen atmosphere could be produced by photodissociation of water [see Chapter 16]. In addition, I wonder whether an intelligent anaerobic organism, who finds oxygen a poison gas, would conclude very readily that an extensive oxygen atmosphere can only be the product of biological activity. △

▽ If Martian astronomers had an instrument which permitted very sensitive examination of the visible spectrum of the Earth at one wavelength of light, they would have observed an apparent major increase in the abundance of such gases as neon, argon, mercury, and sodium in the spectrum of the night sky of the Earth over the past few decades. Whether they would attribute this change to instrumental error, improvements in terrestrial illumination engineering, or an imminent catastrophe is a matter of conjecture.

▽ Routine spectroscopic measurements of the Earth would reveal the presence of quantities of oxygen and water on the Earth that are enormous, especially when compared with Mars. Our temperatures would seem uncomfortably high, and the absence of ultraviolet light from the surface would be noted. It is quite possible that the Martian scientists, arguing from Martian analogy, would conclude that with no convincing evidence for life on Earth, and with such an unpromising environmental inventory, further searches for life on Earth should be abandoned. △

However, there is another method which might be used to detect life on Earth. Let us assume that there are Martian observatories equipped with a modern radiotelescope—an instrument which permits us to detect, measure, and record the radio emission from various celestial objects. The Martian astronomer, like his Earthly counterpart, would investigate the radio emissions of the planets. ▽ He would find that Venus is a radio source, probably because its surface is hot; that Jupiter is a radio source, because the electrons in its magnetic field are emitting synchrotron radiation; and so forth. △ Turning his radiotelescope to Earth, however, he would make an amazing discovery: at meter wavelengths, the otherwise unassuming planet Earth emits almost the same power of radio radiation as does the sun in a period of low sunspot activity! ▽ A planet as bright as a star! △ In the meter wave band, the Earth radiates a million times more radiation than Venus or Mercury. This discovery could be made on Mars by using only a modest radiotelescope.

Further investigation would show that different regions on the surface of our planet radiate unequally; a periodic relation would be found between the intensity of radio emission and the rotation of the Earth on its axis. For example, when Africa or South and Central Asia were facing Mars, the radio intensity would fall sharply; when Europe and North America were facing Mars, the power emitted would sharply increase. If observations had been continued over a long period of time, the Martian astronomer could make an even more astounding discovery— today the Earth is emitting radio radiation which is 10^6 times more intense than what it emitted a few decades ago. ▽ The Martian scientists would perhaps attempt a "natural" explanation for the phenomenon; such attempts would eventually prove unsuccessful. △ The clever Martian astronomers would come to realize that the radio emission could not be explained by the action of natural forces, but could only be produced by artificial means. They would conclude that intelligent life exists on Earth—a remarkable discovery indeed.

Several thousand television transmitters exist on the Earth. If we take into account the average power of each transmitter (approximately 20 kilowatts), the frequency bandwidth emitted, the average operating period of each transmitter (say, 6 hours out of every 24), and the fact that all wavelengths in television transmission (1.5–6.0 meters) pass unobstructed through the atmospheres of the Earth and Mars, we can calculate the power transmitted from Earth to Mars.

Radio astronomers may be interested to know that the so-called "brightness temperature" of the Earth at television wavelengths is some hundreds of millions of degrees. This is 100 times greater than the radio brightness of the sun at comparable wavelengths, during a period of low sunspot activity. In addition to television transmitters, there are a large number of radio stations, and other installations which emit radiation strongly in the ultra-high frequency wavelength range. ▽ The United States' Ballistic Missile Early Warning System (BMEWS) would, some years ago, every now and then, detect the moon on its radar screens.

▽ We have presented this fantasy of a Martian observatory investigating the Earth because it illustrates the actual difficulties and potential triumphs of remote investigations of planetary biology. If the hypothetical Martians could not find any sign of life on Earth except at radio frequencies, it should not surprise us that unambiguous, indisputable, rigorous evidence for life on Mars is not yet forthcoming. Such searches as have been made for intelligible radio transmission from Mars have yielded entirely negative results. The radio emission from Mars is the random noise of thermal emission. △

In the example of radio emission from Earth, we have encountered for the first time, the cosmic implications of the biological activity of intelligent beings. Due to the presence of a technical civilization on our planet, there has been a drastic modification of an important feature of the Earth as seen from afar—the nature and power of its radio emission. ▽ Arduous work by an extraterrestrial astronomer could probably convince him that the signals have intelligible content (despite the quality of many television programs). △ The Earth has become strikingly different from all the other planets in our solar system. An essential attribute of intelligent life is that sooner or later its activity will attain a cosmic character. In Part III of this book, we shall elaborate this possibility.

Does the absence of strong, nonthermal, and intelligible radio emission from Mars imply, in itself, that there are no highly developed life forms on that planet? Generally speaking, no. Much of the radiation associated with television transmission is dissipated into space. Perhaps the radio emission from Mars is not sufficiently powerful to reach the Earth. It is natural to assume that as technical civilizations become more advanced, less wasteful methods of utilizing electromagnetic energy will be devised. Electromagnetic waves will probably be focused into tight, discrete beams, and scattering of this energy away from the intended source will be minimized. ▽ Thus, if a Martian civilization is somewhat more advanced than our own, it may have devised economical means of electromagnetic communication which do not permit eavesdropping from Earth. Nevertheless, if a civilization exists on Mars which is substantially in advance of our own, it is surprising that we have no sign of its existence (although if they have monitored *our* television transmission, perhaps we have some clue to their absence!).

▽ The American radio astronomer Frank Drake of Cornell University has pointed out that no serious search for narrow band radio transmission from Mars has actually been carried out. Mars has been observed with broad-band receivers, to measure its subsurface temperatures, but searches for intelligible signals have been carried out, at best, unofficially and unsystematically. On the other hand, Drake argues, the likelihood for success of such a program is probably small. If the Martians were as much as 50 years ahead of us, we should (with the reservations noted above) have had some other signs of their existence. If they are as much as 50 years behind us, they are incapable of radio transmission. These estimates are based on terrestrial analogy, and assume that the almost discontinuous recent advances in our technical civilization are characteristic of civilizations elsewhere. We certainly do not know that this is the case; on the other hand, it is the most reasonable assumption we can make—there are no known counterexamples! Since both the Earth and Mars have existed for 5×10^9 years, the probability of a successful search for intelligible Martian radio emission is $50/(5 \times 10^9) = 10^{-8}$, or a millionth of a percent. Thus, in budgeting no time for such investigations of Mars, the directors of radio observatories have probably chosen wisely. Yet because of the interest of the search, it will not be surprising if occasional moments are stolen informally, between observing programs, to peer, with an amalgam of wistfulness and hope, at distant Mars. △

19

The planet Mars

. . . I am apt to believe that the Land in Mars is of a blacker Colour than that of Jupiter or the Moon, which is the reason of his appearing of a Copper Colour, and his reflecting a weaker Light than is proportionable to his distance from the Sun. . . . His Light and Heat is twice, and sometimes three times less than ours, to which I suppose the Constitution of his Inhabitants is answerable.

Christianus Huygens, *New Conjectures Concerning the Planetary Worlds, Their Inhabitants and Productions* (c. 1670)

▽ We now come to discuss our enigmatic planetary neighbor Mars, which seems to provide the best opportunity, in the immediate future, for the study of extraterrestrial life. In this chapter we will discuss the physical environment of Mars and the possibility that life could have come into being in the ancient Martian past and survived to the present day. In the following chapter we will discuss the observational evidence which has suggested more directly that Mars may harbor life, and the experiments which have been planned for future programs of Martian exploration.

▽ Seen for the first time through a telescope, Mars is a disappointing sight. You see an orange-buff or ochre colored disk of varying brightness and flickering visibility, swimming erratically across the telescope's field of view. The evanescent, will-o'-the-wisp appearance of Mars is due to "seeing," erratic atmospheric motions near the base of the Earth's atmosphere which change the directions of photons journeying from Mars to Earth and thereby distort the image of Mars which we see in reflected sunlight. To obtain a better image of the Martian surface, we should construct our observatory at higher altitudes, leaving the bulk of the atmospheric turbulence below us. The best visual and photographic observations of Mars have been made from telescopes situated on high, usually isolated, mountain peaks. Among the best observatories for studying Mars are those in the American Southwest, and at the Pic du Midi, in the French Pyrenees. There we find that the image of Mars is much more steady, and we can make out surface details quite clearly. Yet Mars never appears so large that it fills the entire field of view of the telescope. Generally, it appears as a small orange disk, with an angular diameter no larger than a modest-sized lunar crater.

▽ If we carry out observations over a period of time, we find that some of the surface features are disappearing over the west edge, or "limb," of Mars, and that others are appearing over the east limb. We are observing the planet's rotation. In time, we see familiar features reappearing at the east limb; we have observed a complete rotation. Mars rotates once about its axis every 24 hours and 37 minutes, just 41 minutes longer than the period of the Earth's rotation. The rotation of Mars can be seen in parts A, B, and C of Figure 19–1. The feature in the center of the disk in view A is Sinus Meridiani, which has disappeared over the eastern limb of the planet in view C. By observing the rotation of Mars, we can demarcate the Martian equator, and therefore, the axis of rotation. The Martian axis of rotation is inclined about 24 ° to the perpendicular to the plane of its orbit. The inclination of the Earth's axis of rotation is $23\frac{1}{2}$ °. Because the Martian period of rotation is similar to ours, Mars has a familiar day-night cycle. Since the axes of rotation of the two planets have such similar inclinations, the seasons on Earth and Mars have quite

259

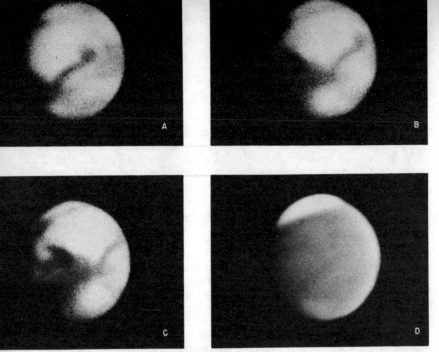

FIGURE 19-1. *Four photographs of Mars. Contrary to the usual astronomical convention, south is here at the bottom. Figures A, B, and C are taken in red light and illustrate the rotation of the planet. Figure D is taken in blue light, and illustrates the absence of surface detail in the blue and violet, a phenomenon known as the blue haze. (Courtesy of Mt. Wilson and Palomar Observatories.)*

similar forms. No one knows why the periods of rotation and the axial inclinations of Earth and Mars are so nearly identical. It may be merely a coincidence, or it may indicate some deeper connection between Earth and Mars, dating to the time of the origin of the solar system.

▽ Because Mars is about 50 percent further from the Sun, on the average, than is the Earth, its year is much longer—about 687 of our days. Thus, while winter lasts for the same fraction of the year on Mars as it does on Earth, its actual duration is almost 200 days—a long and, as we shall see, very cold winter indeed.

▽ Observing Mars under superior seeing conditions [Figure 19–2], we can make out three general regions: brilliant white polar caps; generally neutral gray dark areas, often concentrated in the equatorial regions; and the buff or orange ochre-colored bright areas, which give Mars its ruddy hue. The polar caps, which wax and wane with the seasons, are at least in part a form of thin and loosely packed water ice known as hoarfrost. This identification is based on a variety of independent lines of argument. Just as spectral absorption lines are formed when light passes

260

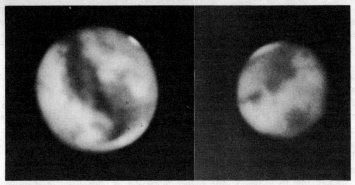

FIGURE 19-2. *Two photographs of Mars taken at the Observatoire du Pic du Midi in the 1940's. These pictures illustrate the wealth of surface detail which can be photographed under excellent seeing conditions. The photograph at left, taken during late spring on Mars, shows a very small southern polar cap. The triangular shaped region in the lower right is Syrtis Major. Above it and to its left are Mare Tyrrhenum and Mare Cimmerium. At the right, a photograph taken during late fall, we see a fairly extensive southern polar cap. The region to the bottom right is Mare Acidalium. Directly above it at the top of the picture is Solis Lacus. (Courtesy of Dr. A. Dollfus and the Meudon Documentation Center of the International Astronomical Union.)*

through an absorbing gas [see Chapter 4], so are absorption bands formed when light is reflected off a solid. In reflection, the light actually penetrates a small distance into the solid, and those wavelengths which correspond to the characteristic absorption wavelengths of the material are subtracted from the reflected light. Ice has a characteristic reflection spectrum in the near infrared which is matched by the near infrared reflection spectrum of the Martian polar caps.

▽ When sunlight is reflected off a solid, it tends to acquire a characteristic polarization, not as pronounced as in synchrotron emission [see Chapter 7], but nevertheless detectable. The polarization of sunlight reflected off the Martian polar caps is exactly matched by the reflection of sunlight off hoarfrost in the laboratory. Finally, the brightness of the polar caps is consistent with the brightness of hoarfrost. Thus, even a quick glance at Mars through a modest telescope under good seeing conditions shows the polar ice cap, and the polar ice cap suggests there is water on Mars. Since we have found water to be intimately involved with terrestrial life processes, this simple observation justifies some first hope that Mars may also have its own biology. More recent evidence suggests that the caps may also contain frozen carbon dioxide.

▽ Two stages in the regression of the northern polar cap of Mars can be seen in Figure 19–3, two drawings re-sketched as if we were looking down on the polar cap. The two views are about two Earth months apart, during northern Martian spring. We see that as the cap retreats towards the pole, small islands of hoarfrost are left behind. It has been suggested that these regions are elevations, which hold the hoarfrost longer because they are at higher and colder altitudes. One such locale,

THE PLANET MARS   261 where the hoarfrost is regularly left behind, is called the Mountains of Mitchell. However, elevations are not necessarily colder, on Mars, and these areas may be colder simply because they reflect more sunlight.

▽ From the rate of regression of the Martian polar caps in local spring, we can compute the thickness of the caps. We know how much sunlight is striking the caps, and how much of it is absorbed by the ice. This sunlight tends to heat the ice and make it evaporate. A very thick ice cap would appear to shrink very slowly; a thin ice cap, rapidly. For the amount of sunlight available, the ice cap regresses at a rather rapid rate; this permits us to conclude that the thickness of the cap is generally about a centimeter or less. All the water in the ice cap, if melted, would perhaps fill the Great Lakes of North America. Thus, while the caps may indicate the existence of water on Mars, they do not point to very large amounts.

▽ Actually, there seems little chance that lakes of pure water exist on Mars.

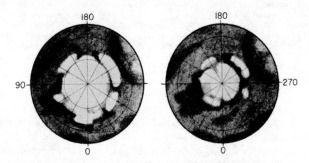

FIGURE 19–3. Two phases in the average seasonal development of the northern polar ice cap. These drawings are based on observations in the 1946, 1948, 1950, and 1952 oppositions. (Courtesy of Dr. A. Dollfus.)

In order for a liquid to form at a given temperature, the atmospheric pressure must exceed a certain value. The atmosphere provides a kind of lid over the body of water. In a vacuum, the water would vaporize almost instantly. The total atmospheric pressure on Mars, discussed below, is so small that no effective lid is available to keep a pool of water liquid. Instead, if ice on Mars is heated, it will turn directly into water vapor; just as on Earth, under atmospheric pressure, we can observe that dry ice (frozen carbon dioxide), when heated, is converted into gaseous CO_2. But we never observe liquid CO_2 at 1 atm pressure.

▽ There is other evidence for the absence of open bodies of water on Mars. At certain angles of observation, we should see a bright image of the Sun reflected off the mirror-like surfaces of the hypothetical Martian lakes; despite much searching, no such image has ever been seen. We can conclude with some confidence, then, that no open pools of pure water exist on Mars.

▽ While the polar caps wax and wane with the seasons, the bright and dark areas of Mars generally maintain their relative configurations. Figure 19–4 is a

LIFE IN THE UNIVERSE

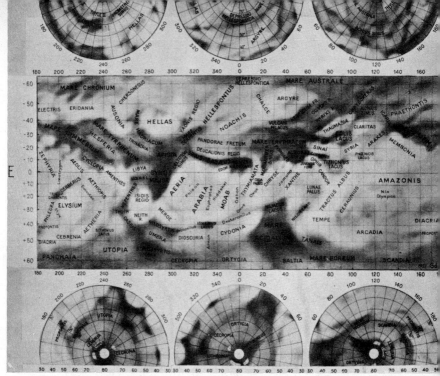

FIGURE 19-4. *The International Astronomical Union Mars cartography. Illustrated in this map are only those features which have been photographed during several recent oppositions. The smallest features depicted are some hundreds of kilometers across.*

map of Mars in mercator projection, like many maps of the Earth. The vertical scale shows latitude; the horizontal scale shows longitude. Because astronomical telescopes invert images, astronomers tend to think of south as being "up," a convention which is followed in this map. The features shown and named are those which have been repeatedly photographed, year after year. Under the best seeing conditions, observers of Mars have noted that the dark areas seem actually to be composed of many very dark spots, now referred to as the dark nuclei [Figure 19–5]. When the seeing conditions are not excellent, the dark nuclei appear smeared together, and we see Mars roughly as it appears in the map in Figure 19–4. There are other more elusive features, which have not been photographed but which can be seen visually through a large telescope under good seeing conditions. These we shall describe later.

▽ Around the turn of the century, the Martian bright and dark areas were given names, usually of Latin or Greek origin and sometimes with copious allusions to classical antiquity. Thus, Mare Erythraeum is the "Red Sea," although it is neither red nor a sea; Hellespontus is "The Greek Bridge," though neither in fact;

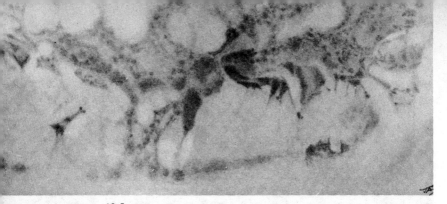

Solis Lacus is "The Lake of the Sun"; Sinus Meridiani is "Meridian Bay" because the zero meridian of Mars, corresponding to the meridian of Greenwich on Earth, passes through it. This is, of course, a terrestrial convention; Martian cartographers, if any, will have other conventions. And as a hopeful augury for the future, at 250° longitude, +55° north latitude is a locale that many have been seeking. It is an arresting thought that these unearthly places with strange names—Trivium Charontis, Tithonius Lacus, Thoth-Nepenthes—places until now observed only with large telescopes over immense distances, will, one day in the lives of most of us, be trod by men.

▽ While the general configurations of the bright and dark areas have, with a few exceptions, remained fixed for decades, we sometimes see a transient incursion of a bright area into a dark. It is as if a small piece of dark area becomes eaten away, replaced with buff-colored material typical of the bright areas. The incursion may continue, obscuring large fractions of the dark areas. There is every reason to believe that such incursions are great dust storms. The polarization of the light reflected from the bright areas indicates that they are covered with innumerable small, opaque particles. The incursions of bright areas into dark have just the same polarization properties as the bright areas. We conclude that the bright areas of Mars are vast deserts, and that occasionally the winds carry large amounts of desert material over the dark areas, temporarily obscuring them from our view. In 1956, a dust storm of planet-wide proportions was observed; for about a month it obscured almost all detail on the planet. Yet even after the most striking of these dust storms, the winds subside and the dark areas reappear. If the dark areas are at higher elevations than the bright areas, we can understand how they can be obscured by a dust storm, and later, scoured by the winds, reappear to the view of the astronomer on Earth. Recently the American astronomer James Pollack and I have found radar evidence suggesting that the dark areas are at systematically higher elevations than the bright deserts.

▽ The polarization of the light reflected from the bright areas not only tells us that the bright areas are covered with dust; it also tells us something of the composition of this dust. Of hundreds of terrestrial minerals examined in the laboratory, only one shows the same polarization properties as the Martian bright areas—a mineral called limonite. Each molecule of limonite is an iron oxide polyhydrate—that is, a compound of iron and oxygen, Fe_2O_3, which has several molecules of water loosely bound to it. Limonite explains both the polarization properties of the Martian deserts and their color and brightness.

▽ The dark areas of Mars have also been examined polarimetrically and spectroscopically. The polarization of light reflected from the dark areas shows them also to be covered by or composed of small, opaque particles, which are even more opaque than the already very dark particles in the Martian deserts. Pollack and I believe that larger particles of limonite, several tenths of a millimeter across, can also account for the polarizing properties and the darkness of the dark areas. In general, larger particles are darker. The nature of the Martian dark areas carries us directly to the question of the possible existence of life on Mars, but we wish first to describe some other features of the Martian environment.

▽ Just as we saw, in Chapters 3 and 4, how the physical conditions in the stars could be determined from the light they emitted, so the physical conditions of planetary atmospheres and surfaces can be partially deduced from an examination of the sunlight that they reflect and the infrared and radio radiation that they emit. Sunlight which is reflected off the Martian surface passes twice, at a slant angle, through the Martian atmosphere. The molecules in the Martian atmosphere preferentially remove the sunlight at their respective absorption wavelengths, and the reflection spectrum of Mars contains lines and bands, just as does the emission spectrum of a star [Chapter 4]. In this way, the gases CO_2 and H_2O have been identified in the Martian atmosphere. The amount of water vapor in the atmosphere is roughly equal to the amount of water locked as hoarfrost in the polar caps. It is about 0.1 percent of the amount of water vapor in our own atmosphere. On the other hand, the amount of carbon dioxide in the Martian atmosphere is much larger than in the Earth's atmosphere—perhaps thirty times more, although the exact figure is still in question. Oxygen has been searched for unsuccessfully. If it is present at all, it exists as a trace constituent. The absence of oxygen, of course, does not necessarily preclude the existence of life on Mars, even in fairly advanced forms [see Chapter 14].

▽ If there is no oxygen in the Martian atmosphere, then we expect no ozone. In the Earth's atmosphere, ozone absorbs ultraviolet light between 2000 and 3000 Å, light which would otherwise be lethal to most terrestrial organisms. Does the absence of ozone mean that the Martian surface is bathed in ultraviolet radiation? If some other atmospheric absorber were present, either as a gas or a solid aerosol, the ultraviolet light might not reach the surface. When Mars is observed in ordinary visible light, it appears as in Figure 19–1 A, B, and C. On the other hand, when we observe Mars in ultraviolet light, we see something like Figure 19–1D. The polar region shows up very prominently, but almost all surface detail in the bright and dark regions has vanished. The source of this mysterious phenomenon is called the "blue" or "violet haze," although it may not be a haze, and it certainly is not blue or violet. If it is a haze, it absorbs blue, violet, and ultraviolet light, and transmits light of longer wavelengths. If we had some of it—whatever it is—in a bottle, it would appear red. If the Martian blue haze is some unidentified atmospheric absorber, then the intensity of ultraviolet sunlight at the surface of Mars may still be small. However, a recent rocket observation of Mars in ultraviolet light implies the absence of atmospheric absorbers effective at these wavelengths on Mars. What, then, causes the blue haze? We have suggested that limonite particles cover both bright and dark areas, but that bigger particles exist in the dark areas. With the particle sizes necessary to explain both brightness and polarization, Pollack and I find that dark and bright areas reflect light equally well at violet and ultraviolet wavelengths. On this basis we expect the contrast between bright and dark areas to disappear in the violet and ultraviolet. Thus, the "blue haze" may be purely a surface effect; if this view is correct, there should be substantial penetration by ultraviolet light to the surface, posing, perhaps, an additional hazard for organisms on Mars.

▽ Many other gases besides oxygen have been searched for in the Martian atmosphere with negative results. From a radio experiment on the U.S. Mariner IV space vehicle and from the shape of absorption lines in the Martian atmosphere, it is possible to determine the total atmospheric pressure at the surface of Mars. This figure is about 10^{-2} atm—that is, about 1.0 percent of the total atmospheric pressure at the Earth. If we add up the carbon dioxide and water vapor which has been identified in the Martian atmosphere, we find that some of the atmosphere of Mars is unaccounted for. Some other gas which we have not yet identified is present. Certain molecules, such as N_2 and the noble gases, have their absorption lines in ultraviolet wavelengths which cannot be observed from the surface of the Earth because of absorption in the terrestrial atmosphere. Nitrogen is present in large quantities in our own atmosphere (78%), and its cosmic abundance is high. For these reasons, astronomers have concluded that some of the Martian atmosphere is composed of N_2. But this is an argument by default, and direct ultraviolet observations of Mars should be performed—for example, from Orbiting Astronomical Observatories above the atmosphere—to check the presence and abundance of nitrogen on Mars.

▽ Mention should be made of another gas, one which has been used in arguments about the presence of life on Mars. In 1956, the American astronomer C. C. Kiess, of Georgetown University, and his collaborators obtained a spectrum of Mars which seemed to show certain weak absorption features in the blue, green, and yellow parts of the spectrum. They attempted to match these features with a variety of gases and concluded that only nitrogen dioxide, NO_2, could explain the observations. Kiess and collaborators maintained that the quantities of this poison gas on Mars were so large as to exclude the possibility of any indigenous life on that planet. This discussion was taken up and extended by others; it was used to argue that future biological exploration of Mars by space vehicles was unnecessary, because life on Mars was impossible.

▽ This conclusion must certainly be considered premature. Kiess and his collaborators never actually computed how much nitrogen dioxide their observations implied. If this computation is performed, the quantity of NO_2 in the Martian atmosphere is shown to be about 0.001 percent.

▽ But might this not still be large enough to constitute at least a chemical embarrassment to the Martians? The amount of NO_2 in our own atmosphere can be measured in quite analogous ways. For example, a spectrometer may be pointed at the Sun, and the absorption by NO_2 in the overlying atmosphere recorded on a photographic plate. Since NO_2 is a primary constituent of smog and other urban pollution, such studies are performed almost routinely in cities such as Los Angeles. There, the NO_2 content of the atmosphere varies with time. A typical pattern has maximum NO_2 abundances at 8:00 A.M. and at 5:00 P.M., and subsidiary peaks at 7:00 P.M. and 11:00 P.M. (all Pacific local time). These peaks correspond to the morning and evening rush hours, and probably to evening car-borne social activities of the inhabitants of that exotic city. Such studies open up entire new fields of research, such as spectrochemical sociology. But the important point is that the average amount of NO_2 above the city of Los Angeles is greater than the average amount of NO_2 in the atmosphere of Mars. Conditions in Los Angeles, while inclement by some standards, do not quite preclude life there; the same conclusion applies to Mars.

▽ By observing the infrared and radio emission which Mars radiates to space, it is possible to obtain an approximate picture of what the local surface temperatures are. At an average locale in the Martian desert, at the equator, in summer, near noon, a typical temperature might be as high as 20°C (68°F), or warmer than room temperature in Great Britain. Yet that very night, the temperature will plunge to 70 or 80° below zero (−94 to −112°F). Mars has been described as having an extreme continental climate. As we move closer to the poles, the average temperatures become less, and the diurnal fluctuation becomes smaller. A temperature average over latitude, longitude, season, and time of day, might be −30 or −40°C (−22 to −40°F). There is no spot on Mars which stays above the freezing point of water during any 24-hour day. Still, some locales tend to be much warmer than others. Despite out terrestrial tendency to consider deserts as being hotter than other places, the Martian bright areas tend to be cooler than the dark areas, in part because being brighter, they absorb less sunlight during the day. The dark nuclei of the dark areas are very dark indeed; therefore, they absorb significantly more sunlight than the deserts. While even in the dark nuclei, the night-time temperatures tend to be low, during local spring and summer the average daytime temperature of a dark nucleus tends to stay above the freezing point of water.

▽ Mars therefore appears to be generally cold, arid, and oxygen-poor. A man transplanted to Mars with no protective equipment would asphyxiate before he would freeze. Otherwise, he might die of thirst or be scorched by ultraviolet light. But men are not the only organisms on Earth. The most ubiquitous terrestrial life forms are the microorganisms. What happens if we inoculate a simulated Martian environment with terrestrial microorganisms? Such experiments have in fact been performed. A chamber is prepared which may contain dried limonite powder, an oxygen-free atmosphere composed mostly of CO_2 and N_2 is introduced under reduced pressure; an ultraviolet lamp shines on the limonite; and the entire chamber is taken through a daily freeze-thaw cycling. Such chambers are, of course, known as "Mars jars." Perhaps remarkably, when samples of terrestrial soil rich in microorganisms are introduced into such an environment, while some of the microorganisms die, mostly after the first freeze-thaw cycle, a significant fraction survive indefinitely. The survivors include a wide variety of microorganisms, including types which form spores and types which do not. The ultraviolet light kills the microorganisms unlucky enough to be exposed. Those microorganisms which hide under rocks survive. They do not need oxygen, the temperatures do not bother them, and the very low water content is adequate for their needs. If the water content is increased, corresponding, say, to what may happen in local Martian spring, the surviving organisms are found to grow and reproduce. △

It is important to remember that people in the Antarctic live at temperatures which are within the ranges found in the Martian polar regions. The lowest temperature ever recorded on Earth, in the Antarctic, was $-82°C$ ($-116°F$). Man living in the Antarctic creates his own artificial biosphere, but organisms have a great capacity for evolutionary adaptation to severe environmental conditions. The inclemency of the Martian climatic conditions does not in itself exclude the possibility of life.

▽ Such simulation experiments are clearly relevant to the question of life on Mars. They indicate that perfectly adequate biological mechanisms exist for survival under average Martian conditions, and for growth when the conditions are relatively favorable. Since there are few natural terrestrial environments quite as rigorous as those on Mars, it is remarkable that terrestrial organisms have Martian survival capability; but they do. These experiments, a kind of natural selection on a laboratory scale, have only been carried out for periods of months. If we imagine them carried out over very long periods, we can see that through mutation and selection, an evolutionary process will occur in which the survivors are increasingly better adapted to the Mars jars. In just the same way, we can imagine Martian organisms evolving, in the Martian environment, into forms well adapted to it. For all we know, life forms much more advanced than microorganisms might have evolved under such circumstances. While these experiments increase the plausibility of indigenous life on Mars, they, of course, do not prove that life exists on Mars.

▽ But such experiments do have relevance to the question of biological contamination of Mars. Suppose that in future attempts at Martian exploration, a space vehicle were to impact the Martian surface. On its journey from Earth to Mars, such a spacecraft would have been externally sterilized by solar ultraviolet radiation. This radiation does not penetrate into the spacecraft interior, and any organisms which were there at the launch of the spacecraft would survive the impact of the spacecraft on Mars. If the spacecraft fractures on impact, terrestrial microorganisms will be deposited on the Martian surface. If precautions are not taken before launch, all interior materials of the spacecraft will have a large complement of terrestrial microorganisms of many varieties. Martian winds and dust storms are, as we have seen, prevalent; the microorganisms would be distributed over the entire surface of Mars. It is still possible that little ultraviolet radiation reaches the surface of Mars, and that the microorganisms—or "bugs," as microbiologists affectionately, but inaccurately, call them—would not be killed by germicidal sunlight. Even if the ultraviolet flux is large, bugs adhering to particles of dust might survive nicely.

▽ There is a certain "compound interest" to microbial reproduction. In the absence of predators or competitors, the bugs reproduce exponentially. As a simple example, consider a bug which is deposited in an environment in which it grows very slowly. Some terrestrial microorganisms reproduce once an hour; imagine the microorganism in question reproducing on Mars once every thirty days. Thus, at the end of thirty days, we have two organisms; at the end of sixty days, we have $2 \times 2 = 4$ organisms; after ninety days, $2 \times 2 \times 2 = 8$ organisms; and after $30 \times n$ days, 2^n organisms. After 300 days ($n = 10$), we would have 2^{10}, or approximately 10^3 microorganisms. After 1500 days ($n = 50$), or slightly longer than two Martian years, we would have $2^{50} = (10^3)^5 = 10^{15}$ microorganisms. After eight Earth years (about 3,000 days; $n = 100$), we would have $2^{100} = (10^3)^{10} = 10^{30}$ microorganisms, a number which is larger than the entire microbial population of the planet Earth. This example illustrates the seriousness of biological contamination of Mars.

▽ We suspect that there are already at least some microorganisms on Mars, and we wish to examine them in detail. What do they look like? How are they constructed? How do they function? Are they composed of cells? Is the basic hereditary material made of nucleic acids? Are proteins used as catalysts? There is a long list of basic biological questions to be asked.

▽ Now imagine that despite the danger of biological contamination, we send unsterilized spacecraft to Mars—for example, to learn more about its physical environment. In later missions, we send instruments designed to search out and characterize indigenous Martian organisms, if any. We find microorganisms on Mars—in fact, microorganisms which are very similar to some terrestrial bugs. What do we conclude? That similar forms have developed independently on the two planets? That Mars and Earth have had some common biological contact in the distant past? Or that a spacecraft from Earth inadvertently deposited organisms on a previous mission? Biological contamination of Mars would be a major scientific disaster. For this reason, a program of space vehicle decontamination and sterilization has been announced by the National Aeronautics and Space Administration of the United States. But the United States is not the only spacefaring nation. The Soviet Union has an imminent capability for Martian landings, and other nations may, in the not-too-distant future, also participate in the search for life on Mars. It matters little if contamination of Mars is effected by a Russian or an American bug; the microorganisms know no nationalities. Without some effort on our part, they may not even respect interplanetary boundaries. For this reason, it is cheering that the Soviet Union has shown signs of willingness to sterilize its spacecraft. Efforts were made to sterilize the Soviet lunar rocket Luna II, and a resolution calling for rigorous sterilization of space vehicles launched to Mars was approved in May, 1964, by Soviet representatives at the meeting of the Committee on Space Research of the International Council of Scientific Unions. In this area of space exploration, the peoples of the planet Earth appear to have a common purpose singularly apposite for our first venture of another world.

▽ We have assayed the known environment of Mars. We find it rigorous, but probably not too rigorous for indigenous organisms. Yet it is clear that organisms could not have originated and evolved on a planet similar to contemporary Mars [see Chapter 16]. Might the conditions have been more clement on primitive Mars? As we have seen in Chapters 11–13, there is good evidence to support the belief that all the planets in the solar system were formed in an analogous manner, out of the same cloud of gas and dust, which had a common reducing chemistry. There is no reason to doubt that the primitive atmosphere of Mars was reducing; that due to an atmospheric greenhouse effect, the temperatures were warmer; and that some open bodies of water may have been in existence—although these matters are not rigorously demonstrated. The change from the primitive to the contemporary Martian environment must have had the same cause as the transition from the primitive to the contemporary terrestrial environment—namely, atmospheric escape. Mars has a lower mass and therefore provides a greater opportunity for escape of a given molecule from its gravitational field. As the atmosphere of Mars slowly boiled off to space, during eons of geological time, the atmospheric conditions became less reducing, the surface temperatures declined, and eventually most of the water evaporated to space or was frozen subsurface. These changes were gradual, and we can easily imagine the adaptation through natural selection of Martian organisms to the changing conditions.

▽ Some independent support for this picture is provided by the composition of the Martian deserts. As we saw earlier in this chapter, the polarization of light reflected from the deserts strongly suggests that they are composed of limonite, $Fe_2O_3 \cdot nH_2O$. Limonite appears on Earth primarily in equatorial climates, mixed with hematite and bauxite as lateritic soil. Limonite and lateritic soil are both highly oxidized, and have large water content. Limonite is generally five to ten percent water by mass. Terrestrial limonite and lateritic soils are formed, geologists believe, only in the presence of oxygen in hot, humid environments. Contemporary Mars has no oxygen; it is cold and arid. We can understand the presence of large quantities of limonite on Mars only if we postulate the existence of earlier conditions much like those in the tropical zone on the Earth. If limonite requires molecular oxygen for its formation, we then have evidence that at one epoch in its history Mars held an oxidizing atmosphere, an atmosphere which presumably has by now escaped to space or has reacted chemically with the Martian surface.

▽ The oxygen in the terrestrial atmosphere, as we saw in Chapter 16, is probably produced by plant photosynthesis. Might that also have been the case for Mars?

Was Mars once lush and verdant? While oxygen may not be necessary for advanced life forms, the only examples which we have here on Earth point to its usefulness in extracting energy from foodstuffs. Could advanced life forms have developed at some epoch in the distant Martian past, only to be destroyed at a later time by the escape of oxygen to space and its reaction with the crust? Or might organisms on Mars have continued to adapt to the changing Martian environment, in ways at which we now can only dimly guess? △

20

The quest for
life on Mars

Where stars are shining in the mist,
In measured steps the Martian treads.
On hillocks of monastic hue
No grass, no trees, no, none of these . . .

    I. Smelianov

Brothers . . . stoop not to renounce the quest
Of what may in the sun's path be essayed,
The world that never mankind hath possessed.

    Ulysses, in Dante, *Inferno,* XXVI

The origin of life on primitive Mars seems not unlikely. The present physical environment of Mars does not exclude life. We have seen, in Chapter 18, the difficulties in remote detection of life on Earth from a Martian vantage point. How can we say anything more about life on Mars? Remarkably enough, there are a variety of observations which have been interpreted, with varying degrees of success, as indicating life on Mars. Some of the early arguments we now know to be almost certainly erroneous, but even the most recent pieces of evidence do not unambiguously demonstrate the existence of life on Mars. A coherent picture can be gained only by considering all the facets of this enigmatic subject.

∇ Some decades ago, it was commonly reported that the Martian dark areas were green. If the dark areas were green, what could they be made of? The most common greenish materials on Earth are plants, and it was readily concluded that vegetation was thriving on Mars. But the detection of colors by astronomical observation is a thorny problem. It is possible to be deceived for physical reasons and for psychophysiological reasons. Around the turn of the century, it was common to use refracting telescopes, which employ lenses to collect light. Today, almost no refracting telescopes are being constructed for professional astronomical work; instead, reflectors, using large mirrors, are the rule. One of the advantages of reflectors is that they are not plagued by chromatic aberration, as are refractors. Chromatic aberration occurs because light of different colors is brought to different focuses in transmission through a lens. Thus, if the yellow wavelengths of sunlight, reflected off Mars into the telescope, are in focus, many other colors will be out of focus. In particular, the extrafocal blue and green light is smeared over the image of Mars. Mixed with the red-orange coloration of the bright areas, there is little apparent change in color; but mixed with the neutral gray of the dark areas, a distinct blue-green coloration appears. The use of reflecting telescopes largely removes such problems of chromatic aberration.

∇ There remain, however, psychophysiological problems. When a neutrally colored area is placed alongside a brightly colored area, it tends to acquire a complementary color. This corresponds to no real coloration in the neutral area, but is simply a quirk of human color vision. The colors complementary to the red-orange Martian bright areas are greens and blues; and again, neutrally colored dark areas on Mars are invested with a spurious blue-green coloration. Confusion due to extrafocal light and to color contrast effects can both be removed by using a diaphragm with a large reflecting telescope. The diaphragm isolates a dark area, so that the adjacent ruddy bright areas are not seen; the reflecting telescope removes the extrafocal blue light. Under these circumstances, the dark areas appear an almost neutral gray. There is some tendency for the dark areas to appear slightly reddish; this is not surprising, because some of the dusty material from the bright areas must also be present in the dark areas. Occasional subtle and delicate colors have been observed in recent years, but they are a far cry from earlier days, when "chocolate," "carmine," "kelly green," and "dragon's blood" could be found in scientific descriptions of Mars.

▽ Color changes which have been reported on Mars are probably also largely illusory. As we have mentioned, given a brightly colored area with a red or orange hue adjacent to a neutral gray area, the eye invests the dark area with some blue-green color. Now, if the dark area changes its darkness—that is, varies its contrast with the bright area—it will appear to vary in color. The eye's interpretation of contrast variations as color variations is, in fact, one of the principles of the Land process of color photography. Thus, if the Martian dark areas change their brightness, it should not surprise us that they also seem to change their colors.

▽ If, then, the Martian dark areas are neutrally colored and not green, is the possibility of vegetation in the dark areas excluded? It is true that the most easily seen terrestrial plants are colored green. The color arises from a highly specific and ubiquitous molecule known as chlorophyll. Chlorophyll, a photon-acceptor, is involved in the first step in the long photosynthetic chain which converts the energy of sunlight into the energy-rich bonds of the ATP molecule [see Chapters 14 and 17]. Chlorophyll appears green because it absorbs in the red and the blue; the middle of the spectrum is reflected back from the plant, to give it its greenish hue.

▽ The absorption properties of chlorophyll are critically dependent on its molecular structure. A slight change in molecular side groups can produce a major change in the absorption properties of the molecule. A large part of the solar spectrum is in the yellow and green wavelengths which chlorophyll tends to reject. To utilize these yellow and green photons, plants on Earth have made many special adaptations. Many plants use a wide range of accessory pigments, molecules quite different from chlorophyll, such as the carotenoids, which give carrots their distinctive color. Here, it is the orange and red parts of the spectrum which are mostly not utilized, and the shorter wavelengths, including the green and yellow light, which are absorbed. Higher plants concentrate large amounts of chlorophyll, so that the relatively weak absorption in the yellow and green is compensated by the large number of absorbers. There seems to be no particular adaptive advantage to greenish coloration in plants. Most likely, it is an historical accident; that is, at the time of the origin of plants, chlorophyll molecules absorbing primarily in the red and the blue were evolved, and all of subsequent plant evolution has been built upon these early adaptations. Instead of changing the fundamental ground plans, plants have made accessory adaptations to correct the grosser photosynthetic deficiencies.

▽ On another planet, it is entirely possible that other pigments evolved early in the origin of life; there really seems no reason to expect extraterrestrial vegetation to be green. In fact, a neutral color such as brown, gray, or black has a subsidiary advantage on chilly Mars: no part of the spectrum is rejected; all photons are used, either for photosynthesis or for simple heating of the plant. Neutral colorations may make much more sense for Martian plants than greens. This point has been stressed by G. A. Tikhov, the former director of the world's first and only Institute of Astrobotany, at Alma Ata, Kazakhstan, U.S.S.R. This institute, now defunct, was an early focus of Soviet enthusiasm for extraterrestrial life, at a time when the subject was lacking both solid observational techniques and the support of the scientific community.

▽ While some Martian surface features, such as Syrtis Major, were probably observed as early as the eighteenth century, the first systematic mapping of Mars, with the aid of adequate telescopes, did not occur until the last half of the nineteenth century. Many of our present names for Martian surface features derive from that time. A leader in early Martian cartography was an Italian astronomer, Giovanni Schiaparelli. In 1877, during relatively routine observations of Mars, under conditions of relatively good seeing, Schiaparelli was surprised to find long, dark, rectilinear features which seemed to connect dark area with dark area, traversing thousands of kilometers of the Martian deserts. Schiaparelli called these features "canali," which, in Italian, denotes channels, or grooves. The word was, however, translated into English as "canals," a word embracing the distinct implication of intelligent design.

▽ The existence and significance of the canals were most eloquently championed, some decades later, both in the scientific and the popular literature, by Percival Lowell, an American diplomat turned astronomer, who established an observatory in Flagstaff, Arizona, for the express purpose of studying Mars. The seeing conditions in Arizona were superior to those of most other observatories at the time. The further observations which Lowell and his associates recorded were developed into a coherent picture of Mars, which went something like this: long, rectilinear features are observed crossing the Martian deserts. They apparently undergo seasonal brightness and color changes. Occasionally, one such line apparently geminates into two. The lines never stop at some desert locale, but always continue from dark area to dark area. Straight lines, Lowell argued, are not natural features; therefore, they must be artificial. If the canals are in fact artifacts, what is their function? Even at the turn of the twentieth century it was known that the gravitational field of Mars was not likely to hold an extensive atmosphere, and that liquid water was not in great abundance on the Martian surface. Lowell therefore proposed that the canals were canals—carrying liquid water from the polar ice caps to the thirsty Martians residing in the dark equatorial regions. Small, dark nuclei which were observed at the interconnections of several canals were appropriately called "oases."

▽ Two immediate scientific objections to the canal theory were disposed of by Lowell and collaborators with arguments which retain their validity today. First, it was suggested that the reported widths of the canals were too small to be detected with the resolving power of the telescopes used. Lowell showed that long, rectilinear features against high-contrast backgrounds can be seen even if their widths are far below the theoretical resolving power. He performed an experiment with overhead transmission wires in Flagstaff, Arizona, showing that he could station himself far from the wires and still detect their presence.

▽ The second objection was that the canals were too wide—many kilometers across, much wider than necessary to carry water from the polar ice caps. Lowell countered as follows:

> The fundamental fact in the matter is the dearth of water. If we keep this in mind, we shall see that many of the objections that spontaneously arise answer themselves. The supposed herculean task of constructing such canals disappears at once; for, if the canals be dug for irrigation purposes, it is evident that what we see, and call by ellipsis the canal, is not really the canal at all, but the strip of fertilized land bordering it,—the thread of water in the midst of it, the canal itself, being far too small to be perceptible. In the case of an irrigation canal seen at a distance, it is always the strip of verdure, not the canal, that is visible, as we see in looking from afar upon irrigated country on the Earth.

▽ With these successes in the scientific dialogue, Lowell and his followers constructed an inverted pyramid of deductions upon the apex of the canal observations. The canals were a massive engineering work; therefore, the Martians are in substantial technological advance of contemporary human society. The canals obviously cross what we would term international boundaries; hence, a world government exists on Mars. One of Lowell's followers went so far as to place the capital in Solis Lacus (latitude −30°, longitude 90°, in Figure 19–4). The hydraulic engineering required was discussed, and Lowell painted moving verbal portraits of a race of superior beings, engaged in heroic attempts to maintain their civilization on a dying planet. Lowell's ideas were incorporated into fictional form by Edgar Rice Burroughs, in a series of books about John Carter, a terrestrial adventurer cavorting on Mars, which introduced Lowell's ideas to an even larger public.

▽ Lowell developed a long chain of argument, ultimately based on the reality of the canals as a genuine Martian surface feature. But were the canals really on Mars, or, as with other beauty, in the eye of the beholder? An acrimonious scientific debate ensued, stretching over decades in time. Although largely resolved, it can still be heard echoing occasionally in contemporary scientific literature. Had Lowell been less articulate, had he not directed his eloquence to the general public, the debate would probably have terminated much earlier. It became so bitter, and seemed to many scientists so profitless, that it led to a general exodus from planetary to stellar astronomy, abetted in large part by the great scientific opportunities then developing in the application of modern physics to stellar problems. The present shortage of planetary astronomers can be largely attributed to these two factors. To savor the spirit of this debate, consider the following two scientific reports from eminent and experienced planetary observers:

> I have been watching and drawing the surface of Mars. It is wonderfully full of detail. There is certainly no question about there being mountains and large greatly elevated plateaus. To save my soul I can't believe in the canals as Schiaparelli draws

them. I see details where he has drawn none. I see details where some of his canals are, but they are not straight lines *at all*. When best seen these details are very irregular and broken up—that is, some of the regions of his canals; I verily believe— for all the verifications—that the canals as depicted by Schiaparelli are a fallacy and that they will so be proved before many favorable oppositions are past. (E. E. Barnard, 1894)

At the first glance through the 32¾-inch on 1909, September 20, I thought I was dreaming and scanning Mars from his outer satellite. The planet revealed a prodigious and bewildering amount of sharp or diffused natural, irregular detail, all held steadily; and it was at once obvious that the geometrical network of single and double canals discovered by Schiaparelli was a gross illusion. Such detail could not be drawn; hence only its coarser markings were recorded in the notebook. (E. -M. Antoniadi, 1916)

Other observers were similarly unable to record the existence of canals, even under very good seeing conditions. W. H. Pickering, a supporter of Lowell, countered one such report as follows:

Dr. Van Biesbroeck records that he saw no canals or lakes on that evening in spite of the excellent seeing. The main reason for this is that on that evening, at that time, there were no canals or lakes visible.

But Lowell's rejoinders were more eloquent:

The straightness of the lines is unhesitatingly attributed to the draughtsman. Now this is a very telling point. For it is a case of the double-edged sword. Accusation of design, if it prove not to be due to the draughtsman, devolves *ipso facto* upon the canals . . . Let us not cheat ourselves with words. Conservatism sounds finely, and covers any amount of ignorance and fear.

▽ Under fine seeing conditions, some observers saw the canals; others did not. Did one group have superior visual acuity, or did the other have superior powers of imagination? The answer seems to be this: when the atmospheric seeing conditions are moderately good, the polar cap, bright areas, and dark areas can be discerned, as in Figures 19–1 and 19–2, but no canals appear. When the seeing conditions improve, many observers suddenly glimpse the canals standing out, as Percival Lowell put it, "like the lines in a fine steel etching," in a complex and interlacing pattern encompassing the whole planet. But at the best observing sites, such as Pic du Midi, under superb seeing conditions, experienced observers have found that the canals can be resolved into disconnected fine features, the "bewildering amount of sharp or diffused natural, irregular detail" of Antoniadi. Then, as the seeing conditions become worse, and the image shimmers, the canals reappear. The eye has a compulsive need for order, and in the few moments of superior seeing, in which we must glimpse, remember, and record the surface of Mars to sketch in our notebooks, it is far easier to remember a few straight lines than a multitude of fine detail. Similar results have been demonstrated in laboratory experiments. When observers are left to glimpse and record disconnected, mottled features under poor seeing conditions, they tend to construct straight lines where none exist.

▽ A comparison of a given region of Mars under conditions of good and of superb seeing, where the canals are, respectively, glimpsed and resolved, is shown in Figure 20-1, taken from Antoniadi's book *La Planète Mars,* 1929. This result has been confirmed by the French astronomer Audouin Dollfus and by other workers in recent years. Thus, the problem of the Martian canals, as with so many other apparent observables on Mars, appears to be largely psychophysiological rather than astronomical.

▽ There have been no photographs of the thin, straight canals of Mars, the nub of the Lowellian controversy, although there are photographs of broader features, sometimes called canals, such as Thoth-Nepenthes (longitude 260°, latitude

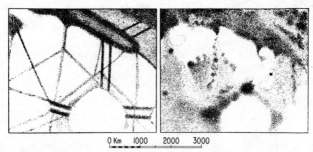

0 Km   1000   2000   3000

FIGURE 20-1. *Example of the resolution of the "canals" of Mars into fine detail. On the left are observations of the region of Elysium as observed by Schiaparelli between 1877 and 1890. There is a network of fine linear canals, both single and double. On the right is a drawing of the same area, as observed by E.-M. Antoniadi, between 1909 and 1926. By squinting and alternately looking at the left- and right-hand illustrations, the reader may test the hypothesis that the Martian surface features are actually as depicted on the right and that, when the atmospheric seeing conditions become poor, are glimpsed as in the illustration on the left. (Reproduced from* La Planète Mars *by E. M. Antoniadi, Hermann et Cie, 1930.)*

+20° in Figure 19-4, left-hand photograph in Figure 19-2). The photographic plate has the advantage of objectivity. Rarely will wishful thinking introduce a canal in a photograph where none was originally. But photography has the disadvantage that Mars must be viewed in a time exposure, encompassing moments when the seeing ranges from poor to superb. The photographic plate records an average, while the eye can remember the one moment of superb seeing. To record on photographs the details which Schiaparelli and Lowell interpreted as canals requires resolution which cannot be obtained from the surface of the Earth. We are like fish in the ocean depths, longing to view the flights of eagles.

▽ Telescopes lofted by balloon to the stratosphere, or taken on spacecraft nearer to Mars, should, in the not-too-distant future, obtain for us an accurate photographic representation of the features formerly interpreted as canals. The features must have some significance; although there is disconnected detail on the Moon, which is observed through the same telescopes as Mars, no one has ever reported canals on the Moon. There are characteristic features on Mars, unlike the canals of Lowell, but which are the basis of the canal reports. One recently suggested possibility is that they are strings of sand dunes. Thus, while the canals are almost certainly not the massive engineering works of an advanced Martian civilization, their study may yet give us some further insights into the Martian environment. Meanwhile, the controversy has served at least the useful purpose of emphasizing the dangers of too many conclusions from too little data. As the Swedish chemist, Svante Arrhenius, put it (1918):

> The theory that intelligent men exist on Mars is very popular. With its help everything can be explained, particularly if we attribute an intelligence vastly superior to our own to these beings, so that we not always are able to fathom the wisdom with which their canals are constructed . . . The trouble with these "explanations" is that they explain anything, and therefore in fact nothing.

▽ Most of the present evidence suggesting life on Mars is of a different character. Each year, as the Martian ice caps recede towards the poles, sizable quantities of water vapor are released into the atmosphere. The Martian atmospheric circulation is apparently adequate to transport this water vapor across the equator, so that the water released by the retreat of one polar cap is available for the reformation of the polar cap in the opposite hemisphere. The radius of Mars, R, is 3380 km. The circumference of Mars is $2\pi R$, so the distance from pole to pole is πR. It takes half a Martian year for the water vapor to travel from pole to pole, or about $687/2 =$ 344 days. The average rate at which the water vapor travels from pole to pole is therefore $\pi R/344$, or about 30 km per day.

▽ At the same time that the water vapor is being transported through the atmosphere, a remarkable phenomenon, known as the wave of darkening, occurs on the surface. The dark areas become progressively darker, and their contrast with the unchanging bright areas increases. This occurs in a wavelike movement, the front of the darkening wave progressing from the vaporizing polar cap towards and across the equator, and into the opposite hemisphere. Half a Martian year later, the wave of darkening proceeds in the opposite direction. The wave of darkening is not subject to the uncertainties of eyeball astronomy; it has been repeatedly photographed, and quantitatively measured on telescopes equipped for photometry. The wave of darkening proceeds according to recent measurements by the Greek astronomer J. H. Focas of the Athens Observatory, at an average rate of 35 km per day, close enough to the presumed rate of transport of water vapor in the atmosphere to suggest that the two phenomena are connected. It is this seasonal contrast enhancement which is the source of reports of seasonal color changes on Mars.

▽ Now what is the origin of the wave of darkening? Svante Arrhenius, whom we have just encountered attacking the Lowellian dogma, proposed an inorganic explanation of the darkening wave. Arrhenius suggested that salts exist in the dark areas of Mars (but not in the bright areas) which change their darkness and color with the humidity. Materials of this general type, such as cobalt chloride, are known on Earth, and in fact, are used to measure humidity changes. The amount of water released by the polar cap, if distributed over the entire planet, is very small, about 10^{-3} gm over each square centimeter of the planet, some thousand times less than the water vapor content of the Earth's atmosphere. At the moving front of the wave of darkening, the water vapor content may be ten times larger, or 10^{-2} gm over each square centimeter. No materials on Earth are known which change their darkness (or color) in the manner observed on Mars due to such a small increase in the absolute quantity of moisture. Also, those materials whose absorption properties are responsive to humidity, the so-called hygroscopic salts, polarize the light reflected from them in a manner inconsistent with the observed polarization of sunlight reflected from Mars. The bright areas of Mars, we recall, are composed of limonite, a very dark, very strongly absorbing material. The dark areas of Mars are darker still, and cannot be composed of a semitransparent salt.

▽ There is an alternative explanation of the wave of darkening. Mars appears to be an arid world. If there are organisms there, we might expect them to be very responsive to the availability of water. Mars is further from the Sun than Earth is, and we might expect any photosynthetic plants on Mars to be more hungry for photons than are plants on Earth. We observe that when the local humidity increases, the Martian dark areas become darker. Are we in fact observing the seasonal growth and proliferation of Martian vegetation? The suggestion is a natural one, and was proposed as long ago as 1884 by the French astronomer E. L. Trouvelot, who mused:

Judging from the changes that I have seen to occur from year to year in these spots one could believe that these changing grayish areas are due to Martian vegetation undergoing seasonal changes.

▽ Visual observation of the wave of darkening indicates that the darkening changes in the individual dark nuclei occur in periods characteristically as short as a week. The changes cover vast areas of Mars. The sudden flourishing of plant life over sizable areas of the Earth is a fairly common occurrence. Algal blooms are one example. A possibly more relevant example is the rapid growth of vegetation during the annual rainy season in many terrestrial deserts. Figures 20–2 and 20–3 illustrate the dramatic changes in a landscape which occur within about a month of a significant increase in the amount of available moisture. If the wave of darkening is a biological phenomenon, it follows that life on Mars is widespread and, furthermore, responds very rapidly to slight increases in the local moisture content. What an extraordinary conclusion to draw, from fifty million miles away! Yet we must recall the demise of the canals. Have we considered all alternatives? Is Martian biological activity the only reasonable explanation for the wave of darkening, or is there another, inorganic explanation, closer to the truth, which has eluded us up to now?

▽ Probably related to the wave of darkening is the dark collar which surrounds the retreating polar ice cap on its journey towards the pole. The collar has variously been described as black, brown, or blue. It is a real Martian phenomenon, not a contrast effect, as can be demonstrated by blotting out the polar cap at the telescope and noting that the collar is still much darker than the surrounding regions. The polarization of light reflected from the polar collar shows that it is not simply due to dampening of the Martian soil. Something else is going on.

▽ At the edge of the receding polar ice cap, there is probably a greater supply of atmospheric water vapor than in any other region on Mars. There is even the bare possibility of temporary and shallow pools of liquid water, although this has never been confirmed polarimetrically. It seems to make some sense for organisms on an arid planet to proliferate at the edge of the polar cap. Despite the low average temperatures on Mars, daytime summer temperatures in the dark nuclei near the polar cap tend to be mild, even by terrestrial standards. The edge of the summer polar cap seems an ideal place to search for life on Mars.

▽ In addition to these seasonal variations, Mars exhibits striking secular changes. While the relative configurations of the bright and dark areas generally retain their integrity for many decades, some areas of Mars characteristically undergo marked, rapid, erratic changes. In Figure 20–4, we see four drawings, three of them made by the Greek astronomer Antoniadi. The upper drawings were made in 1877 and 1911; the lower drawings, in 1924 and 1926. The region is Solis Lacus, erstwhile capitol of Mars in the Lowellian *Weltansicht*. As an example of the superiority of visual to photographic observations, compare Antoniadi's drawings of Solis Lacus with the representation of Solis Lacus in Figure 19–4 (longitude 90°, latitude −30°), taken from photographic plates alone. The dotted lines in the lower two pictures indicate areas covered by clouds at the time of observation. Something extraordinary happened in Solis Lacus between 1877 and 1911, and in the even shorter period of time between 1924 and 1926. From the scales of these figures, we see that the changes have been major. Areas 1000 km on a side are involved. Great variations in fine detail have occurred. Some dark areas have appeared in a desert; elsewhere, deserts have encroached into the dark areas. What is happening? Perhaps the Martian secular changes represent ecological successions on Mars. On the Earth, due to changing geological and climatic conditions, often a species of organism will arrive in a previously uninhabited area and there proliferate mightily in a relatively brief period of time. At other times, the climatic conditions may prove so severe that the species is locally destroyed.

▽ Possibly related to the secular changes is the reappearance of the dark areas after a dust storm. We observe material from the Martian deserts blown by winds over the Martian dark areas, which are consequently obscured. The dust storm does not move on; yet, after a short period of time, characteristically about a week, the dark area reappears. Where has the dust gone? Has Martian vegetation grown through the dust in the short period of a week, as the Estonian-Irish astronomer Ernst Öpik has suggested? Do the Martian plants shake themselves clean? Or is there an inorganic explanation, related to elevation differences?

▽ In Chapter 19, we alluded to the identification of limonite in the Martian bright areas, from analysis of the polarization of the sunlight which they reflect.

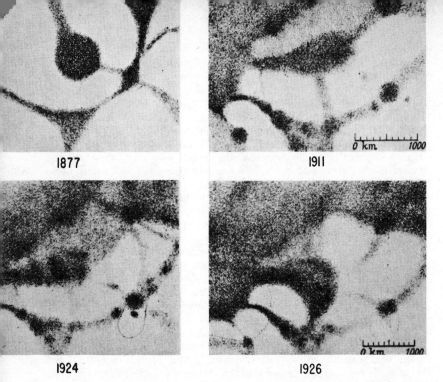

1877

1911

1924

1926

FIGURE 20-4. *Examples of secular changes on Mars. These are four drawings of the same area of Mars, the region of Solis Lacus. The drawing in upper left was made by Schiaparelli. The remaining three drawings were made in 1911, 1924, and 1926 by E.-M. Antoniadi. Even allowing for the difficulties in visual observations and the differences in styles of drawing between Schiaparelli and Antoniadi, it is clear that there have been substantial topographical changes on the Martian surface. (Reproduced from* La Planète Mars *by E.-M. Antoniadi, Hermann et Cie, 1930.)*

The polarization of the Martian deserts is independent of the Martian seasons; the polarization curves have the same character in Martian summer as in Martian winter. However, in the dark areas, the polarization depends very much on the season of the year, being much more striking in local Martian spring and early summer than in late fall and winter. To reproduce anything like these seasonal polarization changes in the laboratory, Dollfus was forced to conclude that the particles in the Martian dark areas change their darkness or their size— probably both—periodically with the seasons. We have already encountered seasonal changes in the wave of darkening and the reports of color changes in the Martian dark areas. But changes in the particle size are something else.

▽ To match the polarimetric observations, in the Martian spring we need some particles which are larger than the average winter particle size, which is perhaps

0.1 mm. Such a redistribution of particle sizes is exactly what we might expect from biological activity. If there is growth and proliferation in the Martian spring, we can understand why larger particles should then exist.

▽ Yet a non-biological explanation of these seasonal and secular changes appears to be possible. We have mentioned (p. 265) that the dark areas seem to have systematically higher elevations than the bright areas, and that both may be covered with a finely granulated material resembling limonite. The existence of dust storms shows that winds can distribute dust over substantial distances on Mars. The seasonal changes in brightness and in polarization of the Martian dark areas can be understood in terms of seasonal changes in particle sizes. If, in local spring, the dark highlands are scoured by the winds and the small bright particles carried down to the deserts below, the dark areas will appear to darken and the average particle size in them will appear to increase. If, in the Martian autumn, the small particles are carried back up to the highlands by local turbulent winds, the contrast between the dark areas and bright areas will diminish, and the average particle size in the dark areas will decrease. Pollack and I have shown that the particle sizes and wind velocities needed for such an inorganic explanation of the wave of darkening are plausible for Mars.

▽ In this view, the reappearance of a dark area after being covered in a dust storm can be understood: the winds soon sweep clean the high lying dark area. In areas where the elevations are not greatly different, perhaps the shifting wind-blown sands sometimes uncover underlying dark material, sometimes cover over pre-existing dark material, thereby giving rise to that other Martian enigma, the secular changes. All of these changes can be understood in terms of the scattering properties of small grains of limonite with diameters roughly equal to the period at the end of this sentence.

▽ The possibility that all the seasonal and secular changes on Mars—previously attributed to biological activity on that planet—can be understood by winds and dust and elevation differences does not, of course, disprove life on Mars. In our studies of the earth with the Tiros and Nimbus meteorological satellites, we were unable to detect seasonal changes in cultivated crops or in forests. Earth-based observations of Mars can detect much finer contrast gradations than the meteorological satellites can, but at the same time their ability to resolve fine details is much worse than for the meteorological satellites. For such gross changes as have been observed on Mars to be due to biological activity there, life would have to be much more extensive on Mars than on earth. For all we know, the planet may have a complex variety of organisms, yet there may be no means of ascertaining this fact over interplanetary distances.

▽ A final category of modern evidence relating to life on Mars is provided by infrared spectroscopy. Organic molecules have characteristic absorption features at a wavelength near 3.5μ in the infrared. The reflection spectra of most terrestrial organic materials show such absorption features. As the photons penetrate a small distance into the sample before being reflected, they are absorbed by vibration of carbon-hydrogen groups in the sample. The American astronomer William

Sinton has observed similar features in the spectrum of sunlight reflected from Mars. Sinton finds three features that can be understood if material on Mars contains large quantities of the methyl group, CH_3, the methylene group, CH_2, and the aldehyde group, CHO, as constituents of larger molecules.

▽ Sinton's observations were very difficult to perform, because of the small amounts of infrared radiation reflected from Mars and the limitations in terrestrial infrared detector systems. Using the 200-inch Hale telescope at Mt. Palomar, California, Sinton seemed to show that the absorption features preferentially appear in the Martian dark areas. The existence of the Sinton bands has been confirmed by the Soviet astronomer V. I. Moroz, at the Crimean Astrophysical Observatory. But more recently, Sinton and the Canadian-American spectroscopist D. G. Rea, of the University of California, Berkeley, have suggested that two of the three Sinton bands may, nevertheless, be due to inorganic molecular contaminants in our own atmosphere, and not due to organic matter on Mars. The remaining Sinton band is apparently a true Martian feature. For the moment, we can only suspend judgment on whether organic molecules have been detected in the Martian dark areas. The problems in obtaining and identifying the Sinton bands illustrate the great difficulties in spectroscopic observations of faint features over interplanetary distances and the desirability of observations from closer range.

▽ The observations we have described are tantalizing. They are considered evidence for life on Mars by many. △ Although the information taken as a whole may indicate the presence of life on Mars, we will have a rigorous answer only when new observational techniques are developed.

Our success to date in mastering space enables us to plan experiments designed to solve this ancient mystery. ▽ We may observe Mars in many ways: from a fly-by vehicle which spends only an hour or less within close range of Mars; from an orbiter, a spacecraft in orbit about Mars which performs observations, perhaps over many months; from an atmospheric entry probe which determines information regarding atmospheric physics before it reaches the Martian surface, but which performs no experiments on the surface; from a small soft-lander which performs a few experiments of biological relevance over a short period of time; and from a larger, automated biological laboratory which performs a wide range of interconnected biological investigations over a long period of time on Mars. Any strategy of Martian exploration will involve some mixture of these systems. △ A fly-by carrying an automatic camera can scan the Martian landscape from a distance of several thousand kilometers. The photographic images can be transmitted, ▽ slowly, point-by-point, △ to Earth by television. The experiment of the Soviet lunar rocket Luna III, which photographed the far side of the Moon [Chapter 21, Figures 21–7 and 21–8], indicates the complete feasibility of such an experiment.

▽ A typical contemporary American vehicle is Mariner IV, shown in Figure 20–5. It was designed to take 22 pictures of Mars from a distance of a few thousand kilometers. Planetary photography was the only Martian experiment directed to the surface of Mars from Mariner IV. The unsuccessful Soviet fly-by spacecraft

Mars-1 is shown in Figures 20–6 and 20–7. In addition to television equipment, Mars-1 was equipped with infrared and ultraviolet spectrometers, and a system to detect long wavelength radio emission. △ Fly-by photography will allow us to study details as small as one kilometer across on the Martian surface. We will then be able to study the surface of Mars in the same detail with which astronomers can, using Earth-based facilities, study the surface of the Moon. After such investiga-

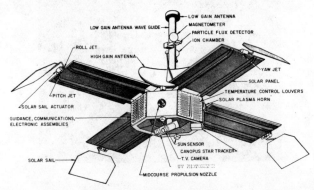

FIGURE 20–5. *Diagram of the United States spacecraft Mariner 4 which flew by Mars on 14 July, 1965. Most of the experiments depicted were designed to measure interplanetary particles and magnetic fields. The ultraviolet photometer was an experiment removed from the spacecraft before launch. (Courtesy of NASA.)*

tions are carried out, many of the problems concerning the nature of the Martian dark areas and the controversial canals will be resolved.

▽ On 14 July, 1965 the United States spacecraft Mariner IV successfully flew by Mars, performing a variety of scientific observations. In one elegantly simple experiment, the spacecraft flew behind Mars, and its radio signal to Earth was gradually eclipsed by the planet's atmosphere. From the rate of fading of the radio signals, information on the temperature and pressure variation of the Martian atmosphere was obtained. Experiments directed at finding a planetary magnetic field and the associated Van Allen radiation belts gave negative results. The absence of a magnetic field on Mars is of some interest. The earth's magnetic field is thought to arise from its liquid iron core, formed through geological time by the migration of iron downward through the surface and mantle. The absence of a magnetic field on Mars suggests that the iron on Mars has not made a similar migration, and therefore that substantial quantities of iron may still exist near the Martian surface. This may be the explanation of the limonite, an iron oxide, which seems to exist on Mars.

▽ Mariner IV successfully acquired some fourteen or fifteen photographs of the Martian surface in the day-lit hemisphere. No usable information was acquired from photographs of the night side. In Figure 20–8 we see three renditions of the

FIGURES 20-6 and 20-7. Two views of the Soviet spacecraft Mars 1, which was launched on an unsuccessful voyage towards Mars on 1 November, 1963. Mars 1 had a much larger and more sophisticated instrumental payload than did Mariner 4, as is evident by comparing these photographs with Figure 20–3. The Soviet spacecraft Zond 2 may have been similar in design to Mars 1. (Courtesy of Sovfoto, Moscow.)

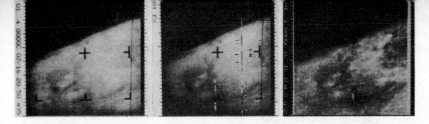

FIGURE 20–8. *Three transcriptions of Frame 1 of the Mariner IV picture sequence of the Martian surface. A possible cloud may be visible above the planetary horizon in the last two renditions. The center of the picture corresponds to approximately 35°N. latitude, 172°E. longitude, primarily a desert area.* (*Courtesy of NASA.*)

same first frame of the Mariner photographic sequence. The radio signals from Mars gave, as in the transmission of newspaper wirephotos, information on the darkness of each bright or dark point comprising the picture. The numbers can then be rendered into a picture and the apparent contrast of the Martian surface features can be increased or decreased on Earth at will. Three different choices of surface contrast are shown here. Among the bright and dark markings which we see, there is a curious dark line paralleling the horizon. Its nature is unknown. A bright patch may also be seen above the horizon in the sky in one of these pictures. Whether this is a dust cloud sitting in the Martian atmosphere, or an optical defect in the lens system is still an open question.

▽ The area covered by the Mariner IV photographs comprises primarily Martian deserts west of Amazonis and eventually regions of the dark area Mare Sirenum [cf. Figure 19–4]. In the early photographs of the bright areas, the Sun was approximately overhead; shadows were short, and details were difficult to see. In Figure 20–9, a rendition of Frame 7, several circular markings can be seen. Figure 20–10 is a rendition of Frame 11, taken near Mare Sirenum, when the Sun was at a low angle, permitting longer shadows. It is now quite clear that the circular markings previously seen are craters like those on the Moon.

▽ The large lunar craters [see Chapter 21] are almost certainly produced by the impact of objects many kilometers across onto the surface of the Moon. Many of these impacting objects are believed to be fragments of asteroids wandering more or less erraticly in the inner part of the solar system. Since Mars is much closer to the asteroid belt than is the moon, it should be subject to many more impacts—perhaps 25 times as many. Yet the number of craters of a given size in a given area on the Martian surface is no larger than the comparable number on the moon. This must mean that processes exist on Mars which efficiently erode even large impact craters. In Figure 20–10 we see a very large crater, over 100 kilometers across, whose ramparts have been seriously breached. Major erosion of its walls has occurred. Is the erosion due to windblown dust, or perhaps, as on earth, to running water? We find that the craters on the Martian bright areas are shallower, more eroded, and have their bottoms more filled in than the craters in the Martian dark areas. This is an explicable circumstance when we recall that the bright areas prob-

FIGURE 20-9. *A transcription of Frame 7 of the Mariner IV photographic sequence. The Sun is now 29° from the zenith, and circular markings are beginning to become visible. The center of the picture corresponds to approximately 13°S. latitude, 186°E. longitude, primarily a desert area. (Courtesy of NASA.)*

ably have substantial amounts of drifting dust, which tend to fill in and erode craters formed there.

▽ There is certainly no extensive liquid water on the Martian surface today; however, it is not out of the question that water erosion was important hundreds of

288   LIFE IN THE UNIVERSE

millions of years ago. Because of the efficiency of Martian crater erosion—regardless of the mechanism—the surface we see is not that of a very ancient Mars, and it is therefore impossible to judge from the Martian geology viewed in these photographs whether there were extensive bodies of liquid water in the early history of Mars. Some curving depressions which look very much like fluid flows can be seen in some of the photographs, e.g. in Frame 11, Figure 20–10; this need not necessarily be due to running water. Although it is not easily visible in the reproduction of Figure 20–10 shown here, a straight line extending from the lower left to the middle right, traversing the large eroded crater, can be seen on the original. Whether this feature has anything to do with the classical Martian canals, or whether it is an easily understood feature such as a fault, remain open questions.

▽ The best ground resolution obtained in the Mariner IV photographs was a few miles. We have already seen in Chapter 18 that photographs of the planet Earth with comparable resolution give no sign of life, intelligent or otherwise. The Mariner IV television experimenters, Robert B. Leighton, Bruce C. Murray, and their colleagues, have been careful to emphasize that the Mariner IV photographic experiment was not designed to search for life on Mars, and that it neither demonstrated nor precluded the existence of life on that planet. Neither has it resolved the canal controversy. It has demonstrated the utility of remote planetary photography and pointed out the need for greatly improved resolution in future space missions.

▽ A Mars orbiter permits us to garner information about even smaller scale features on Mars; but, more important, it permits us to gather this information over many months. Since the bulk of the astronomical evidence suggesting life on Mars is seasonal in character, it would be of enormous interest to examine the Martian dark areas, for example, during the passage of the wave of darkening. The best opportunities for such investigations lie in the years 1969 and 1971. Perhaps we can gain information on the distribution of organic matter over the surface of Mars. Some organic molecules may characteristically be present in one dark area; other organic molecules, in other dark areas. From an orbiter, observations with a resolution of 10 meters or better should be possible. Observations of the Earth with similar resolution show unambiguous signs of life, although most of these are signs of human habitation. Due to the fact that Mars is an exterior planet, lying further from the Sun than the Earth, no one has ever observed any region of Mars in the middle of local night. If life on Mars is not distributed over the whole planet, but is localized in a few favored high-temperature, high moisture environments, an orbiter may be the ideal vehicle for finding such "hot spots." In infrared night-time observations, a large Martian hot spot would be easily detectable. The potentialities of an orbiter for Martian exploration are many; there seems little doubt that orbiters will be used in the early stages of the biological investigation of Mars.

▽ But before very long, we will want to land scientific instruments on the Martian surface. In addition to the simple question, "Is there life on Mars?" biologists are interested in the anatomy, physiology, genetics, biochemistry, ecology, and behavior of Martian organisms, to name only a few sub-disciplines. Such information can only be acquired on the spot. In the design of instrumentation for

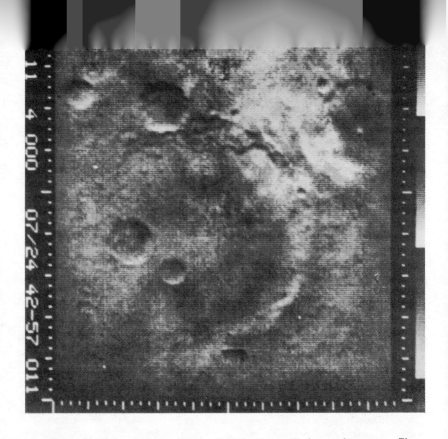

FIGURE 20–10. *A transcription of Frame 11 of the Mariner IV photographic sequence. The Sun is now 47° from the zenith, and impact craters are clearly visible. At the Northern ramparts of the large central eroded crater, a sinuous flow pattern may be seen; a straight line exists traversing the Southern ramparts of this crater diagonally. The center of the picture corresponds to approximately 31°S. latitude, 197°E. longitude, a region localized in a dark area. The contrast of features in this frame is difficult to compare with the contrasts of other frames. (Courtesy of NASA.)*

the detection and characterization of life on Mars—a major occupation of some biologists today—there are two fundamental questions: First, is life on Mars ubiquitous, or localized in only a few areas of Mars? Second, how close are the Martian life forms to those on Earth? Can an automated biological laboratory land anywhere on Mars, or are some places vastly preferable to others? We have presented arguments that some locales, such as the edge of the retreating polar ice cap during Martian spring, are favorable habitats for Martian organisms. Other areas, such as Syrtis Major and Solis Lacus, show striking seasonal or secular changes. Yet the Martian winds should distribute small organisms essentially uniformly over the planet, and we find on Earth today that microorganisms can be found in essentially every locale, from the Sahara and Gobi deserts to the Mindanao Deep; from the top of Mt. Everest to the top of the Empire State Building. Human beings are not so uniformly distributed, and an extraterrestrial expedition to Earth, seeking indigenous life, would be well advised to look for microorganisms: there are more microorganisms, and they are more readily caught. Yet any biological inventory of Earth should, we know, consider organisms larger than microbes.

▽ How, in fact, will an automated biological laboratory detect life on Mars? One set of possible experiments, which are actively being pursued at the time of writing, involves landing a nutrient medium on Mars, inoculating it with samples of Martian soil, and looking for signs of growth and reproduction. As the microorganisms grow, they may increase the turbidity of the nutrient medium or change its acidity. Alternatively, the Martian microorganisms, like many terrestrial organisms, including people, may give off carbon dioxide in the course of metabolizing the food brought from Earth. The Martian biological experiment, Gulliver, shown in Figure 20–11, is such a CO_2 monitor. But what if the Martians fail to find the food sent from Earth palatable? What if their tastes are more exotic? The nutrient medium will be inoculated, but the Martian organisms present will not grow; there will be no turbidity changes, no acidity changes, no CO_2 given off. The experiment will send negative results back to Earth. Shall we conclude that there is no life on Mars?

▽ An alternative experiment is to look for particular categories of enzymes on Mars. We have seen that phosphorus compounds play a fundamental role in metabolic energy transfer and other terrestrial metabolic activities. If phosphorus is also important in Martian metabolism, we might expect enzymes known as phosphatases, which transfer phosphorus groups in metabolism, to be present in the Martian soil, as they are in terrestrial soil. A device called Multivator, designed to search for phosphatase and other signs of Martian metabolism, is shown in Figure 20–12.

▽ But what if the Martian organisms do not contain phosphatases? Phosphorus is present in terrestrial organisms in an abundance far out of proportion to the cosmic abundance. Perhaps some other atom takes the place of phosphorus on Mars. The fluorescence technique used to search for phosphatases will give spurious positive results for some relatively rare minerals. Perhaps such minerals are present on Mars, and the positive result will not actually indicate the presence of phosphatases on Mars. It is for such reasons that a combination of different experimental approaches in an automated biological laboratory is necessary for a thorough search for and characterization of life on Mars. There is no single "life detector."

▽ As an example of the advantages which a combination of experimental techniques provides, consider the following device, which is under preliminary study in the United States: Individual particles of the Martian soil are made to

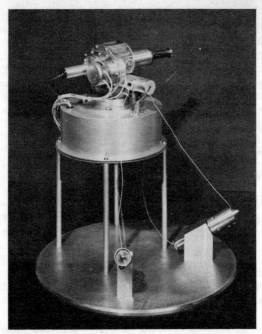

FIGURE 20-11. *Model of the Mark III Gulliver. The two projectiles on the disk are the sample collectors. When fired they would drag a length of sticky string over the Martian surface, which, when reeled back into Gulliver, would have samples of the surface adhering. The strings are then drawn into a nutrient broth containing radioactively labelled carbon compounds. If Martian microorganisms adhering to the string metabolize the labelled broth and release carbon dioxide, this event would be recorded and radioed back to Earth. (Courtesy of Dr. Gilbert V. Levin, Hazelton Laboratories, Inc., and Prof. Norman H. Horowitz, California Institute of Technology.)*

adhere electrostatically to a moving belt, which is carried through an infrared spectrometer. Individual particles 0.1 mm in diameter and smaller are automatically analyzed by infrared spectroscopy. If their infrared spectrum is characteristic of minerals, as the spectra of most of the particles will be, the belt moves on to the next particle. But when a particle is scanned which has the infrared spectrum of organic matter, it is also photographed through a microscope. Such a device can, in principle, sift through large numbers of uninteresting particles to determine something about the chemistry and morphology of what we consider the interesting particles. Only the spectra and photographs of the interesting particles would be transmitted by radio back to Earth. If we now imagine this procedure amplified, with many devices examining samples of Martian soil for their physical and chemical properties, their possible metabolic activities, and their responses to new

FIGURE 20-12. *Cutaway view of a test model of Multivator. Martian dust would be drawn up by a small vacuum cleaner, and deposited into a number of different reaction chambers, each containing its own enzyme or metabolite. Each chamber is then observed by a photometer for changes in turbidity due to growth of the acquired Martian organisms, for fluorescence due to the presence of enzymes, etc. (Courtesy of Prof. Joshua Lederberg and Dr. Elliot Levinthal, Stanford University Medical School.) A somewhat similar device, not pictured here, called Wolf Trap, was designed by Prof. W. Vishniac of the University of Rochester.*

stimuli, we see that an automated biological laboratory controlled by a computer can be a very powerful tool in the quest for life on Mars.

▽ In order that high-risk, high-return possibilities are not completely over-looked, such a device should also obtain periodic television scans of the Martian landscape. A laboratory of this type should be mobile—we may think of it as a small tank. It is heavy, but well within the range of possible payloads deliverable to Mars by the booster rockets being planned by the United States and the Soviet Union for manned exploration of the Moon. Perhaps the television pictures will be unspectacular—rocks, lava flows, sand dunes. An occasional scraggly plant would not be unexpected. But there are other possibilities—fossils, footprints, minarets. . . . We will know only when we drop our instruments on the surface of Mars. △

21

The Moon

The Surface of the Moon then is found, by the least Telescopes of about three or four Foot, to be diversified with long Tracts of Mountains, and again with broad Valleys. For in those Parts opposite to the Sun you may see the Shadows of the Mountains, and often discover the little round Valleys between them, with a Hillock or two perhaps rising out of them. Kepler from the exact roundness of them would prove that they are some vast work of the rational Inhabitants. But I can't be of his mind, both for their incredible Largeness, and that they might easily be occasioned by natural Causes. Nor can I find anything like Sea there . . .

What then, is it credible that this great Ball was made for nothing but to give us a little Light in the Night-time, or to raise our Tides in the Sea?

Christianus Huygens, *New Conjectures Concerning the Planetary Worlds, Their Inhabitants and Productions* (c. 1670)

Though I am old with wandering
Through hollow lands and hilly lands,
I will find out where she has gone,
And kiss her lips and take her hands;
And walk among long dappled grass,
And pluck till time and times are done
The silver apples of the moon,
The golden apples of the sun.

William Butler Yeats, *The Song of the Wandering Aengus*

Each of the nine planets, their thirty-one satellites, and the innumerable smaller objects of our solar system has its own individuality. While certain broad relationships exist—for example, within the terrestrial and Jovian planetary groups—the differences are more striking. To the interplanetary explorer of the next century, the differences among these objects will be far more vivid than, for example, the differences among the major ports of call of the last century. In this and the following two chapters, we will briefly describe the environments of these diverse worlds—within the rather restricted limits of present knowledge—and examine them for the possible presence of life.

▽ Our nearest neighbor is our familiar satellite, the Moon. It revolves about the Earth, of course, about once a month. Since, from our terrestrial vantage point, we always see approximately the same face of the Moon, we conclude that it must be rotating about its axis at the same rate that it revolves about the Earth, thus always keeping the same face to the Earth. This reluctance of the Moon to expose her backside is a coyness probably shared by the other thirty satellites in our solar system. Such synchronous rotation is due to tidal friction—that is, to the tides introduced in the body of the satellite by the more massive planet. Operating over the four and a half billion year lifetime of our solar system, such body tides are very efficient in producing synchronous rotation. Once the periods of the satellite rotation and revolution are equal, however, the tidal forces are usually unable to slow down the satellite's rotation any further.

▽ While the Earth has slowed the Moon's rotation, tides produced by the Moon in the body and oceans of the Earth have slowed the rate of rotation of the Earth. This tidal "braking" increases the day by about 0.002 second per century, an amount which, while incredibly small, is still within the range of detectability of astronomical techniques. The tidal retardation of the Earth has produced no perceptible lengthening of the day during the span of Man's sojourn on this planet; but one billion years ago, if the rate of retardation is constant, the day must have been 2×10^{-5} sec yr^{-1} $\times$ 10^9 yr = 2×10^4 seconds, or roughly six hours shorter. An apparent confirmation of these astronomical deductions on the tidal braking of the Earth has come from an unlikely source.

▽ In the Bahamas, there is a reef coral called *Acropora palmata,* which has ringed ridges on its skeletal structure. The ridges are formed by the growth of the coral, and each ridge corresponds to one year's growth. When the rings are examined in closer detail, it is found that they are composed of large numbers of much finer ringed markings—roughly 360 to the annual band. The American geologist John W. Wells, of Cornell University, has postulated that these finer rings represent a daily growth of the coral.

▽ Now consider a sample of the coral from much earlier times—say, the Middle Devonian, a time about 350 million years ago. The length of the year should not change with time. But if the length of the day was shorter in the Middle Devonian than it is now, we should expect to see more fine lines per yearly band in a Middle Devonian fossil than in a contemporary fossil. Wells has in fact examined Middle Devonian fossils, and finds that they have about 400 ridges per year. Thus, 350 million years ago, there were some 400 days per year, and each day was about $(365/400) \times (24 \text{ hrs}) = $ about 21.9 hours long. The astronomical data give essentially the same result for the Middle Devonian. This is one of many examples of the connection between astronomy and biology. Indeed, this book is devoted to the examination of such a connection.

▽ Everyone knows that through a small telescope the Moon looks something like the view in Figure 21–1. There are bright areas and dark areas, the so-called *continentes* and *maria,* designations dating from the time of their discovery by Galileo, who thought that the dark areas were indeed lunar bodies of water. We now know that there is no liquid water at all on the lunar surface, and that the *maria* are dark, relatively flat, depressions.

▽ In order to study the bright and dark areas more accurately, new photographic methods are being used. A photograph of the Moon is projected onto a blank globe and then rephotographed from any desired angle. Such a procedure, called rectification, removes the effects of foreshortening near the edges, or limbs, of the Moon. The rectified photograph in Figure 21–1 is therefore a view of the Moon that no human being has yet seen. At the center of the figure appears the great lunar rayed crater Tycho, which ordinarily appears far to the south, in naked eye observations or astronomical photographs. The bright rays may be seen emanating from Tycho and traversing substantial distances across the lunar surface. Figure 21–1 is based on a photograph taken at full moon—that is, when the Moon, the observer, and the Sun are approximately in a straight line, with the observer in the middle. At full moon, the lunar surface takes on the high-contrast guise seen in Figure 21–1. The rays of craters like Tycho then become extremely prominent.

▽ At other times, such as half moon, however, when the sunlight is striking the center of the lunar disk from an angle, a given area of the Moon seems much less bright, the contrast between *maria* and *continentes* declines, and the rays all but disappear. In other photographs of the Moon, Tycho, apart from its rays, is in fact a very modest and unspectacular crater.

▽ A more usual photograph of a smaller region of the Moon is shown in Figure 21–2, a non-rectified photograph of the region of Mare Imbrium, a large circular *mare* in the northwest quadrant of the Moon. We see that the *mare* floors are rugged, occasionally pockmarked with craters of all sizes. Towards the bottom edge of this picture is the lunar terminator, the range of locales on the lunar surface at which the Sun has just set. In the late lunar afternoon, shadows of mountains become long, as in the lower left-hand corner of the photograph, and it is possible to compute from the length of these shadows the height of lunar

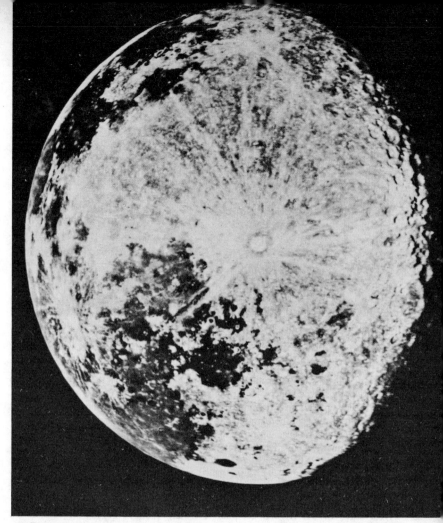

Figure 21–1. *Rectification of a full moon photograph showing the rayed crater, Tycho, at the center of the disk. (Courtesy of Dr. Ewan Whittaker, and Dr. G. P. Kuiper, Lunar and Planetary Laboratory, University of Arizona.)*

features. In this way, it has been possible to determine that there are mighty mountain ranges on the Moon, some of them approaching, if not surpassing, the altitude of the Himalayas. The mountains in the upper left-hand corner of the picture are called the Alps, after their terrestrial counterparts; the slash through the Alps, going towards the extreme left-hand corner of the picture, is called the

FIGURE 21-2. *Unrectified photograph of the region of Mare Imbrium. (Yerkes Observatory photograph courtesy of Dr. G. P. Kuiper, Lunar and Planetary Laboratory, University of Arizona.)*

Alpine Valley. Close inspection of the Alpine Valley reveals it to be filled with a set of closely spaced craters, unlike typical valleys known on Earth.

▽ Far superior resolution of the Moon has been obtained from the U.S. Ranger spacecraft. A typical photograph of the Moon obtained by Ranger VII appears as Figure 21-3. The dense clustering of craters in this photograph occurs along the path of a lunar ray, much as the craters of the Alpine Valley are arranged along the cut through the Alps. Many of the lunar craters, such as Archimedes, the large crater towards the center of Figure 21-2, are more appropriately described as ring walls, or walled plains. Because the radius of the Moon is so small, the lunar horizons are much closer to the observer than on Earth. If one stood at the center of a large lunar crater, or ringed plain, the walls would be beyond the horizon and out of sight.

▽ The relation between the depth and width of the lunar craters follows the same mathematical law which impact craters of all sizes follow on the Earth. This and other evidence have convinced the majority of astronomers that the larger lunar craters have been formed by the impact of some objects from interplanetary space.

▽ The alternative view is that the lunar craters are of volcanic origin. A study of the close-up photographs of the Moon by the Ranger series of space vehicles has recently convinced many students of the Moon that the smaller lunar craters—

LIFE IN THE UNIVERSE

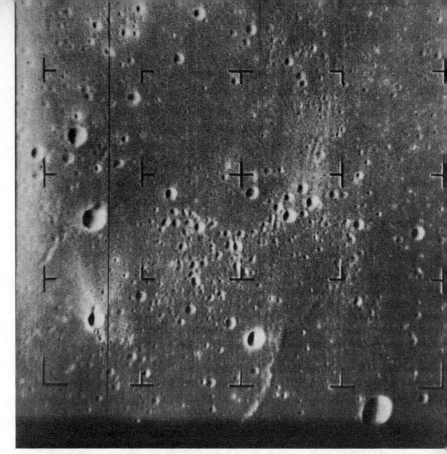

FIGURE 21-3. *Ranger VII photograph of a cluster of craters in the floor of the newly named Mare Cognitum.* (*Courtesy of NASA.*)

particularly those which are too small to be visible from the Earth—may be in part of volcanic origin. One line of evidence supporting this view can be seen in Figure 21-4, a close-up of the lunar crater Alphonsus. The dark region to the center and below is the crater floor. In the crater floor we see a set of rills—slightly meandering cracks in the lunar surface. Oriented along one of these rills is a sequence of at least six fair-sized craters. This correlation between the rills and the craters is too striking to be attributed to mere chance. Either the craters caused the rills, the rills caused the craters, or both have a common cause. It has been argued that the most likely of these alternatives is that both rills and volcanic craters are formed along faults by stresses in the lunar surface. In some cases long chains of craters have been observed which are far too orderly to be an accidental configura-

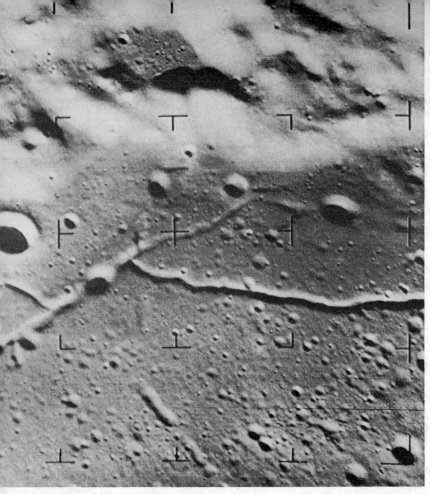

FIGURE 21-4. *Ranger IX photograph of the eastern edge of the floor of the lunar crater Alphonsus. The photograph was taken from an altitude of 115 miles above the lunar surface, at a time 1 minute and 17 seconds before impact. (Courtesy of NASA.)*

tion produced by impacting projectiles from interplanetary space. (In the vicinity of ray craters, however, the clustering of craters along the ray can be understood as the result of the debris flung out by the explosion forming the crater.)

▽ Some—perhaps all—of the *maria* show a roughly circular shape. Figure 21-5 is a rectified photograph of Mare Humorum, in the southwest quadrant of the lunar hemisphere which faces the Earth. The *maria* may in fact be nothing more than a group of very large craters, produced by just the same impact mechanism

FIGURE 21-5. *Rectification of a Meudon Observatory photograph of Mare Humorum. Note the partially destroyed circular craters around the periphery of Mare Humorum. (Courtesy of Dr. G. P. Kuiper, Lunar and Planetary Laboratory, University of Arizona.)*

that produced the craters. The Alpine Valley would then be exactly analogous to a lunar ray, a gash carved out of the lunar Alps by debris from the giant impact which formed Mare Imbrium.

▽ If the lunar craters are formed by impact of large meteorites and asteroidal-sized objects, should we not see an occasional crater being formed? Should astronomers invest time in the comparison of photographs of the same region of the Moon, taken years apart, to look for the appearance of new craters? We can easily convince ourselves that this is a profitless enterprise. There are about 10^5 craters visible in the lunar hemisphere which faces the Earth, on photographs obtained with large astronomical instruments. If we assume that these craters were formed uniformly throughout the last 5 billion years of lunar history, then we see that new craters should be formed about once each $(5 \times 10^9)/10^5 = 5 \times 10^4 = 50,000$ years. We should wait, on the average, some 50,000 years before seeing the next crater formed; even then, it is unlikely to be very spectacular.

▽ Similar impacts must have occurred on the Earth during the same 5×10^9 year period. Yet the Earth is not prominently marked with large circular craters. This discrepancy can be understood entirely in terms of erosion by wind and water on the Earth's surface. Structures become eroded on the Earth in periods of time very short compared with the history of the planet. In fact, in recent years, such structures as the Riss Kessel, in Germany, have been identified as fossil meteor impact craters. The number of such recent craters on the Earth, extrapolated through its history, gives a total number of terrestrial craters entirely consistent with the number on the lunar *maria*.

▽ Why are some craters rayed, like Tycho, and others, like Archimedes, not, if both types of craters are formed by the same process—the collision with the Moon of some interplanetary derelict? There is now reason to believe that erosion occurs on the lunar surface, both from the impact of innumerable micrometeorites on the Moon each day, and by the re-impact on the Moon of lunar material ejected after collisions of larger objects. Some sign of this erosion can be seen in Figure 21–5. In and around Mare Humorum are several "ghost craters," circular features which evidently were once craters, but which now have been partly eroded away. It is also possible that lava flows attended at least some of the earlier and larger lunar impacts, thereby obscuring preexisting features.

▽ Another eroding influence is solar radiation and the solar wind. When materials are bombarded by solar ultraviolet radiation and x-rays, and the ejected charged particles of the solar proton wind, their crystalline structure tends to break down; the recombination of these molecular fragments forms chemical groups which impart color to the objects; and we are left with a very dark, fine powder. Spectroscopic searches have failed to find any sign of a lunar atmosphere. When a cosmic radio source such as the Crab Nebula passes behind the Moon, it instantaneously "winks out," rather than slowly fading, as it would if the Moon possessed even a modest atmosphere. Especially in the absence of an atmosphere, small particles tend to sinter; that is, they become welded to each other, not solidly but rather with only one or two points of contact. The result is a low-density fluff of unimaginable complexity, which has been called a "fairy castle structure." Such a material explains many of the spectroscopic, polarimetric, and radio properties of the lunar surface.

While the lunar surface is known to be covered by such low-density material, there is still some debate on the depth of this layer. Most astronomers believe that its thickness is of the order of a few centimeters or less. Thomas Gold believes that the depth may run to kilometers. Such a material, even if very deep, has an appreciable bearing strength, and would probably feel "crunchy" to the first astronaut who treads it.

▽ When a small asteroid, let us say, impacts the Moon, it blasts out a fragment of lunar surface material, some of which escapes to space; the remainder is distributed over the lunar surface. The larger chunks produce secondary craters when they impact. The material of the asteroid and the impact site are both ground into a fine rock flour, which, when distributed over the lunar landscape, gives the appearance of the rays. As time progresses, the ravages of solar radiation and the solar proton wind will cause a gradual deterioration in the brightness of the rays. In about 10^6 years, the highly reflecting character of the ray material will be destroyed, and except for the secondary craters there will be no sign of their previous existence. It may be that ray craters such as Tycho are not very many millions of years old.

▽ We have already alluded to laboratory experiments, in which fine powders were irradiated in vacuum by protons simulating the solar proton wind. In experiments of this type, performed by the American astronomer Bruce Hapke of Cornell Universty, it is found that, almost independent of the composition of the irradiated material, the powder becomes as dark as the lunar surface is today after the equivalent of 10^6 years' solar proton irradiation. Continued irradiation tends to make the materials darker yet. Thus, to explain the fact that the Moon is not even darker than it is, we must postulate that underlying brightly colored material is stirred up, in timescales of a million years or less. This is clearly related to the erosion processes which we have already mentioned.

▽ We then have an interesting model of the superficial layers of the lunar surface. Underneath perhaps only a few centimeters of the dark, irradiated, sintered, pulverized material, is a layer of brighter sintered material which has not been recently exposed to the solar proton wind. However the footprints left by the American Surveyor 1 spacecraft, and the digging experiment performed by Surveyor 3, show that the underlying material is darker, not lighter, than the surface material. This apparent contradiction has not yet been resolved.

▽ The darkening effect of solar radiation is, of course, not restricted to the Moon. It should apply to all bodies in the solar system which have little or no atmospheres and small magnetic fields (so that solar protons reach their surfaces). In this category are probably most of the satellites in the solar system, perhaps the planet Mercury, and the dust and debris which fill the spaces between the planets. The vast lanes of dust which fill the plane of the solar system, and which we see as the zodiacal light, are composed of very dark particles—undoubtedly darkened by solar protons.

▽ Erosion of the lunar surface tends to wipe away small craters in times short compared with the age of the Moon, but is unable to destroy the larger craters. Since there are more impacts of small particles than of large ones, there must be more smaller craters formed than larger ones. The combined result of impact and erosion must produce a certain distribution of crater sizes on the lunar surface. Studies of crater counts in the Ranger photographs are being used to reconstruct the history of lunar crater formation and destruction.

▽ One of the most striking conclusions of the Ranger photographs is the general uniformity of the lunar surface. Figure 21–6 is a Ranger IX photograph in the crater Alphonsus. The white circle is the impact area of the Ranger IX spacecraft on the lip of a small crater. Parts 1, 2, and 3 of Figure 21–6 were taken with progressively improved resolution. Thus the crater near which impact occurred, as seen in Part 1 is barely detectable, but in Part 3, it is clearly visible. What is striking is the similarity in form of craters of very different sizes and the general uniformity of the lunar landscape at different resolutions. The largest craters in Part 1 and Part 3 (Figure 21–6) are practically indistinguishable, yet one

FIGURE 21–6. *The last three frames of the P1 camera of the Ranger IX spacecraft. Frame three was taken 0.45 seconds before impact from an altitude of three quarters of a mile above the lunar surface. (Courtesy of NASA.)*

is about ten times larger than the other. The best Ranger IX photographs were able to see detail as small as a few inches across. Unlike the Earth there is no qualitative novelty which appears on the lunar surface when we increase our ability to see fine detail. The Soviet spacecraft, Luna IX, soft-landed on the Moon, revealed a lunar landscape remarkably similar in general character to that seen with the incomparably poorer resolution obtainable with Earth-based telescopes.

▽ By noting which craters have partially destroyed other craters, and by counting the number of asteroidal fragments in the vicinity of the Moon, astronomers have been able to reconstruct something of the history of lunar crater formation. The craters within the *maria* can be accounted for by asteroidal fragment impact during the last few billion years. The lunar *maria* must have been formed earlier, probably three to four billion years ago. There are too many craters in the lunar *continentes* to be accounted for by contemporary impact rates. Also, enormous objects—many hundreds of kilometers across—are necessary to produce such major and lasting scars on the face of the Moon as the *maria*. Thus, many of the lunar surface features must be due to the impact of debris present in the vicinity of the Moon shortly after the time of its origin. It may be that this debris was the final fragments of the swarm of bodies which gravitationally condensed to form the Moon. △

▽ Figure 21–7 is a montage, prepared by the Anglo-American selenologist E. A. Whittaker, of the Lunar and Planetary Laboratory, University of Arizona. It is made from photographs taken primarily of the far side of the Moon by the Soviet cosmic rocket Luna III, when that side of the Moon was in direct sunlight. (The near side was therefore dark, at the phase that we on Earth call new moon. There is an unfortunate tendency to call the far side of the Moon the "dark" side of the Moon. This is obviously an error; it is probably related to the unconscious feeling of some people that the Earth, if not at the center of the universe, is at least the source of all light.)

▽ The large, circular *mare* at left center is Mare Crisium, and is identical, when rectified, with this *mare* as seen from the Earth. Except around the edges, where there is overlap with what is seen from the Earth, all the features are new, discovered by Luna III. A rectified and recentered photograph of the overlapping region—that photographed by Luna III and by ground based telescopes both—can be seen in Figure 21–8. Comparisons of Figures 21–7 and 21–8 show the quality of the Luna III photographs and give a good idea of the relation of the newly discovered features on the lunar surface to those known earlier. There seems to be

LIFE IN THE UNIVERSE

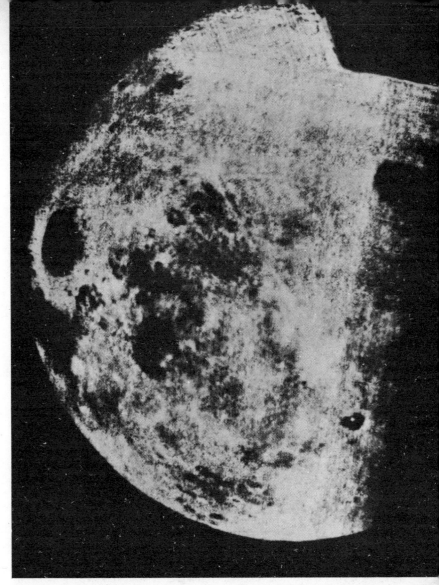

FIGURE 21-7. *A montage of Luna III photographs of the far side of the Moon.* (*Courtesy of Dr. Ewen A. Whittaker, Lunar and Planetary Laboratory, University of Arizona.*)

a puzzling lack of *maria* on the far side of the Moon, a fact which is connected with unanswered questions of origin. Some 5 to 10 percent of the Moon has not been observed by Luna III, by the later Soviet spacecraft Zond III, or from Earth, and remains to be discovered and named by future lunar spacecraft.

▽ The Moon's scarred and pitted face is a treasure trove of clues to the early history of the solar system. Because there is no erosion by wind or water, subsurface features have remained relatively undisturbed. What erosion there is, due to micrometeorites, secondary meteorite impacts, and the solar proton wind, operates very slowly, and may not disturb the lunar subsurface to great depths. There is consequently a possibility that as we dig beneath the lunar surface, we will find intact objects of earlier and earlier ages, until we reach material essentially as formed at the time of the origin of the solar system.

▽ In Chapters 16 and 17, we argued that the origin of life resulted from the production of organic molecules in a secondary reducing atmosphere, outgassed from the primitive Earth. A similar outgassed atmosphere must have accompanied the early Moon. The Moon today has essentially no atmosphere; its mass is so low that it is unable to gravitationally bind even the heaviest gases to it. Instead, they dissipate to space by the process of gravitational escape. In primitive times, atmospheric escape must have been equally efficient on the Moon. Thus, the Moon could have retained an atmosphere for, say, 10^9 years only if the gases escaping to space were continually replenished by outgassing from the lunar interior. There is some reason to suspect that such outgassing occurred, and that the Moon may have retained an atmosphere, and even a hydrosphere, in its early history. If so, organic molecules must have been abiologically produced in appreciable quantities. If life never developed on the Moon, such material may now be sequestered below the layer of micrometeoritic material which gently rained down through the primitive lunar atmosphere.

▽ We do not know how long the Moon retained an atmosphere and hydrosphere. It seems possible, although unlikely, that a primitive form of life arose in the early history of the Moon. It certainly could not survive on the lunar surface today. Any terrestrial organism placed on the surface of the Moon would be killed by conditions far more rigorous than those of Mars. During the lunar day (one of our months), the surface temperatures range from the normal boiling point of water to $-180°C$. There is no atmosphere, and no liquid water. The solar ultraviolet radiation alone is adequate to destroy in a period of hours the most radiation-resistant microorganism known. Along with solar x-rays and the solar proton wind, even dead organic matter would be charred in a few years.

▽ The possibility of life on the surface of the Moon has been proposed from time to time, on the basis of supposed color and other changes which have been reported. For example, the American astronomer William H. Pickering, observing in Mandeville, Jamaica, in the 1920's and 1930's, reported many observations of periodic color changes in the floors of craters, in step with the local time of day on the Moon. He reported, for example, that the floor of the crater Stevinus became reddish-brown as the Sun rose high in the lunar sky, while the floor of the large

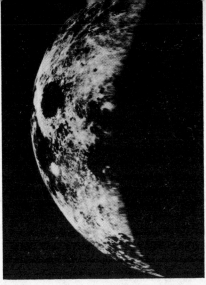

FIGURE 21–8. *Rectified and recentered photograph of the region of the Moon observable from the surface of the Earth and also observed by the Soviet spacecraft Luna III. Figure 21–8 and the left-hand portion of Figure 21–7 show the same region of the Moon photographed under comparable lighting conditions. (Courtesy of Dr. Ewen A. Whittaker, Lunar and Planetary Laboratory, University of Arizona.)*

crater Grimaldi became increasingly green towards local noon. Pickering also reported seeing moving spots in the crater floors, some bright and some dark. The moving bright spots he attributed to clouds on the almost airless Moon; the moving dark spots, to the rapid growth of plants across the crater floor, or even, in some cases, to the movements of large migratory insects!

▽ Similar observations have been made up to the present day, although the interpretations have become less facile. Many of these reports can be attributed to the seeing conditions in the Earth's atmosphere, the dependence of the reflecting power of the lunar surface on the Sun's angle, and the motion of shadows across crater floors when the Sun is low in the lunar sky. There is no good evidence for life on the surface of the Moon; and indeed, the physical conditions there provide a strong independent argument against a lunar surface biology. But may not conditions be less inclement below the lunar surface?

▽ The Moon, like every other object in the solar system, is a source of radio radiation. The more intense the radio radiation, the hotter the Moon must be. At short radio wavelengths, radiotelescopes "see" close to the lunar surface and derive a temperature close to that determined by infrared and other techniques, figures which we have already quoted. But as we go to radiotelescopes tuned to longer and longer wavelengths, we are in effect observing the Moon at greater and greater depths. The Soviet astronomer V. I. Troitskii of Gorkii University finds a systematic increase of this derived "brightness temperature" with wavelength, corresponding to an increase in temperature by about 1.6 C° per meter. The source of this temperature increase must be the heat of the lunar interior. The temperature beneath the Earth's surface similarly increases, as temperature measurements in borings and mines have shown.

▽ In addition to the average temperature increasing with depth, the daily temperature fluctuations are greatly reduced as we go below the lunar surface, because of the excellent insulating properties of the lunar surface material. The particles in the "fairy castle" structure have few points of contact with each other; therefore it is difficult for heat from the Sun to propagate downwards. At a depth of roughly 50 meters below the lunar surface, comfortable temperatures by our standards can be expected, temperatures which remain constant through the lunar day and night. At similar depths, several astronomers and geologists have suggested, there should be subsurface water which is prevented from escaping to the surface by an overlying layer of ice, in exact analogy to the permafrost of the terrestrial antarctic regions. If there is a region below the surface of the Moon which has warm temperatures, liquid water, and the possibility of primitive organic matter, then it seems premature to exclude the possibility of life on the Moon. Indigenous life seems highly unlikely because there is no energy source besides the chemical energy locked in the organic matter and other subsurface materials. This energy is limited at best; if life once arose at such depths, it would, in a brief period of time on the astronomical timescale, have died of malnutrition. But the lunar subsurface does seem able to support terrestrial microorganisms, a fact which is the basis for concern about biological contamination of the Moon.

▽ By the beginning of 1966, a dozen vehicles have impacted the Moon: the Soviet spacecraft Luna II, IV–IX, and the United States spacecraft Rangers IV, VI, VII, VIII, and IX. While attempts were made to sterilize Luna II and Ranger IV, there does not seem to have been a thorough sterilization of any of these vehicles. The difficulties in the sterilization procedure would have impaired the progress of the national space programs involved; as a result, the sterilization requirements were relaxed. Fortunately, the risk is not nearly as grave as that which would attend the biological contamination of Mars. We have no independent evidence for life on the Moon; but there is, as we saw in Chapter 20, some suggestion of life on Mars. If terrestrial microorganisms are to replicate on the Moon, they must find their way down some tens of meters below the lunar surface. In addition, while there is a mechanism for widespread atmospheric distribution of replicating contaminants on Mars, no comparable mechanism exists on the Moon.

▽ There may, however, be direct evidence for subsurface lunar organic matter. From time to time, there have been reports of gas clouds, mists, and reddish glows observed on the lunar surface. The earliest such report appears to be that of Sir William Herschel, the discoverer of the planet Uranus. His accounts follow:

May 4, 1783. I perceived in the dark part of the Moon a luminous spot. It had the appearance of a red star of about the fourth magnitude. It was situated in the place of Hevelli Mons Porphyrites [a feature which we call today the crater Aristarchus].

The instrument with which I saw it was a 10 feet Newtonian Reflector of 9 inches aperture. Dr Lind's lady who looked in the telescope immediately saw it, tho' no person had mentioned it, and compared it to a star . . .

***

Last night I had an opportunity to view the Moon in a favorable situation and found that the volcano of which I saw the eruption last month was still considerably luminous. The crater seemed to glow with a degree of brightness, which I should not have been able to account for, if I had not seen the eruption last month. It appeared to me as if the crater was nearly doubled in its dimension since last month . . .

***

This is all I can give you at present. Believe me, Sir, I have not the least desire of keeping such observation to myself, but have so many subjects (which I think of greater consequence to astronomy) in hand at present that I had postponed giving an account of them to some other opportunity.

Quite analogous glows were seen in Aristarchus in 1963 by the American astronomers, Edward Barr and James Greenacre at the Lowell Observatory, Flagstaff, Arizona. Their observations were confirmed by several other observers at another telescope.

▽ The lunar crater Alphonsus had already been the subject of reports of low-lying gas clouds, or ground hazes, which obscured surface detail, when the Soviet astronomer N. A. Kozyrev performed a remarkable observation of the Moon on 3 November, 1958, at the Crimean Astrophysical Observatory. While photographing the spectrum of the sunlight reflected from Alphonsus, Kozyrev noticed a reddish cloud enveloping the central peak of the crater. (A Ranger IX photograph of Alphonsus is seen in Figure 21–9. It is the largest crater and is in the left-hand portion of the photograph. The featureless central mountain peak may also be viewed. A close-up of the crater floor of Alphonsus is seen in Figure 21–4.) He immediately obtained another spectrum, and after about thirty minutes, observed the cloud to have dissipated. He then obtained a final spectrum. Kozyrev's first and third spectra showed the usual spectrum of the Moon—namely, no lunar features at all; merely the solar spectrum superimposed on the absorption features of the Earth's atmosphere (since we are looking at sunlight reflected off the Moon and passing through the atmosphere of the Earth). The second spectrum, however, showed a broad spectral feature confined to the region of the central peak of Alphonsus that was absent on the other two spectra. Kozyrev identified this feature as due to the molecule C_2. This identification has stood the test of time and a number of critical analyses of the observation.

▽ C_2 is not a molecule encountered in everyday life on the Earth, because it is highly reactive, and combines, for example, with oxygen to form CO_2. C_2 is, however, a constituent of comet tails, where it apparently is the breakdown product of a more complex organic molecule. Similarly, the presence of C_2 on the Moon must be attributed to some larger molecule which contains two carbon atoms. The simplest such molecule is acetylene, C_2H_2, although more complex organic

FIGURE 21-9. *Ranger IX photograph of the lunar crater, Alphonsus, at left. The central peak in this crater is the apparent source of the gas emission seen by Kozyrev and others. The peak shows no central opening. (Courtesy of NASA.)*

molecules are also possible. In the reconstruction of events now accepted, acetylene or a more complex molecule was outgassed from the lunar interior, escaping in the vicinity of the central peak of Alphonsus. The molecule was then bombarded by solar radiation, which broke it down into simpler fragments, including C_2. The C_2 molecule was then excited by sunlight; the absorption and emission of light by C_2 account for Kozyrev's spectrum.

▽ Although Kozyrev, like Herschel, attributed what he saw to lunar volcanism, there seems little evidence for active volcanism of the terrestrial type on the Moon. But as Kozyrev's observations showed, outgassing from the lunar interior may be a contemporary process. Also in the crater Alphonsus, there are craters which are surrounded by dark halos. A general discoloration can be seen in the region of the large crater at the bottom center of Figure 21–4, in the floor of

Alphonsus. It has been suggested that such dark halo craters are also the result of the outgassing of material from the lunar interior. One possibility for such a material is acetylene. Kozyrev's observations, the halo craters, and the more frequent reports of glows and gas clouds do suggest the presence of organic matter beneath the lunar surface and the occasional penetration of the surface by escaping organic materials.

▽ The United States and the Soviet Union have extensive programs for the scientific exploration of the Moon, first by unmanned orbiters and landing vehicles, and followed by scientific exploration parties. Such explorations have the promise not only of determining the physical conditions at the time of the origin of the solar system, but also, through organic chemical analysis of subsurface material, of illuminating the processes which led to the origin of life on Earth. △

22

Mercury and Venus: environments and biology

. . . I have often wonder'd that when I have view'd Venus . . . she always appeared to me all over equally lucid, that I can't say I observed so much as one Spot in her . . . is not all that Light we see reflected from an Atmosphere surrounding Venus?

Christianus Huygens, *New Conjectures Concerning the Planetary Worlds, Their Inhabitants and Productions* (c. 1670)

I. Mercury

▽ Until recently, the planet Mercury was described as both the hottest and the coldest place in the solar system. Because it is the planet closest to the Sun and because it absorbs almost all the sunlight reaching it, its illuminated hemisphere should be very hot. But since the planet was thought to rotate synchronously, always keeping the same face towards the Sun, it seemed that the dark side would be heated primarily by the heat flow from within and by starlight—energy sources so feeble that the temperatures on the dark side were estimated at 20 or 30 degrees above absolute zero (about −240°C).

▽ Measurement of the infrared and radio emission of the bright side confirmed the theoretical expectation of high temperatures; values around 350°C were obtained. Recently, the first accurate measurements of the temperature on the dark side of Mercury have been made by the American astronomer Kenneth Kellerman at the Parkes radiotelescope near Sidney, Australia. Kellerman found that temperatures on the dark side were in the vicinity of 0°C, the normal melting point of ice. Thus, since the bright side of Venus is hotter, and the clouds of the Jovian planets colder, Mercury is neither the hottest nor the coldest place in the solar system.

▽ How is the temperature on the sunless side maintained? One possibility is that Mercury is not in synchronous rotation. The observations which led to deductions of synchronous rotation, by Schiaparelli, Antoniadi, and Dollfus, are very difficult to perform. Figure 22–1 shows three drawings of the Mercurian surface made by Dollfus at the Pic du Midi Observatory in the French Pyrenees, among the finest observing locales on Earth. Each drawing is based on observations made on a different night. Except for the wobble in the position of the axis of rotation of Mercury—an effect known as libration—they show approximately the same regions. While the general configuration of the markings is very similar in each of the three drawings, the differences from drawing to drawing illustrate the difficulties in observing so small an object as close to the sun as Mercury. The remarkable feature of the maps of all observers of Mercury is that they only show one hemisphere, while if the planet were in nonsynchronous rotation, it should be possible to see, at various times, aspects of both hemispheres.

▽ More recently radar techniques have been used to observe the rotation rate of Mercury. This technique for determining the rate of rotation is exactly analogous to the Doppler effect methods discussed in Chapter 13 for determining stellar rotational velocities. When a radar pulse is reflected from a planetary surface, the edge approaching the Earth changes the frequency of the reflected radar

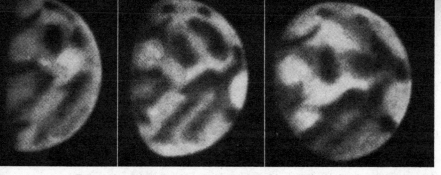

FIGURE 22–1. *Three drawings of the illuminated hemisphere of the planet Mercury made by Dr. Audouin Dollfus in October 1950. Each drawing represents the collation of several observations. Mercury evidently exhibits phases like the Moon. (Courtesy of Dr. Audouin Dollfus.)*

beam to smaller wavelengths, while the edge receding from the Earth Doppler shifts to longer wavelengths. A radar pulse which has a very small range of frequencies will, because of planetary rotation, have a much broader range of frequencies when received back on Earth after reflection. Using the world's largest radiotelescope, a dish of 1,000 ft diameter in Arecibo, Puerto Rico, the American radio astronomers Gordon H. Pettengill and Rolf Dyce of Cornell University have shown that Mercury is apparently not rotating synchronously. Rather than rotating once every eighty-eight days—a period of rotation equal to its period of revolution—these radar results suggest that Mercury is rotating once about every fifty-six. If this is the case, then the problem of maintaining the relatively high temperatures on the dark side of Mercury is solved. Even the coldest place on Mercury would have been in sunlight a few weeks previously, and there would not be sufficient time for it to cool to lower temperatures than are observed. Nevertheless, the conflict between the visual and the radar observations, both of which are difficult to perform, remains nettling, and at the present time we cannot say that the problem is solved.

▽ Polarimetric observations by Audouin Dollfus, in France, and spectroscopic observations by V. I. Moroz, in the Soviet Union, have each indicated that Mercury has a definite, although very thin, atmosphere. The illuminated hemisphere of Mercury has permanent features; these have been drawn in Figure 22–1. Antoniadi, in the 1920's, reported seeing atmospheric "veils" which temporarily obscured the dark features, an apparent analogy to the situation on Mars. The veils also suggest the presence of some atmosphere.

▽ That Mercury has any atmosphere at all is extraordinary. Because of its nearness to the Sun, its exosphere temperature should be very high. The low gravitational field of the planet and the high exosphere temperature together suggest that any but the most massive molecules would have escaped during the history of the solar system. The gas identified by Moroz is carbon dioxide, which is in fact a fairly heavy gas. But even CO_2 would have escaped during the lifetime of Mercury. The presence of an atmosphere on Mercury is probably due to an equilibrium between outgassing and escape. CO_2 and other gases are exhaled from

314

the Mercurian interior, spend a fairly brief period of time in the atmosphere proper, and escape from the exosphere. The gas which we observe at any time is the gas which happens to be in transit between the Mercurian interior and interplanetary space.

▽ If Mercury were in synchronous rotation, its dark side might be heated by hot gases which circulate from the illuminated hemisphere to the dark side, carrying their heat with them. The wind speeds required are enormous—hundreds of miles per hour. If we imagine ourselves standing near twilight on Mercury, the Sun will appear two and a half times its size as seen from Earth, and will be low in the black Mercurian sky. The landscape before us is even more parched, withered, and seared than on our own airless Moon. There is a thin but violent wind blowing towards us. The temperatures on the bright side of Mercury are hotter than the highest temperatures in the average oven; it is difficult for us to imagine any life thriving under that cruel and blazing sky.

▽ Behind us is the dark side. We think the temperatures there are equable, but we know nothing else about it. An extensive atmosphere is probably absent on the dark side, because it would recirculate to the bright side and boil off into interplanetary space. Liquid water may be present there temporarily, and we may therefore begin thinking about the possibility of life on the night side of Mercury. In the absence of sunlight, we cannot expect photosynthesizing plants. There are other energy sources, but because of the paucity of our knowledge, it does not seem profitable to speculate upon them. Yet in any inventory of biologically interesting planets Mercury must be included. Hopes have been expressed by the United States' National Aeronautics and Space Administration that unmanned exploration of the Mercurian surface may begin in the late 1970's.

II. Venus

▽ Seen through a large telescope, Venus is an even more disappointing sight than Mars. When the planet is full, we see a completely featureless disk. In the course of months, Venus exhibits crescent phases like those of the Moon, since it, too, passes between us and the Sun, and we are often presented with some combination of the bright and dark hemispheres. The dark hemisphere is invisible against the blackness of space beyond, and the crescent shape of the illuminated hemisphere is all we see [Figure 22–2]. When the planet is photographed in ultraviolet light, faint, evanescent markings can be discerned [Figure 22–3]. Venus is surrounded by an extensive, unbroken cloud deck whose composition was, until very recently, unknown. Both in the visible and in the ultraviolet, we are seeing only the clouds of Venus.

▽ Before we can proceed with the discussion of Venus, there is a semantic problem which must first be solved. Except for the Earth, the names of the planets are derived from the gods of Roman mythology. Corresponding to each god, there

FIGURE 22–2. *Venus, photographed in blue light in crescent phase. At all visible frequencies photographs of Venus such as this show no discernible markings on the disk. (Courtesy of Mt. Wilson and Palomar Observatories.)*

is a certain character, personality trait, or geological term which is commemorated in adjectival form: Mercury, mercurial; Mars, martial; Jupiter (or Jove), jovial; Saturn, saturnine; Neptune, neptunian; and Pluto, plutonic. In the case of Venus, the corresponding adjective is "venereal." Long after most of these words were ensconced in the English language, astronomers discovered the need for planetary adjectival forms which would not be confused with similar adjectives of different meaning. For some planets there was no problem. Thus, Mercury, Mercurian; Mars, Martian; Jupiter, Jovian; Saturn, Saturnian; and Uranus, Uranian. Since almost no astronomical work has been done on the physical environments of Neptune and Pluto, there is little confusion in the use of Neptunian and Plutonic.

▽ But what to do for Venus? The proper word, by analogy, is "Venerean," but many astronomers felt it to be too closely associated with its cognate, and preempted by other areas of human activity. The Italian-American astronomer Luigi Jacchia, of the Smithsonian Astrophysical Observatory, has suggested that "Venerean" be used, nevertheless, and *honi soit qui mal y pense:* but "Venerean" has not proved at all popular in the scientific literature. One sometimes finds "Venusian" as an alternative; but this is a barbarism, comparable to "Marsian,"

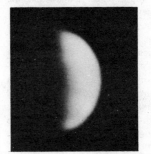  

FIGURE 22-3. *Six photographs of Venus taken in ultraviolet light. At these frequencies, markings can sometimes be discerned, especially near the terminator—the line dividing the bright and dark hemispheres. The ultraviolet features vary from day to day—perhaps from hour to hour—as these photographs show. In ultraviolet, as in visible light, we are looking at the Venus cloud level, and the variations in ultraviolet indicate, at most, violent movements of the Venus clouds. (Courtesy of Mt. Wilson and Palomar Observatories.)*

"Jupiterian," or "Earthian." The Greek goddess corresponding to Venus is Aphrodite. The appropriate adjective here, "Aphrodisian," or "Aphrodisial," again has other connotations, which some astronomers, in the interests of clarity and decorousness, prefer to avoid. The currently accepted alternative is "Cytherean," from the Ionian island of Cythera, onto which Aphrodite is said to have emerged from the sea. It is portrayed in the right foreground of Botticelli's celebrated painting, "Birth of Venus."

▽ Having clarified these monumental issues, let us consider further the Cytherean environment. Because Venus is enshrouded by clouds, direct telescopic examination of its surface was beyond the ability of the early planetary observers. In the absence of direct observations, they adduced a variety of differing and mutually inconsistent environments. Since only water clouds were familiar, the apparent thickness of the Cytherean cloud layer seemed to argue for a great abundance of water. From there, it was only a step to the assertion, seriously put forth in 1918 by Svante Arrhenius, that

everything on Venus is dripping wet . . . a very great part of the surface of Venus is no doubt covered with swamps. . . . The constantly uniform climatic conditions which exist everywhere result in an entire absence of adaptation to changing exterior conditions. Only low forms of life are therefore represented, mostly no doubt, belonging to the vegetable kingdom; and the organisms are nearly of the same kind all over the planet.

Arrhenius, it will be remembered, had criticized Lowell for deducing too much about Mars from too little data.

▽ Spectroscopic observations of such a wet world should easily demonstrate, one would think, the presence of atmospheric water vapor. Thus, it was with some surprise that observers in the 1920's found that they were unable to detect any water vapor above the clouds of Venus at all. Thus, the Carboniferous swamp model was generally abandoned, and replaced by the arid, planetary desert model. The clouds could not then be water; they were instead attributed to a permanent pall of dust, raised from the windswept surface.

▽ Unsatisfied with such an explanation of the brilliant white clouds of Venus as dust, the American astronomers Donald H. Menzel and Fred L. Whipple, of Harvard University, pointed out in 1955 that the absence of spectroscopically detectable water vapor was not a good argument against water clouds. The situation can be demonstrated by the simple analogy of a pan of water whose temperature can be controlled. At a given moment, some fast-moving H_2O molecules have broken the weak chemical bonds which bind them to their neighbors and are escaping from the pan. At the same moment, some other H_2O molecules are reentering the pan from the overlying atmosphere. Just as in the atmosphere of Mercury, the amount of water vapor above the pan depends on the equilibrium between two processes. As we reduce the temperature of the pan, there are far fewer fast-moving molecules in the liquid and therefore far fewer water vapor molecules in the atmosphere above. If the temperature of the water is sufficiently low—say, many tens of degrees below 0°C, so that the water has frozen to ice— then the amount of water vapor above the pan will be very small indeed.

▽ From the infrared emission of Venus, it was determined that the temperature of the clouds of Venus is about −40°C (by coincidence, this is also −40°F). If the clouds of Venus were made of ice crystals at a temperature of −40°C, the amount of water vapor above them would be undetectable, and no contradiction with the spectroscopic results would be implied. Menzel and Whipple then went on to argue that if large amounts of water existed in the clouds, even larger amounts must exist on the surface. In the previous unsuccessful searches for water vapor, it had been found, quite by accident, that great quantities of carbon dioxide existed in the atmosphere of Venus. Menzel and Whipple proposed, in effect, that the surface of Venus was largely covered by carbonated oceans—seltzer water.

▽ As a final example of the variety of descriptions of Venus which could be derived from the very limited data then available, let us consider the model proposed, also in 1955, by Fred Hoyle. In the early history of any planet, there will be a certain amount of water and other materials outgassed from the planetary interior, as we saw in Chapter 16. In the upper atmosphere of the planet, the water vapor tends to be photodissociated by solar ultraviolet radiation; the hydrogen escapes to space, and the oxygen remains behind to oxidize the atmosphere [see Chapter 16]. If the planet initially has much more water than hydrocarbons, all the hydrocarbons will eventually be oxidized, and an aqueous, oxidizing environment will result as on Earth. But if the initial complement of hydrocarbons greatly exceeds the amount of water, all the water will be used up in partially oxidizing the hydrocarbons to CO_2, and a CO_2 atmosphere with a large residue of surface hydrocarbons will result. While the atmosphere of Venus is thought to be largely composed of N_2, by the same argument from default that we encountered for Mars (Chapter 19), the proportion of CO_2 is perhaps a hundred times greater than in the Earth's atmosphere. Hoyle therefore proposed that the surface of Venus was covered with oil, or other hydrocarbons, and that the cloud layer was smog.

▽ The state of our knowledge of Venus in 1956 is amply illustrated by the fact that the Carboniferous swamp, the windswept desert, the planetary oilfield, and the global seltzer ocean each had its serious proponents. Those optimists planning, in 1956, eventual manned missions to Venus must have had considerable difficulties in deciding whether to send along a paleobotanist, a mineralogist, a petroleum geologist, or a deep-sea diver. We now know that none of these models is correct, and that a proper description of Venus incorporates features from several of the early models.

▽ In 1956, a team of American radioastronomers at the U.S. Naval Research Laboratory, headed by Cornell H. Mayer, first turned a large radiotelescope towards Venus. The observations were made near inferior conjunction, the time when Venus is nearest the Earth, and when, also, we are looking almost exclusively at the dark hemisphere of the planet. Mayer and his colleagues were astounded to find that Venus radiated as if it were a hot object at a temperature of about 300°C. Subsequent observations at a variety of wavelengths have confirmed these observations and have shown that the deduced temperature of Venus increases away from inferior conjunction—that is, as we see more and more of the illuminated hemisphere. The most natural explanation of these observations is that the surface of Venus is hot—far hotter than anyone had previously imagined. Venus is about 0.7 A.U. from the Sun. By the inverse square law it should therefore receive $1/(0.7)^2$, or about twice as much solar energy as does the Earth. On the other hand, its clouds are very highly reflecting. When both effects are considered, it turns out that despite its smaller distance from the Sun, Venus absorbs less sunlight than the Earth. Ordinarily, it should not even be as hot as the Earth; yet it was 300° warmer.

▽ Some early difficulties in providing a detailed explanation of the high surface temperatures led to an alternative explanation of the intense radio radiation from Venus. Douglas E. Jones, an American physicist at the Jet Propulsion Laboratory of the National Aeronautics and Space Administration, proposed that the high temperatures apply not to the surface of Venus, but to a dense ionized layer, or ionosphere, high in the Cytherean atmosphere. The difference between the hot surface and hot ionosphere models can be understood by reference to Figures 22–5 and 22–6. The radio spectrum of Venus at inferior conjunction is

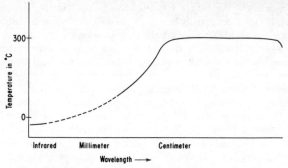

FIGURE 22-4. *Schematic representation of the long wavelength spectrum of Venus. The temperature observed rises from about −40° C, at infrared wavelengths, to over 300° C at centimeter wavelengths. Any model of the Venus environment must be able to explain this spectrum.*

given roughly by Figure 22–4. At centimeter wavelengths, the same temperature—about 300°C—is deduced at all wavelengths. But at millimeter wavelengths, there is a sharp decline in temperature, as we would expect, since the spectrum should join smoothly to the temperature of −40°C deduced in the infrared.

▽ In the hot surface model [Figure 22–5], the centimeter wavelength radiation arises from the surface and is transmitted by the atmosphere and clouds, which must be transparent at those wavelengths. At millimeter wavelengths, however, the atmosphere and clouds must absorb the radiation, so that in fact the shorter wavelength radiation arises from higher, and therefore cooler, levels of the atmosphere. In the infrared, we are observing the cold clouds.

▽ In the hot ionosphere model, however, at centimeter wavelengths we are observing emission by the ionosphere. A dense ionosphere becomes transparent towards shorter wavelengths. In the ionospheric model, at millimeter wavelengths

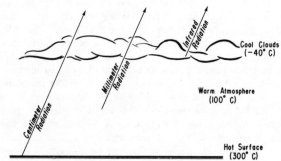

FIGURE 22–5. *Schematic representation of the hot surface model of Venus.*

LIFE IN THE UNIVERSE

we are seeing radiation emitted directly by the surface [Figure 22–6]. Note that the ionospheric model preserves the possibility of relatively low surface temperatures and therefore of the possibility of life on Venus. This is its great appeal.

▽ A distinction between the hot ionosphere and hot surface models can be gained if we imagine a radiotelescope scanning across the disk of Venus, tuned to a wavelength of about one centimeter. In the hot surface model, the atmosphere and clouds are slightly absorbing at 1 cm wavelength. Thus, when the radiotelescope looks towards the edge of the disk, there is more absorbing material in the light path than when the radiotelescope points to the center of the disk [Figure 22–7]. Thus, in the hot surface model, there should be less radiation coming from the edges, or limbs, of Venus than from the center, a circumstance known as limb-darkening.

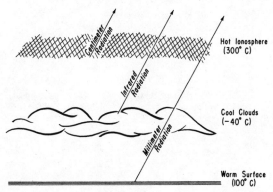

FIGURE 22–6. *Schematic representation of the hot dense ionosphere model of Venus.*

▽ In contrast, consider the hot ionosphere model [Fig. 22–8]. Here, the semitransparent ionosphere is the primary source of emission at 1 cm wavelength. At the center of the disk, the radiotelescope sees a smaller thickness of the emitting ionosphere than at the limbs. Where there is more emitting material, there should be more emission. Thus, the hot ionosphere model predicts limb-brightening. Unfortunately, the available radiotelescopes on Earth are unable to resolve, or scan across, Venus. At 1 cm wavelength, they could only determine the average emission over the entire disk. A relatively small radiotelescope, flown to the vicinity of Venus, could distinguish between limb-brightening and limb-darkening by scanning the Cytherean disk; this was a primary mission of the United States spacecraft Mariner II.

▽ A photograph of Mariner II may be seen in Figure 22–9. The extended horizontal panels are solar cells for the conversion of sunlight into electricity. At the very bottom is a directional antenna for radioing scientific results back to Earth. The radiotelescope used to scan the disk of Venus is the small disk sitting just above the main hexagonal electronics housing.

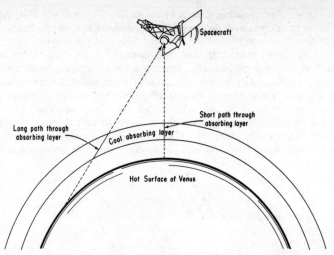

FIGURE 22–7. *Illustration of limb-darkening expected at 1 centimeter wavelength if Venus has a hot surface and a cool absorbing layer. When the spacecraft looks towards the limb of the planet, it is looking through a greater quantity of absorbing material and therefore sees a lower effective temperature.*

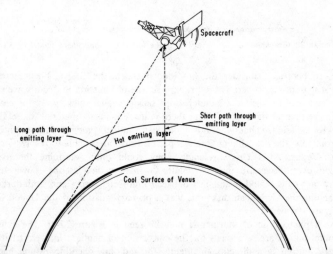

FIGURE 22–8. *Representation of expected limb-brightening on the ionospheric model of Venus. Here, when the spacecraft looks towards the limb, it sees a greater path of emitting material and therefore enhanced emission.*

FIGURE 22–9. *A photograph of the Mariner II space vehicle as it may have looked when flying by Venus on 14 December, 1962. The microwave and infrared radiometers are mounted on the disk set in the wire superstructure just above the middle of the spacecraft.* (*Courtesy of NASA.*)

▽ On 14 December, 1962, Mariner II passed within 35,000 to 40,000 km of Venus, and scanned across the disk at two wavelengths near 1 cm. Mariner II found no limb-brightening. Instead, a distinct limb-darkening was observed. These results contradict the ionospheric model and provide support for the hot surface model.

▽ This Mariner II experiment is an excellent example of the role of space vehicles in the investigation of planetary environments. A specific model of Venus had been proposed which explained most of the observations then available. The model had predictable consequences, which were different from the consequences of other models, but which could not be tested from the vicinity of the Earth. A space vehicle was needed. The spacecraft and the radiotelescope were designed and built together. Despite the fact that some expectations for the mission were not fulfilled, both the spacecraft and the radiotelescope worked well enough to provide the critical tests of the theoretical model.

▽ If, then, the ionospheric model is invalid, what makes Venus hot? From a variety of observations at visual, infrared, and radio frequencies, it has recently been established that the clouds of Venus are indeed made of water: ice crystals in the colder cloudtops, which are seen in ordinary photographs [Figures 22–2 and 22–3]; and water droplets in the bottom of the clouds, which are "seen" at long wavelengths. The CO_2 and H_2O in the Cytherean atmosphere, plus the water in the clouds, combine to produce a very efficient greenhouse effect. The atmosphere is in convective motion. Sunlight is deposited either in the clouds or directly on the surface. The sunlight which is deposited on the surface heats it immediately; the sunlight which is deposited in the clouds or atmosphere is transported by the downward convective motions, to heat the surface. The hot surface attempts to radiate in the infrared, but the absorption by the atmospheric CO_2 and H_2O and the water clouds is so great that very little heat from the surface or lower atmosphere escapes directly to space. The surface temperature must then be sufficiently high so that the small fraction of radiation which does escape to space equals the intensity of the sunlight which is absorbed by Venus.

▽ The American astronomer James B. Pollack of the Smithsonian Astrophysical Observatory and I have explored the role which water clouds can play in determining the characteristic features of the Venus environment. We find that a fairly thick layer of ice crystal clouds with water droplets below can explain in detail the spectrum of infrared and microwave radiation emitted from the planet, the limb-darkening at microwave frequencies observed by Mariner II, the variation of the centimeter wavelength temperatures with the phase of Venus, the limb-darkening observed in the infrared, and the polarization properties of the Venus clouds at optical frequencies. In addition, these clouds can explain, through the greenhouse effect, the high surface temperatures deduced from radio observations. While there are still a number of unsolved problems about Venus, the hypothesis that the clouds are water explains, in a straightforward way, a wide variety of observations.

▽ When a radar pulse is sent to Venus at centimeter wavelengths, it is transmitted by the atmosphere and clouds and strikes the surface, where it is partially absorbed and partially reflected. The part which is reflected is then returned to Earth, where it can be detected with a large radiotelescope. The ability of Venus to reflect radar gives a clue to its surface composition, just as the brightness and color of an object in reflected visible light can be used for estimating its composition. For example, extensive oceans of water or hydrocarbons can be excluded. In addition, the rotation of Venus causes a Doppler broadening of monochromatic radar pulses reflected from the planet, and the rate of rotation of Venus can be deduced.

▽ When the passive radio observations and these active radar observations are combined, some interesting conclusions about the body of Venus emerge. Venus is rotating very slowly, approximately once every 250 days; but more remarkable yet, it is rotating backwards. Except for Uranus, which is a marginal case, all the other planets in the solar system have direct rotation; that is, they are rotating in the same direction that they are revolving about the Sun. If we stand above the Earth's north pole and observe the Earth rotating from West to East beneath us, we will find that it is rotating in a counterclockwise direction. From the same vantage point, we would see the Earth revolve about the Sun, also counterclockwise. This is called direct rotation. But if we were able to make the same observation at Venus, we would find that while it revolves about the Sun in a counterclockwise sense, it rotates clockwise about its axis. This is called retrograde rotation. The cause of the retrograde rotation of Venus is unknown, but it and the slow rotation period are both probably related to tidal friction. The rotation and revolution of Venus together imply that the time from local sunrise to sunrise—the "day" on Venus—is about 116 of our days. The nights on Venus are long and hot.

▽ The surface of Venus is not covered with liquid water or pools of hydrocarbons. But any one of a large number of pulverized common terrestrial minerals could account for the properties of the Cytherean surface as determined by radio measurements. The coldest temperature on Venus is about 200°C; the warmest, about 700°C. At these temperatures, any familiar terrestrial organisms would be scorched. It is perhaps premature to exclude the possibility of completely novel organisms, based on exotic chemistry, but, from our present vantage point, the prospects for life on the surface of Venus appear very bleak indeed.

▽ The Cytherean water clouds are, perhaps, another story. They are at moderate temperatures, bathed in sunlight, abundantly supplied with water, and must contain small amounts of minerals convectively transported from the underlying surface. It is possible to imagine organisms carrying out their entire life cycle in such an environment. The clouds of Venus appear to be a possible habitat for microorganisms from Earth, if not indigenous Cytherean organisms. We will discuss this possibility further in Chapter 34.

▽ As for the surface of Venus, it is appallingly hot; because of the thick clouds, it is overcast and gloomy even in the daytime. The temperatures are so high that in some places the surface should glow with the deep ruby red of its own heat. Venus, the bright morning star, has for millennia been called and identified with Lucifer. The identification is curiously appropriate. Venus is very much like hell. △

23

The solar system
beyond Mars:
environments and biology

The inhabitants of Jupiter must . . . it would seem, be cartilaginous and glutinous masses. If life be there, it does not seem in any way likely that the living things can be anything higher in the scale of being than such boneless, watery, pulpy creatures . . .

William Whewell, 1854

I. Jupiter

▽ Moving outwards from the Sun, we glimpse the familiar Earth and ruddy Mars, which we have already discussed. If we pass those mountains of erratically drifting rubble and debris, the asteroids, we arrive at mighty Jupiter, eleven times larger than the Earth, three hundred times more massive, where the day is ten of our hours and the year is twelve of our years. The nearest and best-known of the Jovian planets, Jupiter is still far less understood than Venus or Mars.

▽ When we look at Jupiter, we see a whirling, turbulent mass of clouds and gases. The atmosphere of Jupiter is composed primarily of hydrogen and helium, with smaller amounts of ammonia, methane, and probably water. The clouds of Jupiter [Figure 23–1] are thought to be composed of frozen crystals of ammonia, but this is not certain. The temperature at the clouds is about −100°C. In this environment of unfamiliar substances and low temperatures, spots are observed suddenly to appear in the Jovian clouds. Due to the differential rotation of Jupiter (it rotates faster at the equator than near the poles), the spots are stretched out into the conspicuous, brightly colored bands which are one hallmark of the Jovian planets. The Great Red Spot of Jupiter, seen in the upper left central portion of Figure 23–1, is a generally brick-red feature observed probably for the last three centuries. It is of unknown composition and unknown origin. Jupiter is a powerful source of radio emission, but unlike that of Venus this emission does not come from any underlying surface; instead, it is probably synchrotron radiation such as that which characterizes supernova remnants [Chapter 7]. It is believed that Jupiter has an intense magnetic field which traps charged particles from the solar wind and produces the Jovian analog of the terrestrial Van Allen belts. These charged particles are accelerated by the magnetic field of Jupiter, and are thereby induced to emit synchrotron radiation.

▽ No one knows what lies far beneath the clouds of Jupiter. As in all planetary atmospheres, the density of the air must increase with the depth below the clouds. From the motions of the satellites of Jupiter, it can be concluded that there is not a solid surface a short distance below the clouds. The atmosphere is extensive, and very high densities (for a gas) will be reached only a few hundred kilometers beneath the clouds. The atmosphere of Jupiter must have densities which approach the densities of ordinary solids. Under these enormous pressures, materials take on unfamiliar properties; walking through the lower reaches of the Jovian atmosphere would be very similar to swimming. In a sense Jupiter is a vast planetary ocean, not of water, but of hydrogen and helium, with smaller amounts of methane, ammonia, and water. Far below, in the innermost recesses of the Jovian

FIGURE 23–1. *Jupiter in blue light showing bands and belts parallel to the equator, and, in the upper left-hand corner, the Great Red Spot. (Courtesy of Mt. Wilson and Palomar Observatories.)*

interior, according to the German-American astronomer Rupert Wildt of Yale University, metallic hydrogen abounds, a form of hydrogen uncommon to everyday experience, produced only under enormous pressures.

▽ It has been customary to dismiss instantly the possibility of life on Jupiter, with a reference to poisonous gases and freezing temperatures. But the gases of the Jovian atmosphere, let us recall, are far from unambiguously poisonous; indeed, they are just the components of the primitive atmosphere in which life arose on Earth [Chapter 17]. And while the temperatures at the visible cloudtops are very low, temperatures approaching room temperature will almost certainly be found a few tens of kilometers further down. Ultraviolet light supplies energy to the upper atmosphere, and lightning discharges must be common in the clouds. With an atmosphere of hydrogen, methane, ammonia, and water, an abundance of energy sources, and equable temperatures, we have exactly the conditions used in experiments on the origin of life on Earth [see Chapter 17]. Theoretical models of the Jovian atmosphere below the visible clouds, constructed by the French astronomer Roger Gallet, at the U.S. National Bureau of Standards, even predict the existence of a thick liquid water cloud. It therefore seems inescapable that large quantities of organic molecules are being produced abiologically in the atmosphere of Jupiter today, and that such conditions have been maintained for the past 4.5×10^9 years. Jupiter is in fact an immense planetary laboratory in prebiological organic synthesis.

▽ It is much more difficult to say anything about the possibility of the origin and present existence of life on Jupiter. For example, we can imagine organisms in the form of ballasted gas bags, floating from level to level in the Jovian atmosphere, and incorporating pre-formed organic matter, much like plankton-eating whales of the terrestrial oceans. However, such speculations are profitless, except as an encouragement to future studies. But when the preliminary detailed reconnaissance of our solar system is completed a century hence, it may well turn out that the greatest surprises and the most striking advances for biology attended the exploration of Jupiter.

II. Saturn, Uranus, Neptune, and Pluto

▽ The other Jovian planets, Saturn, Uranus, and Neptune, are believed to be similar in their general structure and composition to Jupiter; but since they are further from the Sun, their cloudtops are colder, and since they lie further from us, they are more difficult to study. Saturn [Figure 23–2] has spots and atmospheric bands similar to those of Jupiter, but in addition it possesses one extraordinary feature: its rings. The rings, rather than being a thin sheet, as some early astronomers naïvely supposed, are an immense swarm of small particles orbiting Saturn, much as the planets and asteroids orbit the Sun. The innermost constituents of the rings revolve about Saturn in significantly less time than the outermost. The thickness of the rings has been determined by the American astronomer Fred Franklin, of the Smithsonian Astrophysical Observatory, as at most a few centimeters. The spectra of the rings and other theoretical considerations indicate that they may be composed of ordinary water ice; if not, they are at least covered by ice. Thus, the rings of Saturn are, more or less, made of snowballs.

▽ A photograph of the outermost planet, Pluto, is shown in Figure 23–3, compared with standard photographs of Mars, Jupiter, and Saturn. Pluto is 40 astronomical units from the Sun, and even in this photograph by the world's largest optical telescope it is indistinguishable from the background stars.

III. Satellites of the Jovian Planets

▽ The 31 natural satellites of planets in the solar system vary greatly in size, appearance, and over-all density. What they have in common is our ignorance

Figure 23–2. *Saturn and its ring system. A system of bands and belts on the body of Saturn can be seen as can one of several divisions in the rings. (Courtesy of Mt. Wilson and Palomar Observatories.)*

about them. The distribution of satellites in the solar system is as follows: the Earth, of course, has one; Mars, 2; Jupiter, 12; Saturn, 9; Uranus, 5; and Neptune, 2. By the late 1970's or the early 1980's investigation of the satellites of the Jovian planet by space vehicles may begin. Until then we must be content with our very limited knowledge and the names which astronomers have granted to the satellites. Particularly exotic are the names of the satellites of Saturn, which are, in order of distance from Saturn, Mimas, Enceladus, Tethys, Dione, Rhea, Titan, Hyperion, Iapetus, and Phoebe.

▽ The satellites vary in size from the satellites of Mars, Phobos, and Deimos, which are only several kilometers in radius, to Ganymede, the giant satellite of Jupiter which is half again as large as our moon. Roughly the same size as our moon are the satellites Triton of Neptune, Titan of Saturn, and the satellites of Jupiter, Io, Europa, and Callisto. Galileo discovered Io, Europa, Callisto, and Ganymede, and for this reason they are called the Galilean satellites of Jupiter. The average densities of these satellites vary from the density of a typical rock—our moon, for example—to densities apparently below the density of water—as in the case of some of the satellites of Saturn. Such low density satellites may be nothing more than large balls of icy fluff.

　　　　　　　　　　　　　　　　　　　LIFE IN THE UNIVERSE

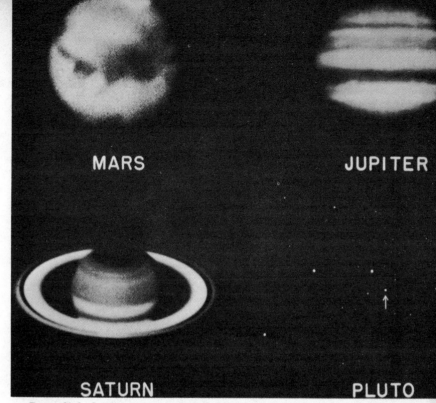

FIGURE 23-3. *Comparison of typical photographs of Mars, Jupiter, Saturn, and Pluto.* (*Courtesy of Mt. Wilson and Palomar Observatories.*)

▽ Aside from our own satellite, we know most about the Galilean satellites of Jupiter, Io, Europa, and Callisto. Crude maps of them have been prepared from visual observations and are displayed in Figure 23–4. Because they are so small and so far away, the Galilean satellites are even more difficult to observe than Mercury. All four, like Mars, show irregular patterns of dark and bright features, with some concentration of dark features towards the equator. The nature of the dark areas is entirely unknown. Similar dark features on Mars are thought by some to be connected with biological activity [Chapter 20]. The surface temperatures on these bodies are very low, −100°C or less in the bright areas; somewhat warmer in the dark areas. We are largely ignorant of possible biological processes indigenous to such low temperatures.

▽ Figure 23–4 does not give a completely adequate picture of the relative brightness of the Galilean satellites. Io is about three times brighter in the visible than Callisto, for example (and Titan reflects even less light than Callisto.) The colors of Io and Europa vary with position on their surfaces to a much greater

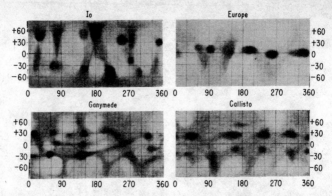

FIGURE 23–4. *Maps in Mercator projection of the four Galilean satellites of Jupiter, Io, Europa, Ganymede, and Callisto. These maps are based on visual observations, although very recently some photographs of the Galilean satellites showing surface detail have been obtained. (Courtesy of Dr. Audouin Dollfus, Meudon Observatory of Paris.)*

extent than do the colors of, for example, the other Galilean satellites. Both Io and Saturn's satellite Titan are extremely red; they reflect much less light at short visible wavelengths than at long. This fact may be connected with the presence of an atmosphere on these two satellites. Titan is known, on spectroscopic grounds, to have an atmosphere containing methane and there is some indirect evidence for an atmosphere on Io. The bright areas of the Galilean satellites are very likely to be snow, but whether this is snow of H_2O, NH_3, or CH_4, we do not yet know.

IV. Comets

▽ Comets have been a subject of fear, awe, and reverence from the beginnings of recorded history. Comets are seen as brilliant streaks against the familiar backgrounds of stars, as in Figure 23–5. Generally they do not perceptibly move against this stellar background during a single night's observing. A period of months characteristically elapses between the time when they are first seen and the time when they are too distant to be seen. New comets are discovered each year, but only rarely are they visible to the naked eye. One naked eye comet is Arend-Roland, shown in Figure 23–5, and named after the two amateur astronomers who discovered it.

▽ When a bright comet appears that is visible to the naked eye, interesting public reaction sometimes follows. When Halley's Comet last appeared, in 1910, the Earth passed through the comet's tail, which was known to be composed of poison gases. Many people expected the asphyxiation of everyone on Earth, an expectation which led to several celebrated sybaritic parties saluting the end of the

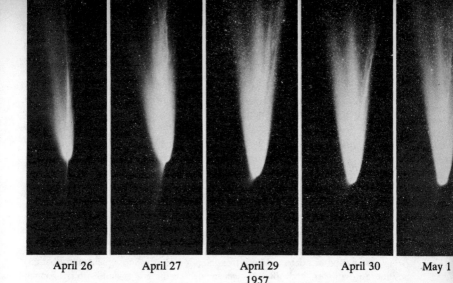

April 26	April 27	April 29	April 30	May 1
		1957		

FIGURE 23–5. *Five views of the comet Arend-Roland, all but one taken on consecutive nights. (Courtesy of Mt. Wilson and Palomar Observatories.)*

world. Their outcomes were somewhat anticlimactic: the density of matter in comet tails is so extraordinarily small that there were no detectable consequences on Earth, except the aftermaths of the celebrations.

▽ The spectral analysis of sunlight reflected from comets (which do not shine by their own light) has indicated the presence of the molecules C_2, C_3, CN, CH, NH, NH_2, OH, CO, CO_2, and N_2, either in neutral or in ionized forms. Many of these molecules—C_2 and C_3, for example—are unfamiliar because they are chemically highly reactive. They exist in comet heads and comet tails only because the density there must be very low, so that the probability of one of these molecules colliding and interacting with another molecule is small. The molecules therefore have lifetimes long enough to absorb incident sunlight and be detected by Earth-based astronomical spectroscopy. The low density of the comet tails is attested to by the fact that we can see stars, and in some cases, the Sun, through the tail and even, in some cases, through the head of the comet. The only dense portion of the comet is the nucleus, which is about 10 km across. The diffuse tail, on the other hand, may be 10^7 to 10^8 km long.

▽ The most widely accepted theory of the nature of comets, due to the American astronomer Fred L. Whipple, of the Smithsonian Astrophysical Observatory, holds them to be conglomerates of methane, ammonia, and water ices, with an admixture of impurities. Many comets are in extremely elongated orbits about the Sun. They are not observed until they are at about the distance of the orbit of Mars. At that point, the intensity of sunlight and the solar proton wind is sufficient to excite the molecules in the nucleus, force them outward from the Sun by radiation and particle pressure, and produce the prominent cometary tail. The radiation pressures involved are physically just the same as the pressures discussed in the context of the panspermia hypothesis [Chapter 15].

▽ When radiation falls upon such an orbiting snowbank, chemical interactions among H_2O, CH_4, and NH_3 will produce organic molecules, as has been demonstrated in laboratory experiments on simulated comets. The dissociation of these organic molecules by solar radiation leads to the molecular fragments, like C_2 and C_3, which are observed spectroscopically. The tails so produced are sometimes multiple, as in Figure 23–5, showing a great complexity in the fine structural details which may vary from day to day. When the comets are receding from the Sun, their tails precede them in their flight.

▽ Many comets are thought to arise from a region several hundred thousand Astronomical Units from the Sun, essentially in interstellar space. The Dutch astronomer Jan Oort, of the University of Leiden, believes that there is a vast population of cometary nuclei in orbit around the Sun at these enormous distances; these are occasionally perturbed by passing stars into orbits which enter the inner solar system and are detected by astronomers on Earth. Subsequent perturbations by the Sun, Jupiter, and other planets may drive the comets into orbits of much smaller size, so that their periodic returns may occur frequently enough to be noted on Earth. Halley's Comet has a period of about 76 years, and has been observed in historical records some 29 times. The next return of Halley's Comet will be in 1986.

▽ If comets are ordinarily denizens of interstellar space (although in orbit about the Sun), then their detailed examination would give significant clues on the still unexplored regions between the stars. In addition, many theories of the origin of the solar system hold that the comets are similar to the original material from which the solar system was formed. A detailed chemical analysis of cometary nuclei might be useful in studies of the early history of the solar system, including primitive organic chemistry. Comets approach sufficiently closely to the Earth that a rendezvous between a comet and a spacecraft is almost within the range of present technology. Interests in a cometary probe have been expressed by the European Space Research Organization, a joint establishment of many Western European countries for the scientific exploration of space.

V. The Asteroids

▽ Between Mars and Jupiter a vast horde of particles, ranging from Ceres, 350 km in radius, down to pea-sized grains and smaller, are orbiting the Sun. This is the asteroid belt. Repeated collisions among asteroids over the history of the solar system have produced a great number of small particles. The asteroid belt has been called a "cosmic grist-mill." The collisions frequently inject material into elongated orbits; some of them intersect the orbit of the Earth, and a small fraction, quite by accident, collide with the Earth in its travels about the Sun. These asteroidal fragments are the meteorites. They are divided into two general varieties, the irons and the stones, whose composition is approximately indicated by their names.

▽ The Earth can be considered divided into two regions: the core, which is composed, we think, primarily of iron; and the mantle and crust, which are composed primarily of silicates. Were the Earth shattered by some unimaginably powerful explosion, we could imagine interplanetary space littered with debris similar to the meteoritic irons and stones. There are, indeed, serious scientists who hold that the asteroids are the fragments of a destroyed planet. The total mass of the present asteroid belt is roughly equivalent to a sphere with the same density as the Earth, but with a diameter of about 1000 km. This is equivalent to the mass of a small Jovian satellite, and not to a planet. But for all we know, much of the material may have escaped during the explosion.

▽ If the asteroids are a shattered planet, we may wonder if some previous technical civilization blew its world apart. We may point out that the destruction of a planet by a technical civilization requires a state of advance—if that is the word—far beyond our present capabilities. For example, the great meteor crater in Arizona was produced by a very minor asteroidal fragment, but the energy expended in carving out the meteor crater by explosive impact is comparable to an explosion of a 20-megaton nuclear weapon, close to the present technological limits on thermonuclear devices.

▽ The bulk of astronomers who have studied the problem believe that the asteroids are not the result of a titanic explosion, but rather the remnants of a planet which never formed, perhaps because of the tidal perturbations from the nearby massive planet Jupiter.

▽ The major fraction of the stony meteorites are known as chondrites, because of the chondrules, small, glassy inclusions in the stones. Of the chondrites, a small fraction are called carbonaceous, because they contain significant quantities of organic matter. About 2% of the known meteorites are carbonaceous chondrites, and about 0.5% of the carbonaceous chondrites by mass are made of organic matter. Thus, about 10^{-2} percent of all meteoritic material which has fallen on the Earth is organic matter. For comparison, the mass of the Earth is 6×10^{27} gm; the mass of the biosphere—all the living and non-living organic matter on Earth—is a few times 10^{17} gm. Thus, the Earth is composed of something like 10^{-8} percent organic matter, and most of this is of biological origin. Why is there a million times more organic matter in the asteroid belt than on the Earth?

VI. The Carbonaceous Chondrites

▽ The carbonaceous chondrites have been used in three different ways to argue for the presence of extraterrestrial life. First, there is the organic matter itself. In 1864, a meteorite that fell near Orgueil, in southern France, was analyzed by Jon Jacob Berzelius, of Sweden, and several other of the famous chemists of the day.

They were astonished to find a large content of organic matter. The possibility of contamination by terrestrial organic matter—for example, in the soil on which the meteorite fell—was shown to be insubstantial, and the possibility of living organisms on the parent body of the Orgueil meteorite was seriously raised in the scientific literature.

▽ In recent times, Orgueil and other carbonaceous chondrites have been subjected to a rigorous and multifaceted chemical analysis. There seems little doubt of the existence of indigenous high molecular weight paraffins, long-chain aromatic hydrocarbons like tar, fatty acids, and porphyrins, the building blocks of chlorophyll. We know today, as Berzelius did not, that very complex organic molecules may be produced in the absence of life, under reducing conditions [see Chapter 17]. Thus, in itself, the demonstration that organic matter exists in the meteorites does not prove that life also exists on the meteorite parent body. It has been argued that the relative abundance of organic molecules in the carbonaceous chondrites is similar to that in undisputed samples of biological origin—for example, recent sediments, or even butter. But not enough is known about the relative distribution of organic molecules in prebiological synthetic reactions to give much weight to this argument.

▽ An even more intriguing discovery has been made by the Hungarian-American geochemist Bartholomew Nagy, of the University of California, and his colleagues. We recall from Chapter 14 that the optical activity of organic molecules is one of the hallmarks of their biological origin. With a few insignificant exceptions (insignificant because the conditions used are unlikely to recur in nature), all organic molecules produced under simulated prebiological conditions are racemic mixtures of approximately equal numbers of dextrorotatory and levorotatory stereoisomers [see Chapter 14]. Nagy and his colleagues extracted a certain fraction of the organic matter from the Orgueil meteorite and tested it for optical rotation. They found that the Orgueil organic matter was distinctly levorotatory. As controls for possible sources of contamination, they used dust and wax from the museums in which the Orgueil meteorite has been stored, and pollen, soil samples, and other organic matter. All the samples of terrestrial origin similarly prepared showed dextrorotatory optical activity.

▽ Let us consider the significance of these results. The Orgueil meteorite, like all chondrites, is porous. It had been sitting in a French museum for a century. Sizable opportunity for contamination existed. Yet it appears that all possible contaminants are dextrorotatory, while the meteorite organic matter is levorotatory. Must we then conclude that the meteorite organic matter was initially levorotatory, and that there was biological activity on the meteorite parent body? Not necessarily, for we can imagine how the optical activity may have been generated, even after the meteorite's arrival on Earth.

▽ Suppose that the Orgueil meteorite originally had only a racemic mixture of organic molecules, but that these molecules were palatable to terrestrial microorganisms. Life forms here preferentially metabolize one of the two stereoisomers.

Since most terrestrial organic matter of the type extracted by Nagy and co-workers is dextrorotatory, the dextrorotatory organic matter in Orgueil may have been digested and metabolized by terrestrial microorganisms. The levorotatory fraction would have remained untouched. In time, the meteorite would be left with only levorotatory organic matter as a result of terrestrial biological activity. It seems a pity that, because of the possibility of contamination, we cannot unambiguously deduce biological origins from optical activity. Whether the extracted fraction of Orgueil were levorotatory, dextrorotatory, or racemic, we would be unable to draw any significant conclusions about biological origins. If optical activity is to be used for the detection of extraterrestrial life, it is clear that very stringent sterilization techniques must be used; for biological contamination can destroy the entire utility of the method.

▽ Contamination is also a problem in the second argument from carbonaceous chondrites—the discovery of organized elements. In the course of their investigations of carbonaceous chrondrites, Nagy and the Hungarian-American microbiologist George Claus, of New York University Medical School, discovered that these meteorites seemed full of highly structured forms, roughly 10 microns across, which seemed to them obvious remnants of living microorganisms. Some of them were fairly amorphous, some nondescript spheres; but others had highly provocative features, such as the organized element of Type 5, seen in Figure 23–6. Here was a structure which, when stained, appeared to be of indisputable biological origin, because of the complexity of its form. It was apparently embedded in the meteorite, and resembled no known terrestrial microorganism. Is the organized element of Type 5 the first known example of extraterrestrial life?

▽ We have mentioned that carbonaceous chondrites are porous. In the course of a meteorite's entry into the Earth's atmosphere, it "breathes," and large volumes of air, containing microorganisms, are drawn through its structure. Some of them may easily become embedded in the interior of the chondrite. Although the organized element of Type 5 resembled no known terrestrial microorganism, the Latvian-American geochemist Edward Anders and the American pathologist Frank Fitch, both of the University of Chicago, found that when ordinary ragweed pollen is prepared and stained by the same procedure used by Nagy and Claus, a structure is produced which looks extraordinarily like the organized element of Type 5 [see Figure 23–7]. Two alternatives remain: We may assume that ragweed flourishes in the asteroid belt, as in the illustrations of Antoine de St. Exupery's book *The Little Prince;* or we may assume that the Orgueil meteorite was contaminated by ragweed pollen. Somewhat reluctantly we must choose the latter alternative.

▽ This does not dismiss the wide variety of other identified and named organized elements. But consider the problems inherent in their identification. We would like to be sure that an organized element was present in the meteorite when it fell. In many cases, this is impossible, because of the porosity of the meteorite. If the organized element has an exotic morphology, we should like to be sure that no terrestrial microorganisms can give a similar appearance. This is not always easy.

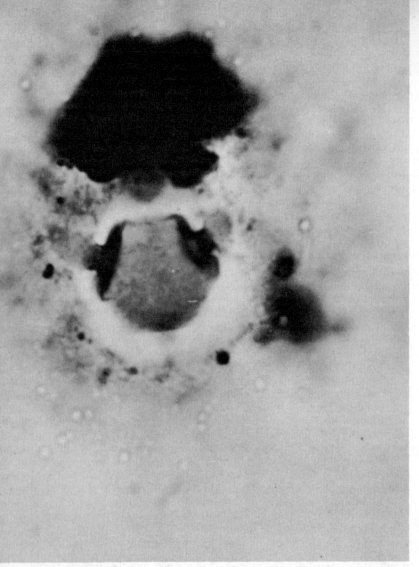

FIGURE 23–6. *The structured object below the black smudge is an organized element of Type 5, in the designation of Claus and Nagy, with an applied Gridley stain. (Courtesy of Prof. Edward Anders and Prof. Frank Fitch, University of Chicago, and Prof. Bartholomew Nagy, University of California.)*

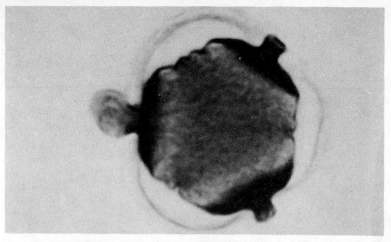

FIGURE 23–7. *Gridley stained* Ambrosia elatior *pollen grain.* (*Courtesy of Prof. Edward Anders and Prof. Frank Fitch, University of Chicago.*)

We should like to demonstrate that the organized elements are in fact themselves composed of organic matter, or a likely fossil replacement; but because they are so small, it is difficult to perform such microchemical analysis.

▽ Finally, even if the organized elements could be proved to be morphologically unique, composed of organic matter, and indigenous to the meteorite, we still have not proved that life exists on the meteorite parent body. As we saw in Chapter 17, experiments related to the origin of life have shown that highly structured forms of organic matter can be produced in the absence of life. These problems are extremely difficult, and a simple solution with a single experiment is unfortunately unrealistic.

▽ In a third category of experiments, some microbiologists have attempted to extract living microorganisms from the interiors of carbonaceous chondrites. They have tried to use extremely careful techniques to extract uncontaminated cores from the interiors of the meteorites, and to perform the microbiological cultures under sterile conditions. But as we have seen, the meteorites are porous, and contamination is virtually unavoidable. The Soviet microbiologist A. A. Imshenetskii, of the Soviet Academy of Sciences, has shown that completely sterilized meteorites become contaminated with microbes even in their deep interiors, simply after sitting on a shelf for a short period of time. △ In recent years, the Soviet scientists Bairiev and Mamedov announced to the press that they had "discovered" a special variety of bacteria in the *iron* Sichotz-Alinscii meteorite. However, it soon became apparent that this "discovery" was invalid because of the crude nature of the investigations. ▽ Similarly, in the United States, Frederick D. Sisler, of the U.S. Geological Survey, cultured samples from the interiors of carbonaceous chondrites and found that after a long period under sterile conditions, his nutrient broth clouded, and several varieties of microorganisms were found to be present. One of them was a facultative anaerobe; that is, although it was capable of living in the absence of oxygen, it also showed a preference for utilizing molecular oxygen. The only planet on which significant quantities of oxygen have been detected is our own. It is out of the question that an extraterrestrial microorganism could have developed the complex electron transfer apparatus required for utilizing molecular oxygen without a long period of evolution in an oxygen environment. Despite the apparent unfamiliarity of Sisler's microorganisms, the fact that one of them was a facultative anaerobe is strong evidence that they are in fact contaminants. △

What conclusions, then, can we draw from the organic substances and inclusions which have been found in the meteorites? Of course, it would be tempting to say that the carbonaceous chondrites constitute definite proof that there is life on other planets. In the history of science, however, there have been many instances where a desired answer was accepted, not because it had been proved correct, but merely because it was the answer sought. An old Chinese proverb states: "The man who eagerly awaits the arrival of a friend should not mistake the beating of his own heart for the thumping hooves of the approaching horse." The true nature of the carbonaceous meteorites—whether they actually contain the remnants of extraterrestrial life, or whether there is some other explanation for the presence of organic matter and organized elements—remains an unresolved question. ▽ The difficulties, frustrations, and scientific debates which this question has engendered may presage the consequences of the first search for life on Mars by an unmanned lander. But the experience gained in the analysis of the carbonaceous chondrites will be invaluable in other searches for extraterrestrial life. △

24

Life in other solar systems

. . . And yet 'tis not improbable that those great and noble Bodies have somewhat or other growing and living upon them, though very different from what we see and enjoy here. Perhaps their Plants and Animals may have another sort of Nourishment there.

> Christianus Huygens, *New Conjectures Concerning the Planetary Worlds, Their Inhabitants and Productions* (c. 1670)

Let us . . . consider a giant man sixty feet high—about the height of Giant Pope and Giant Pagan in the illustrated *Pilgrim's Progress* of my childhood. These monsters were not only ten times as high as Christian, but ten times as wide and ten times as thick, so that their total weight was a thousand times his, or about 80 to 90 tons. Unfortunately, the cross sections of their bones were only a hundred times those of Christian, so that every square inch of giant bone had to support ten times the weight borne by a square inch of human bone. As the human thigh bone breaks under about ten times the human weight, Pope and Pagan would have broken their thighs every time they took a step. This was doubtless why they were sitting down in the picture I remember. But it lessens one's respect for Christian and Jack the Giant Killer.

> J. B. S. Haldane, *On Being the Right Size* (1932)

▽ In previous chapters, we have considered the properties of the stars, the likelihood that other stars have planetary systems accompanying them through space, the requirements for the origin and early evolution of life, and the range of planetary environments which may conceivably support biological processes. Let us now try to collect these results, attempt to specify which stellar types are likely to have inhabited planets, and perhaps even indicate which of the nearer stars are the most likely candidates. While much of what we say will concern life in general, bearing in mind the objectives of Part III of this book, we will also consider at least some minimal criteria for the development of intelligent life.

▽ On our own planet, it has taken at least several hundreds of millions of years for the evolution of simple one-celled organisms from the materials of the primitive atmosphere and oceans. If we consider this a typical figure, it follows that planets of stars of spectral type earlier than A0 have not resided on the main sequence sufficiently long for the evolution of protozoa [see Table V].

▽ Again from terrestrial analogy, an even larger time interval seems to be required △ for the simplest forms of life to evolve into intelligent beings ▽ capable of constructing a technical civilization. △ The driving force behind this evolution is the natural selection of randomly produced mutations. A vast number of mutations must take place before one of them, purely by chance, aids in the development of a more advanced life form. ▽ On our planet, this process has taken about three billion years. If we believe this figure to be typical, then △ technical civilizations will probably be found only on planets associated with stars which have resided on the main sequence for at least several billions of years, that is, stars of spectral type later than F0 [see Table II, Chapter 6]. The argument from stellar rotation [see Chapter 13] has suggested that only stars of spectral type later than F2 are accompanied by planetary systems. Hereafter we shall assume, with one exception, that all main sequence stars of spectral type later than F2 have associated planetary systems.

The one exception is the first-generation stars—the sub-dwarfs [see Chapter 6]. These stars contain only negligible amounts of the heavier elements and are unlikely to have Earthlike planets. ▽ They may, however, have planets of the Jovian type; as we have seen [Chapter 23], the production of complex organic molecules, and perhaps even living systems, seems to be possible on such worlds. But we again emphasize that the general existence of planetary systems of other stars is not yet rigorously demonstrated. The existence of dark companions of the nearest stars, the argument from stellar rotation, and contemporary theories of the origin of solar systems together strongly point to a plurality of habitable worlds.

But only future developments in astronomy can demonstrate beyond the shadow of a doubt the existence of large numbers of such planets. △

All planets and satellites are not habitable. We do not expect to find life on the lunar surface because the Moon is devoid of an atmosphere and lacks surface water, ▽ or other liquids which might perform the biological role of water. △ The chemical reactions necessary for the origin of life can occur only under a certain range of temperatures. If the local climate is too hot or too cold, ▽ the larger synthesized molecules will immediately be broken down by the heat, or the rate of reaction will be so slow that relatively few chemical reactions will have occurred in the lifetime of the planet. △ In either case, life will not arise.

We can imagine each star surrounded by a spherical shell, throughout which planetary temperatures are equable, and the origin and development of life are possible. ▽ We can call this region the "zone of habitability," or the "ecosphere." The science of ecology is concerned with the relation between organism and environment. △ If a planet lies too close to its sun, the high local temperatures may preclude life. A possible example is the planet Mercury, where the temperatures on the surface facing the Sun are higher than the melting point of lead. Similarly, if a planet lies too far from its star, the local temperatures will be too cold for the origin and development of life. ▽ It is difficult, for example, to conceive of life on the planet Pluto, where the temperatures are approximately $-200°C$. △ However, very high temperatures are more hazardous for living processes than very low temperatures. We know that simple forms of life, such as viruses and bacteria, can withstand extremely low temperatures for extended periods of time.

The temperature of a planet is determined first of all by the amount of radiation that it receives from its sun on each unit of area of its surface in a given period of time. For this reason, the size of the ecosphere varies from star to star, depending on the stellar luminosity. If the local sun is of early spectral type, and hence has high luminosity, the dimensions of its ecosphere will be large. On the other hand, if the local sun is a red dwarf (of spectral types between late K stars and M's), the luminosity will be low, and the external radius of the ecosphere will be very small—smaller, in fact, than the radius of the orbit of the planet Mercury.

▽ Let us assume that planetary systems everywhere have the same relative dimensions as our own, the innermost planet lying at about 0.4 A.U. from the Sun, the outermost, at about 40 A.U., and the spacing of the planets also more or less as in our solar system. Then the probability that red dwarfs have even one planet within the local ecosphere is very small. But we do not in fact have any good theory on the expected dimensions of extraterrestrial solar systems. For all we know, the stars of late spectral type have planets which in effect huddle together very close to their star, while stars of early spectral type may have planetary systems which are very distended. △ We cannot exclude the possibility that red dwarfs, in general, have planets within their ecospheres.

If we exclude red dwarfs, and assume that habitable planets occur only around main sequence stars lying between spectral types F2 and K5, then only one to two percent of the stars in our Galaxy simultaneously meet the requirements ▽ for long lifetimes and at least one planet within the stellar ecosphere. △ However, since there are approximately 150 billion stars in our Galaxy, we still arrive at the comforting conclusion that at least a billion may have habitable planets.

▽ The American engineer Stephen Dole, of The RAND Corporation, believes that there is an additional reason that stars of later type than K1 are unsuitable. The luminosity of such stars is so low that planets must be very near their stars, for equable temperatures to be maintained. But the distance to the star must then be so small, Dole believes, that the planets would soon be locked into synchronous rotation, always keeping the same face to their sun. On a planet with no atmosphere, such trapped rotation would lead to very high temperatures in the illuminated hemisphere, and to very low temperatures in the unilluminated hemisphere; therefore life would probably be excluded from either hemisphere. However, as we have seen in the case of the planet Mercury, even a small atmosphere may be sufficient to carry enough heat by atmospheric convection to maintain a fairly balmy climate on the dark side; also, recent studies of Mercury's rotation suggest that synchronous rotation is not the only possibility for a close planet in an elliptical orbit. △

Let us consider another circumstance which might limit our estimate of the number of habitable planets in the Galaxy. Nearly half of the stars belong to multiple systems. The orbit of a possible planet associated with a binary stellar system would, in general, follow a very complex and unclosed path ▽ —that is, an orbit which does not, like familiar circular or elliptical orbits, close back upon itself. △ The calculation of such an orbit is an extremely complex mathematical undertaking, the solution of the so-called restricted three-body problem. Despite its difficulties, this problem is simpler than the general three-body problem, because here the mass of the planet is negligible compared with the mass of the two stars. The planet has no influence on the stellar motion, although its motion is influenced by the more massive stars. Traveling in such a complex orbit in or about a binary system, the planet would at times approach one of the stars very closely; at other times, it would recede to great distances. Thus, its surface temperature would vary greatly ▽ and more or less erratically, posing great difficulties for life, if not excluding it altogether. △

Until recently, it was generally accepted that habitable planets could not be associated with multiple star systems. However, this problem has now been reexamined by the Chinese-American astronomer Su-Shu Huang, of Northwestern University, who has shown that in certain special cases there do exist possible periodic planetary orbits in multiple star systems.

The temperature variation on such planets is within the allowable limits for the development of life. In these special cases, the relative orbits of the stars are approximately circular. Figure 24–1 shows a cross section of the so-called "critical surfaces" in the restricted three-body problem. Clement temperatures are associated with periodic orbits which lie either inside the surface passing through the point L_1, or outside the surface passing through the point L_2. Let us consider the simpler case that the masses of both stars are identical. We express the distance between the stars, measured in Astro-

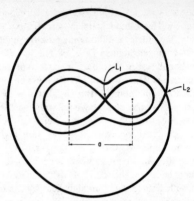

FIGURE 24-1. *Diagramatic representation of the critical surfaces in the restricted three-body problem. Periodic orbits are permitted about each of the stars represented by points, provided these orbits lie within the figure-eight curve. Alternatively periodic orbits are permissible outside the outer curve. Such orbits would circle both stars.*

nomical Units, as *a,* and the luminosity of each star, in units of the luminosity of our Sun, as *l.* ▽ Thus, if *a* = 5, the stars are 5 A.U. apart; if *l* = 0.8, then each star has ⅘ the luminosity of our Sun. △ Huang has shown that inside the surface passing through the point L_1, orbits suitable for the development of life exist, provided that *a* is greater than 2 $l^{1/2}$. When *a* is greater than 13 $l^{1/2}$, it is possible to consider each component of the binary star system as a single star. ▽ Thus, for stars of solar luminosity, appropriate orbits exist if they are separated by more than 2 A.U.; and we may ignore the fact that it is a binary star system if the components are separated by more than 13 A.U. △

In many binary systems, the distance between the components exceeds the critical value of 2 $l^{1/2}$. When the components of the double star system are close to one another, suitable periodic orbits must be outside the surface which passes through the point L_2 [again, compare with Figure 24-1]. The calculations of Huang show that when the components of a binary system have equal mass, orbits suitable for the origin and development of life can exist, provided that *a* is less than 0.4 $l^{1/2}$. Thus, habitable planets are excluded if the distance between the stars is between 0.4 $l^{1/2}$ and 2 $l^{1/2}$. Analogous results can be obtained for the more common case that the masses of the two components are unequal.

Conceivably, multiple star systems are formed in such a way that the simultaneous formation of planetary systems is excluded. ▽ But this is, at the moment, only a conjecture. △ Although it appears much more likely that habitable planets orbit single stars, in principle they can also exist in association with multiple star systems.

The stellar system closest to our own, Alpha Centauri, is in fact a triple system. ▽ The two major components, Alpha Centauri *A* and Alpha Centauri *B,* have spectral types G2 and K4, respectively. Thus, Alpha Centauri *A* has a spectral type very similar to that of our Sun. The third component, Alpha Centauri

C, also called Proxima Centauri, because at times it is the closest star to our Sun, is a red dwarf of spectral type M5e. △ The relative orbits of the two larger components are elliptical. The semi-major axis* of these two components of Alpha Centauri is 23.4 A.U. The distance between these two major components is therefore great enough to permit each of them to have planets with stable periodic orbits of biological interest. However, the extreme eccentricity of the paths of these stars with respect to each other requires special consideration, since the expressions above were deduced for binary systems having circular orbits. Further, Alpha Centauri seems to be a comparatively young system. It is possible that the component stars have not as yet entered the main sequence. ▽ In this case, there would not have been sufficient time for the origin and early evolution of life on planets of the Alpha Centauri system. △

For a star to have a habitable planetary system, the radiation emitted by it must remain approximately constant for perhaps billions of years. ▽ Other factors being equal, a few percent change in the solar luminosity would have drastic effects on the temperature of the Earth [Chapter 16]. △ The overwhelming majority of stars on the main sequence are remarkably constant in their radiation output. Geological studies indicate that our own Sun has varied its luminosity no more than a few tenths of one percent ▽ over the last few hundreds of millions of years △. There is, however, a large class of variable stars where luminosities fluctuate greatly. ▽ Such stars are unlikely to have habitable planetary systems. △

Among other conditions which must be satisfied, if a planet is to harbor indigenous life, are the mass of the planet and the chemical composition of its atmosphere. As we discussed in Chapter 16, these two characteristics are apparently not independent of one another. ▽ We saw there that at a given exosphere temperature and planetary gravitational field, the lighter atoms will preferentially escape to space. As the exosphere temperature becomes higher (because, for example, the planet is nearer its sun), or as the force of gravity declines (because, for example, we are considering a planet of low mass), the rate of escape of all atoms is enhanced.

▽ With the mass, radius, and exosphere temperature of the Earth, hydrogen should escape in geologically brief periods of time, while the rate of escape of oxygen over all of geological time is insignificant. The mass of the Moon, however, is so much less than the mass of the Earth that even if its exosphere temperature were the same as the Earth's, very heavy gases should escape during the lifetime of the solar system. Thus, any residual hydrogen in the Earth's atmosphere, and any residual atmosphere at all on the Moon, must be due to a continuous supply of atmosphere, probably from the interior of these bodies. In the absence of an atmosphere, a planet cannot maintain an ocean of water or of any other kind of liquid; but liquids or very dense gases seem required for molecular interaction in the origin and evolution of life. Thus, except for the fairly remote possibility of the

---

* ▽ The longest straight line that can be drawn through an ellipse is called the major axis; half the major axis is called the semi-major axis. △

subsurface origin and evolution of life, a planet must have an atmosphere to be habitable. △

On the other hand, a very large planetary mass can also be a limiting factor. For example, the giant planets Jupiter and Saturn have almost completely retained their original atmospheres, rich in hydrogen and helium. If a planet preserves the original composition of the medium from which it was formed, its hydrogen-helium atmosphere must be very dense. The possibility of such a planet forming a hard surface is problematical. ▽ Whether Jupiter, Saturn, Uranus, and Neptune are completely gaseous spheres, with their density rapidly increasing towards their centers, or whether they in fact have a crust of rock or of more exotic composition far below the visible atmosphere, is at the present time unknown. △ We have already pointed out that if the mass of a planet were 5 or 10 times greater than that of Jupiter, it would not differ appreciably from a dwarf star. ▽ We have mentioned that the chemical composition of a massive planet of the Jovian type does not necessarily exclude the origin and development of life, although it does imply that the character of that life would be very different from life on Earth. △

In order for life to arise and develop on a planet, the mass of the planet must lie between certain limits. ▽ For a planet with an exosphere temperature similar to the Earth's (about 1500°K), a mass about 10 times smaller than the Earth's would result in a significant escape of the atmosphere into interplanetary space during geological time. If the mass were several tens of times greater than the Earth's, substantial quantities of hydrogen would be retained, and the planetary chemistry would be highly reducing. If the planetary mass were some 2000 times larger than the Earth's, the "planet" would in fact be a small star. But these mass limits for habitability—between 0.1 and 2000 Earth masses—are so broad that the bulk of expected planets will be included. △

The fact that the terrestrial planets lie in the inner and warmer part of the solar system, while the larger Jovian planets, of reducing composition, lie in the outer and colder portions is probably not a simple coincidence. ▽ It may be that planets of terrestrial type always form in the inner regions of the solar system, where the early dissipation of the lighter gases, hydrogen and helium, is facilitated. Jovian-type planets tend to contain the fully reduced gases methane, ammonia, and water vapor, which are very efficient absorbers of infrared radiation. Thus, Jovian planets in general tend to have very efficient greenhouse effects, so that relatively warm temperatures can be expected, at least at some level in their atmosphere or clouds, even if they are very far from their sun.

▽ With the preceding criteria we could make some estimate of the probable habitability of a given extraterrestrial planet, if only we had some information about that planet. Unfortunately, as we discussed in Chapter 11, the identification and characterization of extraterrestrial planets are just beyond our present capabilities. Such information may be supplied by new astronomical techniques within the next decade. All we can do, therefore, is to survey the nearest stars and estimate what fraction of them have appropriate ecospheres.

▽ If we assume that other planetary systems always have the same distribution

TABLE V

THE TWENTY NEAREST STARS OF SPECTRAL TYPE BETWEEN F2 AND K5

Star	Spectral type	Distance in light years
Alpha Centauri A	G2	4.3
Alpha Centauri B	K4	4.3
Epsilon Eridani	K2	10.8
61 Cygni A	K5	11.1
Epsilon Indi	K5	11.3
Tau Ceti	G8	12.2
70 Ophiuchi A	K1	17.3
70 Ophiuchi B	K5	17.3
Eta Cassiopeiae A	F9	18.0
Sigma Draconis	G9	18.2
36 Ophiuchi A	K2	18.2
36 Ophiuchi B	K1	18.2
HR 7703 A	K2	18.6
HR 5568 A	K4	18.8
Delta Pavonis	G7	19.2
82 Eridani	G5	20.9
Beta Hydri	G1	21.3
HR 8832	K3	21.4
p Eridani A	K2	22.0
p Eridani B	K2	22.0

of planets as our own system, we will probably obtain a lower limit on the number of nearby stars likely to have habitable planets. We then find that the nearest stars likely to possess habitable planets are, in order of their distance from the Sun, those of Table V. We have presented the nearest twenty such stars. Designations beginning "HR" refer to the Harvard Revised Catalogue. We emphasize that the list would be very much longer had we included late K and M dwarfs. Since the number of nearby stars increases as the cube of the distance from the Sun, the bulk of these stars lie between 17 and 22 light years from the Sun. We have included components of multiple star systems where they have matched the range in spectral types, although there is a suspicion that the process of formation of multiple star systems may preclude the formation of planets.

▽ If we exclude multiple star systems, we find that the three nearest stars of potential biological interest are Epsilon Eridani, Epsilon Indi, and Tau Ceti. It is reasonable that any search for life beyond our solar system should begin with these stars. If we restrict our attention to single stars of spectral type quite close to that of the Sun—let us say, between F5 and G9—we find that the four closest such stars are Tau Ceti, Sigma Draconis, 82 Eridani, and Beta Hydri. If, despite the implications of present evidence, the formation of planetary systems and the origin of life are rare events, none of the stars listed in Table V would hold inhabited planets. Instead, the nearest life forms would lie at much greater distances beyond the nearest stars.

▽ The range of planetary environments, even in our own solar system, is startling. The airless, waterless surface of our Moon is alternately very hot and very cold. The night side of Mercury, with a very thin atmosphere and no sun at all, nevertheless is at a moderate temperature. Venus, with a massive atmosphere, is at temperatures approaching red heat; Jupiter, with its dense, reducing atmosphere, is very cold at the clouds, and probably very warm beneath them. The force of gravity at the clouds of Jupiter is more than 10 times that at the surface of the Moon. The environments are diverse; each planet and satellite are unique. In other solar systems, we can expect an even greater diversity, although general patterns should also emerge: The distinction between Jovian and terrestrial planets is probably a universal one.

▽ What can we say about the forms of life evolving on these other worlds? We have argued that the early chemical processes leading to the origin of life may be similar on many diverse worlds, although this is far from proved. But it is clear that subsequent evolution by natural selection would lead to an immense variety of organisms; compared to them, all organisms on Earth, from molds to men, are very close relations.

▽ There are limiting sizes to organisms on any given planet. An organism must be large enough to carry out a minimum of metabolic functions required for its continued replication. The smallest organism known on Earth capable of independent replication is called PPLO, for pleuropneumonia-like organism. It is about 10^{-5} cm across. The upper limit to the size of land-dwelling animals derives from several factors. As the Haldane epigraph to this chapter underlines, if an organism is too large, it will be unable to support its own weight. A second limitation concerns the rate of propagation of signals through the animal's nervous system. If the animal is too large, a signal—for example, from the light receptors, saying, "Stop; a crevasse lies immediately ahead"—will be received by the distant legs too late for useful action. As a partial solution to this problem, dinosaurs had extensive neural networks in their posteriors. Larger animals can be maintained if there is a buoyant medium for support, as, for example, in the oceans, or in a very dense atmosphere.

▽ Most familiar organisms have two, four, or six legs, but adaptations to none or to many, as in snakes or millipedes, have occurred. There seems no reason for extraterrestrial organisms to have any particular number of legs—or, for that matter, any legs at all. In other environments, other specialized motility schemes may have been derived. Certainly, at the level of protozoa this is the case, where flagellae, cilia, and even a kind of ramjet, are commonly used for biological propulsion.

▽ The greater the gravity of the planet, the smaller will be the largest animals. On planets with low gravity, there may be organisms which, from our point of view, would be long and spindly. The same, incidentally, applies to architecture in advanced extraterrestrial civilization's. High-gravity worlds should have short and squat structures; low-gravity worlds are at least permitted more delicate forms.

▽ We have mentioned in Chapter 16 that on other worlds respiration may not be required, and that fairly advanced forms may be found even in reducing environments. The size of respiring organisms is also limited by the method of respiration. There are no insects larger than about a foot across, because insects introduce oxygen into the interior parts of their bodies by diffusion, a much slower and less efficient process than the circulation of blood.

▽ The number of possible sensory receptors in extraterrestrial organisms is apparently limited. On planets with fairly extensive atmospheres or oceans, sensory receptors for direct chemical analysis of molecules in the atmosphere or ocean would clearly be useful. While a variety of bioanalytic techniques would be possible, these senses would be roughly equivalent to our senses of taste and smell. The usefulness of a sense of hearing depends on the composition, and temperature, of the atmosphere, which determines the velocity of sound. Pressure receptors, such as our sense of touch, seem useful in almost any environment.

▽ The most efficient means of sensing distant objects is the reception of electromagnetic radiation. Since the velocity of light is so large, the propagation time on a planetary surface is negligible. Almost all stars of interest emit the bulk of their radiation in what we call the visible part of the spectrum. In general, we should expect more reflected visible light to be available than light of any other frequency. Furthermore, the visible part of the spectrum is the wavelength range least likely to be absorbed by atmospheric constituents. Transitions of the electrons in atmospheric gases result in light absorption in the ultraviolet. The vibrations of molecules cause absorption in the infrared. The rotation of molecules causes absorption at infrared and short radio wavelengths. Thus, for fundamental physical reasons, the visible wavelength interval is a "window" region of transparency in all planetary atmospheres. Another window should, in general, be found at long radio wavelengths, beyond 3 cm. However, there is a primary difficulty in imagining organisms which "see" with radio waves: In order to have any useful resolution—that is, detection of fine visual detail—the effective collecting area must be enormous. To have the same resolving power at 5 cm wavelength that the eye has at 5000 Å wavelength, an extraterrestrial microwave "eyeball" would have to be roughly half a mile in diameter. This seems awkward.

▽ In terrestrial organisms, optical senses are used primarily for observations in reflected sunlight. There are occasional instances of animals which emit visible light, such as certain marine animals and fireflies. The female of the latter species winks seductively at the male. Elsewhere—particularly on worlds where sound propagation is not utilized (for example, because of a very thin atmosphere)—we can imagine the more elaborate development of communication by electromagnetic propagation, probably of visible light, but not necessarily. If such a species communicated by radio waves, despite the attendant poor resolution, we would probably attribute extrasensory perception to them. But it should be emphasized that this is "extrasensory" only in that it is a sense we lack. Such an adaptation can be based on perfectly sound physical principles. There is some evidence that human beings can sense high-intensity radar, although the mechanism is at the present time unknown.

▽ One eye gives two-dimensional resolution; a second eye, through binocular vision, gives three-dimensional resolution. Three eyes represent not nearly the same improvement over two that two represent over one. But if placed in the back of the head, for example, a third eye might serve some useful purpose. Some animals in the Mesozoic seem to have had three eyes, all in the front of the head, and some physiologists believe that the human pineal gland is a vestigial remnant of a third eye in the middle of the forehead. Representations of the Buddha sometimes show such a third eye.

▽ Devices for acquiring, reprocessing, and excreting food would probably vary widely from world to world, depending on the nature of the food chain and the relationship of the various organisms. There seems no reason to expect elsewhere the same combination of functions that we find on the Earth, where the vocalizing, breathing, and eating organs have been combined, to a certain degree, as have the organs of excretion and reproduction. Elsewhere, different combinations of functions may prevail.

▽ Even such a brief and tentative excursion into extraterrestrial ecology cannot be tested until we have obtained samples of extraterrestrial organisms. Yet such simple considerations are useful, because they shed some light on the selective advantages of the forms and functions of terrestrial organisms. △

12/31/56

"Want To Know How It Ends?"

"I'm sorry, sonny. We've run out of candy."

INTELLIGENT LIFE
IN THE UNIVERSE

Lights come and go in the night sky. Men, troubled at last by the things they build, may toss in their sleep and dream bad dreams, or lie awake while the meteors whisper greenly overhead. But nowhere in all space or on a thousand worlds will there be men to share our loneliness. There may be wisdom; there may be power; somewhere across space great instruments, handled by strange, manipulative organs, may stare vainly at our floating cloud wrack, their owners yearning as we yearn. Nevertheless, in the nature of life and in the principles of evolution we have had our answer. Of men elsewhere, and beyond, there will be none forever.

Loren Eiseley, *The Immense Journey* (1957)

25

The assumption of mediocrity

. . . That which makes me of this Opinion, that those Worlds are not without such a Creature endued with Reason, is that otherwise our Earth would have too much the Advantage of them, in being the only part of the Universe that could boast of such a Creature . . .

Christianus Huygens, *New Conjectures Concerning the Planetary Worlds, Their Inhabitants and Productions* (c. 1670)

. . . the intelligent part of creation is thrust into the compass of a few years, in the course of myriads of ages; why not then into the compass of a few miles, in the expanse of systems?

William Whewell, *Plurality of Worlds* (1854)

Life, even cellular life, may exist out yonder in the dark. But high or low in nature, it will not wear the shape of man. That shape is the evolutionary product of a strange, long wandering through the attics of the forest roof, and so great are the chances of failure, that nothing precisely and identically human is likely ever to come that way again.

Loren Eiseley, *The Immense Journey* (1957)

▽ **A**re there other intelligences in the universe? Is the Galaxy filled with civilized worlds, diverse and unimaginable, each flourishing with its own commerce and culture, befitting its separate circumstances? Or can it be that we are alone in the universe, that by some poignant and unfathomable joke, ours is the only civilization extant?

▽ The idea that we are not unique has proved to be one of the most fruitful of modern science. The atoms on Earth are the same in kind as those in a galaxy some 5 or 10 billion light years distant. The same interactions occur, the same laws of nature govern their motions. The formal statement summarizing the attraction of massive lead spheres in a terrestrial laboratory can also be used to predict accurately the motions of binary stars, or the orbit of the Moon. One of the major intellectual revolutions of the Renaissance, one for which Copernicus and Galileo fought, and for which Giordano Bruno lost his life, was the idea that the Earth was but one of many planets in our solar system and beyond. △

The power of this idea, ▽ the assumption of our own mediocrity, the thought that our surroundings are more or less typical of any other region of the universe △ has been emphasized by the German astronomer Sebastian von Hoerner at the National Radio Astronomy Observatory in the United States. The ancient Greeks were unaware of the true nature of the stars or the scale of the universe. ▽ Some primitive peoples believe the stars to be lanterns hung from the vault of heaven, or holes cut in the celestial panoply, showing the fires which burn beyond. That the stars are distant suns is a subtler and more powerful idea. △ But in principle, the Greeks could have determined the dimensions of the solar system and the distances to the stars.

Let us assume that the Earth is an average planet, and that the Sun is an average star. Then the diameter of the Earth, its distance from the Sun, and its albedo, or reflectivity, should be characteristic of planets in general. Since the Greeks already knew the approximate dimensions of the Earth (Eratosthenes had performed an essentially correct calculation), a comparison of the apparent brightness of the five planets then known with the apparent brightness of the Sun permits a calculation of the distance from the Earth to the Sun. The value obtained in this way is about twice the true value.

If we were to assume that the ten brightest stars in the sky were also suns like our own, and if we knew how much brighter the Sun appears than these stars, it would be possible to compute *their* distance from the Earth in terms of the distance of the Sun from the Earth. And with the value of the Astronomical Unit obtained from the apparent brightness of the planets, the ancient Greeks could have estimated the average distance between the stars with an error of a mere 10%.

▽ In the seventeenth century, Christian Huygens in fact attempted such a calculation. He constructed a thin metallic plate which could artificially eclipse the image of the Sun. A series of small holes were punctured in the plate, until a hole was made which was so small that the sunlight passing through it seemed no brighter than the star Sirius. Huygens found that his hole had an angular diameter about 1/28,000 that of the Sun. Assuming that Sirius and the Sun have the same intrinsic brightness, Huygens deduced that Sirius was 2.8×10^4 further from the Earth than the Sun. Since one Astronomical Unit is about 1.5×10^{13} cm, Huygens concluded, in effect, that Sirius was 4.2×10^{17} cm, or about 0.45 light years distant. The correct figure is almost a factor 20 larger. The discrepancy is due primarily to Huygens' adoption of the assumption of mediocrity: Sirius, a dwarf star of spectral type A1, has an intrinsic luminosity some 60 times greater than the Sun. △

Thus, although such estimates have only probabilistic character, the assumption of mediocrity will, in many cases, give a valid rough answer, when a detailed scientific justification lies beyond the present capabilities of science.

▽ Nevertheless, the application of this method to areas where we have little knowledge is essentially an act of faith. For example, one exercise which we shall later carry through is to estimate the likelihoods of the origin of life in a suitable planetary system, the origin of intelligence, the origin of technical civilization, etc. Such estimates are, either implicitly or explicitly, based upon terrestrial experience. But it is dangerous to extrapolate from one example. This is why, for example, the discovery of life on one other planet—e.g., Mars—can, in the words of the American physicist Philip Morrison, of the Massachusetts Institute of Technology, "transform the origin of life from a miracle to a statistic."

▽ For the origin of intelligence and of technical civilizations, finding another example may be even more difficult than the detection and characterization of life on Mars. We must recognize the possibility that even with as many as 10^{22} planets in the accessible universe, the probability that one of them possesses a technical civilization may be 10^{-22} or less. We may feel that the probability must be higher, but we do not *know*. Indeed, the determination of such probabilities is one of the major motivations of a search for intelligent extraterrestrial life.

▽ Another question of some relevance to our own time, and one whose interest is not restricted to the scientist alone, is this: Do technical civilizations tend to destroy themselves shortly after they become capable of interstellar radio communication? The establishment of interstellar radio contact may permit an estimate of such probabilities.

▽ As an example of the difficulties inherent in establishing a priori probabilities, consider the question of the origin of intelligent life on Earth. We have emphasized that evolution is opportunistic, not foresighted. We have five digits on each hand and foot not, we think, because there is any intrinsic advantage to five, versus four or six, but because we have evolved from a Devonian predecessor, an amphibian with five bones homologous to our present phlanges. This example is trivial for the question of the origin of intelligence; but suppose that we had some evolutionary patrimony which was not irrelevant, but rather *detrimental* to the development of intelligence—some characteristic so deep-seated, so intimately woven in the fabric of life that the development of intelligence would be unlikely. Surely, all conceivable adaptations are not achieved, even when they may have high selective value. There must be tractable evolutionary pathways from here to there. For example, there are no organisms on the Earth which have developed tractor treads for locomotion, despite the usefulness of tractor treads in some environments. The improbability of achieving such an adaptation through slow evolutionary process must outweigh its potential adaptive advantage.

▽ So we may ask whether the development of human intelligence was a fortuitous occurrence. Intelligence itself arose early, and the development of tool-using capabilities evolved with birds and non-human primates. But the ecological circumstances surrounding the evolution of contemporary human intelligence are essentially unknown. Some anthropologists believe that human communities developed in response to the inclemency of late Pliocene and Pleistocene times, perhaps because of the recession of the forests in which pre-human communities had lived, or perhaps because the cold new climate placed a premium on new habits of dress, food, and habitat. But if there had been no Pleistocene ice ages, would intelligence have developed on Earth?

▽ Some scientists have been especially impressed by the number of individually unlikely events which are together responsible for the development of men and human intelligence. They have emphasized that even if the Earth were started out again from scratch, and only random factors allowed to operate, the development of anything like a human being would be highly unlikely. But others have been impressed with the high selective value of intelligence. Provided that we do not use our intelligence to destroy ourselves, it and the civilization which now accompanies it are among the most significant developments in the history of life on Earth. We have occupied all habitats, tamed or destroyed all competitors and predators, and some of us are about to leave these Earthly confines for other places. Even though the development of humans—or their rough extraterrestrial anatomical equivalents, humanoids—is unlikely, might not the development of their intellectual equivalents be a pervasive evolutionary event?

▽ The development of intelligence and technical civilization has occurred about midway during the main sequence residence time of our Sun. If we were to extrapolate from one example, using the assumption of mediocrity, we would conclude that all planets on which life has flourished for several billions of years have a high probability of the development of intelligence and technical civilization. But this is at best a plausibility argument; we do not know the detailed factors involved in the development of intelligence and technical civilization. △

It would seem, then, that this book is concerned with an unsolved—if not unsolvable—problem. Is it in fact possible to call a book dealing with intelligent life in the universe "scientific"? ▽ We are deeply convinced that the problem can be approached responsibly only if the assumptions involved are stated explicitly, and if the most efficient use of the scientific method is made. Even then, we shall not come to many final answers, but the formulation of the problems has itself significance and excitement.

▽ One conceivable approach is to assume that civilizations in various states of historical development exist throughout our Galaxy, and then to see what observational consequences this assumption implies. Humanity is relatively young; our civilization is in its infancy. Hominids have inhabited the Earth for about 0.1% of its history; our civilization has so far endured only for one-millionth the lifetime of the Earth; and technical civilization, in the sense of the capability for interstellar radio communication, has been present for about one-billionth of geological time. It is then immediately obvious that if there are civilizations on planets of other stars, they should, in general, be much more highly developed than our own. Whether this development includes social, scientific, artistic, or technical aspects, or other aspects which we cannot even imagine, is difficult to foretell. But establishing contact with an extraterrestrial civilization evokes, in exaggerated form, some of the same problems as would face the crew of an Algonquin war canoe, miraculously transported to contemporary Upper New York Bay. △ It would seem an almost impossible task to forecast the development of society for thousands or more years into our future. Historians tend to avoid such problems; ▽ they have difficulty enough understanding the past, without foretelling the future. △ Nevertheless, we believe that some regularities and general tendencies about the evolution of civilizations can be stated.

Judging from our only example, there is an important peculiarity of advanced forms of intelligent life: they strive for active control of the universe. Man is already venturing beyond the Earth and taking his first timid steps toward remaking the solar system. Possible influences of intelligent life in the Galaxy, but on a much grander scale, will be discussed in Chapter 34. For billions of years, the Earth has had only one satellite; ▽ now, there are thousands. △ The artificial satellites are, of course, small; yet they are larger than the tiny satellites of Saturn which form its remarkable rings. Our civilization could establish an artificial ring about this planet, an engineering feat which seems well within the reach of contemporary technology. There appears to be no use for such a ring at present; but if there were, we could create one within a few decades. ▽ In fact, the orbiting of a belt of small needles by the United States Air Force some years ago, in an operation called "Project Westford," demonstrated the feasibility of such an enterprise. △

In Chapter 18, we mentioned that because of the activities of man, the brightness temperature of the Earth in the meter wavelength range has increased a millionfold during the last two or three decades. Intelligent life has made our small planet the second most powerful radio source in the solar system. It is entirely possible that in future decades our planet will—at least at some times and some frequencies—become as powerful a source of radio radiation as the sun.

We shall show in Chapter 28 that an analogous situation can, in principle, be created at optical frequencies. The development of quantum generators of optical radiation—the lasers—opens the possibility of sending narrow beams of almost monochromatic light over vast interstellar distances. At a given frequency and direction, the intensity of optical emission from the Earth may greatly exceed that of the Sun.

These are only a few examples of those cosmic manifestations of intelligent life that can be predicted by modest extrapolations of existing technology. But what will come after? The specific course of the active influence of intelligent life on the universe is not easy to forecast; but the trends in development are entirely obvious. ∇ If there are many technical civilizations in the universe, only a small fraction need have the same urge to expand and control that our species possesses, for there to be a wholesale remaking of the universe.

∇ When we attempt to make a prognosis of the most general aspects of intelligent society in the distant future—say, millions of years hence—modest extrapolations from existing technology do not suffice. We might restrict ourselves only to what is physically possible, even though it may be technically far beyond our present imaginings. But for million-year timescales, even this procedure is hopelessly modest. New scientific principles will of course be discovered, and it is impossible for us to forecast their nature or even their direction. Perhaps a sign of a very advanced civilization will be the abandonment of the urge to expand and control. Perhaps a sign of a truly advanced civilization will be the voluntary abandonment of technical pursuits for activities of another kind. In the Russian edition of the present work, Shklovskii expresses his hope that "Marxist philosophers will become interested in the problem of large-scale predictions of the future of humanity," and apologizes for setting forth his own ideas, because he is not a specialist in scientific augury. But there are no specialists in this subject; there may not even be such a subject. △ But at least, the mistakes made here will encourage more fruitful discussions in the future.

In the remainder of Part III, we will touch upon a large number of problems. First, we shall consider an analysis of some modes of possible reconstruction of the cosmos by intelligent beings. As examples (perhaps not entirely hypothetical), we shall consider the problems of the moons of Mars and of the Dyson shell hypothesis. Then we consider a wide range of possible modes by which contact may be established with intelligent extraterrestrial life. Some of the chapters of Part III contain mathematical calculations which may present some difficulty for the general reader. However, they are required to substantiate some of the conclusions derived. ∇ Since this phase of the subject is so new, it is not possible to refer to standard references. We have tried to construct the analysis in such a way that the detailed calculations can be omitted without substantially impairing comprehension of the major points. To this end, unessential mathematical details are given in small print. △ The material in these chapters is new, and to a certain degree, not previously published.

26

Are the moons of Mars artificial satellites?

. . . Nor has [Mars] any Moon to wait upon him, and in that . . . he must be acknowledged inferiour to the Earth.

> Christianus Huygens, *New Conjectures Concerning the Planetary Worlds, Their Inhabitants and Productions* (c. 1670)

Round the decay
Of that colossal wreck, boundless and bare
The lone and level sands stretch far away.

> Percy Bysshe Shelley, *Ozymandias*

The two moons of Mars are among the most intriguing objects in the solar system. Their existence was first suggested by the English satirist Jonathan Swift. In his work *Gulliver's Travels*, published in 1726, more than 150 years before the Martian satellites were discovered, Swift has Gulliver describe the scientific activities of the kingdom of Laputa, an inhabited island in the sky. In Lemuel Gulliver's account, the following curious sentence appears:

> They [the Laputan astronomers] have likewise discovered two lesser stars, or 'satellites,' which revolve about Mars, whereof the innermost is distant from the centre of the primary planet exactly three of his diameters, and the outermost five; the former revolves in the space of ten hours, and the latter in twenty-one and an half; so that the squares of their periodical times are very near in the same proportion with the cubes of their distance from the centre of Mars, which evidently shows them to be governed by the same law of gravitation, that influences the other heavenly bodies . . .

▽ This Laputan discovery was echoed by Voltaire in his interplanetary romance, *Micromegas*, published in 1752. △

Swift's characterization of the number of Martian moons, their periods of revolution, and their distances from the planet are uncannily close to the truth. There has been some speculation on how Swift arrived at his prognosis. It seems probable that he was not operating on fantasy alone; in a sense, his description was based on the prevalent astronomical ideas of the day. It was known, of course, that the Earth had one moon, and believed that Jupiter had four. (Only the four Galilean satellites had been detected in Swift's time; now we know that the giant planet has 12 moons, many of which can be observed only through the largest telescopes.) Since Mars is situated between Earth and Jupiter, the assumption that there was a geometric progression of the number of satellites for the more distant planets may have led Swift to the deduction that Mars had two moons. We should recall that Pythagorean ideas about the harmony of numbers were widely accepted in those days.

Swift probably believed that the moons were small in size because non-Laputan astronomers had not yet detected them. He may have reasoned that the moons were relatively close to Mars, because even very small satellites could be detected if they were sufficiently distant from their primary. Close proximity, however, would have hidden them in the scattered light of the planet. ▽ The proportionality between the period of revolution of these satellites about Mars and the 3/2 power of their distance from the center of Mars is simply an expression of Kepler's Third Law, which, together with its derivation from the theory of gravitation by Newton, was well known in Swift's time. △

The moons of Mars were actually discovered in 1877 by the American astronomer Asaph Hall, shortly after the completion of a large refracting telescope at the United States Naval Observatory. Since 1877, they have been observed repeatedly, mostly when Mars is at opposition. The outermost of the two moons is called Deimos, and is approximately 23,000 km from the center of the planet. The inner moon is Phobos, some 9,300 km distant. ▽ Phobos and Deimos are Greek for, respectively, "fear" and "panic," the chariot horses of the god of war. △

The period of revolution of Deimos about Mars is 30 hours, 18 minutes; Phobos revolves every 7 hours, 39 minutes. Thus, Swift predicted the period of revolution of Phobos to within 25%, and of Deimos to within about 40% of the true values—a rather remarkable guess. The period of rotation of Mars about its axis is 24 hours, 37 minutes, and 23 seconds. Thus, if we neglect the artificial satellites of Earth, Phobos is the only known moon in the solar system with a period of revolution about its planet which is less than the period of rotation of the planet itself. For this reason, future explorers of the planet Mars will be able to see Phobos rise in the western Martian sky and set in the east; its apparent period of revolution is 11 hours.

▽ In the early decades of this century, the English author Edgar Rice Burroughs published a series of Martian romances based on the adventures of one John Carter, a Virginian miraculously transported to Barsoom (as Mars was called by its inhabitants). The Martian scenarios were based in large part on Percival Lowell's views of Mars, and served to fix Lowell's ideas of the Martian environment in the minds of an entire generation.

▽ Among other preconceptions which are, even today, sometimes difficult to shake, Burroughs populated Mars with an intelligent race of indigenous human beings, breathing an oxygen atmosphere, living in the dry bottoms of oceans long ago evaporated, and drinking water pumped by Lowell's elaborate planetary canal system. One of Burroughs' phrases, "beneath the hurtling moons of Barsoom," has given the impression that Deimos and Phobos, viewed by an observer on Mars, move rapidly and perceptibly through the nighttime sky. In fact, it would take some 5 1/2 hours for Phobos to rise in the West, follow a meridian through the zenith, and set in the East. Those who have watched artificial Earth satellites (whose comparable periods are about 50 minutes) can testify that such motion would be almost imperceptible. △

If the period of revolution of a satellite were exactly equal to the planet's period of rotation, the moon would appear fixed in the sky from one hemisphere of the planet, and never seen from the other. (▽ Such synchronous orbits are the basis of the SYNCOM system of communication satellites under development in the United States; here, three satellites launched into synchronous orbits could, in principle, revolve just as fast as the Earth rotates, so that every locale on the Earth's surface would be in direct line-of-sight communication with one of the satellites, and each satellite would always be in direct view of the other two.) △ The period of revolution of Deimos about Mars is fairly close to the period of planetary rotation. The length of the Deimos "month" from new Deimos to new Deimos is about 132 hours. ▽ The word "month" is, of course, derived from the word "moon." It might be tempting to invent new names for the "months" of satellites of other planets; but since the word "moon" can also be used in a generic sense, we will refrain from wrestling with such splendid barbarisms as "donth" and "phonth." △ The orbits of both Martian satellites lie in the equatorial plane of the planet, and are very close to being circular. The eccentricity of the orbit of Phobos is 0.017, and of Deimos, 0.003. ▽ A perfect circle has an eccentricity of zero; the larger the eccentricity, the more elongated the orbit. △ The angles of inclination—that is, the angles between the satellites' orbital planes and the Martian equatorial plane—are 1'75" and about 1', respectively.

During an average opposition of Mars, the apparent "stellar" magnitudes of Phobos and Deimos are +11.5 and +13, respectively. Thus, if it were not for their proximity to the planet, they could easily be seen from Earth with a telescope of moderate size. ▽ This difficulty in detection is the same one which we encountered in Chapter 11, when we considered the prospects for photographic detection of planets of nearby stars. △

At present, it is impossible to measure the angular dimensions of the two moons—and therefore, their true sizes—by direct observation from Earth, because their diameters are so small. But there is an indirect method which enables us to obtain approximate values of their dimensions. ▽ We know to sufficient accuracy how far the moons are from us, and from the Sun. We can measure their brightness and derive their apparent magnitudes, as given above. Why are they as bright as they are? Because of their reflectivity, or albedo, and because of their size. The higher the albedo and the larger the size, the brighter they should be. Thus, if we make an assumption about the albedo of the satellites, we can deduce their size. △ If we assume that the albedo of the satellites is about the same as that of Mars (some 15%, in the visible), then it can be calculated that Phobos has a diameter of about 16 km, and Deimos, of perhaps 8 km. ▽ If the satellites have albedos comparable to the moon's or Mercury's (values about half that of Mars), then the diameters will be somewhat larger. △ Phobos and Deimos are, then, the smallest known moons in the solar system. We should note, however, that if satellites of similar dimensions exist very close to Jupiter, Saturn, or the other Jovian planets, they would not be detectable at the present time.

To an explorer on Mars, Phobos would be a brilliant celestial object with a discernible disk. Its angular diameter would approach 10 minutes of arc—that is, one-third the size of the lunar disk seen from Earth—and its luminosity would be about 4% that of our own moon, quite sufficient to cast shadows during the Martian night. Deimos, more distant from its primary, would look very much like a bright star, perhaps ten times brighter than Venus appears from the Earth.

Lowell noted that neither of these moons has the characteristic red color of Mars itself, an observation confirmed by later investigators. ▽ We have seen in Chapter 19 that the red color of Mars is probably due to large amounts of the mineral limonite, which also accounts for the planetary albedo. Thus, it seems clear that the chemical composition of the surfaces of Deimos and Phobos differs from that of Mars. The albedo of the satellites therefore need not necessarily be the same as that of Mars. This underlines the uncertainties involved in the calculation of the diameters of Phobos and Deimos. If the surfaces of these moons initially had compositions similar to that of Mars, subsequent differentiation would have occurred. For example, the Martian atmosphere is thick enough to absorb protons incident upon it from the solar wind. The satellites have no such atmosphere, and the incident protons will strike their surfaces and discolor them as they have discolored our moon [see Chapter 21]. There are also other possible causes for the composition difference, as we shall see. △

In 1945, the American astronomer B. P. Sharpless, ▽ working at the same Naval Observatory at which Hall discovered the satellites of Mars, △ detected a remarkable peculiarity in the motion of Phobos. Comparing a series of old observations made by Hermann Struve with more recent observations, he noted that the orbital velocity of Phobos is increasing. The magnitude of this acceleration is small, but, from his data, apparently real [see Figure 26–1]. ▽ In the case of Deimos, there was less clear evidence for such an acceleration. If we call the angular velocity of Phobos around Mars ω, and $\Delta\omega$ the change in this velocity in some time interval, then $\Delta\omega/\omega$ will be the relative change in angular velocity in the same time period. △ According to Sharpless, this relative change was

$$\Delta\omega/\omega = +(7.98 \pm 0.73) \times 10^{-12}.$$

▽ The first plus sign denotes an acceleration, as opposed to a deceleration; the sign $\pm$ indicates Sharpless' estimate of the uncertainty in the measurements.

▽ Since the period of revolution of Phobos about Mars is 7 hours, 39 minutes,

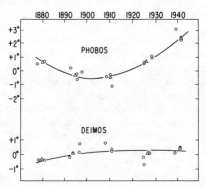

FIGURE 26–1. *Evidence on secular accelerations of Phobos and Deimos gathered by B. P. Sharpless. A satellite with no secular acceleration would show a horizontal line. Within the errors of observation the data points for Deimos are very close to a horizontal line. On the other hand, it is difficult to draw a horizontal line through the points for Phobos, and it is on this basis that Sharpless deduced a secular acceleration of Phobos. (Courtesy of the* Astronomical Journal.)

or about 28,000 seconds, Phobos travels at roughly $(28,000)^{-1} \simeq 3.6 \times 10^{-5}$ revolutions per second. Due to its acceleration, Phobos moves $8 \times 10^{-12} \times 2.1 \times 10^{-5} = 1.7 \times 10^{-16}$ of a revolution faster each second. Since the distance of Phobos from the center of Mars is 9300 km, the acceleration causes a *decrease* in the radius of the orbit of $9.3 \times 10^8 \times 1.7 \times 10^{-16} = 1.6 \times 10^{-7}$ cm each second. In 60 years the orbital radius has shortened some three meters, an extremely small amount; but the consequent changes in the period of Phobos have been detectable from Earth. At this rate, Phobos will impact the surface of Mars, now some 5,900 km below, in 5.9×10^8 cm$/1.6 \times 10^{-7}$ cm sec$^{-1} \simeq 3.7 \times 10^{15}$ sec, or about one hundred million years. △

In celestial mechanics, a continuous, non-periodic change in one of the components, or characteristics, of an orbit is called a "secular change." ▽ This use of the words "secular change" is similar to that introduced in Chapter 20, when we spoke of secular changes in the configuration of dark areas on the surface of Mars. A periodic, and hence more easily predictable, change is called a "canonical" change. The words hark back to the Middle Ages, when the church had calendrical (hence, periodic) responsibilities. Those occurrences not conforming to the ecclesiastic calendar were, by default, secular. △ Thus, Sharpless detected a secular acceleration in the motion of Phobos about Mars. No unequivocal evidence was adduced for a secular acceleration of Deimos.

Since the Martian moons are very difficult to observe, even with the best equipment, it is possible that Sharpless' compilation of the data may contain substantial errors. However, the large magnitude of the secular acceleration, $\Delta\omega/\omega$, suggests that the effect is real. Suppose a hypothetical observer on Mars were to predict the position of Phobos in the sky over a 50-year period, neglecting the effect of secular acceleration. At the end of this time, the actual position of Phobos would be $2°$ from the predicted position—in celestial mechanics, a very large deviation.

Let us assume for the moment that the secular acceleration is a real effect. We will suggest several conceivable causes, ▽ and then examine their consequences △:

1. Atmospheric drag. If Phobos were traversing a sufficiently dense gas during its motion about Mars, the gas would "drag" the satellite, causing its orbit to shrink, and resulting in a net acceleration. This effect strongly influences the motion of artificial satellites of Earth, and is a main factor in determining their lifetime in orbit.

2. Tidal friction, an effect which probably played an important role in the evolution of the Earth-Moon system.

3. Electromagnetic braking of the motion of Phobos by the magnetic field of Mars.

4. The effects of radiation pressure.

5. Classical celestial mechanical perturbations.

Let us now consider each of these possibilities in turn.

1. *Atmospheric drag.* In 1954, the astronomers Frank J. Kerr and Fred L. Whipple, working in the United States, concluded that a gaseous, resisting medium could not explain the secular acceleration of Phobos. They computed the density of the resisting medium required to produce the observed effect. By a variety of assumptions, they arrived at figures for the density of the resisting medium ranging between 3×10^{-16} and 5×10^{-16} gm cm^{-3}. ▽ A more recent estimate of the required gas density in the vicinity of Phobos by the Austrian-American scientist Gerhard Schilling of the Rand Corporation puts it at $\rho \simeq 5 \times 10^{-16} \delta$ gm cm^{-3}, where δ is the bulk density of Phobos itself. Thus, if Phobos were made of ordinary terrestrial surface rocks, or the material which comprises the moon, δ would equal 3.3 gm cm^{-3}, and ρ would then be some 2×10^{-15} gm cm^{-3}. If Phobos were made of ice, δ would be 1 gm cm^{-3}, and ρ would be 5×10^{-16} gm cm^{-3}. Thus, the required density of the resisting medium must be approximately 10^{-15} gm cm^{-3}, if Phobos is a solid object composed of ordinary materials, as, in a preliminary analysis, we would certainly expect it to be. △

Kerr and Whipple then assumed that the resisting force was due to drag of the *interplanetary* gas and dust. The interplanetary medium is about equally dense at the orbits of Deimos and Phobos. Thus, if the secular acceleration of Phobos is caused by a resisting interplanetary medium, Deimos should have a similar secular acceleration. Since this was not the case, Kerr and Whipple concluded that the existence of a damping medium could not explain the secular acceleration of Phobos.

However, if we assume that the opposing medium is the Martian atmosphere, then at a distance of some 23,000 km from the center of the planet, at the orbit of Deimos, the atmospheric density would be much less than in the vicinity of Phobos. Therefore, we must estimate the density of the Martian atmosphere at the various altitudes before we can exclude the resisting medium explanation.

▽ Before the successful completion of the Mariner IV mission to Mars, a calculation of the expected densities of the Martian atmosphere at the distances of Phobos and Demos were beset with many difficulties. The uncertainties included the number density and altitude of the base of the Martian exosphere, the exosphere temperature and its mean molecular weight. As a result of the occultation experiment on Mariner IV (see Chapter 20) some of these parameters are now known to better accuracy. The base of the exosphere—the region from which gravitational escape can occur—now appears to be at an altitude of less than 200 km, as compared with the approximately 1,500 km that had been previously computed. The exosphere temperature appears to be a few hundred °K, much colder than had previously been thought, and the mean molecular weight at this level appears to be close to 44, the molecular weight of carbon dioxide. However, at greater altitudes, the major constituent should become atomic oxygen, and at still greater altitudes, atomic hydrogen, arising from the photo-dissociation of water vapor. With these figures, the number density at the base of the Martian exosphere is approximately 2×10^9 cm^{-3}, a factor of 200 larger than the best previous theoretical estimates. At the altitude of Phobos, the number density will, of course, be much less.

▽ Let n_P be the density of the Martian exosphere at the distance of Phobos, and n_b be the density at the base of the exosphere. If the distances of Phobos and the base of the exosphere from the surface of Mars are, respectively z_P and z_b, then

$$n_P = n_b \exp\{ - R^2/H \left[1/(R + z_b) - 1/(R + z_P) \right] \}$$

Here, R is the radius of Mars, and $H = kT/mg$ is the scale height of the atmosphere, a measure of how rapidly the atmospheric density declines with altitude. k is Boltzmann's constant, T is the absolute temperature, m is the mass of the atmospheric constituent in question, and g is the acceleration due to gravity at the surface of Mars. The equation takes into account the variation of g with altitude; the dependence is as the inverse square of the distance from the center of the planet. This equation does not hold exactly because we are considering the exosphere, where collisions are infrequent. However, it should apply to first approximation.

▽ Putting numbers into this equation, and noting that the Martian exosphere will be composed over most of its extent of atomic hydrogen, we find that the number density at the distance of Phobos, some 6,000 km, is about $2 \times 10^5 f_H$, where f_H is the fractional abundance of atomic hydrogen at the base of the exosphere. We do not know the value of f_H, but we suspect it to be very small by analogy with the small amount of hydrogen (about 0.3%) at the base of the terrestrial exosphere; in particular, the source of hydrogen in the Martian atmosphere must be the photo-dissociation of water, and there is about 1/1,000 as much in the Martian as in the terrestrial atmosphere. It would be very surprising if f_H were larger than, say, 10^{-3}. We then find that an upper limit to n_P is about 2×10^3 cm^{-3}. For comparison, we found that the required mass density of the exosphere to explain the secular acceleration of Phobos by atmospheric drag was $5 \times 10^{-16} \delta$ gm cm^{-3}. For a hydrogen exosphere, this is the same as 3×10^8 δ cm^{-3}. For ordinary values of δ, we see that the atmosphere is more than 100,000 times too diffuse at the altitude of Phobos for this explanation to be viable. Calculations based on the numbers thought to apply prior to Mariner IV gave a smaller discrepancy of about a factor of 1,000.

▽ Thus, we have reached the conclusion that the density of the Martian exosphere in the vicinity of the satellite Phobos is probably 100,000 times too diffuse to explain its secular acceleration, if Phobos has a density characteristic of ordinary solid materials.

▽ In the discussion immediately following, we analyze the alternative explanations of the secular acceleration of Phobos. The over-all conclusion is that explanations 2 through 5 cannot account for the secular acceleration of Phobos. The reader who does not wish to trouble himself with these technical details may take up the discussion again on page 373. △

2. *Tidal friction.* Another possible explanation of the secular acceleration of Phobos is tidal friction, a problem investigated by the British geophysicist Sir Harold Jeffreys of Cambridge University. Since there are no large bodies of liquid on the surface of Mars, tidal friction can arise only in the solid body of the planet. Jeffreys assumed that

the viscoelastic properties of Mars are the same as for the solid body of the Earth. His calculations indicate that tidal friction could account for only 10^{-4} of the observed secular acceleration of Phobos.

However, the question of the viscoelastic properties of the solid material of a planet is quite controversial. Recently, the Soviet geophysicist N. N. Pariiskii ▽ and, independently, the American geophysicist G. J. F. MacDonald of the University of California at Los Angeles, △ concluded that body tides in the Earth (and, by analogy, in Mars) are significantly greater than Jeffreys anticipated. According to the calculations of Pariiskii, body tides are necessary in order to explain the secular motion of our moon and might also account for the secular acceleration of Phobos.

However, we now have evidence, from entirely different considerations, that the secular acceleration of Phobos cannot be explained by tidal friction. According to Jeffreys, the theoretical value of the secular acceleration of a satellite by viscoelastic tidal friction in the solid body of a planet can be represented by the expression

$$\frac{d\zeta}{dt} = \frac{9}{4} \frac{m\omega}{M} \left(\frac{R}{r}\right)^5 \psi \sin 2\theta,$$

where m is the mass of the moon, M is the mass of the planet, R is the radius of the planet, r is the radius of the orbit of the satellite at any time, ω is the average angular velocity of the moon at any time, and θ is the angle of lag of the tidal bulge. The quantity ψ depends only on the viscoelastic properties of the planet. Furthermore, according to Jeffreys,

$$\sin 2\theta = \frac{\Phi}{2(\Omega - \omega)},$$

where Ω is angular velocity of rotation of the planet, and Φ depends only on the viscoelastic properties of the planet. From the above equations and Kepler's Third Law, we can determine the time it takes for the radius of the circular orbit of the moon to pass from r to r_0 because of tidal effects:

$$t(r) = t_0(1 - \omega/\Omega)^{-1}\{[(r/r_0)^{13/2} - 1] - (13\omega/10\Omega)[(r/r_0)^5 - 1]\};$$

$$t_0 = 3\omega_0/13(d\omega/dt)_0.$$

Here, ω_0 and $(d\omega/dt)_0$ are the current values of the average angular velocity of the moon and its variation with time, ▽ and $r_0 \simeq 2.8\ R$ is the current value of r. △ We note that in the case of Phobos, $r < 2.17\ r_0$ (the distance from the center of Mars for which $\omega_0 = \Omega$); otherwise, this moon would not approach Mars, but would recede from it. Having carried out these calculations, we obtain

$$t(r < 2.15\ r_0) < 5 \times 10^8 \text{ yrs.}$$

But 500 million years as an upper limit on the time which has passed since the formation of Phobos is an inadmissibly small value. Five hundred million years ago, conditions on Mars (which has itself existed for 4 to 5 billion years) were not significantly different from contemporary conditions. Accordingly, it is inconceivable that in such a recent epoch a moon could have been formed having an almost circular orbit and lying practically in the plane of the equator of the planet.

There is another possibility: let us suppose that Phobos was formed at a distance of 2.15 $r_0 < r < 2.17 r_0$, and that its period of revolution was almost exactly equal to the period of rotation of Mars. We must also suppose that Deimos was formed at the same critical distance; at this distance the tidal forces of Mars would not noticeably influence the motion of the moons. One could then assume further that for various reasons the moons moved out of their almost stable orbits—that Phobos was swept toward the planet and Deimos was swept in the opposite direction. For small displacements, the tidal forces would be very small, and a large amount of time could pass before Phobos' r became smaller than, for example, 2.1 r_0.

However, this is a highly improbable explanation for the origin of the moons. Why would the moons necessarily be formed at the precise distance where the condition $\omega = \Omega$ is fulfilled? All other satellites revolving about planets in the solar system are found at relatively great distances from the planets. Furthermore, it is difficult to understand why Deimos, on which tidal forces have practically no influence (because of its small mass), should move away from the planet, out of the orbit at which $\omega = \Omega$ (where, according to our supposition, it was formed).

One must bear in mind that over several billions of years, the period of rotation of Mars could have changed substantially. Such a fact would invalidate the hypothesis that satellites were formed at a distance simply determined by the contemporary value of the period of rotation of Mars. However, these considerations strongly suggest that the observed secular acceleration of Phobos cannot be explained by tidal friction in the solid body of Mars.

3. *Magnetic braking.* In principle, electromagnetic effects might lead to the observed secular acceleration of Phobos. Let us assume a satellite which is a good conductor of electricity. Also let us assume that Mars has a magnetic field. Then, the movement of the moon in the magnetic field gives rise to an electric field $E' = [v \times H]/c$. This field would polarize the satellite; that is, charges of different signs would migrate to opposite sides. The electric field of these charges in the space surrounding the satellite would be of the same order as E', so that the electric potential with respect to the ions it meets would be $x = Es$, where s is the characteristic dimension of the satellite. The value of x in volts is 300 $E's = 300 vHs/c$. Assuming that $v = 2 \times 10^5$ cm sec^{-1}, $H = 10^{-3}$ gauss, and $s = 10^6$ cm, we find that $x = 2$ volts. Since this energy is comparable to the thermal energy of the interplanetary gas, it follows that positive ions would settle on the negatively charged surface of the satellite and all electrons would be repulsed. On the reverse side, which is positively charged, the ions would be repulsed, and some of the electrons would settle. Then the current, I, would be equal to the flow of positive ions through the hemisphere. Since the velocity of the satellite is close to the velocity of the ions, v_i, we have: $I = n_i v_i e A$, where $A \propto s^2$ is the cross-section of the satellite, e is the charge on the electron, and n_i is the number density of ions. The damping force is $f = IHs/c \simeq n_i e v_i s A H/c$, and the magnitude of the acceleration is

$$\left(\frac{dv}{dt}\right) = \frac{n_i e v_i s A H}{mc} \simeq \frac{n_i v_i e H}{c\delta},$$

where m is the mass of the satellite and δ is its density. The time of damping will be

$$t \simeq \frac{v}{dv/dt} \simeq \frac{vc\delta}{n_i v_i e H} \simeq \frac{2 \times 10^{15} \delta}{n_i} \text{ years,}$$

where we assume that at a distance of 6,000 km from the surface of Mars, $H = 10^{-3}$ gauss (probably an overestimate). Since $n_i < 10^5$ cm^{-3} while $\delta \simeq 2.5$ gm cm^{-3}, then $t > 5 \times 10^{10}$ years. $\triangledown$ Thus, the timescale for magnetic damping of a conducting satellite would be longer than the age of the solar system. $\triangle$

If the conductivity of the satellite is sufficiently small, then the current across it will be determined by the electrical conductivity, λ, and not by the flow of interplanetary charged particles. In this case,

$$I = \lambda E' A \simeq \lambda v H A / c$$
$$f = IHs/c \simeq \lambda^2 H^2 As/c^2$$
$$t' \simeq \frac{v}{dv/dt} \simeq \frac{c^2 \delta}{\lambda H^2}$$

Down to $\lambda \leqq 10^9$ sec^{-1} (which is significantly greater than the conductivity of rocks), $t' > t$. For $\lambda > 10^{10}$ sec^{-1}, taking into account the polarization, the time of the electromagnetic drag will be determined by t.

In summary, we must conclude that it would be impossible to explain the observed secular acceleration of Phobos by magnetic forces.

4. *Radiation pressure.* We could try to explain the secular acceleration by the Poynting-Robertson effect. Owing to the aberration of light, the force of light pressure on a moving body will have a component directed against the motion, which leads to a continuous drag on the body. This is known as the Poynting-Robertson effect. Due to this effect, dust with dimensions greater than 0.5μ which revolve in orbits about the sun will fall into the sun $\triangledown$ in a time shorter than the age of the solar system. $\triangle$ If an ordinary particle has a dimension which is less than 0.6μ (but greater than 0.2μ), the force of the light pressure will exceed the force of gravitational attraction. Such particles will be ejected beyond the limits of the solar system (see Chapter 15).

However, I am convinced that this effect, which here depends both on direct solar radiation and on the light reflected from Mars, would give a secular acceleration some six to eight times less than the observed secular acceleration.

5. *Classical celestial mechanical perturbations.* Finally, we shall consider the possibility of a purely celestial mechanical explanation for the secular acceleration of Phobos. For example, the effect of the sun on Deimos, in theory, could lead to the appearance of long-period terms in the planetocentric longitude of Phobos. The perturbations of the motion of the satellites of Mars by the sun, and also their mutual perturbations, was recently investigated by the Soviet astronomer M. P. Kosachevskii. According to his calculations, the mutual perturbations are more significant than the solar perturbations; moreover, the motion of Deimos is far more strongly affected than the motion of Phobos. This is completely understandable, since Deimos is further from Mars than Phobos. The absolute magnitudes of the perturbations of the two moons, according to Kosachevskii's calculations, are very small.

Thus, all of the mechanisms we have discussed apparently cannot explain the secular acceleration of Phobos. Of course, we repeat, there is a slight possibility that Sharpless' observations are in error. However, at the present time this seems unlikely to me.

In 1959, I proposed a new and radical hypothesis concerning the motion of Phobos. ▽ Let us reconsider the discussion on page 369. There, we saw that for the secular acceleration to be explained by the action of a resisting medium, the density of this resisting medium had to be about $3 \times 10^8 \, \delta$ cm^{-3}, where δ was the density of Phobos. We also saw that the expected Martian exospheric densities in the vicinity of Phobos are less than 2×10^3 cm^{-3} △ Thus, if the mean density of Phobos were about ▽ 10^{-5} gm cm^{-3}, or, with the older numbers, △ 10^{-3} gm cm^{-3}, then its secular acceleration could be explained by the resistance of the Martian exosphere.

But how can a natural satellite have such a low density? The material of which it is made must have a certain amount of rigidity, so that cohesive forces will be stronger than the gravitational tidal forces of Mars, which will tend to disrupt the satellite. Such rigidity would ordinarily exclude densities below about 0.1 gm cm^{-3}. Thus, only one possibility remains. Could Phobos be indeed rigid, on the *outside* —but hollow on the inside? A natural satellite cannot be a hollow object. Therefore, we are led to the possibility that Phobos—and possibly Deimos as well —may be artificial satellites of Mars.

▽ They would be artificial satellites on a scale surpassing the fondest dreams of contemporary rocket engineers. If the density of Phobos ranges between 10^{-3} and 10^{-5} gm cm^{-3}, then its mass must range from tens of millions to billions of tons although the solid outer shell might be no more than a foot thick. For comparison, the most massive artificial satellites hitherto launched from this planet are in the 10-ton range, and artificial satellites much beyond the 100-ton range do not seem to be feasible projects, at least for the next few decades. △ (If it turns out that the visual albedo of the Martian satellites is high—for example, 0.60 to 0.80—then their dimensions will be 2 or 3 times less than these calculations indicate, and their mass, 5 to 10 times less.)

The idea that the moons of Mars are artificial satellites may seem fantastic, at first glance. In my opinion, however, it merits serious consideration. A technical civilization substantially in advance of our own would certainly be capable of constructing and launching massive satellites. Since Mars does not have a large natural satellite such as our moon, the construction of large, artificial satellites would be of relatively greater importance to an advanced Martian civilization in its expansion into space. The launching of massive satellites from Mars would be a somewhat easier task than from Earth, because of the lower Martian gravity. ▽ Conceivably, the capture and hollowing of a small asteroid may be technically more feasible than the construction in orbit of an artificial satellite with material brought from the surface. △

It is quite possible that in several centuries the Earth will have satellites with dimensions of some kilometers. ▽ Manned orbiting laboratories in the 100-meter size range have already been designed. △ Let us imagine that through the next several centuries, massive artificial Earth satellites are launched and maintained. ▽ Over a much longer timescale—say, 10^7 or 10^8 or 10^9 years—the evolution of human society and of life on Earth will not remain static. Perhaps mankind will destroy itself; or develop a society unconcerned with technological triumphs; perhaps a society will evolve which leaves the Earth altogether; or natural catastrophes, tectonic or climatological, may destroy civilization on Earth. We cannot reasonably assess these possibilities, but it does seem conceivable that the lifetime of our artificial satellites may exceed the lifetime of our civilization. △ These satellites would then remain as unique and striking monuments to a vanished species which had once flourished on the planet Earth.

Perhaps we are observing an analogous situation on Mars. According to the distinguished American cosmochemist Harold C. Urey, of the University of California, some billions years ago Mars may have possessed extensive oceans suitable for the origin of life, and perhaps even an oxygen atmosphere, ▽ although this latter is much less certain. △ Perhaps Phobos was launched into orbit in the heyday of a technical civilization on Mars, some hundreds of millions of years ago.

▽ The Soviet writer F. Zigel has made a more bizarre suggestion. Why, he wonders, were Phobos and Deimos not discovered by Herschel during the favorable Martian opposition of 1862, but found instead by Hall, with a smaller telescope, during the favorable opposition of 1877? The only explanation which occurs to Zigel is that the moons of Mars were launched into orbit between 1862 and 1877; it would then follow that an advanced technical civilization exists on Mars today. But the Naval Observatory telescope of 1877 was superior in several important respects to its predecessors. And the history of astronomy is full of similar incidents. After the discovery of Pluto in 1930 by Clyde Tombaugh at Lowell Observatory, the planet was found on photographic plates taken a decade earlier, with the larger telescope at other observatories. Uranus and Neptune were observed many times before their formal discovery, but their significance passed unnoticed. We have seen in Chapter 20 the unlikelihood of an extant civilization on Mars. If the moons of Mars are artificial—and we have at best only a plausibility argument to support this contention—they are much more likely mute testaments to an ancient Martian civilization than signs of a thriving contemporary society.

▽ While the birthdate of Phobos is difficult to estimate, some idea of the date of its death can be obtained more reliably. As we have seen, it is possible to compute the date on which Phobos will plunge through the lower Martian atmosphere and strike the surface; just as it is possible to compute the decay of an artificial Earth satellite. △ Careful calculations from the magnitude of the secular acceleration indicate that Phobos will impact Mars in some 10 or 20 million years. At that time, the planet itself will have existed for several billion years. This circumstance points out another difficulty in the assumption that Phobos has a natural origin, for it means that we are now observing Phobos during the last fraction of a percent of its lifetime, ▽ an unlikely, but not impossible coincidence. △

When, in the comparatively near future, unmanned and then manned expeditions are landed on Mars, the fascinating problem of the nature of its moons will be solved. ▽ If, some hundreds of millions of years ago, a Martian civilization was advanced enough to launch 10-million-ton satellites, then their works on the planet must have been mighty indeed. Are the sands of Mars today drifting over the edifices and monuments of an ancient civilization? If that society were still extant, it seems likely that we should have some sign of it; and if it is now extinct, evidence of its past existence, character, and achievements can likely be garnered by the first Martian exploration teams. △

A partial test of my hypothesis can be made earlier, from the surface of the Earth. Precision photoelectric photometry of Phobos and Deimos obtained over a long period of time can lead to a determination of the shape of the satellites and a characterization of their axial rotation. If it transpires that the satellites have some particular and special shape, this could conceivably provide a serious argument for artificial origin. Neither the observations nor their interpretations are very easy to perform.

Photographs of Phobos and Deimos can be obtained at close range by Mars flyby vehicles, and the data telemetered back to Earth. This is, however, a delicate operation, requiring precise guidance and faultless operation of the automatically-controlled photographic equipment. In particular, the camera would have to be aimed precisely at Phobos and Deimos. However, such technical problems will likely be solved during the next decade.

As soon as it was published, in the form of a newspaper interview, the hypothesis of the artificial origin of the moons of Mars became the subject of wide discussion. The majority of scientists were skeptical, a reaction which of course is completely understandable. However, not one scientific argument was advanced against the hypothesis. An article in the American press by the American astronomer G. M. Clemence, of the U.S. Naval Observatory, stated that the British astronomer G. A. Wilkins, who worked for some time at the Naval Observatory, had obtained results indicating that Sharpless' data were in error. In response to my inquiry, Wilkins indicated that no new results had been obtained concerning the motion of the moons of Mars. Thus, the assertion in the American press was repudiated by Wilkins himself.

▽ Subsequent to the publication of the Russian edition of this book, Dr. Wilkins kindly supplied the following information for this edition:

"So far I have re-reduced practically all of the observations of the satellites of Mars that were made from their discovery up to 1941—i.e., for the period covered by Sharpless' note. . . . The values found for the secular variations of the mean motions were insignificant, but I have not yet fully confirmed this result nor taken into account even those later observations that have been made available to me.

"There is no doubt that visual observations of the positions of these satellites with respect to the centre of the disk of the planet are difficult to make, but I do not have sufficient evidence to be able to state that Sharpless' determination was based on inadequate observations or that the method of treatment was not suitable. I consider that the question of existence of the secular accelerations should be regarded as an open one until a new and more complete analysis of the observations is made; I do not consider that the evidence is sufficiently strong to justify any attempt to look for artificial causes." △

It is possible that Sharpless' results are incorrect. In this case, the hypothesis that Phobos and Deimos have an artificial origin would lose its scientific support. Only when new and very precise observations are carried out will we be able either to disprove or verify Sharpless' results. ▽ A reanalysis of the previous observations, in particular those from 1941 to the present time, could also shed some light on this tantalizing subject. △

Even if future observations indicate that the reported secular acceleration of Phobos is spurious, the hypothesis that the moons of Mars are of artificial origin has nevertheless been provocative, and thereby has served a useful purpose. It reminds us that the activity of a highly developed society of intelligent beings could have cosmic significance and could produce artifacts which would outlive the civilizations that constructed them. This conclusion, as we shall see in the following chapters, has significant implications for the problem of intelligent life in the universe.

27

Radio contact among galactic civilizations

I know perfectly well that at this moment the whole universe is listening to us—and that every word we say echoes to the remotest star.

Jean Giraudoux, *The Madwoman of Chaillot*

In previous chapters, we have presented arguments to support our contention that there are several billion planetary systems in our Galaxy, and that of them about a billion worlds are populated with their own varieties of living organisms. On some of these planets, life may have existed for such a long period of time that there may have evolved intelligent forms which, in turn, may have produced technologically advanced civilizations. The assumption that technical civilizations must *necessarily* make an appearance, even after many billions of years of biological evolution, implies that the ultimate purpose, or goal, in the formation of stars and planets is the production of intelligent beings and technical civilizations, an idealistic and teleological view. We must not forget that the Earth existed for billions of years before highly intelligent life forms and technical civilizations arose.

On the other hand, as we discussed in Chapter 25, the rise of intelligent life in a universe filled with planetary systems seems to be a likely phenomenon. At the present time, since we do not adequately understand the factors leading to the evolution of intelligence and technical civilizations, we cannot reliably estimate the probability that intelligence and technical civilizations will emerge. At one extreme, this probability may be close to one; at the other extreme, the Earth may be the only cradle of intelligence in the Galaxy. We believe—but this is a belief, not a demonstrated fact—that there are a certain number, perhaps even a large number, of planets in the Galaxy which have highly developed technical societies.

▽ We cannot guess what the character of such advanced extraterrestrial civilizations would be. But the laws of physics are universal in character, and the same discoveries that have been made on Earth will be made on planets of other stars, although perhaps not in the same sequence. The ability to generate and receive radio waves has developed on our planet in tandem with the development of electromagnetic theory, in the last quarter of the nineteenth century. An important verification of the electromagnetic theory of the British physicist James Clerk Maxwell was provided by the German physicist Heinrich Hertz, who showed that an oscillating dipole, which is oppositely charged at its two ends, generates electromagnetic waves, including radio waves. Similar discoveries have probably been made countless times on other worlds, during the lifetime of our Galaxy. Advanced technical civilizations have likely developed radio transmission and reception for long-distance communication, as we have.

▽ If familiarity with electromagnetic theory and radio waves is a common patrimony of all technological civilizations in the Galaxy, is it possible to establish radio contact among Galactic civilizations? △ We need not question the great importance of such communication. If we were to succeed in establishing contact with an extraterrestrial civilization, especially one possessing a high degree of scientific development, the impact on our lives, our society, and our philosophical outlook would be incalculable.

▽ The possibility of radio contact with intelligent beings on other planets was clearly held by such pioneers in the development of radio transmission as Marconi and Tesla, each of whom, incidentally, believed they had detected intelligent signals of extraterrestrial origin. Their preliminary reports resulted in a deluge of popular interest and scientific skepticism. This double-pronged attack reduced Tesla and Marconi to silence, and the accounts available today of the signals which these radio pioneers claimed to have detected are fragmentary at best. In 1959, the prospect of interstellar radio contact was revived by the Italian-American physicist Giuseppe Cocconi and the American physicist Philip Morrison, then both at Cornell University. △ They concluded that electromagnetic radiation is the most natural and feasible interstellar communication medium. There are two obvious advantages: the signal is propagated at the highest possible velocity—the velocity of light; and the energy can be concentrated within relatively small areas in the sky without significant scattering into other directions.

Because of absorption and scattering by the interstellar medium and by the atmospheres of the planets involved, the range of potentially useful wavelengths for interstellar communication is restricted. Cocconi and Morrison pointed out that if wavelengths longer than 300 meters (corresponding to a frequency of one megacycle per second = 10^6 cps) were used, the radiation would be absorbed by the interstellar medium. (▽ A frequency of one megacycle per second—1000 kilocycles per second—is the frequency in the middle of the ordinary AM broadcast band. △) Radiation near a frequency of one megacycle per second tends to be absorbed by the charged particles in planetary ionospheres. There is reason to believe that all planets have ionospheres of varying extents, and only radiation of wavelength less than about 10 or 15 meters can pass through such ionospheres and reach the surfaces of the planets. Planetary atmospheres also limit radio propagation at short wavelengths. For example, a planetary atmosphere of the terrestrial type absorbs radiation at wavelengths of about 1 cm or less, because of the presence of water vapor molecules. Thus, allowing for absorption by the interstellar medium and by familiar planetary ionospheres and atmospheres, interstellar radio communication should be restricted to the wavelengths between 3 cm and about 10 or 15 meters. ▽ Ordinary radar operates at wavelengths of 3 cm and longer. △ Of course, if the receiver and transmitter were located above the planetary atmosphere and ionosphere—for example, in an artificial satellite—then the upper limit to the wavelength interval useful for interstellar communication could be as large as several kilometers, and the lower limit could be as small as desired.

The interstellar medium and the planetary atmosphere and ionosphere are not, however, the only factors which limit the range of wavelengths useful for interstellar communication. Of equal importance is the natural "noise level" of the universe.

▽ All the matter in the universe radiates at all wavelengths, including radio wavelengths. Much of the interstellar material is very cold (see Chapter 5), so the intensity which it radiates at radio wavelengths is low. △ But because of the vast distances which must separate planetary civilizations, the power of the received signals will also be extremely weak. The radio radiation from the Galaxy and the metagalaxy will seriously interfere with the detection of weak signals of artificial origin. Cosmic radio radiation has a continuous spectrum, and its intensity (per unit frequency interval) increases towards longer wavelengths. The thermal radio radiation emitted by the molecules in planetary atmospheres would also interfere with interstellar radio contact. Here, the intensity decreases as the wavelength increases. In Figure 27–1, we see how these two types of interference are related

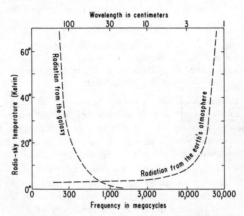

FIGURE 27–1. *Estimated noise levels in the radio frequency spectrum. Shown are two principal sources of background noise; the radio noise of galactic origin which dominates at low frequencies and the radio noise which arises in the Earth's atmosphere, which dominates at high frequencies. The sum of these two curves has a minimum near 2000 megacycles, which corresponds to a wavelength of about 15 cm. (Courtesy of Dr. Frank Drake and* Sky *and* Telescope.)

to frequency. It is apparent that the lowest level of potential interference occurs in the frequency interval between 10^3 and 10^4 megacycles per second, corresponding to the wavelength interval between 3 cm and 30 cm.

Now let us assume that a given planet somewhere in the Galaxy holds a highly developed technical civilization which wishes to make its presence known. The inhabitants of this planet, which we shall call planet A, decide to send a radio signal in the direction of a suspected planet B, which orbits a distant star and which is suspected to contain a technical civilization. However an immediate difficulty is encountered. The star which planet A orbits is a powerful source of continuous radio emission. ▽ The radio receivers on planet B will be unable to distinguish a signal radiated by planet A from a similar signal radiated from the star about which planet A orbits. △ Thus it appears on first examination that to transmit an artificial radio signal we must have radio transmitters which are at least as powerful as the radio emission of our sun at the same wavelengths if the signal is to be detected by a distant civilization. Actually, the required conditions on the transmitter power are not quite this stringent, as we shall see.

▽ In order to estimate how powerful the planetary emission must be, so it can be detected above the local stellar interference, △ let us assume that the sun of the transmitting civilization radiates at radio frequencies in the same way as does our Sun during a period of low sunspot activity, when it is relatively "quiet." So that we can calculate specific numbers, we will consider a wavelength of 10 cm. At this wavelength, the quiet Sun radiates as if it were a blackbody with a surface temperature of approximately 50,000°K. Using the Rayleigh-Jeans approximation to the blackbody intensity distribution, we can write the intensity of solar radio emission per unit frequency interval as

$$W_\odot = 4\pi R_\odot^2 (2\pi k T_B / \lambda^2),$$

where the wavelength $\lambda = 10$ cm, the Boltzmann constant $k = 1.38 \times 10^{-16}$ erg$(K°)^{-1}$, the radius of the Sun $R_\odot = 7 \times 10^{10}$ cm, and the brightness temperature of the quiet Sun at 10 cm wavelength is $T_B = 50,000°K$. Inserting the numerical values, we obtain $W_\odot = 2.6 \times 10^{10}$ erg sec^{-1} (cps)$^{-1} = 2.6 \times 10^3$ watts (cps)$^{-1}$.

We must bear in mind that the Sun radiates at all frequencies. The total power emitted by the quiet Sun is of the order of tens of billions of kilowatts. In addition, the Sun radiates isotropically—equally in all directions. By contrast, the artificial signal has a very narrow bandwidth, perhaps only a few thousand, or even a few hundred, cycles per second. If a sufficiently large antenna is used, almost all the power of the artificial signal can be concentrated within the limits of a narrow cone, of angular size approximately equal to λ/D, where D is the diameter of the antenna dish. This cone is determined by the principal lobe of the antenna, shown in Figure 27–2, ▽ a typical diagram of the directivity of a radiotelescope. The figure shows the power output in various directions. Since the straight line is perpendicular to the antenna dish, we see that the bulk of the power emitted or received by a radio antenna—it may do either—is in the direction to which the telescope is pointing.

▽ The gain of a radio antenna, a measure of the directivity, is the ratio of the power transmitted or received in the direction the dish is pointing to the smaller amounts of power received from other directions in the side lobes. △

The antenna gain is given by $G = 4\pi A/\lambda^2$, where A is the effective area of the antenna, a quantity close to its geometric area. If we use an antenna with a diameter of 100 meters (well within the limits of contemporary radio technology), then at 10 cm wavelength, the antenna gain $G \simeq 10^7$. ▽ With the 1000-foot semi-steerable radiotelescope of Cornell University, in Arecibo, Puerto Rico, even larger gains are possible. △

If the total power radiated by the antenna at 10 cm wavelength were equal to that of the Sun, the antenna would radiate ten million times more power in the direction to which the dish is pointed than will the Sun. The power of the transmitter need only be 10^{-4} watts (cps)$^{-1}$ for the signal in the principal lobe to be approximately the same as that of the Sun. Such a highly directional, narrow-band, artificial radio signal would permit us to obtain information from a space vehicle even when it is headed towards the Sun ▽ and must contend with the noise of the solar radio emission. The direct investigation of at least the outer reaches of the solar atmosphere is one objective of space exploration in the next decade. △

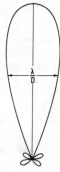

FIGURE 27–2. *A typical diagram of the directivity of a radio antenna, imagined to be at the apex of the rosette. The large lobe is oriented perpendicular to the antenna and indicates that by far the greatest reception of the antenna is in the approximate direction to which it is pointing. The four smaller lobes indicate that some weak reception will be made of signals incident from the sides of the radio telescope. In the principle lobe the radio telescope is capable of an angular resolution of λ/D where λ is the wavelength of the radio frequency observed and D is the aperture of the antenna. Were this same antenna being used for radar transmission rather than passive reception the same directivity diagram would apply.*

Thus, the natural radio emission of the local sun will not necessarily interfere with interstellar communication undertaken by an advanced technical civilization. A far more important source of interfering noise is the background cosmic radio radiation, from which the artificial signal must be discriminated by the receiving civilization.

In radio astronomy, the ability to so discriminate is determined by the so-called antenna temperature, T_A, which is defined as

$$T_A = \left(\frac{\pi^2}{16k}\right) \; \left(\frac{W}{r^2}\right) \; \left(\frac{D_1^2 D_2^2}{\lambda^2}\right),$$

where D_1 is the diameter of the receiving antenna, D_2 is the diameter of the transmitting antenna, r is the distance between civilizations, and W is the power per unit bandwidth of the transmitter. Thus, to discriminate the artificial signal from the background, the antenna temperature due to the artificial radio emission must not be less than T_B—here, the brightness temperature of the sky at the same frequency. ▽ From Figure 27–1 we see that the brightness temperature of the sky at 10 cm is about 10°K. △ Thus, the condition for detection of signals is

We should note, however, that in a number of cases the signal can be extracted from the noise even when T_A is less than T_B—for example, when $T_A = 0.1\ T_B$. But for the present we consider only the case that $T_A \geq T_B$.

Assuming $D_1 = D_2 = 100$ meters, $W = 100$ watts (cps)$^{-1}$, $\lambda = 10$ cm, and $T_A = T_B = 10°$K, we find that $r \simeq 10^{19}$ cm, or about 10 light years, corresponding to the distance to the nearer stars.

Thus, transmitting and receiving civilizations at the present terrestrial level of technology are capable of radio communication over interstellar distances. This remarkable fact is often very hard for the layman to comprehend. Older generations can remember when transatlantic radio contact was first established. In 1945, a radar signal was bounced off the Moon for the first time. Fourteen years later, in 1959, Venus was located by radar. Radar contact with Venus is a much more difficult problem than radar reflection from the Moon, because the power required for a radar transmitter to make contact with a target must be proportional to the fourth power of the distance to the target. In 1961, a Soviet cosmic rocket was launched in the direction of Venus, and radio contact was maintained up to a certain point in its trajectory.

▽ The United States spacecraft Mariner II sent meaningful signals over 86 million km of interplanetary space on January 3, 1963, with a transmitter operating on three watts of power. Three watts is barely enough to light an electric bulb to incandescence! How can it possibly be adequate for communication over interplanetary distances? The answer is that the transmitted beam is directed and monochromatic. Instead of radiating in all directions, as an electric light bulb does, the antenna of a spacecraft is beamed directly towards the Earth. Instead of radiating over the entire electromagnetic spectrum, as an electric light bulb does, the spacecraft antenna radiates in a narrow frequency range, or bandwidth. In addition, substantial advances in receiver sensitivity have been made in recent years. By pouring all the transmitter power into a very small bandwidth and a very tight beam, and by improving receiver sensitivity, communications over immense distances may be achieved with small power. Spacecraft communications over a distance of several billions of kilometers are now feasible. △

But the radio transmitters of interplanetary space vehicles are necessarily of low weight and therefore of low power. For radio contact over interstellar distances, very large, stationary, groundbased antennas are available. ▽ Figures 27–3, 27–4 and 27–5 show photographs of three of the largest radiotelescopes now in operation. In Figure 27–3, we see the world's largest radio dish, the Arecibo radiotelescope of Cornell University, in Puerto Rico. The diameter of the Arecibo dish is 300 meters. If we were to repeat the calculations we just performed but assume that both transmitting and receiving civilizations were able to use equivalents of the Arecibo dish, interstellar radio communication over a distance of 100 light years would be possible. △

In addition to the increase in the dimensions of radio dishes, there have been

FIGURE 27-3. *The Arecibo Ionospheric Observatory, the world's largest radio telescope now in operation. It has an aperture of 300 meters and is semi-steerable. The cables comprising the antenna itself are layered down into a deep depression smoothed out into an already existing valley in Arecibo, Puerto Rico.*

improvements in recent years in the sensitivity of the receiving apparatus for radiation of centimeter and decimeter wavelengths—that is, between 1 and 100 cm. These refinements have been achieved through the wide application of quantum amplifiers—the so-called masers. Such devices, in conjunction with increased precision in the manufacture of radio dishes, will enable us to detect signals from a point source even when the antenna temperature is significantly less than the brightness temperature of the sky.

Let us consider this problem in more detail. Even if an antenna receives a signal of constant intensity, the output detected by the receiver will not be quite constant. One measurement will differ slightly from the next. These fluctuations can be minimized, but never completely eliminated, because they are inherent in the receiver itself. It is customary, in radio astronomy, to characterize the receiver by T_N, the noise temperature, ▽ proportional to the energy of the noise which originates within the receiver. △ An average value (actually, the root-mean-square value) can then be expressed as

$$\Delta T_N = T_N (\tau \, \Delta f)^{-\frac{1}{2}},$$

FIGURE 27–4. *The 85 foot radio telescope at the National Radio Astronomy Observatory, Greenbank, West Virginia which was used in project Ozma.*

where τ is the integration time during which the recording apparatus at the receiver output accumulates information about the incoming power, and Δf is the receiver bandwidth—that is, the range of frequencies admitted by the receiver.

To detect a weak signal, the antenna temperature, which is dependent on the signal, must not ordinarily be less than the noise fluctuation ΔT_N. Otherwise expressed, $T_A \geq \Delta T = T(\tau \Delta f)^{-\frac{1}{2}}$. At centimeter wavelengths, the brightness temperature of the sky is approximately $10°K$ (cf. Figure 27–1). With masers now in use, the receiver noise temperature is 50 to $100°K$. Therefore, the level about which the fluctuations occur is primarily determined by the receiver noise, and not by the cosmic background noise. These expressions can be rewritten as

$$r \leq (\pi /4)(W /kT_N)^{\frac{1}{2}} (\tau \Delta f)^{\frac{1}{4}} (D_1 D_2 /\lambda),$$

FIGURE 27—5. *An array of eight 15-meter dishes used in the Soviet Union for tracking Soviet space flights. This array is also of great utility for radio astronomy and an instrument like it may have been used in the Russian studies of the radio source CTA 102.*

an expression relating the range of interstellar radio communication to the transmitter power, the dimensions of the transmitting antennas, and the characteristics of the receiver.

▽ Note that in the algebraic expression above, the distance of interstellar communication, r, is proportional to the square root of W, where W is not the total transmitter power, but the transmitter power per unit bandpass—that is, per cycle per second. If the total transmitter power, therefore, is funnelled into a bandpass of 1 cps, interstellar radio contact can be effected over a hundred times greater distance than if the power is spread over a bandpass of 10^4 cps. But then we must pay the price of bandpass compression elsewhere—for example, in a longer integration time. △ For numerical values, let $D_1 = D_2 = 100$ meters, $\tau = 100$ seconds, and $\Delta f = 10^4$ cps.

What, then, must be the power of a transmitter, in order to establish contact over a distance of 10 parsecs, or about 30 light years? This equation indicates that the required power would be about 10 kilowatts ▽ spread over the 10,000 cycles per second, △ a very modest figure in terms of contemporary radio technology. ▽ At 10 cm wavelength, transmitters exist today which deliver 500,000 watts of power with a frequency bandpass of 1 cps. If we imagine transmitting and receiving antennas of the size of the Arecibo dish (300 meters), we find that interstellar radio communication over distances approaching 100 parsecs becomes possible at the present stage of terrestrial radio technology. How might we improve this figure even further? We may increase the power per unit frequency interval of the transmission, decrease the noise temperature of the receiver, increase the apertures of the transmitting and receiving antennas, or decrease the wavelength of the transmission. Because of the small exponent, the communication distance does not depend sensitively on the integration time of the receiver. These parameters cannot, however, be varied independently of one another. They are mutually dependent variables. It does not seem unlikely that civilizations in moderate advance of our own can, in the absence of interstellar absorption, communicate over much greater distances than 100 parsecs—perhaps even over distances comparable to the dimensions of our Galaxy. △

By astronomical standards, the power required is insignificant. For example, the power of the radio emission of the quiet Sun at wavelengths between 10 and 100 cm is approximately 10^9 kilowatts. Yet the emission of even the nearest star at these wavelengths cannot be detected, because stars radiate equally in all directions (isotropically), and over a wide range of wavelengths. On the other hand, an artificial radio signal of this power, transmitted from the nearest star, would be easily detectable, because it would be narrow-beam and monochromatic.

We indicated earlier that the most effective wavelengths for negotiating interstellar radio contact lie between 3 cm and 300 m, ▽ or, when the effects of cosmic radio noise are considered, between 3 and 30 cm. These wavelength intervals are fairly broad. △ It seems almost impossible for the target civilization to detect an interstellar signal, unless the frequency of transmission were known beforehand. ▽ 3 cm wavelength corresponds to 10^{10} cps; 30 cm wavelength corresponds to 10^9 cps. If the bandpass of the transmission is 1 cps, there are nine billion possible transmission frequencies between 3 and 30 cm. If we multiply the number of possible frequencies by the number of possible inhabited planets, we see that even in a Galaxy heavily populated with technical civilizations, the establishment of interstellar radio contact may be an intractable problem.

▽ However, if every civilization which approached the problem could arrive at an identical conclusion on the preferred transmission frequency, interstellar radio contact would be greatly simplified. △ Cocconi and Morrison arrived at the elegant idea that nature itself provides a standard calibrating frequency within this wavelength range—namely, the 21 cm (1420 megacycles per second) radio frequency line of neutral hydrogen [see Chapter 5]. Each advanced civilization must have discovered this line in the spectrum of cosmic radio radiation at an early stage of its technological development. Hydrogen is the most abundant element in the universe, and 1420 Mc sec^{-1} may be considered the fundamental frequency of nature. Radioastronomical observations at this wavelength provide a powerful tool for the investigation of the Galaxy, as we have seen [Chapter 3]. On other worlds as well there must be very sensitive apparatus tuned to this wavelength. Cocconi and Morrison concluded that there is a language of nature comprehensible to technical societies throughout the universe.

▽ No matter how obvious this choice of wavelength is to us, there still remains the question of whether Earthly clarity may be extraterrestrial nonsense. If technology has advanced at a different pace, and discoveries have been made in a different sequence on other worlds, the 21 cm wavelength may not be the preferred interstellar communications channel. Beyond this, there are other reasons to examine alternative frequencies. △ The background radiation of the sky is appreciable at 21 cm wavelength. When contact at distances beyond 3000 light years is attempted—beyond our present capabilities, but within the grasp of a more advanced civilization—the signal would be strongly absorbed by interstellar hydrogen. This would be particularly true if the signal were confined to a small angle within the plane of the Galaxy. Within the Galactic plane, the brightness temperature of the sky at 21 cm wavelength can reach 50 to 100°K. But at shorter wavelengths (see Figure 27–1), it is less than 10°K. ▽ At those shorter wavelengths, there seems to be no natural frequency such as the hydrogen line at 21 cm. △ There is always the possibility that the signal frequency may be a whole multiple of the fundamental hydrogen frequency, for example, ▽ 2840 megacycles per second (10.5 cm wavelength), or 4260 megacycles per second (7 cm wavelength).

▽ There are other possibilities as well. Recently, an interstellar radio frequency line due to the molecular fragment OH has been discovered near 18 cm wavelength. Perhaps the preferred communications channel is 18 cm, or 12 cm, or 6 cm. There must be other radio absorption lines which have not yet been discovered. Still, even if some score of such natural frequencies and their overtones exist, a search for communication at these channels is vastly simpler than the nine billion possible channels of a random search in frequency. △ We may conclude that if intelligent life is widespread in the universe, and civilizations are removed from each other by distances of tens or hundreds of light years, the most probable communication channel is 1420 megacycles per second. (▽ Note, however, that this is for local transmission only; long distance communications—for example, with the dense star clouds of the Galactic center—require other frequencies. △)

The 1420 megacycle per second channel is noisy, as we have said. How do we recognize an artificial signal? ▽ First, we might expect it to have a narrow-band character. △ Second, we would expect the power of such a signal to vary regularly with time; that is, the signal would be modulated. It could consist of a regular sequence of relatively short pulses, one sequence separated from another by distinct time intervals. The number of pulses in each sequence might represent a natural series of numbers—e.g., 1, 2, 4, 8, 16, 32, . . . , etc.—a concept probably common to all technically advanced civilizations. The length of each pulse must not be too short; otherwise, it would be impossible to obtain a long enough integration time, τ, for the reception of the signals. The necessity for a long time period per pulse increases with distances. ▽ We have seen that the communication distance goes as $\tau^{\frac{1}{4}}$; thus, a large increase in τ is required for even a small increase in the communication distance. In our calculation of 100 parsecs as a possible communication distance for civilizations at our state of technical advance, we assumed 100 seconds for the integration time. If we assume 3 hours per pulse instead, leaving the other quantities unchanged, the communication distance increases to about 300 parsecs. △ The length of each pulse may be more than several hours in duration. The signal could contain complex information, but initially it should be quite simple. In Chapter 30, we pursue in more detail the question of the nature of the signals.

After the signal is received, two-way interstellar radio contact could be established, followed by the exchange of information. ▽ Even an exchange of interstellar salutations would take tens or hundreds of years, depending on the separation of the communicants. △ But the immense significance of such an exchange of information would certainly compensate for the somewhat sluggish nature of the conversation.

Even if we are unsuccessful in detecting a regular variation in the power of the signals with time, the artificial character of the signals would soon be revealed by systematic observations. The radial velocity of the transmitter would vary periodically with respect to the receiver, because the transmitting planet is revolving about its star. Because of the Doppler effect, a periodic variation in the frequency of the transmitted signal must occur, ▽ unless it is purposely compensated for by the transmitting civilization. △ Since the orbital velocity of the planet must be several tens of kilometers per second, the amplitude of the periodic variations in frequency may reach hundreds of kilocycles per second, ▽ that is, values much greater than the bandwidth of the transmitted signals. △ The period of such frequency variations could range anywhere from several months to several years, depending on the period of revolution of the transmitting planet about its local sun. Thus, an analysis of an uncompensated signal would immediately yield information about the duration of the year in that distant technical civilization.

We may also expect periodic variation in the transmission frequency due to the rotation of the planet about its axis. Since this velocity is likely to be less than the orbital velocity, frequency variations of rotational origin would probably have an amplitude that is smaller but nevertheless detectable through careful observations. Thus, we could extract from the signal the length of the day on the transmitting planet.

With this information in hand, we could derive many other features of the environment of the transmitting planet. After we identified the star about which the planet is rotating, we could determine the stellar mass from its spectral type; the star would probably be a star of the main sequence [see Chapter 6]. Knowing the period of revolution of the planet, we can find, from Kepler's Third Law, the distance between the planet and the star. Knowing the luminosity of the star, we could then make a rough estimate of the average planetary surface temperature. Knowing the velocity of rotation of the planet about its axis and the length of its day, we could estimate the planetary radius. A more detailed analysis might even allow us to determine the latitude on the planet at which the transmitter is located. Thus, a wide range of interesting physical information could be obtained from systematic observations of the variations in transmission frequency ▽ of an uncompensated signal, even if it were otherwise incomprehensible.

▽ If the Doppler variation of frequency due to planetary rotation and revolution are uncompensated by the transmitting civilization, there are certain attendant difficulties in the reception of the signals. If the receiver bandpass is 1 cps, and yet the frequency variation due to planetary revolution is of the order of 10^5 cps, at any instant there is only one chance in 100,000 that the transmitted signal will be accepted by the receiver. Thus, the receiving civilization, searching the skies with radiotelescopes, may lock onto the transmitting planet, receive no signal, and move on to another star before the transmitted signal fortuitously coincides with the frequency bandpass of the receiver. There are two solutions to this difficulty: First, both transmitting and receiving civilizations may have reasoned as we just have, and utilized only broader bandpasses, comparable to or slightly less than the 100 kilocycle per second frequency broadening due to planetary revolution. Alternatively, the transmitting civilization may exactly compensate for the rotation and revolution of the transmitting planet, and the receiving civilization likewise may compensate for the motions of the receiving planet. This has the advantage that the entire power of the transmitter may be funnelled into a very small bandpass. The communications channel would then be, for example, the exact center of the hydrogen emisson line. The frequency would have to be known to ten significant figures, and even then the relative proper motions of the two stars in question would Doppler shift the frequency off the line center. It remains open to conjecture whether such relative motions could be compensated for in a universe with no absolute standard of rest.

▽ The pace of science is now swift. In earlier times, the suggestion of Cocconi and Morrison would never have been accepted for scientific publication; it would have been considered too speculative by far. Now the temper of the times is different. △ In 1960, the American radioastronomer Frank D. Drake, then at the National Radio Astronomy Observatory in Green Bank, West Virginia, developed a special receiver to detect interstellar radio signals of ·intelligent origin at 21 cm wavelength. ▽ This enterprise was dubbed Project Ozma, after the queen of the land of Oz, in Frank Baum's series of children's stories. △

Figure 27–6 shows a photograph of Drake's receiver. The receiver has a very stable narrow-band, superheterodyne design, since the desired signal must be narrow-band. At the focus of the 27-meter antenna [Fig. 27–4] there are two horns. Radiation from a small area near the star under investigation, where one might expect to find a transmitting planet, enters one horn. Radiation from a neighboring region of the sky enters the other. Each horn alternately feeds into the receiver, with the aid of an electronic switch. Thus, the radiotelescope alternately looks first at the star, and then at a nearby section of the sky. For this reason, the signal consists of short pulses, periodically interrupted, at a rate equal to the switching frequency between the horns. The synchronous detector at the output of the receiver isolates the variable component of the current derived from the radio signal. Similar schemes, widely used in radioastronomy, are described as modulation. They enable us to separate out the desired signal even when it is much weaker than the noise level of the apparatus. Unfortunately, an extremely weak signal cannot be detected by this method, because of the inherent fluctuations due to the recording apparatus itself. However, in a number of cases at least, the modulation scheme enables us to obtain a sensitivity close to the theoretical maximum sensitivity given by the formula we have already encountered, $\Delta T = T(\tau \Delta f)^{-1/2}$.

Four successive conversions of the signal frequency are made. These conversions are required because the expected signal is narrow-banded. Thus, the intermediate frequency of the receiver must be low. As is usual in superheterodyne receivers, the frequency conversion is carried out by mixer stages. The corresponding local oscillators must have very high frequency stability. The frequency must not vary by more than 1 cps in each 100 seconds of operation. Particularly high stability is required of the first local oscillator, since its frequency is very high—1390 megacycles per second.

FIGURE 27–6. *The receiving equipment used by Frank Drake at the National Radio Astronomy Observatory for Project Ozma. The 85 foot radio telescope may be seen out the window. The additional equipment not on hand for ordinary radio astronomical studies which Drake required in this investigation cost a few thousand dollars.*

After these four stages of amplification, the signal is divided into two parts, and then passed through electronic filters. One filter is broad-banded; the other is narrow-banded. These filters are arranged in such a way that their output currents are identical when receiving a broad-band signal. If subsequently the two currents are electronically subtracted from each other, a zero output is obtained. However, if an incoming narrow-band signal passes through the filters, the output current of the narrow-band filter will exceed that of the broad-band filter, and the resulting current, after subtraction, will be different from zero. Thus, the receiver is sensitive only to narrow-band signals. The filters precede the synchronous detector, and pass only the switching frequency. A signal will be obtained at the output of the synchronous detector only when a narrow-band signal enters the receiver and the direction of the arriving signal corresponds to the direction of the star under investigation.

Drake chose the nearby stars Epsilon Eridani and Tau Ceti as the first objects of investigation with this receiver and the 27-meter Green Bank antenna. We have previously encountered these stars in Chapter 24, in our discussion of nearby stars likely to have habitable planets. Epsilon Eridani and Tau Ceti are approximately 11 light years distant. The observations of Project Ozma began in the autumn of 1960, and continued for several months. ▽ The results of Project Ozma were described to a meeting of the American Astronomical Society in approximately the following manner by the Russian-American astronomer, the late Otto Struve, then Director of the National Radio Astronomy Observatory: "I am reminded," he said, "of a cartoon showing the return to Earth of the first astronaut to land on Mars. 'Tell us,' say the reporters, 'is there any life on Mars?' 'Well,' the astronaut replies, 'there's a little on Saturday night, but it's pretty dull the rest of the week.' "Well, ladies and gentlemen," Struve concluded, "it was pretty dull on Epsilon Eridani and Tau Ceti eleven years ago."

▽ These pioneering investigations were unsuccessful; yet the investment of ancillary equipment was only a few thousand dollars. Only two nearby stars were investigated, and the total time actually spent in observing the stars was about 200 hours. Success of this first venture would have been astounding indeed. △ It is highly probable that the nearest technical civilizations are at much greater distances than 11 light years, as we shall discuss in Chapter 29. If the nearest civilizations are 100 light years away, it would be a much more time-consuming task to determine which of the tens of thousands of stars at that distance might hold an advanced technical civilization. The separate investigation of each such star would be a humdrum and expensive task, ▽ one requiring a long-term commitment for a systematic study. But by any reckoning, the consequences of success would more than balance the pains which went before. △ Only the first tentative steps have been taken so far, on our planet, towards interstellar radio contact. Perhaps we shall soon be able to broadcast our own existence. This would not be immodest. What would happen if all Galactic civilizations worked only on receiving, and not on transmitting interstellar radio signals?

▽ Drake has suggested that it may be possible for us to "eavesdrop" on local planetary radio communications of a distant civilization. The radio signals which a civilization uses for its own purposes have a certain characteristic distribution in frequency. If we point our radiotelescope at such a civilization and scan in frequency, we record the frequencies characteristically utilized by the civilization. Perhaps none of the signals will be detectable individually. But if a second such frequency scan is performed, the two records can be checked for cross-correlation. The frequency distribution of cosmic radio noise will show no such cross-correlation; artificial transmission will. Drake estimates that such cross-correlation techniques can increase the distance over which we may detect radio transmission by a factor of ten—with present equipment, from 300 light years to 3000 light years.

▽ Conversely, our civilization may be detectable over interstellar distances, even though we make no effort to announce our presence. Large-scale radio communication on Earth has been in operation for only some 40 years. We may imagine those earliest radio transmissions—for example, a cadenza sung by Enrico Caruso —traveling forever at the speed of light across interstellar space from the position which the Earth was in some 40 years ago. By now, the signal has propagated some 40 light years into space. If there is an advanced technical civilization within 20 light years of the Sun, they may have received that signal 20 years ago, correctly interpreted it as the result of another technical civilization, and immediately beamed their response to us. We should receive that signal any day now. But if the nearest technical civilization is many hundreds of light years away, we will have to wait a little longer. A relatively nearby civilization in substantial advance of our own may be able to detect some of our domestic radio transmission. There are two general channels which are in heavy commercial use and which are transmitted by the terrestrial ionosphere. One is the entire television band; the other is the high frequency end of the AM broadcast band, between about 1000 and 1400 kilocycles per second, which is occasionally transmitted by the ionosphere. Thus the characteristic signs of life on Earth which may be detectable over interstellar distances include the baleful contents of many American television programs and the mindless outpourings of rock-and-roll stations. It is a sobering thought indeed that the Beverly Hillbillies may be our only interstellar emissaries.

▽ In our discussion up to this point, we have considered only interstellar radio contact among civilizations at or just slightly beyond our present state of technical advance. Yet the bulk of technical civilizations in the universe may be immensely more advanced than ours—perhaps even billions of years beyond. The Soviet astrophysicist N. S. Kardashev, an associate of I. S. Shklovskii at the Sternberg Astronomical Institute, has considered the possibility of the detection of signals from such greatly advanced civilizations. He classifies possible technologically advanced civilizations in three categories: (I) A level of technological advance close to that of the contemporary terrestrial civilization. The rate of energy consumption is about 4×10^{19} ergs sec^{-1}. (II) A civilization capable of utilizing and channeling the entire radiation output of its star. The energy utilization would then be comparable to the luminosity of our Sun, about 4×10^{33} ergs per second. In Chapter 34, we will consider a specific proposal for the harnessing of such power. (III) A civilization with access to the power comparable to the luminosity of an entire galaxy, some 4×10^{44} ergs per second.

▽ Kardashev then examines the possibilities in cosmic communication which attend the investment of most of the available power into communication. A Type II civilization could transmit the contents of 100,000 average-sized books across the Galaxy in a total transmitting time of 100 seconds. It would, of course, take some tens of thousands of years for the signals to make the journey. The transmission of the same information intended for a target 10 million light years distant, a typical intergalactic distance, would take a few weeks' transmission time. A Type III civilization could transmit the same information over a distance of 10 billion light years, approximately the radius of the observable universe, with a transmission time of 3 seconds. The journey would take, of course, 10 billion years. Thus, enormous, almost unbelievable quantities of information can be communicated over immense distances, if such civilizations exist. Signals from one Type II civilization among the nearby galaxies, or one Type III civilization in the observable universe— transmitting appropriately long ago in the past—would stand out as a beacon in the dark, if only we knew how to look.

▽ Kardashev has called attention to two cosmic radio sources with the California Institute of Technology designation numbers CTA 21 and CTA 102. They display small angular diameters and had not been identified with any known source of visible radiation at the time Kardashev was writing. Moreover, the peak emission of CTA 102 seems to be at approximately 32.5 cm; of CTA 21, at approximately 37 cm. These are not quite at the wavelengths of minimum cosmic noise, nor at what we have concluded are probably the natural communication frequencies. Furthermore, CTA 21 and CTA 102 have bandpasses some thousands of megacycles wide, an apparently extravagant inefficiency. The radio signals of a Type II or a Type III civilization should have small angular diameter, as seen from Earth, and should probably be associated with no known optical object. We expect its wavelength to be between 3 and 30 cm, and probably at some natural and universal radio frequency or an overtone thereof. The frequency considerations, however, have been derived in the interest of economy. A Type II or Type III civilization can probably afford to be extravagant. We must recall that a bandpass of 10^9 cps makes detection immensely easy. The radio emission of CTA 21 and CTA 102 might profitably be examined for possible content.

▽ Following the publication of Kardashev's paper, the Soviet radio astronomer G. B. Sholomitskii of the Sternberg Astronomical Institute undertook a study of the radio source CTA 102 with a large radiotelescope—probably the array of eight 15 meter dishes shown in Figure 27–5. Sholomitskii announced that CTA 102 was varying significantly in intensity with an apparent period of about 100 days. At the time of this announcement in early 1965, speculation on its significance was rife, especially because of the previous interest which had been expressed in this radio source. It was speculated that the oscillation might serve the purpose of a beacon, calling attention to CTA 102, and that on a much shorter time-scale than 100 days individual words of an interstellar communications channel might be deciphered. It was also suggested that the oscillations corresponding to individual words had a time scale of 100 days, implying centuries even to receive the simplest message. In the Soviet press Kardashev was quoted as concluding that CTA 102 was definitely an artificial radio source, but this news report was roundly criticized the following day by Shklovskii in a press conference. Attempts to confirm Sholomitskii's announcement have been equivocal. The Norwegian radio astronomer P. Maltby and the American radio astronomer A. T. Moffet at the Owens Valley Radio Observatory of the California Institute of Technology were unable to find in records of CTA 102 for 1961 and 1962 any sign of a systematic variation in the intensity of this source. More recently, other observers have found no variation. In Figure 27–7, Sholomitskii's observations over a period of many months are displayed.

▽ The great interest in the radio spectrum of CTA 102 has encouraged improved optical studies of this region in the sky. The astronomer J. D. Wyndham of the California Institute of Technology has obtained a photograph of a faint object which is just in the radio position of CTA 102. [Figure 27–8] From its spectrum Wyndham and Sandage have identified CTA 102 as a quasar [see Chapter 9] with a probable distance of some billions of light years from the Earth. Quasars have been known to vary in intensity at optical frequencies with periods comparable to 100 days. Sholomitskii's discovery, if confirmed, will be the first time that a quasar has been observed to oscillate at radio frequencies. The great distance which now seems likely for CTA 102 does not in itself dispose of the possibility of intelligent origin of its radio emission; we might consider it a product of a civilization of Type III. But the argument for the artificial origin of the CTA 102 radio source does seem considerably eroded by its identification as a quasar, despite the fact that we do not fully understand the origin and nature of quasars [see Chapter 9].

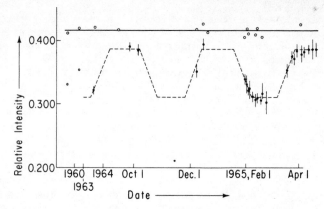

FIGURE 27–7. *A summary of observations of the radio source CTA–102 as measured by G. B. Sholomitskii. The open circles represent the intensity of the radio source CTA–21, relative to the intensity of the radio source 3C–48. The closed circles represent the intensity of CTA–102, relative to the presumably unchanging intensity of 3C–48. We see that over the five year period represented here, CTA–21 has varied its intensity a negligible amount and its emission can be represented by the solid horizontal line. CTA–102, on the other hand, has varied significantly, by far more than the probable error of a single measurement, as indicated by the short vertical slashes. The radio emission from CTA–102 can be represented approximately by the dashed line, suggesting an intensity variation with a period of about 100 days, at a wavelength near 32.5 cm.*

▽ The most recent observations of CTA 102 have interesting implications. Sholomitskii's observations were performed near the maximum in the emission spectrum of CTA 102; negative searches for variation have been performed in recent years at longer and at shorter wavelengths, but not near Sholomitskii's wavelength of 32.5 cm. From the optical red shift, we can show that the radio emission maximum of CTA 102 has a wavelength near 18 cm *if measured at CTA 102*. This is a wavelength previously proposed for interstellar communication, particularly over intergalactic distances, when the 21 cm line will be noisy (cf. p. 389). In general, we expect Type III civilizations to have their signals significantly shifted to longer wavelengths, because of the expansion of the universe. While it is not yet even likely, the possibility should be borne in mind that CTA 102 has a general radio spectrum designed to call attention to the wavelength of peak emission, at which information is being transmitted. It will be interesting to see, after CTA 21 is observed optically, if it is receding at an even larger velocity than CTA 102— in order to account for its longer wavelength of maximum emission; and if it is varying near 37 cm.

▽ More narrow-band searches for Type I civilizations should be encouraged. Except by the sheerest stroke of fortune, interstellar radio communication will be detected by our just-emerging technical civilization only after a commitment to a long and careful search. But imagine if one day the contents of 100,000 books of a

396

N

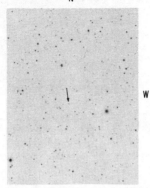

W

FIGURE 27-8. *A photograph of the star field around the radio source CTA 102, itself indicated by the arrow. (Courtesy of Dr. J. Wyndham, Mount Wilson and Palomar Observatories.)*

Type II civilization suddenly fluttered through the receivers of our radiotelescopes, a kind of Encyclopedia Galactica for children! The rewards of success are inestimable. △

Such pioneering investigations as those of Frank D. Drake are of the greatest potential value to our civilization. As Cocconi and Morrison have quite properly pointed out, the chances for success in such an endeavor are not great; but they are zero, if nothing is attempted.

28

Optical contact among galactic civilizations

Our eye-beams twisted, and did thread
Our eyes upon one double string;
So to intergraft our hands, as yet
Was all the means to make us one;
And pictures in our eyes to get
Was all our propagation.

John Donne, *The Ecstasy* (1633)

The possibility of radio communication among Galactic civilizations, which we discussed in the last chapter, has a number of valuable advantages. A relatively modest transmitter can send signals over distances of some tens of light years. The artificial signal can easily be separated from the thermal radio radiation of the local sun. The excellent frequency resolution of contemporary radio receivers enables us, after detailed study of a signal, to obtain significant information about distant planetary systems and the intelligent beings which may inhabit them. But is the radio band the only frequency range useful for interstellar communication? In this chapter, we discuss the possibility of using much higher frequencies, near the spectral region of visible light, to effect interstellar contacts.

At first glance, it might seem that sending a narrow beam of light from one planet to another would be a simple communications mode. But we soon encounter difficulties in trying to devise a practical light source for interstellar communication. Even the best projectors of the usual type do not send parallel beams of light. The rays are always slightly diverging, and it is impossible to produce a point source of light in focus from such a beam. Although this divergence is relatively unimportant over terrestrial distances, it poses a problem over interplanetary and interstellar distances.

As an example, suppose that the divergence in angle of a cone of radiation beamed by our light source is 30 minutes of arc, corresponding to the tightest beam which can be achieved by ordinary contemporary projectors. Such a beam, transmitted from one point on Earth to another 50 km away, will have a diameter of 450 meters when received. If the power level of the projector is 10 kilowatts, the energy flux at the distance of 50 km would be 5×10^{-6} watts cm^{-2}, a quantity some tens of thousands of times smaller than the solar flux during daytime, but nevertheless a detectable flux at nighttime.

Now imagine that such a projector is used to transmit a light beam to the nighttime hemisphere of the Moon. Since the average distance to the Moon is 380,000 km, the illuminated area on the Moon would be approximately 3,000 km across. The resulting illumination of the Moon would be extremely feeble—about 10^7 times smaller than the illumination of the nighttime hemisphere of the Moon by Earthshine, sunlight reflected from the Earth. $\triangledown$ Studies of Earthshine reflected from the dark hemisphere of the Moon have permitted scientists to estimate that on the average the Earth reflects about 40 percent of the sunlight shining on it back to space. But such measurements are extremely difficult to perform. $\triangle$ Thus, the artificial beam reflected back from the Moon could obviously not be detected. However, the projector would be seen by an observer on the Moon as a star of approximately the third magnitude, even against the bright background of the

Earth, illuminated by the Sun. At a distance of 100 million km—roughly corresponding to the distance to Mars or to Venus—the light from our projector, if raised above the Earth's atmosphere, would be visible through a fairly large telescope as a weak star of the fifteenth magnitude. The beam would have approximately the same magnitude as the moons of Mars, observed from Earth. Of course, the beam would have to be directed precisely at the planets, in order to be observed from them.

Thus, optical projection techniques of the conventional sort would be useless for interstellar contact. Not only could the beam not be detected over such vast distances; in addition, the visible radiation of the Sun in the direction in which the projector is pointing would be vastly more intense than the radiation emitted by the projector itself.

Despite these difficulties, we must not discount optical devices as a possible means of future interstellar contact. Recently, intensive research has been performed on quantum generators and amplifiers of radiation. At radio frequencies, this has led to the development of receivers of ultra-high sensitivity, called *masers.* ▽ "Maser" is an acronym for "microwave amplification by stimulated emission of radiation." △ The same principles, applied to the optical and infrared frequencies, have led to the development of devices called *lasers,* ▽ a parallel acronym for "light amplification by stimulated emission of radiation." △ Of special interest to us here are the lasers, which are generators of intense, narrow beams of visible and infrared radiation.

Many contemporary lasers (as well as masers) utilize synthetic ruby crystals, although other substances have also been used. Under certain conditions, these crystals can be induced to emit relatively short pulsed beams of radiation with a power level approaching 100 kilowatts, or pulses of longer duration with power levels approaching 10 kilowatts. In addition, there are lasers which operate continuously, with appreciably less power, around 2×10^{-2} watts. In this latter case, the reflecting surface of the artificial ruby is approximately 1 cm in diameter. Undoubtedly much larger crystals will be made in the near future. The wave emitted by this laser is in phase over the entire reflecting surface. ▽ In optics, the angular resolution of a telescope of aperture D is approximately λ/D, where λ is the wavelength of the observed light, and the angular resolution is measured in units of radians (2π radians $= 360°$). If the telescope mirror were used to transmit radiation, rather than receive it, the angular size of the transmitted beam would still be about λ/D, provided that the transmitted beam is in phase. Hence, contemporary lasers with a diameter of only 1 cm, operating at a wavelength of 5000 Å $= 5 \times 10^{-5}$ cm, have a beam width of approximately 5×10^{-5} radians. But 1 radian $= 360/2\pi° \times 60$ minutes per degree $\times 60$ seconds per minute, which is approximately 200,000 seconds. Therefore, laser beams with a beam width of 10 seconds of arc are entirely realistic. △ If such a beam were projected onto the Moon, the illuminated area of the lunar surface would be approximately 20 km across. ▽ Since the power would not be distributed over as large an area as by conventional projection systems, the laser radiation reflected from the dark hemisphere of the Moon could be detected by telescopes on the Earth. Such experiments have, in fact, been performed successfully, both in the United States and in the Soviet Union. △ The angular size of the beam could be made significantly smaller, if the laser were combined with special optical systems.

Consider a lens of high quality, with its diameter equal to its focal length. If such a lens were placed in a beam of light, then the entire image would have a diameter of λ in the focal plane. Let this image coincide with the focal plane of another ideal lens (or mirror) of significantly greater diameter, A, and let the focal length of the larger lens be $\geqq A$. In this case, the beam emerging from the larger mirror would have an angular width, limited by diffraction at its aperture, of λ/A. Although such a system has not yet been developed, it is theoretically feasible. The difficulties in its construction are great, but they are problems of technology, not of science. It would be necessary, for example, to develop a system which would automatically correct the geometry of the large mirror's surface for distortion due to the heat of the high-intensity laser beam.

Another important advantage of the lasers is the extremely pure monochromaticity of the beam. Contemporary lasers, which produce a continuous beam, have frequency bandwidths as small as 10 kilocycles sec^{-1}—more than 10^{10} times smaller than the frequency of the optical radiation. We shall see later that a high degree of monochromaticity is a very valuable property for interstellar communication.

At the present time, great efforts are being made ▽ in both the United States and the Soviet Union △ to develop more powerful lasers. In the United States, the government is spending millions of dollars each year, and more than four hundred firms are working on the problem. This interest is not accidental. Lasers of great power could provide a new type of weapon with extraordinary destructive capabilities. A laser of advanced design would not be dissimilar to the famous "heat ray" of H. G. Wells' *The War of the Worlds*. Such a laser could probably also be a very effective anti-missile weapon. ▽ Similar interests in the possible military potentialities of lasers have been manifested by the Soviet Union. △ Of course, we fervently hope that the vast potential of the laser will be employed only for peaceful purposes. This new technology can be used in a number of fields of practical interest to mankind, but most particularly in cosmic communications.

The first men seriously to consider using the laser for interstellar contact were the American physicists C. H. Townes and R. N. Schwartz of the Massachusetts Institute of Technology. ▽ Townes had previously played a very prominent role in the development of the maser. △ As their basic equipment, Townes and Schwartz suggested two laser systems, neither of which has as yet been developed, but both of which are feasible in principle:

SYSTEM A:
Power level, 10 kilowatts, continuous;
Wavelength, 5000 Å;
Bandwidth, 1 megacycle per second (or, in wavenumbers, 3×10^{-5} cm^{-1});
Diameter of light-collecting area, $D = 500$ cm (maximum size of present telescopes);

Beam width, $\lambda/D = 10^{-7}$ radians, or 2×10^{-2} seconds of arc.

SYSTEM B: A group of 25 lasers, each with the same individual characteristics as in System A, but with an effective system aperture, $A = 10$ cm, and therefore a beam width of 5×10^{-6} radians, or 1 second of arc. The entire group of 25 lasers is to be pointed in the same direction, within the accuracy of the beam width.

If System A were implemented on the surface of the Earth, the beam width, ▽ because of seeing conditions in the Earth's atmosphere, would be restricted to about one second of arc. △ The performance of the laser would be accordingly limited. Therefore, it would be expedient to place such a system in an artificial satellite beyond the atmosphere. System B, however, could work from the surface of the Earth, within the seeing limitations.

Townes and Schwartz formulated two fundamental conditions for detecting extraterrestrial laser signals: (1) the beam must be sufficiently intense to be detected with a practical telescope and in a reasonable time; and (2) the signal must be distinguishable from the background radiation of the local star of the transmitting civilization. At radio frequencies, this second condition is satisfied almost automatically; but in the optical frequency range the separation of an artificial signal from the background radiation of a star constitutes a very difficult problem.

Let us assume that a signal is sent by means of System A, operating from just outside the Earth's atmosphere. Let the distance, r, from the receiving planet to the Earth be 10 light years, or 10^{19} cm. Then the flux of radiation being beamed from the vicinity of the Earth will be $F = W/r^2 \Omega$ watts cm^{-2}, where W is the transmitter power, and Ω is the solid angle of the beam. Substituting $W = 10$ kW and $\Omega = 10^{-14}$ radians^2, we find $F = 10^{-20}$ watts cm^{-2}. We may compare this figure with the flux due to the sun at a distance of 10 light years. ▽ The luminosity of the sun is 4×10^{33} ergs/sec or 4×10^{26} watts. The sun does not radiate in a tight beam as does the laser, but radiates into a solid angle Ω of 4π radians^2. Using the same equation for the flux that we just used in the laser application we find that the solar flux at a distance of ten light years is 3×10^{-13} watts cm^{-2}. △ Knowing the ratio of the flux from the laser to the flux from the Sun, it is easy to calculate the apparent stellar magnitude of the laser as seen from any distance. △ Corresponding to any flux, F, there is an apparent stellar magnitude, m; the relation between them has been touched upon in Chapter 3. △ The well-known astronomical equation which relates them is

$$m_1 - m_2 = 2.5 \log (F_2/F_1)$$

▽ The difference in apparent magnitude between the Sun and the laser beam as seen from a distance of 10 light years is therefore $2.5 \log (3 \times 10^{-13}/10^{-20}) = 18.7$ magnitudes. At a distance of 10 light years the sun has an apparent magnitude of about 2.2 magnitudes. △ Therefore the apparent magnitude of the laser at the same distance is about $m_1 = 21$. ▽ This is the approximate apparent magnitude of the faintest visible stars observable with the 200-inch telescope at Mt. Palomar Observatory, in California.

Thus, if a large telescope were used at a distance of 10 light years, such a laser beam could be detected. However, in order to insure detection, it would be advisable that the power of the transmitter be increased several tens of times above the power level proposed by Townes and Schwartz.

The radiation flux from System B would be 100 times less than from System A, ▽ corresponding to an apparent magnitude of about 26 at a distance of 10 light years. △ Therefore, System B does not seem suitable for interstellar communications ▽ among civilizations at the level of technological advance assumed in this discussion. △

How would it be possible to separate the signal of the laser (with flux ∼ 10^{-20} watts cm^{-2}) from the signal of the Sun (flux ∼ 3×10^{-13} watts cm^{-2})? Such discrimination can be achieved only by exploiting the high degree of monochromaticity of the laser radiation. Let us consider a star which has a maximum radiation output near 5000 Å—such as our Sun. Then the radiation intensity per unit frequency interval and per unit solid angle will be 4×10^{10} watts (c.p.s.)$^{-1}$ sterradians.$^{-1}$ ▽ (A steradian can be considered a square radian.) △ The radiation from the laser will exhibit an intensity which is equal to the radiation flux divided by the solid angle of the beam and by the laser bandwidth. **Thus:**

$$\frac{10^4 \text{ watts}}{10^{-14} \text{ ster} \times 10^6 \text{ c.p.s.}} = 10^{12} \text{ watts (c.p.s.)}^{-1} \text{ ster}^{-1}.$$

Because the laser has all its radiation concentrated in a very narrow frequency band one megacycle wide, its spectral intensity is 25 times that of the Sun, ▽ despite the vastly greater flux from the Sun over all visible wavelengths. △ If the laser operated at ultraviolet or infrared frequencies, its spectral intensity would exceed that of the Sun, since the spectral intensity of the Sun will be less there than near 5000 Å. The spectral intensity of the Sun at wavelengths greater than 15,000 Å or less than 2500 Å is more than 10 times less than at 5000 Å; at wavelengths greater than 40,000 Å or less than 2000 Å, it is hundreds of times less than at 5000 Å.

In addition, we may recall that there are many Fraunhofer absorption lines in the solar spectrum. These lines have frequency bandwidths significantly greater than the bandwidth of the laser. At the frequencies of these lines, the spectral intensity of the Sun is decreased by several orders of magnitude, ▽ and, as Townes and Schwartz have emphasized, the detectability of the laser signal will be even further enhanced. △

The Earth's atmosphere completely absorbs ultraviolet radiation of wavelength less than 2900 Å, and a significant fraction of the infrared radiation. If a laser operating near 1500 Å could be sent aloft in a satellite above the atmosphere of the Earth, it could attain a spectral intensity some tens of thousands of times greater than that of the Sun. However, we must bear in mind the great technical difficulties which must be overcome, to produce an operational system at these wavelengths. Not only would such a laser be very difficult to construct; but also the reflectivity of the mirrors—the system needs mirrors—abruptly declines towards ultraviolet wavelengths. If we used a laser operating in the infrared part of the spectrum, we would also run into difficulties, but of a different nature: the beam produced by the laser has an angular width of λ/D. Thus, at longer wavelengths, the divergence of the beam would increase. With these limitations in mind, it appears that the most suitable laser for interstellar communications ▽ (at least for the near future for terrestrial technology) △ would operate at visible frequencies in the middle of a strong absorption line in the solar spectrum—for example, at the well-known H and K lines due to ionized calcium. The spectral intensity of the laser we have described, with a frequency bandwidth of one megacycle sec⁻¹, would then be some 300 times greater than that of the Sun.

If such a laser were directed towards the Earth from a distance of 10 light years, and the beam were observed through a very narrow band filter, the radiation emitted by the laser could be discerned from the background radiation of the star. In other words, if a good spectrum of the star could be obtained, then the very narrow lines due to the laser could also be detected. However, it is technically difficult to construct good narrow band filters. Moreover, the resolving power of the spectrograph is a limiting factor.

What resolving power must a spectrograph have, in order to discriminate a line of artificial radiation from the background radiation of the star? Ideally, to be detected, the intensity of the line would have to be only 10 percent greater than the continuous spectrum. Unfortunately, even an intrinsically very narrow spectral line seems to be spread over neighboring frequencies by the limited resolving power of the spectrograph. The intensity of the line, per unit frequency interval, is thereby reduced. If, for example, the resolving power of the spectrograph were 1 Å (in frequency units, about 10^{11} c.p.s.) then the intensity of a very narrow laser line spread over this frequency interval would be 300 times less than the intensities at neighboring frequencies of the stellar spectrum. Thus, to obtain a 10 percent contrast of the laser line over the stellar background with the laser systems we have been discussing, the resolving power of the spectrograph must be 0.03 Å. This resolving power is extremely high but can be obtained by using high precision spectrographs and interferometric techniques. Thus, for the systems we have been describing, it would be possible to detect a weak spectral line of artificial origin in the spectra of the nearest stars, by using the largest existing telescopes. If, however, the power of the transmitter were increased by a multiple of 10, the detection of such a line would not be extremely difficult, even for telescopes of moderate dimensions, provided good spectrographs were used.

There is yet another obstacle to overcome in making such observations: due, for example, to the rotation of the transmitting planet, or the revolution of a transmitting satellite about its planet, there will be continuous changes in the velocity of the artificial radiation source, a velocity change which, through the Doppler effect, will induce a frequency variation in the signal. In order to detect the laser beam, its frequency must not vary during the time when the spectrum of the star is photographed—say, about an hour—beyond the frequency limits defined by the resolving power of the spectrograph. ▽ But as in the case of radio frequency communication over interstellar distances, the transmitting civilization may be able to compensate for the motion of the source. △

To summarize, in order for an artificial laser signal to be distinguishable from the natural radiation background, the following characteristics are necessary: First, the emitted intensity must be confined to an exceedingly narrow frequency bandpass. Second, it must in some respect be distinct from any known ▽ stellar emission △ lines. Finally, if it is to be used for the transmission of information, as a kind of light telegraph, the intensity in the spectral line must vary with time.

As soon as the presence of an artificial line is detected in the spectrum of a star, it can be recorded in detail through the use of photoelectric techniques which permit us to increase the integration time of a signal (analogous to a time exposure in photographic observations) up to several minutes. This is desirable for deciphering a ▽ slowly △ modulated light signal. All of our discussion on the detection of optical signals of artificial extraterrestrial origin has assumed that the very narrow cones, or beams, of light are aimed precisely at the Earth. Since the assumed beam width of the laser—10^{-7} radians, or 0.02 seconds of arc—is very small, the pointing accuracy of the signal must be maintained to within 10^{-7} radians. This degree of accuracy is barely within the limits of contemporary terrestrial astronomical technology.

If our solar system is viewed from a hypothetical planet surrounding one of the nearest stars, the angular diameter of the Earth's orbit is approximately one second of arc. For the laser systems we have discussed, the width of the beam transmitted by the extraterrestrial civilization will be about 10 million km across by the time it reaches the solar system. This is one-fifteenth of the distance between the Earth and the Sun. Since the extraterrestrial civilization will presumably not know beforehand where our planet is located, the laser beam will have to be moved about within the speculated limits of our solar system, in order to find the Earth. For this reason, the Earth will be exposed to the laser beam only occasionally, and the possibility of detection of this beam will be accordingly decreased. I believe that this is a very important consideration which Townes and Schwartz failed to take into account. It might decrease significantly the value of lasers for interstellar communication. ▽ However, Professor Townes has since suggested that the beaming civilization might be able to determine the position of habitable planets in the target solar system. △

The difficulty can also be circumvented by assuming that the width of the beam is several times greater than the distance between the Earth and the Sun. For the laser system we have previously discussed, and for stars tens of light years distant, the power of the laser beam would have to be increased by several thousand times. This increased power requirement does not, however, constitute a decisive argument against the possible use of lasers for interstellar communications. In fact, we are convinced that lasers, after optimal improvement, will be entirely suitable for interstellar contact, ▽ at least over the distances discussed to this point. △ As we mentioned previously, there is good reason to believe that laser power levels will be greatly increased within the next few decades, because for lasers to be of substantial military significance their power levels must be increased to millions of kilowatts.

▽ With a power level of millions of kilowatts, a laser beam which fills the entire inner solar system of the target star would be useful for interstellar contact over hundreds of light years. If the light-gathering devices of the receiving civilization involve collecting areas more than 200 inches (500 cm) in diameter, communications over much greater distances are possible. Note that the collecting area need not have the fine optical properties of the mirrors of reflecting telescopes. We are interested not in forming a point image of the transmitting star —only in obtaining a high-resolution spectrum of the transmitting laser beam. For this purpose, we could use a large, perhaps faceted, "light bucket," composed not necessarily of glass, but rather of metals or plastic materials, and much more easily constructed than a conventional reflecting telescope of comparable dimensions. When such substantial improvements become possible, it may be that the limiting factor in the range of interstellar communication at optical frequencies will be absorption by the interstellar medium, a limitation particularly relevant for any attempt to communicate with civilizations in the direction of the Galactic center. △

At the present stage of terrestrial technology, radio wavelengths—for example, near 21 cm—are more economical means of interstellar communication than optical wavelengths. However, our criteria of economy may not be the same as those of other planetary civilizations. ▽ Townes and Schwartz point out that in the evolution of terrestrial technology, the development of the laser might well have antedated the development of radiotelescopes. △ We are basing the technical and economic possibilities of interstellar communication on contemporary conditions, but these conditions may change.

▽ While discussing optical frequency interstellar contact, we should mention independent suggestions by Drake and Shklovskii that, if not the communication of large amounts of information, at least the communication of the presence of a technical civilization, can be effected through the use of *markers*. Drake and Shklovskii envision the dumping of a short-lived isotope—one which would not be ordinarily expected in the local stellar spectrum—into the atmosphere of the star. In any case, the material of the marker should be of a type that is difficult to explain, except as a result of intelligent activity. Drake considers an atom with a strong, resonant absorption line, which may scatter about 10^8 photons sec^{-1} in the stellar radiation field. A photon at optical frequencies has an energy of about 10^{-12} ergs, so each atom will scatter about 10^{-4} erg sec^{-1} in the resonance line. A typical line width might be about 1 Å, and we assume that a 10 percent absorption will be detectable. We must then scatter about

$$\frac{1 \text{ Å}}{5000 \text{ Å}} \times 10^{-1} = 2 \times 10^{-5}$$

of the total solar flux. The solar flux is 4×10^{33} erg sec^{-1}, so for the line to be detected, it must scatter about 8×10^{28} erg sec^{-1}. Thus, we need $(8 \times 10^{28})/10^{-4} = 8 \times 10^{32}$ atoms. The weight of a hydrogen atom is 1.66×10^{-24}

gm; the weight of an atom of atomic weight μ is $1.66 \times 10^{-24} \times \mu$ grams. Thus, if the atom has an atomic weight of 10, we must distribute some 10^{10} grams, or 10^4 tons of it into the stellar spectrum. If the atom has an atomic weight of 100, we must inject 100,000 tons. If a one percent absorption were detectable, 1,000 tons would be adequate for an atom of atomic weight 10. The injection of 1,000 tons of material into the Sun does not seem vastly beyond contemporary rocket technology.

▽ Remarkably enough, the spectral lines of one short-lived isotope, technetium, have in fact been found in stellar spectra. Its half-life is around 2×10^5 years. However, technetium lines have not been found in stars of solar spectral type, but rather only in peculiar stars known as S stars. In fact, as we saw in Chapter 8, the discovery of technetium in the S stars has been used as an argument for contemporary stellar nucleosynthesis. This example illustrates one of the difficulties with such a marker announcement of the presence of a technical civilization. We must know a great deal more than we do about both normal and peculiar stellar spectra before we can reasonably conclude that the presence of an unusual atom in a stellar spectrum is a sign of extraterrestrial intelligence. △

To conclude this chapter, let us consider the possibility of optical contact between planets within our own solar system. If the laser system we have described in this chapter as System A were directed at Mars during its closest approach to the Earth, when it is some 50 million km distant, the diameter of the laser beam on the Martian surface would be between 5 and 7 km. To the Martian observer, the laser flash would appear as a bright star of magnitude −7, that is, approximately 10 times brighter than Venus appears in the sky of the Earth. Such a bright light source could be modulated to transmit any type of information to a small region of Mars. Such a beam, directed at the unilluminated hemisphere of the Moon, would produce a spot with a diameter of only 40 meters, and the illumination would be only 100 times less than that of direct solar radiation. Thus, we see that the prospects for laser communication within the confines of the solar system are very favorable.

29

Distribution of technical civilizations in the galaxy

Far and few, far and few,
    Are the lands where the Jumblies live:
Their heads are green, and their hands are blue;
    And they went to sea in a sieve.

Edward Lear, *The Jumblies*

▽ In the last two chapters, we have seen that the prospects for interstellar communication over distances of some tens of light years seem reasonable; over hundreds of light years, more difficult; and over thousands of light years, only possibly by civilizations in substantial advance of our own. If it seemed likely that technical civilizations existed on planets only 10 or 20 light years away, or civilizations greatly in advance of our own, at larger distances, a serious effort to establish contact might be justified. On the other hand, if we can only reasonably expect civilizations at about our level of technical advance thousands of light years away, attempts at communication would not seem profitable, at least at the present time. In the present chapter, we shall make some effort to compute the number of extant technical civilizations in the Galaxy, which will permit us to estimate the average distances between civilizations. To perform such estimates, we must select numerical values for quantities which are extremely poorly known, such as the average lifetime of a technical civilization. The reliability of our answers will reflect this uncertainty. △ The analysis will have an exclusively probabilistic character, ▽ and the reader is invited to make his own estimate of the numerical values involved, and to draw his own conclusions on the numbers of advanced technical civilizations in the Galaxy. △ However, these analyses are of undoubted methodological interest and illustrate very well the potentialities and limitations of this type of investigation.

▽ We shall be concerned with two general approaches: first, a simple discussion due essentially to Frank Drake, and then a more elaborate treatment due to the German astronomer Sebastian von Hoerner, when he was working at the National Radio Astronomy Observatory, Green Bank, West Virginia.

▽ We desire to compute the number of extant Galactic communities which have attained a technical capability substantially in advance of our own. At the present rate of technological progress, we might picture this capability as several hundred years or more beyond our own stage of development. A simple method of computing this number, N, was discussed extensively at a conference on intelligent extraterrestrial life, held at the National Radio Astronomy Observatory in November, 1961, and sponsored by the Space Science Board of the National Academy of Sciences. Attending this meeting were D. W. Atchley, Melvin Calvin, Giuseppe Cocconi, Frank Drake, Su-Shu Huang, John C. Lilley, Philip M. Morrison, Bernard M. Oliver, J. P. T. Pearman, Carl Sagan, and Otto Struve. While the details differ in several respects, the following discussion is in substantial agreement with the conclusions of the conference.

▽ The number of extant advanced technical civilizations possessing both the interest and the capability for interstellar communication can be expressed as

$$N = R_* f_p n_e f_l f_i f_c L.$$

R_* is the mean rate of star formation, averaged over the lifetime of the Galaxy; f_p is the fraction of stars with planetary systems; n_e is the mean number of planets in each planetary system with environments favorable for the origin of life; f_l is the fraction of such favorable planets on which life does develop; f_i is the fraction of such inhabited planets on which intelligent life with manipulative abilities arises during the lifetime of the local sun; f_c is the fraction of planets populated by intelligent beings on which an advanced technical civilization in the sense previously defined arises, during the lifetime of the local sun; and L is the lifetime of the technical civilization. We now proceed to discuss each parameter in turn.

▽ Since stars of solar mass or less have lifetimes on the main sequence comparable to the age of the Galaxy, it is not the present rate of star formation, but the mean rate of star formation during the age of the Galaxy, which concerns us here. The number of known stars in the Galaxy is $\sim 10^{11}$, most of which have masses equal to or less than that of the Sun. The age of the Galaxy is $\sim 10^{10}$ years. Consequently, a first estimate for the mean rate of star formation would be ~ 10 stars yr^{-1}. The present rate of star formation is at least an order of magnitude less than this figure, and according to the Dutch-American astronomer Maarten Schmidt, of Mt. Wilson and Palomar Observatories, the rate of star formation in early Galactic history is possibly several orders of magnitude greater. According to present views of element synthesis in stars, discussed in Chapter 8, those stars and planets formed in the early history of the Galaxy must have been extremely poor in heavy elements. Technical civilizations developed on such ancient planets would of necessity be extremely different from our own. But in the flurry of early star formation, when the Galaxy was young, heavy elements must have been generated rapidly, and later generations of stars and planets would have had adequate endowments of the heavy elements. These very early systems should be subtracted, from our estimate of R_*. On the other hand, there are probably vast numbers of undetected low-mass stars whose inclusion will tend to increase our estimate of R_*. For present purposes, we adopt $R_* \sim 10$ stars yr^{-1}.

▽ From the frequencies of dark companions of nearby stars, from the argument on stellar rotation, and from contemporary theories of the origin of the solar system [see Chapters 11–13], we have seen that planets seem to be a very common, if not invariable, accompaniment to main sequence stars. We therefore adopt $f_p \sim 1$.

▽ In Chapter 11, we saw that even many multiple star systems may have planets in sufficiently stable orbits for the origin and development of life. In our own solar system, the number of planets which are favorably situated for the origin of life at some time or another is at least one, probably two, and possibly three or more [see Chapters 16, 19, 20, and 23]. We expect main sequence stars of approximately solar spectral type—say, between F2 and K5—to have a similar distribution of planets, and for such stars, we adopt $n_e \sim 1$. However, the bulk of the main sequence stars—well over 60 percent—are M stars; as we mentioned in

Chapter 24, if the planets of these suns are distributed with just the same spacings as the planets of our Sun, even the innermost will be too far from its local sun to be heated directly to temperatures which we would consider clement for the origin and evolution of life. However, it is entirely possible that such lower-luminosity stars were less able to clear their inner solar systems of nebular material from which the planets were formed early in their history. Further, the greenhouse effect in Jovian-type planets of M stars should produce quite reasonable temperatures. We therefore tentatively adopt for main sequence stars in general $n_e \sim 1$.

▽ In Chapters 14–17, we discussed the most recent work on the origin of life on Earth, which suggests that life arose very rapidly during the early history of the Earth. We discussed the hypothesis that the production of self-replicating molecular systems is a forced process which is bound to occur because of the physics and chemistry of primitive planetary environments. Such self-replicating systems, with some minimal control of their environments and situated in a medium filled with replication precursors, satisfy all the requirements for natural selection and biological evolution. Given sufficient time and an environment which is not entirely static, the evolution of complex organisms is, in this view, inevitable. The finding of even relatively simple life forms on Mars or other planets within our solar system would tend to confirm this hypothesis. In our own solar system, the origin of life has occurred at least once, and possibly two or more times. We adopt $f_l \sim 1$.

▽ The question of the evolution of intelligence is a difficult one. This is not a field which lends itself to laboratory experimentation, and the number of intelligent species available for study on Earth is limited. In Chapter 25, we alluded to some of the difficulties of this problem. Our technical civilization has been present for only a few billionths of geological time; yet it has arrived about midway in the lifetime of our Sun on the main sequence. The evolution of intelligence and manipulative abilities has resulted from the product of a large number of individually unlikely events. On the other hand, the adaptive value of intelligence and of manipulative ability is so great—at least until technical civilizations are developed—that if it is genetically feasible, natural selection seems likely to bring it forth.

▽ The American neurophysiologist John C. Lilley, of the Communication Research Institute, Coral Gables, Florida, has argued that the dolphins and other cetacea have surprisingly high levels of intelligence. Their brains are larger than those of human beings. These brains are as convoluted as our brains, and their neural anatomy is remarkably similar to that of the primates, although the most recent common ancestor of the two groups lived more than 20 million years ago. Dolphins are capable of making a large number of sounds of great complexity, which are almost certainly used for communication with other dolphins. The most recent evidence suggests that they are capable of counting, and can mimic human speech. Large numbers of anecdotes supposedly illustrating great intelligence in the dolphins have been recorded, from the time of Pliny to the present. The detailed study of dolphin behavior and serious attempts to communicate with them are just beginning and hold out the possibility that some day we will be able to communicate, at least at a low level, with another intelligent species on our planet. Dolphins have very limited manipulative abilities, and despite their apparent level of intelligence, could not have developed a technical civilization. But their intelligence and communicativeness strongly suggest that these traits are not limited to the human species. With the expectation that the Earth is not unique as the abode of creatures with intelligence and manipulative abilities, but also allowing for the fact that apparently only one such species has developed so far in its history, and this only recently, we adopt $f_i \sim 10^{-1}$.

▽ The present technical civilization of the planet Earth can be traced from Mesopotamia to Southeastern Europe, to Western and Central Europe, and then to Eastern Europe and North America. Suppose that somewhere along the tortuous path of cultural history, an event had differed. Suppose Charles Martel had not stopped the Moors at Tours in 732 A.D. Suppose Ogdai had not died at Karakorum at the moment that Subutai's Mongol armies were entering Hungary and Austria, and that the Mongol invasion had swept through the non-forested regions of western Europe. Suppose the classical writings of Greek and Roman antiquity had not been preserved through the Middle Ages in African mosques and Irish monasteries. There are a thousand "supposes." Would Chinese civilization have developed a technical civilization if entirely insulated from the West? Would Aztec civilization have developed a technical phase had there been no *conquistadores?* Recorded history, even in mythological guise, covers less than 10^{-2} of the period in which the Earth has been inhabited by hominids, and less than about 10^{-5} of geological time. The same considerations are involved here as in the determination of f_i. The development of a technical civilization has high survival value at least up to a point; but in any given case it depends on the concatenation of many improbable events, and it has occurred only recently in terrestrial history. It is unlikely that the Earth is very extraordinary in possessing a technical civilization, among planets already inhabited by intelligent beings. As before, over stellar evolutionary timescales, we adopt $f_c \sim 10^{-1}$.

▽ The multiplication of the preceding factors gives $N = 10 \times 1 \times 1 \times 1 \times 10^{-1} \times 10^{-1} \times L = 10^{-1} \times L$. L is the mean lifetime in years of a technical civilization possessing both the interest and the capability for interstellar communication. For the evaluation of L there is—fortunately for us, but unfortunately for the discussion—not even one known terrestrial example. The present technical civilization on Earth has reached the communicative phase (in the sense of high-gain directional antennas for the reception of extraterrestrial radio signals) only within the last few years. There is a sober possibility that L for Earth will be measured in decades. On the other hand, it is possible that international political differences will be permanently settled, and that L may be measured in geological time. It is conceivable that on other worlds the resolution of national conflicts and the establishment of planetary governments are accomplished before weapons of mass destruction become available. We can imagine two extreme alternatives for the evaluation of L: (a) a technical civilization destroys itself soon after reaching the communicative phase (L less than 10^2 years); or (b) a technical civilization learns to live with itself soon after reaching the communicative phase. If it survives more than 10^2 years, it will be unlikely to destroy itself afterwards. In the latter case, its lifetime may be measured on a stellar evolutionary timescale (L much greater than 10^8 years). Such a society will exercise self-selection on its members. The slow, otherwise inexorable genetic changes which might in one of many ways make the individuals unsuited for a technical civilization could be controlled. The technology of such a society will certainly be adequate to cope with geological changes, although its origin is sensitively dependent on geology. Even the evolution of the local sun through the red giant and white dwarf evolutionary stages may not pose insuperable problems for the survival of an extremely advanced community.

▽ It seems improbable that surrounded by large numbers of flourishing and diverse galactic communities, a given advanced planetary civilization will retreat from the communicative phase. This is one reason that L itself depends on N. Von Hoerner has suggested another reason: He feels that the means of avoiding self-destruction will be among the primary contents of initial interstellar communications. If N is large, the values of f_l, f_i, and f_c may also be larger as a result. In Chapter 15, we mentioned the possibility of the conscious introduction of life into an otherwise sterile planet by interstellar space travelers. In Chapter 33, below, we shall discuss the possibility that such interstellar space travelers might also affect the value of f_c.

▽ Our two choices for L— $< 10^2$ years, and $>> 10^8$ years—lead to two values for N: less than ten communicative civilizations in the Galaxy; or many more than 10^7. In the former case, we might be the only extant civilization; in the latter case, the Galaxy is filled with them. The value of N depends very critically on our expectation for the lifetime of an average advanced community. It seems reasonable to me that at least a few percent of the advanced technical civilizations in the Galaxy do not destroy themselves, nor lose interest in interstellar communication, nor suffer insuperable biological or geological catastrophes, and that their lifetimes, therefore, are measured on stellar evolutionary timescales. As an average for all technical civilizations, both short-lived and long-lived, I adopt $L \sim 10^7$ years. This then yields as the average number of extant advanced technical civilizations in the Galaxy

$$N \sim 10^6.$$

Thus, approximately 0.001 percent of the stars in the sky will have a planet upon which an advanced civilization resides. The most probable distance to the nearest such community is then several hundred light years. (In the Space Science Board Conference on Intelligent Extraterrestrial Life, previously mentioned, the individual values of N selected lay between 10^4 and 10^9 civilizations. The corresponding range of distances to the nearest advanced community is then between ten and several thousands of light years.) △

We now take up von Hoerner's alternative discussion of the probable distance between Galactic civilizations. He defines v_0 as the number of stars about which habitable planets could exist; T_0 as the time that elapses between the formation of a given planetary system and the appearance of a technically advanced society; and L as the lifetime of a technically advanced society. Further, let T be the age of the oldest stars, and let v be the number of stars around which technically advanced civilizations in fact currently exist.

Von Hoerner then assumes that the rate of star formation remained constant over the period T, ▽ an assumption which, as we have seen, is probably not quite valid. △ It then follows that

$$v = v_0(T - T_0)/T$$

if $L \geqq T - T_0$, and

$$v = v_0 L/T$$

if $L \leqq T - T_0$. Let d_0 be the average distance between neighboring stars. Then the average distance between neighboring technical civilizations will be

$$d = d_0 v^{-\frac{1}{3}}.$$

Von Hoerner considers the following five possibilities on the limitation of the lifetime of a technical civilization: (1) the total obliteration of all life on the planet; (2) destruction of only the higher forms of life; (3) physical or intellectual degeneration and decay; (4) the loss of interest in science and technology; and (5) no limitations on L at all. Von Hoerner believes that condition (5) is entirely inconceivable, ▽ although it does not appear inconceivable to us. △ He also believes that in cases (2) and (3), a new civilization might arise on the same planet, out of the ashes of the old, or from unaffected lower forms of life. The time required for such a reestablishment of civilization would probably be short compared with T_0. ▽ Fred Hoyle has suggested that the reestablishment of civilization may not be as easy as it sounds. Our civilization developed using fossil fuels as an energy source. The coal and oil in the Earth's crust are the residues of hundreds of millions of years of biological evolution and decay. At the present rate of growth, in another 50 or 100 years we will have exhausted all fossil fuels on Earth. If our civilization were to destroy itself at that time, the absence of fossil fuels would make the development of a successor civilization unlikely, at least for a few hundreds of millions of years. △

We shall denote the average lifetime on these five hypotheses as L_1, L_2, L_3, L_4, and L_5; and the likelihood, or probability of realization, of each hypothesis as P_1, P_2, P_3, P_4, and P_5, respectively. Thus,

$$v = (v_0/T)P_1L_1 + P_2L_2 + P_3L_3 + P_4L_4 + P_5(T - T_0)Q,$$

where Q, equal to $[1 - (P_2 + P_3)] - 1$, takes into account the possibility of the reestablishment of a destroyed civilization. Since $L = P_1L_1 + P_2L_2 + P_3L_3 + P_4L_4 + P_5(T - T_0)$ is the average lifetime of a technical civilization, this expression may be simplified to

$$\nu = QL\nu_0/T.$$

What is the probable age of the first extraterrestrial civilization with which we might make contact? A simple discussion by von Hoerner shows that this time is

$$\tau = [P_1L_1^2 + P_2L_2^2 + P_3L_3^2 + P_4L_4^2 + P_5L_5^2]/2L,$$

and the probability that there was at least one previous civilization on a given planet is

$$P_2 = (Q - 1)/Q.$$

To obtain concrete numerical estimates from these general formulae, it is necessary to assign values to the various L_i and P_i. Von Hoerner's estimates for these quantities, $\triangledown$ like anyone else's, $\triangle$ are quite subjective. But note that if we combine our expressions for d and ν, we find

$$d = d_0(\nu_0QL/T)^{-\frac{1}{3}}$$

except for extremely long-lived civilizations. Thus, our principal unknown, L, appears with an exponent $-\frac{1}{3}$, and the uncertainty of our estimated L will not strongly influence our estimate of d.

Table VI gives von Horner's estimates of the probable lifetime of an

TABLE VI

An Arbitrary Set of Values for the Lifetimes and Probabilities
of Destruction of Technical Civilizations

(after von Hoerner)

Alternative	Estimated range for L_i, years	Value adopted		P_iL_i, years
		L_i, years	P_i	
Complete destruction	0–200	100	0.05	5
Destruction of higher life	0–50	30	0.60	18
Degeneration	10^4–10^5	3×10^4	0.15	4500
Loss of interest	10^3–10^5	10^4	0.20	2000
No limitation	—	—	0.00	0

advanced technical civilization under each of his five hypotheses. It also gives his estimates of the likelihood, or probability of realization, of each of these modes for the termination of a civilization.

In my opinion, it is logical to assume that the era of technical development on any planet is finite. However, any attempt to estimate the probabilities connected with this idea are subjective and may lead to paradoxical conclusions, a problem which we discuss in some detail later. For the values of L_i and P_i selected by von Hoerner in Table VI, the average lifetime of a technical civilization becomes $L = 6500$ years, and the mean number of reestablishments of destroyed civilizations becomes $Q = 4$. ∇ Note, however, that von Hoerner has assigned a zero probability to an extremely long-lived civilization such as we described earlier in this chapter. Even a very low probability for the occurrence of such a civilization would, in von Hoerner's theoretical development, lead to a very large value of the mean lifetime of a technical civilization. For example, if $L_5 = 10^9$ years, and $P_5 = 10^{-2}$, we find $L = 10^7$ years. $\triangle$ But with von Hoerner's numbers and $T = 10^{10}$ years, $v_0 = 0.06$, and $d_0 = 2.3$ parsecs, the average distance between the Sun and nearest stars, we find that $v = 2.6 \times 10^{-7}$. This means that within the framework of von Hoerner's assumptions, only about one out of every three million stars has a planet which currently sustains intelligent life. The average distance between Galactic civilizations is then $d = 360$ parsecs, or a little over 1000 light years. ∇ Considering the differences in analytic treatments and choices of numerical values in our earlier discussion and in the present discussion of von Hoerner, the agreement of final results is somewhat gratifying. $\triangle$ The most probable age of a technical civilization when we first contact it is $\tau = 12,000$ years. ∇ The level of technical development of such a civilization is difficult for us to imagine. But if it corresponds to the technical civilization of the Earth in the year 14,000 A.D., continuously developed from the present, it must be a civilization different not in degree, but in kind, from our own. $\triangle$ There is a 75 percent probability that this civilization is the successor to an older civilization which previously flourished on the same planet, but which was subsequently destroyed. The calculations indicate that there is only a small probability—about 0.5 percent—that any given interstellar contact would be with a civilization at the same phase of development as our own. ∇ Thus, in any interstellar contact, we very likely have much more to learn than to teach. $\triangle$ We again emphasize that all the foregoing numerical estimates are valid only to the extent that the initial values for L_i and P_i are valid, and these values are necessarily arbitrary.

If these estimates are at all accurate, however, we can conclude that it would be useful to attempt to detect interstellar radio signals by the methods of Project Ozma [see Chapter 27]. If the nearest technical civilization were 1000 light years away, how could the inhabitants single out our Sun from among the millions of stars within 1000 light years of them, and convey information or inquiries in our direction? It is more reasonable to suppose that the signals would be sent out in all directions, and would initially be designed to make the existence of their technical civilization known, an announcement signal. ∇ Only after a similar signal had been received would two-way conversation be initiated. $\triangle$ Since $d = 1000$ light years in this case, the time interval between inquiry and answer, t_0, would be greater than 2000 years. It would hardly be a hurried conversation. Since the lifetime of the technical civilization would be limited, the number of possible conversations would also be limited. With the results of von Hoerner's calculations, there would be time for only about ten two-way conversations, and the exchange of information would be limited. ▽ But while limited, the amount of information transmittable would not be small [see Chapter 27]. △

The situation would be radically different if we were to take into account what von Hoerner calls the "feedback effect." This effect, also considered by the Australian-American radioastronomer Ronald Bracewell of Stanford University, may be understood as follows: If the waiting time, t_0, were significantly greater than the lifetime, L, of the technical civilization, answers to the transmitted inquiries would of course never be obtained, and interest in communication would eventually dissipate. But if t_0 were significantly less than L, it is entirely possible that a fruitful and productive exchange of information could take place. ▽ It would in fact be to the advantage of the communicating civilizations to increase the lifetime of their communication partners, if they wished to continue the conversation. △ The various civilizations, distributed through the Galaxy, could be of mutual benefit and assistance from the radio or optical contacts. As a consequence, the local value of L in any given system would undoubtedly increase, perhaps by a significant factor. Von Hoerner calls this the feedback effect.

We believe, however, that even if t_0 were greater than L, and the conversations turned out to be monologues, feedback would still take place. Any information at all received by a planetary civilization could assist the society in overcoming difficulties which impede its further development. The result would be the lengthening of L.

In the case that $t_0 > L$, where L is the average lifetime of a technical civilization, the quantity $K = L/t_0$ is of significance. Note, incidentally, that $t_0 = 2d/c$, where c is the velocity of light.

Taking von Hoerner's estimates of the most probable values of L and d from Table VI, one finds that $K = 10$. This quantity can also be written as

$$K = (L/L_0)^{\frac{4}{3}},$$

where

$$L_0 = (8d_0T/c^3v_0Q)^{\frac{1}{4}}.$$

If we assume that $d_0 = 2.3$ parsecs, $T = 10^{10}$ years, $v_0 = 0.06$, $c = 3 \times 10^{10}$ cm sec^{-1}, and $Q = 4$, then $L = 4500$ years, comparable to von Hoerner's previous estimates. When $K > 1$, feedback can occur. Thus, if the lifetime of a technical civilization, L, is unaltered by feedback, $L_0 \simeq 5000$ years. We note that L_0 is determined with a relatively high level of confidence, since all the quantities entering into it appear to the $\frac{1}{4}$ power. Therefore, even very large errors in the estimates of d_0, v_0, and Q would not lead to a substantial error in the estimate of L_0. If L is significantly greater than 5000 years, then, due to feedback, L would increase substantially. It is difficult—perhaps impossible—to estimate by how much L would increase. Von Hoerner himself assumes that there is only a small probability that L would increase, for example, to one million years. However, we must emphasize again that von Hoerner's estimates are purely subjective.

Fluctuations in the space-time distribution of extraterrestrial civilizations, even in the case where $t_0 > L$, could have very important consequences for the feedback effect. If the feedback results in a substantial local increase in L, due to such fluctuations, the further development of many technical civilizations could be significantly enhanced. For example, the lifetime of our own technical civilization might increase substantially, and then the lifetimes of technical civilizations in general could increase throughout the entire Galaxy. The rapid multiplication of microorganisms inoculated into a suitable medium is an analogous phenomenon.

It is evident that feedback could have a decisive significance for intelligent life in the universe. Ultimately, it could be the basic method for the development and propagation of knowledge throughout the Galaxy and metagalaxy, a subject we consider in more detail in Chapter 34.

▽ The very tentative conclusions of this chapter may now be summarized: The number of extant civilizations substantially in advance of our own in the Galaxy today appears to be perhaps between 50 thousand and one million. The average distance between technical civilizations is between a few hundred light years and about 1000 light years. The average age of a communicating technical civilization is 10,000 years or more. And the information transmitted by interstellar contact may serve to substantially increase the lifetime of the participating civilizations. △

30

Interstellar radio contact: the character of the signals

But if we allow these Planetary Inhabitants some sort of Reason, must it needs, may some say, be the same with ours? Certainly it must; whether we consider it as applied to Justice and Morality, or exercised in the Principles and Foundations of Science. For Reason with us is that which gives us a true Sense of Justice and Honesty, Praise, Kindness, and Gratitude: 'tis That that teaches us to distinguish universally between Good and Bad; and renders us capable of Knowledge and Experience in it. And can there be any where any other Sort of Reason than this? or can what we call just and generous, in Jupiter or Mars be thought unjust Villany?

Christianus Huygens, *New Conjectures Concerning the Planetary Worlds, Their Inhabitants and Productions* (c. 1670)

et us now discuss the anticipated character of radio ▽ or optical laser △ signals which we might receive from another civilization. Von Hoerner has suggested the nature of the signals would be determined ultimately by (a) the purpose they are to serve; and (b) the most economical transmission channel. There are three general types of signals which we might anticipate: (1) local broadcast, that is, radiation due to local communications on a planet such as from domestic television transmitters. ▽ Eavesdropping on such calls is, under some circumstances, feasible; △ (2) long distance calls, that is, specifically directed radio contact between two particular civilizations; and (3) announcement signals, that is, signals transmitted for the purpose of attracting the attention of any civilization which has not yet been contacted.

Local broadcasting was discussed in Chapter 27. We have noted that due to the activities of mankind, the power of the Earth's radio spectrum at meter wavelengths is approximately 1 watt (c.p.s.)$^{-1}$, and the brightness temperature of the Earth at these wavelengths is some 100 million degrees. If a hypothetical observer were at the distance of the nearest stars, some 10 light years away, the meter radiation flux from the Earth would be about 10^{-35} watts meter^{-2} (c.p.s.)$^{-1}$, a negligible amount. For this radiation to be detected by conventional techniques over interstellar distances, the power would have to be increased some 10^8 times. ▽ However, as discussed in Chapter 27, if cross-correlation techniques are used with a very large frequency bandpass, eavesdropping becomes possible even though the signal may be much less than the noise. △

A long distance call intended for another civilization might be detected on the Earth only if our planet were accidentally interposed in the direct radio path between two communicating Galactic civilizations.

Von Hoerner estimates the probability of such accidental interception as $(\pi/120)q^3\beta^2 n^2$, where β is the beam width of both the transmitting and receiving antennas (assumed identical), n is the number of neighbors with which each civilization maintains contact, and q is the ratio of the distance at which the signal can be detected to the distance at which it can be positively interpreted. The quantity q is always > 1, because it is simpler to detect a signal than to decipher it. Curiously, the interception probability does not depend on L or on d.

Assuming that the interception probability is sufficient to warrant the organization of an interception service (if, for example, this probability is $\frac{1}{2}$), that $q = 5$, and that $\beta = 1$ minute of arc (corresponding to the beam width of current large radiotelescopes), then n would equal 1300. In other words, the signals would be accidentally intercepted only if each civilization was attempting to converse simultaneously with 1300 neighbors. This seems highly improbable. If we require the probability of interception to be

$\frac{1}{4}$, and assume n to be as small as 50, we must have $q = 10$ and $\beta = 10$ minutes of arc, which is again highly improbable.

We can surmise that the probability of accidental interception of interstellar long distance communication signals is very small.

An announcement signal is designed to attract the attention of an unknown civilization. $\triangledown$ One such announcement signal might be the atomic markers in stellar spectra, discussed in Chapter 28. $\triangle$ There is today increasing interest in the most likely character of interstellar signals. Such signals must fulfill two requirements: They must attract attention, but at the same time they must be economical. The consumption of energy and other resources must be a minimum, while the distance over which it is detectable must be a maximum. Of course, the criteria for economy which might seem natural to us as members of a terrestrial civilization may not be identical with the estimates of other advanced societies.

There are several methods which might be used for such an announcement signal. For each method, it is possible to estimate a certain equivalent cost, C, the price which must be paid in order that the probability, P_d, of detecting the signal at the distance d during the time t_d be sufficiently large. We can assume, for example, that $P_d = \frac{1}{2}$, $d = 1000$ light years, and t_d is of the order of several hundred years. One then chooses from among those methods which give acceptably small values for the cost, C.

Von Hoerner has assumed that the quantity C would be a minimum if all the power is sent in a narrow beam at a specific frequency interval which the unknown receiving civilization could reliably guess beforehand. In Chapter 27, we considered the suggestion of Cocconi and Morrison that the most supremely rational frequency for interstellar communication is the natural frequency of the 21 cm radio frequency line of hydrogen. $\triangledown$ We also considered objections to this choice of frequency, and alternative frequency selections. $\triangle$

In order to minimize C, we must also choose an optimum distribution for the transmitted power, both in space and in time. The communication mode might provide for modulation of the signals, and would probably be elegantly simple, rational, and easily understood by the unknown receiving civilization. Since the waiting time for a reply will be quite long, the initial messages will probably contain significant quantities of information, as well as the cynosures of the announcement signals. The information content could be included either in the entire transmitted signal spectrum—for example, through modulation—or by an indication of a separate frequency channel on which the information is being sent.

Attention might be directed to the information channel as follows: The announcement signal could consist of a large number of signals transmitted at various fixed frequencies which are symmetric with respect to a certain central frequency. Approaching this central frequency, the spacing between neighboring signals might become narrower and narrower, and the signals themselves could have much narrower frequency bandpasses. In this way, attention would be drawn to the fact that the central frequency has special significance. $\triangledown$ (Cf. the discussion of CTA 102 in Chap. 27.) $\triangle$ Information could be transmitted at this frequency at definite time intervals, perhaps once every several years, although the time intervals need not necessarily be multiples of terrestrial years, months, or days. The first transmitted information would probably contain an introduction to interstellar linguistics, the language which the transmitting civilization has selected for the clear communication of information.

▽ But how is this possible? Suppose we were to identify an announcement signal and correctly identify the frequency of the communications channel. We might find a modulated signal there of clearly intelligent origin—for example, we might represent it as a sequence of zeros and ones, or dots and dashes. A zero and a one might represent the signals of two neighboring frequencies; the difference between a dot and a dash might be, as in Morse code, the length of the pulse. Zeros and ones might be coming at us at an extremely rapid rate, since the transmitting civilization is likely to be vastly in advance of our own. We would record the information, perhaps on magnetic tape, slow the signals down, and display them in some conventional representation as, for example, zeros and ones. Due to the rotation of the Earth, the area of the sky from which the signal comes would not always be accessible to our largest radio or optical telescopes used for the detection of this hypothetical interstellar transmission. We would receive a long message, but a fragmented one, abruptly terminated when the radio or optical source set below the observatory's horizon. The next day, the source would reappear, and the message would be picked up again in the midst of transmission. With some effort in data-gathering and preliminary analysis, we might note that, for example, a common sequence of zeros and ones is frequently present—for example, the sequence of 551 zeros and ones in Figure 30–1.

▽ An advanced technical civilization is trying to communicate with us. But how can we possibly understand what they are saying? They are not likely to speak English or Russian. They have had a different evolutionary history. They are on a planet with perhaps an entirely different physical environment. Their thought

```
1 1 1 1 0 0 0 0 1 0 1 0 0 1 0 0 0 0 1 1 0 0 1 0 0 0 0 0 0 0 1 0 0 0 0 0 1 0 1 0 0
1 0 0 0 0 0 1 1 0 0 1 0 1 1 0 0 1 1 1 1 0 0 0 0 0 1 1 0 0 0 0 1 1 0 1 0 0 0 0 0 0
0 0 1 0 0 0 0 0 1 0 0 0 0 1 0 0 0 0 1 0 0 0 1 0 1 0 1 0 0 0 0 1 0 0 0 0 0 0 0 0 0
0 0 0 0 0 0 0 0 0 1 0 0 0 1 0 0 0 0 0 0 0 0 0 0 1 0 1 1 0 0 0 0 0 0 0 0 0 0 0 0 0
0 0 0 0 0 0 0 1 0 0 0 1 1 1 0 1 1 0 1 0 1 1 0 1 0 1 0 0 0 0 0 0 0 0 0 0 0 0 0 0 0
0 0 0 0 1 0 0 1 0 0 0 0 1 1 1 0 1 0 1 0 1 0 1 0 0 0 0 0 0 0 0 0 1 0 1 0 1 0 1 0 1
0 0 0 0 0 0 0 0 0 1 1 1 0 1 0 1 0 1 0 1 1 1 0 1 0 1 1 0 0 0 0 0 0 0 0 1 0 0 0 0 0 0
0 0 0 0 0 0 0 0 0 1 0 0 0 0 0 0 0 1 0 0 0 1 0 0 1 1 1 1 1 1 0 0 0
0 0 1 1 1 0 1 0 0 0 0 0 1 0 1 1 0 0 0 0 0 1 1 1 0 0 0 0 0 0 0 1 0 0 0 0 0 0 0 0 0
1 0 0 0 0 0 0 0 0 1 0 0 0 0 0 0 0 1 1 1 1 1 0 0 0 0 0 0 1 0 1 1 0 0 0 1 0 1 1 1 0
1 0 0 0 0 0 0 0 1 1 0 0 1 0 1 1 1 1 1 0 1 0 1 1 1 1 1 0 0 0 1 0 0 1 1 1 1 1 0 0 1
0 0 0 0 0 0 0 0 0 0 1 1 1 1 0 0 0 0 0 0 1 0 1 1 0 0 0 1 1 1 1 1 1 1 0 0 0 0 0
1 0 0 0 0 0 1 1 0 0 0 0 0 1 1 0 0 0 0 1 0 0 0 0 1 1 0 0 0 0 0 0 0 0 1 1 0 0 0 1 0 1
0 0 1 0 0 0 1 1 1 1 1 0 0 1 0 1 1 1 1
```

FIGURE 30–1. *A hypothetical interstellar message due to Frank Drake. The 551 zeros and ones are representations of the two varieties of signals contained in the message. The problem is to convert this sequence of 551 symbols into an intelligible message, knowing that there has been no previous communication between the transmitting and receiving civilizations.*

patterns, conventions, and cultural values may be entirely alien to our own. At first sight, it seems no more likely that we might understand their transmission than that the content of the first message directed at us is "Are you chaps Presbyterians?"

▽ If you ponder this problem briefly, it will soon become apparent that the initial transmission of words, no matter how simple, in the language of the transmitting civilization, will not be useful for interstellar communication. What we desire is a picture. The adaptive value of vision is very high, and, as we discussed in Chapter 24, there are good reasons for supposing that extraterrestrial biological radiation receptors will work at visible frequencies. Since both transmitting and receiving civilizations are very likely to "see" in some sense, the initial messages must be pictures.

▽ After the first scientific meeting held in the United States on intelligent extraterrestrial life [see Chapter 29], Frank Drake sent through the mails to each of the participants the hypothetical interstellar message of Figure 30–1 and asked us to propose a solution. We had not discussed the probable content of the first interstellar messages, and had not even agreed yet that a picture would be the most likely initial message. The participants met this challenge with varying degrees of success, although all participants did not decode the message. In order to represent more realistically the probable circumstances attending the reception of the first interstellar message, I prepared a message identical to Drake's, but with one of the zeros missing. The radio or optical channels are noisy, and perfect fidelity after transmission over interstellar distances cannot be expected. If the same message is repeated many times, intercomparison will rapidly indicate the points of error, a technique, incidentally, probably used by the cell in decoding the instructions of the genetic material (cf. Chapter 14). This altered message was pondered by a distinguished group of physicists, chemists, and biologists assembled for a private party in Cambridge, Massachusetts. Although several hours were spent in the attempt to decode the message, and despite the fact that the idea of transmission of a visual image was agreed upon early, the altered message was not decoded. The longer the message, the more danger there is that an error in transmission or detection will obscure a major fraction of the message. Thus, both to insure fidelity of content and to allow for the fact that the telescopes of the receiving planet are unable to observe the transmitted signal for an entire period of rotation, all messages should be repeated several times.

▽ With this warning, the reader is invited to inspect the decoded message in Figure 30–2. An explanation of the rationale of the message and its contents, prepared by Drake, follows:

The first step in the solution of this message is to determine, if possible, the number of dimensions in which the message is written. If one dimensional, it will be similar to an ordinary telegram; if two dimensional, it will be similar to a conventional TV picture, although other than Cartesian coordinates might be employed, etc. We would not expect the number of dimensions to be large, simply because ease of decipherment calls for few dimensions. To make headway in this, one may see what factors may be divided into 551. This test reveals that 551 is the product of only two factors, 19 and 29, both prime

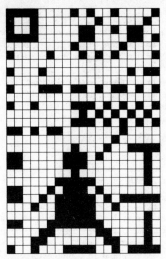

FIGURE 30–2. *The correct decoding of the message in Figure 30–1. The ones have been represented as dark spaces, the zeros as light spaces, and the 551 characters have been arranged into an array of 29 groups of 19 characters.*

numbers, of course. This is a good indication that the message is two dimensional. Trial and error with Cartesian coordinates shows that breaking the message into 29 groups of 19 characters, and arranging these as in a conventional TV raster, gives a clearcut picture, which is obviously the correct decipherment of the message. ▽ Arrangement into 19 groups of 29 characters gives the meaningless result shown in Fig. 30–3. △

The interpretation of the picture is as follows:

1. The figure of the manlike creature at the bottom of the picture is obviously a

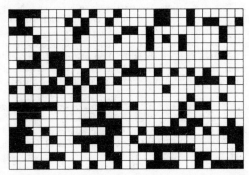

FIGURE 30–3. *An incorrect deciphering of Figure 30–1. Here the zeros and ones have been arrayed into 19 groups of 29 characters.*

drawing of the being sending the message. We see that it resembles a primate, with a heavier abdomen than we have, and that it carries its legs more widespread than we do. Its head is also more pointed than ours (or else it has a single antenna). One may speculate from this physiognomy that the gravitational acceleration is greater on the home planet of this creature than it is on earth.

2. The large square in the upper left-hand corner, accompanied by nine smaller objects strung along the left-hand margin, is a sketch of the planetary system of the creature. We see that there are four small planets, a larger planet, two large planets, another intermediate planet, and one last small planet. The system thus resembles our own in basic morphology.

3. The two groups in the upper right-hand corner may be recognized as schematic drawings of the carbon and oxygen atoms. We deduce from this that the creature's biochemistry is based on the carbon atom, as ours is, and that the oxidizer used in its chemistry is oxygen, also as with terrestrial animals.

4. A key group of symbols are those occurring just to the right of the four minor planets and the fifth planet. Inspection of these symbols shows that they are simply a modified binary representation of 1, 2, 3, 4, 5, written in sequence alongside the first five planets. The modification made to the basic binary numbers is the addition to the ends of the numbers of parity bits, where necessary, so that the number of 1's in every binary number is odd. This is similar to computer practice on earth. It is apparently not used here as a check on transmission, but rather to designate a symbol as a number. In future communications, symbols will certainly also be used for words of language. We may deduce from the creature's careful setting down of the binary number system that he will use this, with parity bits, for numbers henceforth. It follows that we may expect words of language to have even numbers of 1's. In this way, the creature has established a number system and has enabled us to recognize words of language.

5. Knowing this, we may interpret the portions of the message located above the creature and below the atoms. We note that there are three groups of characters all having an odd number of 1's. These are then numbers. The lower group is connected to the creature by a diagonal line, signifying that it has something to do with him. We further note that the arrangement of these groups are mutually consistent only if no parity bits are present. The lower group, which was too long to place on one line, is about 7×10^9 in decimal notation. The next is about 3000, and the upper group is 11. Noting that these groups are connected to the creature, and written alongside planets 2, 3, and 4, we reach the apparent interpretation that these numbers are the population of the creature on those planets. There are about 7 billion creatures on planet 4, evidently the home planet. There are about 3000 on planet 3, from which we can deduce the fact that astronautics is more developed than on earth, and there is a sizable colony on planet 3. Lastly, there are 11 of the creatures on planet 2, evidently a small scientific or exploratory group.

6. The figure to the right of the creature contains one binary number, and a symmetric configuration of symbols of even parity, probably not words, and certainly not numbers. One symbol is level with the top of the creature's head, and the other his feet. This is apparently telling us the size of the creature—it is 31 somethings tall. The only unit of length our two civilizations have in common is the wavelength at which the message was sent, so we conclude that the creature is 31 wavelengths tall.

7. Lastly, there is a symbol of even parity, with four 1's, underneath the creature. This is evidently an effort by the creature to use up all the "words" allotted him in his

message. We may suspect, in keeping with the discussion in (4), that this is a word of language, and is very likely the symbol that the creature will use for himself in future messages. This behavior would seem to reinforce the conclusions of (4), but we will have to wait for future messages for proof that this conclusion is correct.

A few remarks:

The content of the message was designed to contain the data we would first like to know about another civilization, at least in the opinion of many scientists who have thought about this problem.

In preparing the message, an attempt was made to place it at a level of difficulty such that a group of high quality terrestrial scientists of many disciplines could interpret the message in a time less than a day. Any easier message would mean that we are not sending as much information as possible over the transmission facilities, and any harder might result in a failure to communicate. In trying this puzzle on scientists, it has been true so far that scientists have understood the parts of the message connected with their own discipline, but have usually not understood the rest. This is consistent with the philosophy behind the message.

The use of two dimensions has made possible the transmission of a great deal of information with few bits. This is because it is possible to arrange the symbols of the message in positions relative to one another such that even the arrangement carries information, when we employ logic and our existing knowledge of what may possibly occur in another planetary system. Thus the 551 bits are equivalent to approximately 25 English words, but the information content of the message appears much greater than that. This is because much of the message tells us, by the placement of a single symbol, which of several complicated possibilities is the one that has occurred in the other planetary system, without using bits to spell out precisely the possibility that has occurred.

▽ Each of the zeros and ones in the message of Figure 30–1 is called a "bit"— a unit of binary information. It is a "yes" or "no" answer to a specific question— the absence or presence of a dark picture element against a white background at a specific place in the illustration. △ It is amazing that such a large amount of information is contained ▽ within 551 bits. △ This example vividly illustrates the possibility of exchanging vast quantities of information by transmitting pictures over interstellar distances. This small number of elements could be transmitted in a very narrow frequency band, and over a short period of time. If the frequency band were sufficiently broad, and the period of transmission were lengthy, the amount of information could exceed the entire aggregate knowledge of mankind.

In order to clarify this last statement, let us give an example. Let us assume that the essentials of the knowledge of mankind are contained in one million books composed of ten chapters each. There are in general some 40,000 printed signs per chapter. The total number of such signs in one million books is then 4×10^{11}. ▽ If each symbol were one of two possibilities, this would correspond to 4×10^{11} bits. But terrestrial language is not written in zeros and ones, although it might be; instead, each alphabetical terrestrial language uses perhaps 100 symbols. This corresponds to slightly less than 7 bits, because $2^7 = 128$. △ If each sign is coded in a binary system, and the transmission of information is prefaced even by a vast linguistic introduction, the total number of binary bits transmitted would be $\sim 3 \times 10^{13}$. Let the frequency bandpass transmitting the signal be 100 megacycles sec^{-1}, a value easily obtained at 21 cm wavelength. ▽ Thus, with 10^8 cycles per second, it would take only 3×10^5 seconds for the 3×10^{13} bits to be transmitted. In less than 4 days, the knowledge of mankind could be transmitted.

▽ The transmission of this core knowledge would be preceded by a linguistic introduction which itself would be preceded by an announcement signal. Preliminary information could be transmitted graphically, as our illustration with the 551-bit message showed. Let us now consider how a non-graphic interstellar vocabulary could be developed for the expression of more abstract ideas. As an example, let us consider the artificial language Lincos, recently devised by the Dutch mathematician Hans Freudenthal. △ Lincos is ▽ designed as △ an entirely logical language, free from inconsistencies such as exceptions to grammatical rules, and other irregularities found in the spoken languages of the world. While the study of terrestrial languages includes grammar, syntax, and phonemics, Lincos is devised entirely in terms of semantics.

Lincos cannot be spoken. It consists of a coded system of units. The individual parts of the message are clearly enumerated into chapters, paragraphs, and so forth. This facilitates the interpretation of the message, because the semantic content of the language must be derived from logic external to the linguistic system itself. The clearcut differentiation into separate parts also aids the recipient in deciphering transitions, for example, from a mathematical chapter to a biological chapter.

A transmission in Lincos begins with the most elementary concepts of mathematics and logic. This is because the language must define itself before it can become a system of communication. In other words, it is *progressively synthetic*. The first transmissions might consist of very small units—for example, paragraphs preceded by captions. An introductory transmission might be as follows:

Chapter I. A course in basic mathematics.

PARAGRAPH 1. A series of natural numbers.

▽ (So far, of course, the recipient civilization, having not yet deciphered Lincos, does not know the significance of these captions.) △ The lesson would consist of a series of simple radio pulses, not coded—first one pulse, then two pulses, etc.

PARAGRAPH 2. Code numbers

$$
\begin{aligned}
\text{-} &= 1 \\
\text{- -} &= 2 \\
\text{- - -} &= 3 \quad \text{etc.}
\end{aligned}
$$

From this transmission, the receiving civilization would learn the symbols for equality, and the designations of the ordinal numbers in Lincos. Could the receiving civilization actually make sense of such a transmission? We believe that if an extraplanetary civilization were able to build the apparatus to receive such signals, it would certainly be able to decode a passage based on so simple a language system. Any residual confusion about the contents of the first two paragraphs would tend to be resolved by the next paragraph:

PARAGRAPH 3. Addition

$$1 + 2 = 3$$
$$1 + 3 = 4$$
$$2 + 3 = 5 \quad \text{etc.}$$

Lessons on subtraction, multiplication, and division would be transmitted in the same way. Gradually, the more complicated areas of mathematics could be covered—the transcendental number pi, the base of natural logarithms, algebra, the differential and integral calculus, and all of analysis. Geometry could be transmitted by images in combination with the Lincos words.

During such a course in mathematics, the receiving civilization would find itself introduced to a number of important concepts such as "similar to," "more than," "less than," "different from," "it is true that," "it is not true that," "as an example," "maximum," "minimum," "increase," "decrease," and even that invaluable mathematical phrase, "it is easy to prove that." Each of these concepts would be useful to the recipient civilization in the deciphering of subsequent information.

According to Freudenthal, Lincos could also transmit more complex ideas which characterize human nature—for example, "quick wit," "cowardice," "anger," or "altruism"—by transmitting short theatrical performances among imaginary characters, ▽ a sort of cosmic Mickey Mouse. △ At first, such performances would be only mathematical in character. Let us illustrate:

COURSE: Fundamentals of human behavior.

SUBJECT: Differences in mathematical abilities.

(One man speaking to another is denoted symbolically by →.)

$$A \rightarrow B: \text{How much is } 2 + 3?$$
$$B \rightarrow A: 2 + 3 = 5.$$
$$A \rightarrow B: \text{Correct.}$$

In a series of analogous scenes, Man C appears.

$$A \rightarrow B: \text{How much is } 15 \times 15?$$
$$B \rightarrow A: 15 \times 15 = 220.$$
$$A \rightarrow B: \text{False.}$$
$$A \rightarrow C: \text{How much is } 15 \times 15?$$
$$C \rightarrow A: 15 \times 15 = 225.$$
$$A \rightarrow C: \text{Correct.}$$
$$\text{C is more intelligent than B.}$$

▽ This last is presumably an aside to the cosmic reader. △

After this transmission, a series of more complicated interactions could be portrayed. Sooner or later, the recipient civilization would realize that more than just mathematics was being discussed; that theatrical representations conveying the concepts of emotions, ▽ social conventions, and a wide range of philosophical postures △ were being transmitted into space.

We have already mentioned that linguistic information could be transmitted alternately with pictorial information. Especially in transmitting scientific data, this coupling could be very effective. For example, Mendelyeev's periodic system of the elements could be pictured, accompanied by the corresponding words in Lincos. ▽ We saw in Figure 30–2 how the conventional representations of nuclei with associated electrons could be transmitted into space. The number and distribution of electrons, of course, would indicate the nature of the atom. △ Then, a graph of the number of protons in the nucleus versus the number of neutrons could be transmitted. ▽ By this time, the cosmic discourse is well along into atomic and nuclear physics. △

It would be relatively simple to transmit physical, astronomical, and chemical constants. The unit of length could be expressed in terms of the wavelength of transmission, and all other linear units would be either fractions or multiples of this basic unit. The unit of mass could be the mass of the electron; the unit of time could be defined in terms of the velocity of light (▽ for example, the time for light to cross a distance equal to the wavelength of transmission △). Thus, very complex scientific information could be transmitted economically.

We wish to emphasize that a linguistic system based upon these fundamentals would be far easier to decipher than many of the written languages of ancient civilizations which have been deciphered by archaeologists.

31

Interstellar contact by automatic probe vehicles

. . . So deep is the conviction that there must be life out there beyond the dark, one thinks that if they are more advanced than ourselves they may come across space at any moment, perhaps in our generation. Later, contemplating the infinity of time, one wonders if perchance their messages came long ago, hurtling into the swamp muck of the steaming coal forests, the bright projectile clambered over by hissing reptiles, and the delicate instruments running mindlessly down with no report.

Loren Eiseley, *The Immense Journey* (1957)

In the consideration of contact with advanced extraterrestrial civilizations, the average distance among civilizations is clearly critical. If the average distance to the nearest civilization is approximately 10 light years, as assumed by Cocconi and Morrison, and by Townes and Schwartz, we have seen in Chapters 27 and 28 that contact by participating civilizations at the contemporary level of terrestrial technology appears feasible. ▽ But we also saw, in Chapter 24, that there are only five star systems of approximately solar spectral type within 15 light years—namely, Alpha Centauri, Epsilon Eridani, 61 Cygni A, Epsilon Indi, and Tau Ceti. △ Thus, it would be relatively easy to establish whether any one of these stars were sending artificial radio or optical signals in our direction.

On the other hand, assume (as seems much more likely, on the basis of our discussion in Chapter 29) that the average distance among technical civilizations is some hundreds of light years. The situation is then radically different. There are now many thousands of stars with possible populated planets. It seems probable that many stars would have to be observed over a long period of time, in order to determine which, if any, were transmitting artificial signals. An extensive "Operation Starwatch" would have to be performed. The detection of artificial signals, even in the simplest situations, is a difficult and intricate task ▽ at our present level of advance, provided that we are not listening to a vastly more advanced civilization. △ But it would become incommensurately more difficult if, over many centuries or millennia, we must direct beams of electromagnetic radiation with great precision at tens of thousands of stars, while patiently waiting, perhaps in vain, for a reply. And we must remember that intelligent extraterrestrial civilizations may not even be sending radio or optical impulses in the direction of our solar system. Perhaps, for reasons of their own, they have excluded our Sun from the vast numbers of stars which they believe might possess inhabited planets . . .

▽ We saw in Chapter 29 how the number of technical civilizations in the Galaxy, and therefore the distances between them, is fairly sensitively dependent upon L, the lifetime of the technical civilization. We concluded, by two different analyses, that the probable distance to the nearest technical civilization lies between several hundred light years and perhaps 1000 light years from the Earth. But the range of uncertainty, we again emphasize, is very great. If the average lifetime of a technical civilization is comparable to the lifetime of its star, there may be a billion intelligent civilizations in our Galaxy. If the average lifetime of a technical civilization is only a few decades, ours may be the only civilization in the Galaxy, and even a massive effort to detect signals from an extraterrestrial civilization—in the few decades remaining to us—would prove fruitless.

▽ But let us assume that the nearest civilization is 1000 light years away. The average separation between stars in the solar neighborhood is $d_o \simeq 2.3$ parsecs, or $2.3 \times 3.26 =$ some 7.6 light years. The number of stars in a volume of radius 1000 light years is therefore $(4\pi/3)$ $(1000/7.6)^3$, or about 10 million. Even if we restricted our search to stars of approximately solar spectral type, there would be more than a million candidates. △ How could we possibly predict which one of these stars has a habitable planet supporting intelligent life? In view of this situation, Ronald Bracewell has suggested another means of establishing contact.

Bracewell assumes that in general, the development of a technically advanced civilization will be accompanied by great progress in rocketry and other space vehicle technology. Relatively early in its lifetime, the civilization would be capable of sending small, automatically controlled interstellar probes to the nearest stars, and of placing them automatically into almost circular orbits about their objectives.

Great advances in space technology are already occurring on the Earth. ▽ Guidance systems have been developed which have permitted a close flyby of the Moon by Luna III and Zond III, accurate lunar impacts by, for example, Ranger IX and Luna IX, close flybys of Venus and Mars by Mariners II and IV, and an entry into the atmosphere of Venus by a capsule from Venus III △ Guidance systems exist which enable us to put artificial satellites, ▽ like Luna X, △ in orbit about the Moon. The guidance techniques include the transmittal of in-flight commands for midcourse corrections of the space vehicle's trajectory. Some day, ▽ perhaps fairly soon, △ this technology will also be applied to the orbiting of artificial satellites about the planets—perhaps Venus first, and then Mars. Eventually, automatic probe vehicles could be sent to the nearest stars, where they would become artificial planets.

After the initiation of such an interstellar exploration program, only a few more centuries would be required to place such vehicles in orbit about all stars which are likely to have habitable planets within a radius of 100 light years of the Sun. The velocities of such probes might reach 1 or 2×10^5 km sec^{-1}. Such velocities are very great, but they would still be short of the speed of light, and avoid the effects due to relativity, ▽ described in Chapter 32. △ The probes would, of course, contain exceptionally long-lived radio receiving and transmitting apparatus. The energy required to power this apparatus could come from the light of the star about which the satellite is in orbit.

There are a number of distinct advantages of contacts of this type. ▽ Once in orbit about the local star, the probe would then automatically attempt contact with habitable planets in its vicinity. △ Since the instrumentation of the probe is powered by the local star, its transmitted signal would be much more powerful than a signal sent directly from the Earth. Second, the signal from the probe to the inhabited planet would travel a much shorter distance than if it were sent directly from the Earth. ▽ In the case of optical contact, this might avoid the difficulty we discussed in Chapter 28 (that is, the need for the laser beam to fill a significant fraction of the local solar system for there to be a sizable probability of detection). △ Third, such interstellar exploration need not assume that intelligent extraterrestrial societies are conducting an extensive, continuous survey of the heavens in search of signals from suitable stars. Finally, this program does not depend on a specific choice of wavelengths, such as the 21 cm band.

This program, suggested by Bracewell, could be implemented as follows: At the destination star, the probe would investigate the surrounding regions of space, searching for monochromatic radio transmission. Such a search would cover a wide range of frequencies. Should signals be detected, the probe would record them and immediately transmit them back to their original source without change. A repeated playback would undoubtedly attract the attention of the planetary inhabitants. ▽ The reception of a housewife's daytime television serial, from interplanetary space, would undoubtedly interest terrestrial radioastronomers. △ As a result, a very important goal would be achieved: The extraterrestrial society would discover the presence of a messenger from a distant civilization.

After two-way contact with the probe had been established, the probe would transmit a previously-arranged program of more complex information. Television could be used to great advantage—for example, the probe could transmit to the planet a televised image of the constellation in which the probe's star of origin is located, ▽ that is, in this case, the Sun. △ We would of course have to know beforehand how the Sun would appear in the sky of the planet of destination. ▽ Subsequently, a very large volume of information could be transmitted from the probe to the planet, along the lines suggested in Chapter 30. △

As soon as the inhabitants of the contacted planet learn of the presence of intelligent beings near a particular star in their sky, they could begin their own intensive investigation. They might send modulated optical and radio transmission, and also their own automatic probe vehicles, in the direction of this star. It is conceivable that after several centuries, a lively two-way contact could be established between these civilizations, separated by a distance of, say, some tens of light years.

▽ Note that for contact to be established, it is not necessary that the initial probe inform us of the success of its mission. If its mission is successful, the contacted civilization will make its own contact. △ The volume of information contained in such a probe could be so great that even a simple one-sided contact would be valuable.

It is also possible to conceive of a system of relay stations for the retransmission of signals obtained by the probe vehicle. The interstellar space vehicles used as relay stations would sequentially transmit the acquired information to the Earth.

▽ At first, only civilizations relatively close to one another could be investigated by interstellar probes. △ However, we can assume that highly developed civilizations would investigate the universe in a systematic manner, without unnecessary duplication of contacts. As an end result, it is possible to postulate the existence of a vast network of intelligent civilizations in productive mutual contact.

▽ Such a universe, in which physical contact was effected only by relatively short-range automatic interstellar probe vehicles, would have some interesting properties. For example, it is certainly conceivable that physical objects could be transported in such vehicles to civilizations on neighboring stars. The exchange of cultural artifacts—for example, works of art—would have a salutary influence on the maintenance of contact. Such artifacts might in fact be relayed over substantial distances by the automatic interstellar ferries of a multitude of civilizations. Over long periods of time, such objects would tend to diffuse over large distances within the Galaxy, but the likelihood of encountering them far from their source would be small. If the useful range of interstellar space vehicles were only some tens of light years, one would not expect to find terrestrial artifacts near the Galactic center. If interstellar voyages over distances greater than some tens of light years are undertaken, then this artifact diffusion will tend to loosely connect civilizations of greatly differing levels of technical and artistic development. There would occasionally come our way an object of incredible beauty or devastating power that we were unable either to understand or reproduce. Even in a technical civilization such artifacts might evolve into objects of worship. Similar circumstances and an entire associated mythology have developed under analogous conditions in the contemporary cargo cults of New Guinea—an example of artifact diffusion contact between civilizations at greatly differing levels of technical advance. △

Because of the real possibility that such interstellar probes actually exist, Bracewell believes that it is very important for us to investigate carefully all radio signals of cosmic origin. There is some possibility that probes from distant Galactic civilizations are already present within our solar system. In this connection, Bracewell has called attention to certain phenomena which have been known for many years but never explained in a satisfactory manner. For example, during the 1930's, Störmer and van der Pol, ▽ in pioneering work on the atmospheric propagation of radio waves, △ detected several instances of an unexplained radio echo. The time lag in the reflected signal reached many seconds, and at times as long as a minute, suggesting that the signal was reflected from some object removed a distance of about one million kilometers from the Earth, ▽ a respectable interplanetary distance. △ Might these curious echoes be the transmissions of some automatic vehicle from a distant world? We must not forget that in the past, cosmic radio signals of very great intensity have been missed by terrestrial observers. For example, strong radio emission from the planet Jupiter, with a power $\sim$ 1000 watts $(c.p.s.)^{-1}$ were detected many times during the last decades, but were not identified as Jovian emission until 1954.

If a careful search over a number of years does not lead to the detection of a source of artificial radio signals, we can come to the conclusion that the nearest technically advanced society is so far away that it cannot establish contact with us. For example, it might be that the average lifetime of a technical civilization is $\sim$ 1000 years, and the mean distance between civilizations is about 2000 light years. It is clear that under these circumstances, ▽ two-way △ contact between civilizations would be very unlikely. On the other hand, the situation would be entirely different if the average lifetime of a technical civilization were $\sim 10^7$ years, and the average distance between civilizations approximately 100 light years. Then, after some millions of years of technical development, a civilization would reach a peak from which it could easily investigate several thousand neighboring stars, among which at least one would be inhabited by an advanced technical society.

In the case that the lifetime of a technical civilization is long, it may have reached an exceptionally advanced level of competence and be able to establish contact with civilizations which are thousands of light years distant. Even the most remote regions of the Galaxy might be investigated by direct means. We cannot say what methods of investigation such highly developed civilizations might use— there would be too great a difference between their level of development and ours. Perhaps such embryonic civilizations as those of our own world would be of little interest to them. They might pass us by, deeming it unnecessary to investigate all primitive civilizations which, like butterflies, run the gauntlet from birth to death in a single instant.

($\triangledown$ At this point in the Russian edition of the present work, Shklovskii expresses his belief that civilizations are not inevitably doomed to self-destruction, despite his description of contemporary Western literature as filled with details of atomic holocaust. He expresses his belief that as long as capitalism exists on Earth, a violent end to intelligent life on the planet is probable. There is reason to assume, he asserts, that future peaceful societies will be constructed on the basis of Communism. I am able to imagine alternative scenarios for the future. No one today lives in a society which closely resembles Adam Smith capitalism or Karl Marx communism. The political dichotomies of the twentieth century may seem to our remote descendants no more exhaustive of the range of possibilities for the entire future of mankind than do, for us, the alternatives of the European religious wars of the sixteenth and seventeenth centuries. As Shklovskii says, the forces of peace in the world are great. Mankind is not likely to destroy itself. There is too much left to do.) $\triangle$

32

Direct contact among galactic civilizations

"There is no use trying," she said: "one *can't* believe impossible things."

"I daresay you haven't had much practice," said the Queen. "When I was your age, I always did it for half-an-hour a day. Why, sometimes I've believed as many as six impossible things before breakfast."

Lewis Carroll, *Alice in Wonderland*

"What matters it how far we go?" his scaly friend replied,
"There is another shore, you know, upon the other side.
The farther off from England, the nearer is to France;
Then turn not pale, beloved snail, but come and join
    the dance."

Lewis Carroll, *The Lobster Quadrille*

▽ Among the possible ways of effecting interstellar communication, we have considered automatic interstellar probe vehicles of rather limited range, and methods of electromagnetic communication over somewhat greater ranges. The difficulties in electromagnetic communication over interstellar distances are serious. A simple query and response to the nearest postulated technical civilization would require periods approaching 1000 years. An extended conversation—or even a one-way transmission to a particularly interesting community on the other side of the Galaxy—would occupy much greater time intervals, 10^4 to 10^5 years. Electromagnetic communication assumes that the choice of signal frequency will be obvious to all communities. We saw in Chapter 27 that there has been considerable disagreement about interstellar transmission frequency assignments even on our own planet. Among Galactic communities, we may expect even greater differences of opinion about what is obvious and what is not. △

If there were indeed a lack of coordination in the standard wavelength—even if the wavelength were an integral fraction or multiple of 21 cm—the extraterrestrial societies would find it very difficult to detect the signals. Furthermore, if radio contact were attempted between civilizations separated by more than 2000 or 3000 light years, and if the communication radiation would have to pass relatively close to the Galactic plane, the artificial signal would be absorbed by the interstellar medium. Such absorption could be significantly decreased if we depart slightly (1 to 2 megacycles per second) from the neutral hydrogen frequency (1420 megacycles sec^{-1}); but this would again complicate the search.

▽ No matter how ingenious the method, there are certain limitations on the character of the communication effected with an alien civilization by electromagnetic radiation. With billions of years of independent biological and social evolution, the thought processes and habit patterns of any two communities must differ greatly. While it seemed likely to us, in Chapter 30, that the transmission of pictorial representations and artificial languages such as Lincos would be easily understood by alien civilizations, this is really a conjecture. We do not know what hidden assumptions lie in our proposed communication channel, assumptions which we are unable to evaluate because they are so intimately woven into the fabric of our thinking.

▽ There is a famous story in the anthropological community which illustrates this point:

▽ A husband-and-wife team of anthropologists was studying adjacent villages in a remote Pacific island. Despite their proximity, different languages were spoken in the two villages. One day, the woman anthropologist received an urgent message by bearer from her husband, asking her to come at once. She arrived in

439

haste and found her husband in an ecstasy of anthropological exhilaration. "My dear," he said, "I have stumbled upon a marvelous philosophical insight of the inhabitants of this village." Approaching one of the villagers, he pointed to a palm tree and asked, "What is this?"

The native promptly replied, let us say, "Unga munga." Next, the anthropologist pointed to a pig wallowing in the mud, and illuminated by the late afternoon sun. "What is this?"

"Unga munga," again replied the informant, with identical inflection.

Finally, in triumph, the anthropologist pointed to the village chieftain, and once again, asked "What is this?"

The respondent replied again—this time, somewhat dejectedly, it seemed—"Unga munga."

"You see—they do not make distinctions among different forms of life. Their language incorporates the unity of all living things," exclaimed the anthropologist.

"Dear," suggested his wife gently, "ask him what the word for index finger is."

▽ I can imagine such difficulties amplified by many orders of magnitude, were we to establish tomorrow interstellar radio contact.

▽ As an example of the potential difficulties of a less subtle sort, we can consider the case of Egyptian hieroglyphics. This language was deciphered only after the discovery of the Rosetta Stone, in effect a selective dictionary in two other known languages, Demotic and Greek. But earlier, several generations of European linguists had attempted to decipher the large body of hieroglyphic writing available even then. What is noteworthy is not so much that their efforts were almost uniformly unsuccessful, but rather, that some thought they had succeeded. While the hieroglyphics are mainly syllabic, some of the early linguists thought that they were ideographic, and constructed marvelously fanciful translations in which birds of course played a leading part. The Egyptians did not write their inscriptions for the benefit of another civilization ignorant of their language. In interstellar communication, there will be conscious attempts to make the contents clear. But our partners in the cosmic discourse will not be human beings, and it remains to be seen whether mathematics is the interstellar Rosetta Stone.

▽ Electromagnetic communication does not permit three of the most exciting categories of interstellar contact:

▽ (1) Contact between an advanced civilization and an intelligent but pre-technical society. △ Such contact would be particularly valuable, because the lifetime of the pre-technological era on many planets may be quite long, and the number of pre-technical civilizations in the Galaxy may greatly exceed the number of technically advanced societies.

▽ (2) Direct exploration of alien nonintelligent biologies, of the interstellar medium, of exotic star systems, and of the wide range of physical phenomena unobservable from the solar neighborhood.

▽ (3) The direct exchange of material objects, including biological specimens, among distant civilizations.

▽ If effective interstellar electromagnetic communication is feasible, there is the possibility of a kind of surrogate exchange of material goods, despite the fact that only photons would be exchanged. We might receive, for example, detailed instructions for the construction of material objects, a scale model of the capitol of Delta Pavonis 3, a household appliance of Beta Hydri 4, or perhaps a novel scientific device developed on 82 Eridani 2. It is even possible, as Fred Hoyle has suggested, that we should receive detailed instructions for assembling the genetic material of an extraterrestrial organism, even an intelligent extraterrestrial organism. △ But even then, the demand for actual physical exchange would soon arise.

▽ In electromagnetic interstellar communication, the communicants are far distant, the learning vicarious, and the duration of the discourse long. But if direct interstellar spaceflight were possible, it would sweep away these difficulties; it would reopen the arena of action for civilizations where local exploration has been completed; it would provide access beyond the planetary frontiers. We have already discussed the possibility of automatic interstellar spaceflight. We must now examine the prospect of interstellar spaceflight, manned—this will not be quite the appropriate word—by intelligent beings.

▽ There are two basic methods of achieving interstellar spaceflight within characteristic human lifetimes. One involves the slowing down of human metabolic activities during very long flight times. Let us imagine that society has advanced to the stage where fast non-relativistic interstellar spaceflight is possible, with velocities of, say, 100,000 km sec^{-1}, one-third the speed of light. A one-way voyage to a destination planet 1000 light years distant would take some 3000 years, or slightly longer, allowing for acceleration and deceleration. A round-trip to the Galactic center would take about 60,000 years. If such voyages are to be feasible, the lifetime of our civilization should perhaps exceed the length of the voyage. Otherwise, there will be no one to come home to. Work on metabolic inhibitors is just beginning on our planet. As we discussed in Chapter 19, it is possible to preserve a variety of microorganisms for extended periods of time—perhaps indefinitely—by quick-freezing them to fairly low temperatures. Low-temperature preservation of human blood and sperm is now routine. But the preservation of a whole human being at low temperatures for extended periods of time has never been accomplished. The reason is essentially this: The density of ice is lower than the density of water. (This is why ice floats on ponds in winter.) Therefore, ice occupies a larger volume than the same mass of water. (For this reason, milk bottles placed outdoors on cold days undergo sometimes spectacular distortions.) Consequently, on freezing an animal such as a human being, composed largely of water, serious damage is done to his cells, both during freezing and during thawing. During freezing, the volumes of the cells increase; they encroach upon each other, and their internal structure is disrupted. During thawing, comparable contractions occur. Antifreezing chemicals are, of course, known, but it is difficult to saturate adequately a human being with such antifreezes without killing him first.

▽ But there do exist possibilities which have not yet been explored. As one example, we consider the following idea, developed jointly in conversation between myself and the Swedish biologist Carl-Gören Hedén, of the Karolinska Institute, Stockholm. While freezing preserves, it also kills, as we have just discussed, because of the difference in density between water and ice. But at high pressures, there are other kinds of ice, with different crystal structures and different densities from those of ordinary ice. At pressures of about 3000 atm and temperatures of −40°C (−40°F) or less, ordinary ice, called ice I, becomes ice II, a variety of frozen water which has very nearly the same density as the liquid. If a human being could be safely brought to and maintained at an ambient pressure of several thousand atmospheres, and then quickly and carefully frozen to very low temperatures, it might be possible to preserve him for long periods of time. This is only one of many possible alternatives. It seems possible that by the time interstellar space vehicles with velocities of 10^{10} cm sec^{-1} are available, techniques for long-term preservation of a human crew will also be available. From the same considerations which we developed in Chapter 15, in our discussion of the survival of interstellar panspermia, it follows that even for very long journeys—say, approaching 10^5 years in duration—the background cosmic radiation will not prove a very serious hazard to the survival of the sleeping crew.

▽ There is another possible means of establishing manned interstellar spaceflight over long distances, which does not necessarily involve metabolic inhibitors. This is relativistic interstellar spaceflight.

▽ It has been known for some time that there is a remarkable effect, due to the theory of relativity, which would play a major role in spaceflights at velocities close to c, the velocity of light. The passage of time, as measured by the crew of the space vehicle, would be very slow when compared with the passage of time measured by their friends, relatives, and colleagues on their home planet. As the passengers would travel over immense distances of thousands of light years or more at relativistic velocities, they would become only slightly older. This phenomenon of relativistic time dilation is a specific consequence of the theory of special relativity formulated by Albert Einstein, a theory whose other predictions have been repeatedly verified. Direct experimental confirmations of time dilation itself also exist. For example, the time for an elementary particle called a mu meson to decay at non-relativistic velocities is well known. If, as a result, for example, of the cosmic ray bombardment of the upper atmosphere, a mu meson were to enter the atmosphere of the Earth traveling at a velocity close to the speed of light, but with its ordinary lifetime, it would never reach the surface of the Earth, and would never be detected there. Instead, mu mesons are commonly detected at the surface of the Earth, because the time for them to decay when moving at relativistic velocities is much longer than the time for them to decay at slower velocities. There is no essential difference between biological time and physical time; both are subject to the same physical laws. Aboard a relativistic interstellar space ship, not only would the passengers' clocks move more slowly than their counterparts' on Earth, but they themselves would move more slowly, their hearts would beat more slowly, their awareness of the passage of time would be retarded. Relativistic interstellar spaceflight is in fact a kind of metabolic inhibitor, but one that works on the entire spacecraft.

▽ Let us illustrate the time dilation phenomenon with a concrete example. Let us consider a spacecraft which moves with a constant acceleration as far as the midpoint of its journey, and then decelerates at the same rate to its destination. The acceleration chosen for the trip would very likely be the same as the acceleration due to gravity on the home planet. For example, on the planet Earth, the acceleration due to gravity, that is, the acceleration experienced by any falling body, is 980 cm sec^{-2}, or 32 feet sec^{-2}. If the spacecraft were to move with this same acceleration, called 1 g, the human passengers would feel quite at home, and would experience neither any sense of motion nor any untoward lightness or ponderousness. The inhabitants of a Jovian-type planet would choose accelerations of perhaps 2 g or 3 g. At an acceleration of 1 g it would take only about a year to be traveling close to the speed of light. However continued acceleration would not carry the spacecraft faster than the speed of light but only closer and closer to its value of 300,000 km/sec. This ultimate limit on velocity while unfortunate in the present context is inexorable. The impossibility of information or material objects travelling faster than light is one of the firmest foundations of contemporary physics.

▽ With the above flight plan, it is then possible to compute the elapsed time in years, as measured on board the spacecraft, for a trip to a destination distant S light years from the Earth. These computations are displayed in Figure 32–1 for three choices of on-board acceleration—1 g, 2 g, and 3 g. We see that at an acceleration of 1 g, it takes only a few years, ship time, to reach the nearest stars; 21 years to reach the Galactic center; and 28 years to reach the nearest spiral galaxy beyond the Milky Way. With accelerations of 2 or 3 g, these distances can be negotiated in about half the time. Of course, there is no time dilation on the home planet. The elapsed time in years there approximately equals the distance of the destination in light years plus twice the time required to reach relativistic velocities. This time, at an acceleration of about 1 g, is close to one year. For distances beyond about 10 light years, the elapsed time on the home planet in years roughly equals the distance of the destination in light years. Thus, for a round-trip with a several-year stopover to the nearest stars, the elapsed time on Earth would be a few decades; to Deneb, a few centuries; to the Vela cloud complex, a few millennia; to the Galactic center, a few tens of thousands of years; to M 31, the great galaxy in Andromeda, a few million years; to the Virgo cluster of galaxies, a few tens of millions of years; and to the immensely distant Coma cluster of galaxies, a few hundreds of millions of years. Nevertheless, each of these enormous journeys could be performed within the lifetimes of a human crew, because of time dilation on board the spacecraft.

▽ It is at these immense distances that another curious feature of relativistic interstellar spaceflight emerges. If for some reason we were to desire a two-way communication with the inhabitants of some nearby galaxy, we might try the transmission of electromagnetic signals, or perhaps even the launching of an automatic probe vehicle. With either method, the elapsed transit time to the galaxy would be several millions of years at least. By that time in our future, there may be no civilization left on Earth to continue the dialogue. But if relativistic interstellar spaceflight were used for such a mission, the crew would arrive at the galaxy in

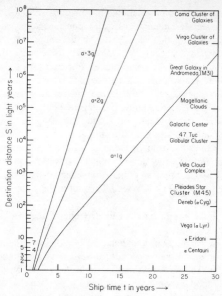

FIGURE 32–1. *An illustration of the potentialities of time dilation in interstellar space flight. A space vehicle is imagined which has uniform acceleration of 1g, 2g, or 3g to the midpoint of its voyage and a uniform deceleration thereafter. It is seen that immense distances —million of light years and more—could be reached by such vehicles during the lifetime of its crew. Yet the time passed on their home planet during the same voyage would amount to millions of years as measured by clocks there.* (*Courtesy of* Planetary and Space Science, *Pergamon Press, London*)

question after perhaps 30 years in transit, able not only to sing the songs of distant Earth, but to provide an opportunity for cosmic discourse with inhabitants of a certainly unique and possibly vanished civilization. Despite the dangers of the passage and the length of the voyage, I have no doubt that qualified crew for such missions could be mustered. Shorter, round-trip journeys to destinations within our Galaxy might prove even more attractive. Not only would the crews voyage to a distant world, but they would return in the distant future of their own world, an adventure and a challenge certainly difficult to duplicate.

▽ It is clear that the ships and engines which we are now barely developing for the exploration of our provincial solar system are but pale shadows of the mighty starships required for relativistic interstellar spaceflight. The primary problem is the construction of a space ship capable of carrying a substantial payload at extremely high velocities over a long period of time. A propulsion system based on contemporary design with the fuel carried on board the spacecraft at launch would require a fantastic quantity of fuel, even if complete conversion of the mass of the fuel into energy were attainable and all the energy so released could be utilized for

INTELLIGENT LIFE IN THE UNIVERSE

thrust. At relativistic velocities and with the above flight plan, the ratio of payload mass to the initial total mass of the spacecraft must be about $2/(1-v/c)$, where v is the maximum velocity. To reach the great galaxy in Andromeda, M 31, during the lifetime of a human crew would require $v = 0.99999\ c$. The initial mass of this ideal fuel would then have to be some 200,000 times greater than the mass of the remainder of the spacecraft. Complete conversion of mass into energy could be obtained only if half the rocket fuel were anti-matter—that is, a form of matter in which our familiar positively charged protons are replaced by negatively charged anti-protons, and in which conventional negative electrons are replaced by positively charged positrons. Anti-matter is uncommon on the Earth for a reason: When it is brought into physical contact with ordinary matter, both become annihilated, in a violent, blinding conversion of mass into energy, often in the form of gamma rays. It is just such an annihilation which would be used to power a hypothetical anti-matter space drive.

▽ The containment of the anti-matter—to say nothing of its production in the quantities required—is clearly a very serious problem. We would not want it to accidentally come into contact with the walls of the spacecraft, themselves composed of ordinary matter. △ Surprisingly, a number of interesting ideas have been put forward which might lead to a successful circumvention of this difficulty. For example, perhaps a special type of non-material, magnetic bottle, employing an intense magnetic field, could be used. Such magnetic bottles are now being investigated in connection with experiments on controlled thermonuclear reactions. ▽ But an interstellar space vehicle powered by anti-matter and requiring a mass ratio of 200,000 does not seem to be an elegant solution to this problem.

▽ A way out of these difficulties which approaches elegance in its conception has been provided by the American physicist Robert W. Bussard, of the TRW Corporation, Los Angeles. Bussard describes an interstellar ramjet which uses the atoms of the interstellar medium both as a working fluid (to provide reaction mass) and as an energy source (through thermonuclear fusion). There is no complete conversion of matter into energy. Such a fusion reactor is certainly not available today, but it violates no physical principles. Its construction is currently being very actively pursued in research on controlled thermonuclear reactions, and there is no reason to expect it to be more than a century away from realization on this planet.

▽ Such an interstellar ramjet would require a large surface area, in order to draw in sufficient interstellar gas to propel the craft. The calculations of Bussard indicate that if there were one atom of hydrogen per cm^3 in the interstellar medium, the surface density of the ramjet would have to be 10^{-8} gm cm^{-2}. In general, the intake surface area of the ramjet is inversely proportional to the concentration n_H of the interstellar gas. If, for example, the mass of the rocket were 100 tons, and n_H equalled 1 atom cm^{-3}, the surface area of the ramjet intake would have to be 10^{15} cm^2, corresponding to a radius of about 700 km. △ In metagalactic space, where $n_H \leqq 10^{-5}$ atoms cm^{-3}, the intake radius would have to be 100 times greater.

▽ These frontal loading areas seem, of course, enormously large by contemporary standards, and perhaps remain absurdly large even when we project the progress of future technology. But we should emphasize that the collecting areas need not be material. Intense magnetic fields are now routinely generated in the laboratory, and even in commercial applications, through the use of what are called superconducting flux pumps. Magnetic fields guide charged particles along a specified trajectory, and if the magnetic lines of force are cleverly arranged, through the design of the flux pumps, the charged particles can be conveyed to any desired region within the magnetic field. Thus, it seems at least possible that the collection of atoms of the interstellar medium by ramjet starships will be accomplished by ionizing the medium ahead of the spacecraft, and guiding the ions into the intake area through the use of intense magnetic fields. △

Should the Bussard ramjet become a reality, our descendants will witness a return, in the interstellar context, of the flight principles used by their ancestors for jet aircraft. The surrounding medium would be necessary for flight.

▽ There is still another very serious difficulty which must be overcome before relativistic interstellar spaceflight can be considered feasible. The ramjet is moving through the interstellar medium with a velocity just short of the velocity of light. This is equivalent to the spacecraft sitting motionless, and the dust grains and atoms of the interstellar medium rushing into it with a velocity almost equal to the velocity of light.

▽ With our previously described flight plan, the maximum velocity of the ramjet would be

$$v = c \left[1 - (1 + aS/2c^2)^{-2}\right]^{\frac{1}{2}}$$

where S is the destination distance, and a is the constant acceleration and deceleration chosen. If S equalled 10,000 parsecs—the distance to the Galactic center—v would differ from c by only one millionth of a percent. At this velocity, each atom of the interstellar medium colliding with the ramjet would appear as a component of the cosmic rays having an energy of 10^{13} electron volts. For 1 atom of hydrogen cm^3 in interstellar space, the spacecraft encounters 10^{13} electron volts cm^{-3}. Since the spacecraft is moving almost with the velocity of light, the flow of equivalent cosmic radiation striking the frontal loading area of the ramjet would be 10^{13} electron volts cm^{-3} × $(3 \times 10^{10}$ cm sec$^{-1}) = 3 \times 10^{23}$ electron volts cm^{-2} sec^{-1}, or 2×10^{11} erg cm^{-2} sec^{-1}. This is penetrating radiation, with an intensity 100,000 times greater than the intensity of sunlight at the surface of the Earth.

The crew would be fried, even on flights to the nearest stars, unless careful precautions were taken.

▽ It is evident, from the large mass ratios already required for "boosted" interstellar flight (for example, using anti-matter), and from the very low frontal loading area surface densities required for an interstellar ramjet, that material shielding would probably never be a practical solution. But it is possible that the same magnetic deflection techniques used to guide interstellar particles to the ramjet's thermonuclear reactor could also be used to deflect particles away from the living quarters and other sensitive areas of the spacecraft. △

These difficulties seem colossal today, but we must remember that a century ago, the prospect of flight in a heavier-than-air vehicle seemed remote ▽ or impossible. △ Now, of course, we take the airplane for granted. Experience in the development of science and technology teaches us that if the basic requirements for an idea do not contradict known scientific principles, sooner or later the problem will be solved. The tempo of scientific and technological development seems to be increasing with each decade. Considering all the possibilities for establishing contact among Galactic civilizations, we cannot exclude direct contact by means of interstellar spaceflight. ▽ Bussard's own concluding remarks on the magnitude of the effort involved in relativistic interstellar spaceflight are worth quoting:

> . . . On any account interstellar travel is inherently a rather grand undertaking, certainly many magnitudes broader in scope and likewise more difficult than interplanetary travel in the solar system . . . The engineering effort required for the achievement of successful short-time interstellar flight will likely be as much greater than that involved in interplanetary flight as the latter is more difficult than travel on the surface of the Earth. However, the expansion of man's horizons will be proportionately greater, and nothing worthwhile is ever achieved easily. △

33

Possible consequences of direct contact

Where are they?

    Enrico Fermi (1943)

. . . Were we to meet with a Creature of a much different Shape from Man, with Reason and Speech, we should be much surprised and shocked at the Sight. For if we try to imagine or paint a Creature like a Man in every Thing else, but that has a Neck four times as long, and great round Eyes five or six times as big, and farther distant, we cannot look upon't without the utmost Aversion, altho' at the same time we can give no account of our Dislike . . . For 'tis a very ridiculous Opinion, that the common People have got, that 'tis impossible a rational Soul should dwell in any other Shape than ours . . . This can proceed from nothing but the Weakness, Ignorance, and Prejudice of Men.

    Christianus Huygens, *New Conjectures Concerning the Planetary Worlds, Their Inhabitants and Productions* (c. 1670)

▽ In the previous chapter, we argued that manned interstellar spaceflight, either at sub-relativistic velocities using metabolic inhibitors, or at relativistic velocities with the Bussard ramjet, is possible without appeal to as yet undiscovered principles. Especially allowing for a modicum of scientific and technological progress within the next few centuries, I believe that efficient interstellar spaceflight to the farthest reaches of our Galaxy is a feasible objective for humanity. If this is the case, other civilizations, aeons more advanced than ours, must today be plying the spaces between the stars.

▽ If interstellar spaceflight is technically feasible, even though an exceedingly expensive and difficult undertaking from our point of view, it is likely to be developed by a civilization substantially in advance of our own. Even beyond the exchanges of information and ideas with other intelligent communities, the scientific advantages of interstellar spaceflight are innumerable. There are direct astronomical samplings—of stars in all evolutionary stages, of distant planetary systems, of the interstellar medium, of very ancient globular clusters. There are cooperative astronomical ventures, such as the trigonometric parallaxes of extremely distant objects; there is the observation and sampling of a multitude of independent biologies and societies. These are undertakings which could challenge and inspire even a very long-lived civilization.

▽ For the civilization lifetimes, L, previously adopted, we see that interstellar spaceflight to all points within the Galaxy, and even to other galaxies, is possible in principle. The voyagers will return far in the future of their departure, but we have already anticipated the civilization will be stable over these immense periods of time. There will still be a record of the departure, a repository for the information collected, and a community interested in results obtainable in no other way. To avoid unnecessary duplication in interstellar exploration, the communicative societies will pool information and act in concert, as Bracewell has already pointed out. Direct contacts and exchange of information and artifacts will exist among most spacefaring societies possessing starships. In fact, over large distances, starship communication will occur very nearly as rapidly as, and much more reliably than, communication by electromagnetic radiation. The situation bears some similarity to the post-Renaissance seafaring communities of Europe and their colonies before the development of clipper ships and steamships. If interstellar spaceflight is feasible, the technical civilizations of the Galaxy will be an intercommunicating whole. But the communication will be sluggish.

▽ It is of some interest to estimate the mean time interval between contacts for a given planetary system. Although the shipboard transit times at relativistic velocities are very roughly the same to any place in the Galaxy, the elapsed time on the home planet is, of course, approximately proportional to the distance of the voyage. Interstellar contact using either metabolic inhibitors or relativistic velocities should be most frequent among neighboring communities, although we can anticipate that occasional very long journeys will be attempted.

▽ Let each of the N planets in the communicative phase launch q starships per year. These vehicles each effect at least one contact per journey, and are most often gone some 10^3 to 10^4 years from the home planet per mission. In the steady state, there are then q contacts per year effected by each of N planets, and about qN contacts per year for the Galaxy as a whole (the units of time here are Earth years). Relative to the economic capacity of such advanced civilizations, a value of $q = 1$ yr^{-1} seems modest. Other choices of q will modify the results in an obvious manner. Thus, each civilization makes about one contact per year, and an average of L contacts during its lifetime. Let us assume, following the discussion at the beginning of Chapter 29, that $N = 10^6$ and $L = 10^7$ years. △ In my opinion, these estimates of Sagan are slightly too optimistic. ▽ Then, each civilization makes an average of 10^7 contacts during its lifetime. The number of contacts per year for the Galaxy as a whole is 10^6, a sizable fraction of which should be between two advanced communities. The mean number of starships on patrol from each technical civilization at any given time is $\sim 10^3$ to 10^4.

▽ If contacts are made on a purely random basis, each star should be visited about once each 10^5 years. Even the most massive stars will then be examined at least once while they are on the main sequence. Especially with a central Galactic information repository, these advanced civilizations should have an excellent idea of which planetary environments are most likely to develop intelligent life. With an average contact frequency per planet of 10^{-5} yr^{-1}, the origin and evolution of life on every planet in the Galaxy can be monitored efficiently. The successive development of metazoa, of cooperative behavior, of the use of tools, and of primitive intraspecific communication schemes would each be noted, and might each be followed by an increase in the interstellar sampling frequency. If the fraction of inhabited planets which have intelligent beings on them, f_i, is about 10^{-1}, then, biasing by rarity, the frequency of contact with intelligent pre-technical planetary communities should be $\sim 10^{-4}$ yr^{-1}. Once a technical civilization has been established, and especially after interstellar contact has been established—for example, by radio—the frequency of direct contact should again increase. If the fraction of planets inhabited by intelligent beings which are also in the communicative phase is $f_c \sim 10^{-1}$, the contact frequency with technical societies should be increased to about 10^{-3} yr^{-1}. Planets of extraordinary interest will be visited even more frequently.

▽ Under the preceding assumptions, each communicative technical civilization should be visited by another such civilization about once every thousand years. The survey vehicles of each civilization should return to the home planet at a rate of about one a year, and a sizable fraction of these will have had contact with other communities. The wealth, diversity, and brilliance of this commerce, the exchange of goods and information, of arguments and artifacts, of concepts and conflicts, must continuously sharpen the curiosity and enhance the vitality of the participating societies.

▽ If these estimates are even approximately correct, we may anticipate extensive interstellar colonization by technical civilizations of planets previously uninhabited. In Chapter 29, we estimated crudely the probability that a given planet suitable for life actually possesses a technical civilization as $f_c f_i \sim 1$ percent. Thus habitable planets lacking technical civilizations will frequently be encountered by spacefaring civilizations. It is not clear what their response will be. They may wish to leave such worlds strictly alone and permit them to slowly evolve their own unique life forms, through the inexorable sieve of natural selection. Direct contact may be delayed until the life forms on a planet develop a technical society at their own pace. Perhaps strict injunctions against colonization of populated but pre-technical planets is in effect in some *Codex Galactica*. But we are in no position to judge extraterrestrial ethics. Perhaps attempts are made to colonize every habitable planet without regard for the indigenous inhabitants, for purposes of prestige, or exploitation, or some non-human motivation which we cannot even guess. A whole spectrum of intermediate cases can also be imagined, in which small colonies are planted on pre-technical planets, not to interfere with or direct the evolutionary development of the local life forms, but merely to observe them. Note that if colonization is the rule, then even one spacefaring civilization would rapidly spread, in a time much shorter than the age of the Galaxy, throughout the Milky Way. There would be colonies of colonies of colonies, such as arose at many sites in the Western Mediterranean during classical times.

▽ But then, every habitable planet would have a technical civilization, and $f_i f_c$ would equal 1. Using our analysis of the beginning of Chapter 29, it would then follow that the number of technical civilizations in the Galaxy at the present time, $N = 10\ L$, where L is the mean lifetime per civilization. If we were to take $L = 10^7$ years, there would be 10^8 technical civilizations in the Galaxy, or on planets orbiting about 0.1 percent of the stars in the sky. The mean distance between technical civilizations would then be, instead of hundreds of light years, tens of light years. If instead we selected von Hoerner's estimate of $L \sim 10^4$ years, the mean distance would remain at several hundreds of light years.

▽ The preceding discussion has two curious applications to our own planet, one to our past, and the other to our future. Figure 33–1 shows a recent reconstruction of the ancestral tree of contemporary man, compiled from painstaking paleontological, archeological, and anthropological analyses. We see that some 25 million years ago, there existed a creature named Proconsul who was probably ancestral both to Homo Sapiens and to the great apes. Proconsul was erect, bipedal, and tool-using. The subsequent evolution in the line of man has been marked, as all evolutionary tracks are, by fits and starts and dead ends. We see, for example, that late Paranthropus, late Java man, and late Neanderthal man all represent evolutionary dead ends. They were intelligent, communicative, and probably had their own simple cultures, but they left no issue. Had the physical environment been slightly different, had the accidents of daily existence occurred another way, Homo Sapiens might have been an evolutionary dead end, and perhaps today there would have been a technical civilization of Pithecanthropi on the planet Earth; or perhaps no civilization at all.

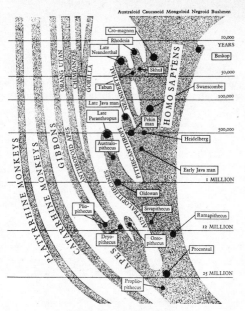

CHART I. The Evolution of Man

FIGURE 33–1. *The evolution of man according to one knowledgable recent view.* (*Redrawn with slight changes after an illustration in* Pre-History and the Beginnings of Civilization *by Jacquetta Hawkes and Sir Leonard Woolley, Harper and Row, 1963; by permission.*)

▽ But these matters, while difficult for us to reconstruct from a distance of millions of years, would have been much clearer to a technical civilization greatly in advance of the present one on Earth, which visited us every hundred thousand years or so to see if anything of interest was happening lately. Some 25 million years ago, a Galactic survey ship on a routine visit to the third planet of a relatively common *G* dwarf may have noted an interesting and promising evolutionary development: Proconsul. The information would have filtered at the speed of light slowly through the Galaxy, and a notation would have been made in some central information repository, perhaps at the Galactic center. If the emergence of intelligent life on a planet is of general scientific or other interest to the Galactic civilizations, it is reasonable that with the emergence of Proconsul, the rate of sampling of our planet should have increased, perhaps to about once every ten thousand years. At the beginning of the most recent post-glacial epoch, the development of social structure, art, religion, and elementary technical skills should have increased the contact frequency still further. But if the interval between sampling is only several thousand years, there is then a possibility that contact with an extraterrestrial civilization has occurred within historical times.

INTELLIGENT LIFE IN THE UNIVERSE

▽ There are no reliable reports of direct contact with an extraterrestrial civilization during the last few centuries, when critical scholarship and non-superstitious reasoning have been fairly widespread [see Chapter 2]. Any earlier contact story must be encumbered with some degree of fanciful embellishment, due simply to the views prevailing at the time of the contact. The extent to which subsequent variation and embellishment alters the basic fabric of the account varies with time and circumstance. For example, M. Eliade's book *Cosmos and History,* mentions an incident in Rumanian folklore, recorded by C. Brailoiu, where only 40 years after a true romantic tragedy, the real story became elaborately embellished with mythological material and supernatural beings. The actual heroine was still alive at the time that the ballad was being sung and attributed to remote antiquity.

▽ Another incident which is more relevant to the topic at hand is the native account of the first contact of the Tlingit people of the northwest coast of North America with European civilization—an expedition led by the French navigator La Perouse, in 1786. The Tlingit kept no written records; one century after the contact, the verbal narrative of the encounter was related to the American anthropologist G. T. Emmons by a principal Tlingit chief. The story was overlaid with the mythological framework in which the French sailing vessels were initially interpreted. But what is very striking is that the true nature of the encounter had been faithfully preserved. One blind old warrior had mastered his fears at the time of the encounter, had boarded one of the French ships, and exchanged goods with the Europeans. Despite his blindness, he reasoned that the occupants of the vessels were men. His interpretation led to active trade between the expedition of La Perouse and the Tlingit. The oral rendition contained sufficient information for later reconstruction of the true nature of the encounter, although many of the incidents were disguised in a mythological framework—for example, the sailing ships were described as immense black birds with white wings. △

As another example, the people of sub-Saharan Africa, who had no written language until the colonial period, preserved their history primarily through folklore. Such legends and myths, handed down by illiterate people from generation to generation, are in general of great historical value.

▽ The encounter between La Perouse and the Tlingit suggests that under certain circumstances, a brief contact with an alien civilization will be recorded in a reconstructible manner. The reconstruction will be greatly aided if (1) the account is committed to written record soon after the event; (2) a major change is effected in the contacted society by the encounter; and (3) no attempt is made by the contacting civilization to disguise its exogenous nature.

▽ On the other hand, it is obvious that the reconstruction of a contact with an extraterrestrial civilization is fraught with difficulties. What guise may we expect such a contact myth to wear? A simple account of the apparition of a strange being who performs marvelous works and resides in the heavens is not quite adequate. All peoples have a need to understand their environment, and the attribution of the incompletely understood to non-human deities is at least mildly satisfying. When interaction occurs among peoples supporting different deities, it is inevitable that each group will claim extraordinary powers for its god. Residence of the gods in the sky is not even approximately suggestive of extraterrestrial origin. After all, where can the gods reside? Obviously, not over in the next county. It would be too easy to disprove their existence by taking a walk. Until very subtle metaphysical constructs are developed—possibly, in desperation—the gods can only live beneath the ground, in the waters, or in the sky. Except, perhaps, for seafaring peoples, the sky offers the widest range of opportunities for theological speculation.

▽ Accordingly, we require more of a legend than the apparition of a strange being who does extraordinary works and lives in the sky. It would certainly add credibility if no obvious supernatural adumbration were attached to the story. A description of the morphology of an intelligent non-human, a clear account of astronomical realities which a primitive people could not acquire by their own efforts, or a transparent presentation of the purpose of the contact would increase the credibility of the legend. △

Such an unusual occurrence would certainly be described in the legends and myths of the people who came into contact with space voyagers. The astronauts would probably be portrayed as having godlike characteristics and possessing supernatural powers. Special emphasis would be placed on their arrival from the sky, and their subsequent departure back into the sky. These beings may have taught the inhabitants of the Earth useful arts and basic sciences, which would also be reflected in their legends and myths.

In 1959, the Soviet ethnologist M. M. Agrest postulated that representatives from an extraterrestrial civilization have indeed visited our planet. ▽ Despite the great dangers of confusion with legends generated in other ways, △ such hypotheses are entirely reasonable, and worthy of careful analysis. Agrest has boldly conjectured that perhaps a number of events described in the Bible were in reality based on the visit of extraterrestrial astronauts to the Earth. For example, the circumstances surrounding the destruction of Sodom and Gomorrah remind Agrest of a nuclear explosion as it might have been described by an observer living in ancient times. ▽ As another example, Agrest considers the incidents related in the apocryphal book *The Slavonic Enoch* to be in reality an account of the visitation of Earth by extraterrestrial cosmonauts, and the reciprocal visitation of several Galactic communities by a rather befuddled inhabitant of the Earth. However, *The Slavonic Enoch* fails to satisfy several of the criteria for a general contact myth, mentioned above: It has been molded into several different standardized supernatural frameworks; the astronomy is largely incorrect; and there is no transparent extraterrestrial motivation for the events described. The interested reader may wish to consult standard versions of the tale. △

Agrest further suggests that certain monuments of past cultures result from direct contact with an interstellar society. However, this idea, in our opinion, is highly debatable. Although certain claims have been made from time to time, no known ancient artifacts have been unambiguously connected with a cosmic visit. The well-known Soviet journalist G. N. Ostroumov recently announced to the world that the famous steel parallelepiped,—▽ purportedly a machine-tooled product of an unfamiliar alloy, found embedded in an ancient vein of coal— △ kept at the Salzburg Museum, was in reality a fraud. It has also been shown that the famous rust-resistant column in India is not the result of a visit by extraterrestrial cosmonauts, but rather, an outstanding example of primitive powder metallurgy. Much commotion was made over the discovery of the image of a "Martian god," complete with space suit, found in cliffs overlooking the Sahara [see Figures 33–2 and 33–3]. It transpired that these Tassili frescoes represented in fact an ordinary human being in a ritual mask and costume. The press in the Soviet Union and in other countries tends to exaggerate and over-publicize such matters. Such publicity is due, of course, to widespread popular interest in the possibility of contact with intelligent extraterrestrials. ▽ But for this very reason, △ we must examine very critically any purported artifacts uncovered. It is wise to bear in mind the ancient Chinese proverb mentioned in Chapter 23.

▽ Some years ago, I came upon a legend which more nearly fulfils some of our criteria for a genuine contact myth. It is of special interest because it relates to the

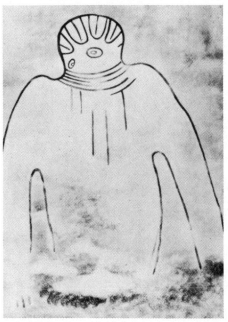

FIGURE 33–2. *A fresco from Tassili-n-ajjer in the central Sahara. Some of these frescoes date to 6000* B.C. *The French archeologist Henri Lhote has called this figure Jabbaren, the "great Martian god," although there is, of course, no evidence to suggest an extraterrestrial origin for the prototype of this illustration. (Reproduced with permission from Henri Lhote,* The Search for the Tassili Frescoes, *E. P. Dutton and Co., New York.)*

FIGURE 33–3. *A Tassili fresco of apparently a somewhat earlier epoch than that of Figure 33–2. Lhote describes this as the style of the round-headed men, "Martian" phase. The originals are in yellow ochre with red ochre lines. (Reproduced from the Soviet film "Planeta Zagadok".)*

origin of Sumerian civilization. Sumer was an early—perhaps the first—civilization in the contemporary sense on the planet Earth. It was founded in the fourth millennium B.C. or earlier. We do not know where the Sumerians came from. Their language was strange; it had no cognates with any known Indo-European, Semitic, or other language, and is understood only because a later people, the Akkadians, compiled extensive Sumerian-Akkadian dictionaries.

▽ The successors to the Sumerians and Akkadians were the Babylonians, Assyrians, and Persians. Thus the Sumerian civilization is in many respects the ancestor of our own. I feel that if Sumerian civilization is depicted by the descendants of the Sumerians themselves to be of non-human origin, the relevant legends should be examined carefully. I do not claim that the following is necessarily an example of extraterrestrial contact, but it is the type of legend that deserves more careful study.

▽ Taken at face value, the legend suggests that contact occurred between human beings and a non-human civilization of immense powers on the shores of the Persian Gulf, perhaps near the site of the ancient Sumerian city of Eridu, and in the fourth millennium B.C. or earlier. There are three different but cross-referenced accounts of the *Apkallu* dating from classical times. Each can be traced back to Berosus, a priest of Bel-Marduk, in the city of Babylon, at the time of Alexander the Great. Berosus, in turn, had access to cuneiform and pictographic records dating back several thousand years before his time. It is important to quote most of the body of the legend, in the form available today. The manner of presentation is as striking as the content. The quoted translations from the Greek and Latin are taken from Cory's *Ancient Fragments,* in the revised edition of 1876:

The account of Alexander Polyhistor:

Berosus, in his first book concerning the history of Babylonia, informs us that he lived in the time of Alexander, the son of Philip. And he mentions that there were written accounts preserved at Babylon with the greatest care, comprehending a term of fifteen myriads of years. These writings contained a history of the heavens and the sea; of the birth of mankind; also of those who had sovereign rule; and of the actions achieved by them.

And, in the first place, he describes Babylonia as a country which lay between the Tigris and Euphrates. He mentions that it abounded with wheat, barley, ocrus, sesamum; and in the lakes were found the roots called gongae, which were good to be eaten, and were, in respect to nutriment, like barley. There were also palm trees and apples, and most kinds of fruits; fish, too, and birds; both those which are merely of flight, and those which take to the element of water. The part of Babylon which bordered upon Arabia was barren, and without water; but that which lay on the other side had hills, and was fruitful. At Babylon there was (in these times) a great resort of people of various nations, who inhabited Chaldea, and lived without rule and order, like the beasts of the field.

In the first year there made its appearance, from a part of the Persian Gulf which bordered upon Babylonia, an animal endowed with reason, who was called Oannes. (According to the account of Apollodorus) the whole body of the animal was like that of a fish; and had under a fish's head another head, and also feet below, similar to those of a man, subjoined to the fish's tail. His voice, too, and language was articulate and human; and a representation of him is preserved even to this day [see Figure 33–4].

This Being, in the day-time used to converse with men; but took no food at that season; and he gave them an insight into letters, and sciences, and every kind of art. He taught them to construct houses, to found temples, to compile laws, and explained to them the principles of geometrical knowledge. He made them distinguish the seeds of the earth, and showed them how to collect fruits. In short, he instructed them in everything which could tend to soften manners and humanise mankind. From that time, so universal were his instructions, nothing material has been added by way of improvement. When the sun set it was the custom of this Being to plunge again into the sea, and abide all night in the deep; for he was amphibious.

After this, there appeared other animals, like Oannes, of which Berosus promises to give an account when he comes to the history of the kings. Moreover, Berosus wrote concerning the generation of mankind; of their different ways of life, and of their civil polity. . .

The account of Abydenus:

So much concerning the wisdom of the Chaldaeans.

It is said that the first king of the country was Alorus, who gave out a report that he was appointed by God to be the Shepherd of the people: he reigned ten sari. Now a sarus is esteemed to be three thousand six hundred years; a neros, six hundred: and a sossus, sixty.

After him Alaparus reigned three sari; to him succeeded Amillarus, from the city of Pantibiblon, who reigned thirteen sari; in his time a semi-daemon called Annedotus, very like to Oannes, came up a second time from the sea. After him Ammenon reigned twelve sari, who was from the city of Pantibiblon; then Megalarus, of the same place, eighteen sari; then Daos, the shepherd, governed

for the space of ten sari—he was of Pantibiblon; in his time four double-shaped personages came out of the sea to land, whose names were Euedocus, Eneugamus, Eneuboulos, and Anementus. After these things was Anodaphus, in the time of Euedoreschus. There were afterwards other kings, and last of all Sisithrus (Xisuthrus). So that, in all, the number amounted to ten kings, and the term of their reigns to one hundred and twenty sari. . . .

The account of Apollodorus:

This is the history which Berosus has transmitted to us: He tells us that the first king was Alorus of Babylon, a Chaldaean; he reigned ten sari; and afterwards Alaparus and Amelon, who came from Pantibiblon; then Ammenon the Chaldaean, in whose time appeared the Musarus Oannes, the Annedotus, from the Persian Gulf. (But Alexander Polyhistor, anticipating the event, has said that he appeared in the first year; but Apollodorus says that it was after forty sari; Abydenus, however, makes the second Annedotus appear after twenty-six sari.) Then succeeded Megalarus, from the city of Pantibiblon, and he reigned eighteen sari; and after him Daonus, the shepherd, from Pantibiblon, reigned ten sari; in his time (he says) appeared again, from the Persian Gulf, a fourth Annedotus, having the same form with those above, the shape of a fish blended with that of a man. Then Euedoreschus reigned from the city of Pantibiblon for the period of eighteen sari. In his day there appeared another personage, whose name was Odacon, from the Persian Gulf, like the former, having the same complicated form, between a fish and a man. (All these, says Apollodorus, related particularly and circumstantially whatever Oannes had informed them of. Concerning these appearances

Abydenus has made no mention.) Then Amempsinus, a Chaldaean from Laranchae reigned, and he, being the eighth in order, ruled for ten sari. Then Otiartes, a Chaldaean from Laranchae, reigned, and he ruled for eight sari.

Upon the death of Otiartes, his son Xisuthrus, reigned eighteen sari. In his time the Great Flood happened. . . .

From the further account of Alexander Polyhistor:

After the death of Ardates, his son, Xisuthrus, succeeded, and reigned eighteen sari. In his time happened the great Deluge; the history of which is given in this manner. The deity Kronus appeared to him in a vision, and gave him notice, that upon the fifteenth day of the month Daesia there would be a flood, by which mankind would be destroyed. He therefore enjoined him to commit to writing a history of the beginning, progress, and final conclusion of all things, down to the present term; and to bury these accounts securely in the City of the Sun at Sippara; and to build a vessel, and to take with him into it his friends and relations; and to convey on board everything necessary to sustain life, and to take in also all species of animals that either fly, or rove upon the earth; and trust himself to the deep. Having asked the deity whither he was to sail, he was answered, 'To the Gods'. . . .

▽ The preceding four fragments from ancient writers present an account of a remarkable sequence of events. Sumerian civilization is depicted by the descendants of the Sumerians themselves to be of non-human origin. A succession of strange creatures appears over the course of several generations. Their only apparent purpose is to instruct mankind. Each knows of the mission and accomplishments of his predecessors. When a great inundation threatens the survival of the newly introduced knowledge among men, steps are taken to insure its preservation. Thereby, the access of Berosus to antediluvian records is formally explained.

▽ The straightforward nature of this account of contact with superior beings is notable. Oannes and the other Apkallu are described variously as "animals endowed with reason," as "beings," as "semi-daemons," and as "personages." They are never described as gods.

▽ Alexander Polyhistor's description of a sudden transition from chaos to civilization after the appearance of Oannes is in accord with the impressions of some, but by no means all, archeologists. For example, the Danish-American Sumerologist Thorkild Jacobsen, of Harvard University, writes:

Thousands of years had already passed since man first entered the valley of the Two Rivers, and one prehistoric culture had followed another—all basically alike, none signally different from what one might have found elsewhere in the world. During these millenniums agriculture was the chief means of support. Tools were fashioned from stone, rarely from copper. Villages, made up of patriarchal families, seem to have been the typical form of settlement. The most conspicuous change from one such culture to another, surely not a very profound one, seems to have been in the way pottery was made and decorated.

But with the advent of the Proto-literate period the picture changes. Overnight, as it were, Mesopotamian civilization crystallizes. The fundamental pattern, the controlling framework within which Mesopotamia is to live its life, formulate its deepest questions, evaluate itself and evaluate the universe, for ages to come, flashes into being, complete in all its main features.

▽ However, since Jacobsen wrote this memorable passage, some evidence has been found for much earlier primitive cities in Mesopotamia, and it now appears possible that the development of Mesopotamian civilization was more gradual than Jacobsen suggested.

▽ Finally, we may mention some relevant ideas of Sumerian mythology. The gods are characterized by a variety of forms, not all human. They are celestial in origin. In general, each is associated with a different star. In fact, in the earliest Sumerian pictographs, which preceded cuneiform writing, the symbols for god and for star are identical. The cosmos is conceived as a state governed by an apparently representative and democratic assembly of the gods, which made the great decisions on the fates of all beings. Within the assembly there was a smaller group of prominent deities called "The Seven Gods Who Determine Destinies." Such a picture is not altogether different from what we might expect if a network of confederated civilizations interlaced the Galaxy.

▽ Some of the astronomical and other ideas of Sumerian and successor civilizations are portrayed on cylinder seals—small cylinders which, when rolled on clay or other impressionable material, left behind the negative of its impression. Unfortunately, the cuneiform notations on each cylinder seal are only very rarely related to the pictorial content of the seal. More often, the cuneiform inscription says something like the Sumerian equivalent of "Joe Williamson: his seal". The illustrations on the cylinder seals have for this reason generally defied attempts to understand them in detail. They refer to mythological material otherwise lost.

▽ In Figure 33–5, we see reproductions of four such cylinder seals, which are now at various museums. In each, there is a clear representation of some celestial object—a central circle, or sphere, surrounded by other, generally smaller circles or spheres. In the upper left-hand illustration of Figure 33–5, we see that the central circle is surrounded by rays and can quite clearly be identified as a sun or star. But what are we to make of the other objects surrounding each star? It is at least a natural assumption that they represent the planets. But the idea of planets circling suns and stars is an idea which essentially originated with Copernicus— although some earlier speculations along these lines were mentioned in ancient Greece.

▽ The cylinder seal in the upper left-hand corner of Figure 33–5 shows, curiously enough, *nine* planets circling the prominent sun in the sky (and two smaller planets, off to one side). The other representations of planetary systems— if we may call them this—show, remarkably, a variation in the numbers of planets per star. In some of the cylinder seals, a star and accompanying planets seem to be associated with a particular deity. An even more enigmatic cylinder seal can be seen in Figure 33–6.

FIGURE 33–5. *Upper left: an Akkadian cylinder seal showing the god of fertility with plow. The seal was in the Vorderasiatische Abteilung der Staatlichen Museen, Berlin, before the War. Upper right: a Mitannian cylinder seal from the British Museum showing, among other interesting objects, what are conventionally described as a hunter and a drinker. Lower left: a late Kassite cylinder seal, showing influence of Mitannian style. This seal is in the Louvre. Lower right: a cylinder seal from the first Babylonian Empire conventionally described as "Marduk and hero with flowing vase". The seal was in the Vorderasiatische Abteilung der Staatlichen Museen, Berlin, before the War. (Reproduced from* Cylinder Seals, *by H. Frankfort, Macmillan, London, 1939.)*

▽ These cylinder seals may be nothing more than the experiments of the ancient unconscious mind to understand and portray a sometimes incomprehensible, sometimes hostile environment. The stories of the Apkallu may have been made out of whole cloth, perhaps as late as Babylonian times, perhaps by Berosus himself. Sumerian society may have developed gradually over many thousands of years. In any event, a completely convincing demonstration of past contact with an extraterrestrial civilization will always be difficult to provide on textual grounds alone. But stories like the Oannes legend, and representations especially of the earliest civilizations on the Earth, deserve much more critical studies than have been performed heretofore, with the possibility of direct contact with an extraterrestrial civilization as one of many possible alternative interpretations.

▽ There are also other possible sources of information. With the numbers we have discussed, it seems possible that the Earth has been visited by various Galactic civilizations many times (possibly $\sim 10^4$, during geological time). It is not out of the question that artifacts of these visits still exist—although none have been found to date—or even that some kind of base is maintained within the solar system to provide continuity for successive expeditions. Because of weathering and the possibility of detection and interference by the inhabitants of the Earth, it might have appeared preferable not to erect such a base on the Earth's surface. The

FIGURE 33–6. *Assyrian cylinder seal of the ninth century* B.C. *On the left is a scorpion-man and a sun disk with wings, both conventional Mesopotamian symbols. The wistful animal at stage center with the cumbersome apparatus on his back is conventionally described as a dragon. Note the dolphin representation just in front of him. The seal was in the Vorderasiatische Abteilung der Staatlichen Museen, Berlin, before the War.* (Reproduced from Cylinder Seals, *by H. Frankfort, Macmillan, London, 1939.*)

Moon seems one reasonable alternative site for a base. Forthcoming high-resolution photographic reconnaissance of the Moon from space vehicles—particularly, of the back side—might bear these possibilities in mind. △ Agrest has independently made a similar conjecture, ▽ as has the Anglo-Ceylonese science writer, Arthur C. Clarke. △ The cosmic visitors would probably reason that by the time man had developed the technology to explore the far side of the Moon, he would also have attained a certain limited degree of advancement and might be called civilized. ▽ Contact with such a base would, of course, provide the most direct check on the possibility of fairly frequent interstellar spaceflight.

▽ The rate of technical advance of our civilization is very great. It is possible that an extraterrestrial society or federation of such societies might want to contact an emerging technical civilization as soon as possible, perhaps to head off a nuclear annihilation—one possible consequence of intensive technological development—or perhaps for other reasons. A visit every few thousand years would not be nearly frequent enough for such a purpose. Drake and Clarke have suggested that an advanced extraterrestrial civilization might deposit an automatic technology monitor, an alarm which beacons across interstellar space when the local level of technological advance has reached a certain point. For example, such a monitor might analyze the content of radioactive elements in the atmosphere. A substantial increase in atmospheric radioisotopes such as has occurred due to nuclear testing during the last two decades would then trigger the alarm. An extraterrestrial resident agent is an alternative possibility. If such an alarm system exists—although it is of course nothing more than the barest supposition—then it has probably been triggered by now. The message may be winging across interstellar space with the speed of light to the nearest advanced technical civilization. But if civilizations are separated by several hundreds of light years, we will have to wait until A.D. 2300 or 2400 for their response.

▽ However it may not have been considered necessary to introduce such a monitor in a developing society. A technical civilization soon indicates its own existence unintentionally. In Chapter 27 we described the possibility of eavesdropping on radio communication intended for local consumption on a planet. Some 40 or 45 light years from the Earth, at the time of writing, there is a wave front propagating away from the Earth due to the first development of extensive commercial radio broadcasting on Earth. In another few hundred years, it may reach the nearest outpost of the community of Galactic civilizations, and it will be a few centuries further into the future before any response, friendly or unfriendly, could be felt on Earth.

▽ In the discussion of interstellar radio communication in Chapter 27, we mentioned that contact would never be achieved if all advanced civilizations were listening, and none were transmitting signals. Some people have suggested that for the present, we might assiduously listen, but should carefully refrain from transmitting, because we do not know the intentions of a superior Galactic society. This argument deserves a closer examination. What might an advanced extraterrestrial civilization want of us? Most of the conventional nightmares can be dismissed. We would not be useful as slaves, because a society capable of mastering interstellar spaceflight would have adequate machine servants. They could not want us for food, even if human beings were composed of especially tasty proteins. Such a society should be capable of synthesizing them in any desired quantity from the constituent amino acids, after the analysis of a single specimen.

▽ There are other possibilities which cannot be so easily dismissed. One of the primary motivations for the exploration of the New World was to convert the inhabitants to Christianity—peacefully, if possible; forcefully, if necessary. Can we exclude the possibility of an extraterrestrial evangelism? While American Indians were not useful for any concrete task in the courts of Spain and France, they were nonetheless transported there for prestige purposes. Is this an emotion alien to extraterrestrial civilizations? Or perhaps human beings have some relatively uncommon talent, of which they are themselves entirely unaware. J. B. S. Haldane once pointed out to me that sea lions and seals have a remarkable ability to balance a rubber ball on their noses, which is part of the reason we maintain them in captivity. Yet such an ability is probably perfectly useless for a seal in the wild state. While any organism or artifact of the Earth could be duplicated by an advanced extraterrestrial society, the original and the duplicate are still different. The American psychologist Ruth Ellen Galper has pointed out in this connection that we carefully distinguish between natural and cultured pearls. Finally, can we exclude even darker motives? Might an extraterrestrial society want to be alone at the summit of Galactic power, and make a careful effort to crush prospective contenders? Or might there even be the "cockroach response"—to stamp out an alien creature simply because it is different, as suggested in the closing scene of Franz Kafka's *Metamorphosis?*

▽ It may be that these gruesome possibilities are real. Or the fact that we can imagine them may be itself only a reflection of how much further we have to go before we will be ready for full membership in a Galactic community of societies. But in either case, there is no way back. It is of no use to maintain an interstellar radio silence; the signal has already been sent. Forty light years out from Earth, the news of a new technical civilization is winging its way among the stars. If there are beings out there, scanning their skies for the tidings of a new technical civilization, they will know of it, whether for good or for ill. If interstellar spaceflight by advanced technical civilizations is commonplace, we may expect an emissary, perhaps in the next several hundred years. Hopefully, there will then still be a thriving terrestrial civilization to greet the visitors from the far distant stars. △

34

Intelligent life as a factor on the cosmic scale

Alexander wept when he heard from Anaxarchus that there was an infinite number of worlds; and his friends asking him if any accident had befallen him, he returned this answer: "Do you not think it a matter worthy of lamentation that, when there is such a vast multitude of them, we have not yet conquered one?"

Plutarch, *On the Tranquillity of the Mind*

Had I been present at the Creation, I would have given some useful hints for the better ordering of the universe.

Alphonso the Wise (c. 1270)

ntelligent life in the universe tends to have an active influence on the character of the cosmos, as we have frequently mentioned in previous chapters. For example, the activities of man have greatly increased the intensity of radio radiation which the Earth emits into space [Chapter 18]. In the second half of the twentieth century, the inhabitants of the planet Earth are beginning to change the over-all organization of the solar system. For billions of years, our planet had only one moon. Now, many artificial satellites orbit the Earth. In the not-too-distant future, artificial satellites may be orbiting our natural moon and other planets of our solar system.

We must note in passing that advances in sciences have, unfortunately, not always been motivated by a desire for the betterment of mankind, but have sometimes been seen as a means for increasing the military power of nations. For purely military reasons, thermonuclear weapons have been exploded high above the atmosphere of the Earth, creating artificial aurorae and magnetic fields. It is hoped that the space sciences of the future will be dedicated solely to the benefit of mankind.

We are only entering the cosmic era. Only a few years have passed since the first artificial satellite was launched. What will the future hold?

Although it is difficult to speculate about the kind of changes which man may bring about in the solar system, several interesting and thought-provoking hypotheses have recently been advanced. For example, Carl Sagan has proposed a way of altering the atmosphere of Venus. ▽ The high surface temperature of Venus appears to be maintained by a greenhouse effect involving both the atmosphere and the clouds [Chapter 22]. Since the amounts of water in the atmospheres of the two planets seem to be roughly comparable, the great difference in temperature must be due at least in part to the fact that the terrestrial atmosphere has several thousand times less carbon dioxide than the Cytherean atmosphere. After the physical environment of Venus has been thoroughly investigated, and if indeed it proves to be lifeless, there will exist the prospect of microbiological planetary engineering.

▽ To prepare Venus for comfortable human habitation, it is necessary to lower the surface temperature and to increase the abundance of molecular oxygen. Both these ends could be accomplished, if a means were found to dissociate carbon dioxide into oxygen and elemental carbon. There is far too much carbon dioxide in the atmosphere for such a goal to be accomplished mechanically. Because of the very rapid growth rate of microorganisms in the absence of predators or competitors, the use of a living organism seems indicated. An organism is needed which can photosynthesize in the cooler parts of the atmosphere of Venus, according to the symbolic equation

467

$$CO_2 + H_2O + light \rightarrow [CH_2O] + O_2 .$$

The oxygen arises from the water; the symbol $[CH_2O]$ represents organic matter. Since the atmosphere is in convective equilibrium, the organisms would in time be carried to lower atmospheric levels where, because of the higher temperatures, they would be roasted and decomposed, ideally according to the symbolic equation

$$[CH_2O] + heat \rightarrow C + H_2O .$$

Although the oxygen is derived from water, the over-all effect would be to restore the water metabolized in photosynthesis to the atmosphere, and to dissociate carbon dioxide to carbon and oxygen. Since the clouds of Venus appear to be composed of water—probably even liquid water, in their lower parts—a suitable water supply for microorganisms seems to be available. The organisms would have to be nitrogen-fixers—that is, capable of removing molecular N_2 from the Cytherean atmosphere. It would also be useful if the organisms were highly temperature-resistant, and could survive temperatures as low as $-40°C$ ($-40°F$). The only photosynthetic, nitrogen-fixing, oxygen-evolving, and temperature-resistant microorganisms in wide abundance on the Earth are the blue-green algae, primarily of the Nostocaceae family.

▽ Before such a scheme can be seriously considered, we must know much more about the physical environment of Venus, and must be quite sure that the clouds are not previously inhabited by some indigenous Cytherean species. Before we can seed the clouds, we must know whether the algae could reproduce at the cloud level more rapidly than they would be destroyed by convection to the hotter, lower layers of the atmosphere; whether atmospheric convection can transport up from the surface the trace elements required for the reproduction of the organisms; and what the products of slow algal thermal decomposition might be. Ideally, we can envision the seeding of the upper Cytherean atmosphere with appropriately developed strains of Nostocaceae, after exhaustive studies of Venus have been performed. As the carbon dioxide content of the atmosphere falls, the greenhouse effect will be rendered less efficient, and the surface temperature will decline. After the atmospheric temperatures decline sufficiently, the decreasing rate of algal decomposition will reduce the water abundance, and hopefully permit the surface to cool below the boiling point of water. At this time, the original mechanism becomes inoperative, because the algae are no longer thermally decomposed; but surface photosynthesis then becomes possible. At somewhat lower temperatures, rain will reach the surface, and the inorganic production of carbonates will reduce the atmospheric carbon dioxide content still further. If we have properly understood the source of the high surface temperature, and if we can find microorganisms which will act in the desired fashion, it may be possible that in geologically short periods of time the temperature of Venus could be lowered; the CO_2 atmospheric content decreased; molecular oxygen introduced into the atmosphere; and liquid water formed on its surface for the first time. △ As an end result, the inhospitable planet Venus might become suitable for human habitation.

INTELLIGENT LIFE IN THE UNIVERSE

To discuss another possible modification of the cosmos by the activities of intelligent beings, consider the following question: Is it possible that in the future—perhaps the distant future—man could so change the solar system that his activities would be visible over interstellar distances? In Chapter 11, we discussed the difficulties in the detection of planets about even the nearest stars, with present techniques. But what of the future? Is it possible that someday we shall be able to conclude, from observed characteristics, that a star is accompanied by a planet populated by an advanced technical civilization? Let us consider some of the ideas of Constantin Edwardovich Tsiolkovskii, an illustrious Russian pioneer in problems of space exploration.

Three quarters of a century ago, this remarkable man suggested a plan for the rebuilding and reorganization of the solar system. In his book *Dreams of the Earth and Sky*, published in 1895, he pointed out that the Earth receives only 5×10^{-10} of the total flux of solar radiation. He speculated that eventually mankind would make use of all the heat and light of the Sun by colonizing the entire solar system. Tsiolkovskii suggested that first the asteroids be rebuilt. The intelligent beings of the future, he predicted, would control the motion of these small planets "in the same way that we drive horses." The energy necessary to maintain the inhabitants of the asteroids would come from "solar motors." Thus, we see that over 70 years ago, Tsiolkovskii predicted the invention of the solar battery, a device which is presently used to provide energy for space vehicles.

The transformed asteroids would form a chain of space cities. The construction materials would initially come from the asteroids themselves, "the mass of which would be dismantled in a day." ▽ Tsiolkovskii's ideas on the re-engineering and relocation of the asteroids have been echoed in recent years by the American engineer Dandridge Cole, of the General Electric Corporation. △ After the asteroidal material is exhausted, Tsiolkovskii envisions the rebuilding of the Moon. He allows several hundred years for this project. Then, the Earth and the larger planets would be reorganized. According to Tsiolkovskii, the entire transformation of the solar system would require hundreds of thousands—perhaps millions—of years. This plan would provide enough heat and light to support a population of 3×10^{23} manlike beings—approximately 10^{14} times more people than presently inhabit the Earth.

Although to his contemporaries the daring ideas of Tsiolkovskii seemed to be merely the daydreams of a provincial school-teacher, his brilliant foresight is readily appreciated today. The eminent American theoretical physicist Freeman J. Dyson, of the Institute for Advanced Study, Princeton, basing his theories on the achievements of contemporary science, has recently independently repeated many of Tsiolkovskii's ideas, without knowing anything of the Russian's work.

Dyson, in a most interesting article published in 1960, attempted to perform a quantitative analysis of the problem of rebuilding the solar system. He first discussed the fact that scientific and technological development takes place very rapidly, after a society has entered its technological phase. The timescale of such development is insignificant, compared with astronomical and geological timescales. Dyson concluded that the one important factor which restricts the scientific and technical development of an intelligent society is the limited available supply of matter and energy resources. At present, the material resources which can be exploited by man are limited roughly to the biosphere of the Earth, which has a mass ∇ estimated variously between 5×10^{17} and 5×10^{19} gm △—that is, less than 10^{-8} the mass of the Earth. The energy required by contemporary mankind per year is approximately equal to that which is liberated in the combustion of 1 to 2 billion tons of hard anthracite coal per year. In terms of heat, we find that contemporary man is expending an average of 3×10^{19} erg sec^{-1}. The Earth's resources of coal, oil, and other fossil fuels will be exhausted in a few centuries.

The question of our reserves of matter and energy becomes more acute when we consider the prospective long-term technological development of our society. Even if we assume that the average annual growth rate in production is only one-third of a percent (a very small figure, when compared to the annual growth rate ∇ of a few percent in modern industrial societies △), our productivity will double in about a century. In 1000 years, the rate of manufacture will increase by 20,000 times; and in 2500 years, by 10 billion times. This means that the energy requirements in 2500 years will be 3×10^{29} erg sec^{-1}, or approximately 0.01 percent of the entire luminosity of the Sun. This figure is approaching cosmic proportions. Will all of our energy resources have been exhausted by the time we achieve this level of productivity?

To answer this question, let us now consider the material resources which are conceivably available to mankind in the future. We shall—perhaps optimistically —assume that we will be able to achieve controlled thermonuclear reactions. The total amount of hydrogen in the Earth's hydrosphere is approximately 3×10^{23} grams, while the amount of deuterium is approximately 5×10^{19} grams. Deuterium would be the basic fuel of a thermonuclear reactor. The amount of energy released by reaction of all the available deuterium would be about 5×10^{38} ergs. In 2500 years, this amount of energy—still assuming an increase in production of one-third of a percent per annum—would be sufficient for only a 50-year period. Even if we assume that controlled thermonuclear fusion can eventually be fueled by ordinary hydrogen, and that 10 percent of the world's oceans can be utilized as an energy source—to burn more would probably be inexpedient—in 2500 years we would be able to provide only enough energy for another few thousand years.

Another possible energy source would be the direct utilization of solar radiation. Each second, approximately 2×10^{24} ergs of solar radiation fall upon the surface of the Earth. This is almost 100,000 times more than the current production of all forms of energy. Yet it is 100,000 times less than the estimated energy requirements for the year 4500 A.D. Thus, direct solar radiation is inadequate to support a stable and sustained increase in production of only one-third of a percent per annum, over a long period of time. From this discussion, we can conclude that the energy resources of the Earth are insufficient to fulfil the long-term requirements of a developing technological society.

Before considering this question further, let us make a slight digression. A

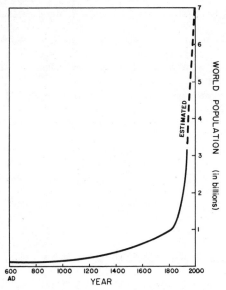

FIGURE 34–1. *Estimated past and extrapolated future rates of human population growth, planet Earth.*

hypercritical reader may claim that the above calculations are similar to the discussions of the English clergyman Thomas Malthus. This is, however, not the case. Malthus predicted that world population growth would outstrip the development of productive forces, and that this would lead to a progressive deterioration of living conditions. His proposed solution was that the poorer classes—that is, the working classes—lower their birthrate. Malthus' views are invalid, because in an intelligent, organized society, the increase of productive forces always outstrips the increase in population. The population of a nation is related, sometimes in a complex way, to its productivity, and in fact is ultimately determined by it. Our discussion of future energy budgets bears no relation to the Malthusian doctrine. We have been discussing only the possibilities of the increase in the productive capacities of a society, which is naturally limited to the material and energy resources available.

▽ The exponential increase in the population of the Earth during historical times is indicated schematically in Fig. 34–1. The required future productive capacity of our society is dramatically illustrated—assuming no major population self-limitation occurs—by extrapolation of the curve to the future. △

Let us ask another question: Will there in fact *be* any appreciable increase in the future productive capability of our society? What is the basis for assuming that mankind's progress will be directly related to an increase in his productive capacity?

Perhaps development will be in terms of qualitative, not quantitative, changes. These problems are philosophical in nature and cannot be discussed in detail here. However, I would like to state that I believe it to be impossible for a society to develop without a concurrent increase in production, both qualitatively and quantitatively. If an increase in productivity were eliminated, the society would eventually die. Note that if a society were to consciously interrupt its productive development, it would have to maintain a very precise level of production. Even the slightest progressive decrease would, after thousands of years reduce the technological potential to essentially nothing. Over these timescales, any civilization which consciously resolves to maintain a constant level of productivity would be balancing on a knife-edge.

Let us now return to the subject of the material resources available to a developing society. After reaching a high state of technical development, it would seem very natural that a civilization would strive to make use of energy and materials external to the planet of origin, but within the limits of the local solar system. Our star radiates 4×10^{33} ergs of energy each second, and the masses of the Jovian planets constitute the major potential source of material. Jupiter alone has a mass of 2×10^{30} grams. It has been estimated that about 10^{44} ergs of energy would be required to completely vaporize Jupiter. This is roughly equal to the total radiation output of the Sun over a period of 800 years.

According to Dyson, the mass of Jupiter could be used to construct an immense shell which would surround the Sun, and have a radius of about 1 A.U. (150 million kilometers). ▽ How thick would the shell of a Dyson sphere be? The volume of such a sphere would be $4\pi r^2 S$, where r is the radius of the sphere, 1 A.U., and S is its thickness. The mass of the sphere is just the volume times its density, ρ, and the mass available is approximately the mass of Jupiter. Thus, $4\pi r^2 \rho S = 2 \times 10^{30}$ grams. Thus, we find that $\rho S \simeq 200$ gm cm^{-2} △ of surface area would be sufficient to make the inner shell habitable. We recall that the mass of the atmosphere above each square centimeter of the Earth's surface is close to 1000 gm. ▽ If the over-all density of the shell were 1 gm cm^{-3} or slightly less, the thickness of the shell, S, would be a few meters. △ Man today, for all practical purposes, is a two-dimensional being, since he utilizes only the surface of the Earth. It would be entirely possible for mankind in the future—say, in 2500 to 3000 years—to create an artificial biosphere on the inner surface of a Dyson sphere. After man has accomplished this magnificent achievement, he would be able to use the total energy output of the Sun. ▽ Every photon emitted by the Sun would be absorbed by the Dyson sphere, and could be utilized productively. △ The inside surface area of the Dyson sphere would be approximately 1 billion times greater than the surface area of the Earth. The sphere could sustain a population great enough to fulfil the predictions made by Tsiolkovskii three quarters of a century ago.

We shall not at this time enter into a discussion of how such a sphere would be constructed, how it would rotate, or how we would guarantee that the inhabitants would not fall into the Sun. The fact is that the sphere would have different gravitational characteristics from those of a solid body. These problems, although complex, are not the principal problems. Dyson himself gave special attention to one interesting circumstance: A number of completely independent parameters—the mass of Jupiter, the thickness of an artificial biosphere, the total energy of the solar radiation, and the period of technological development—all, in Dyson's words,

> have consistent orders of magnitude. . . . It seems, then, a reasonable expectation that barring accidents, Malthusian pressures will ultimately drive an intelligent species to adopt some such efficient exploitation of its available resources. One should expect that within a few thousand years of its entering the stage of industrial development, any intelligent species should be found occupying an artificial biosphere which completely surrounds its parent star.

Up to this point, Dyson's speculations have been essentially the same as those of Tsiolkovskii, but based upon more recent scientific knowledge. At this point, Dyson introduces an idea novel ▽ even to Tsiolkovskii △: How will a civilization living on the inner surface of a sphere surrounding its star appear from outside? Dyson says:

> If the foregoing argument is accepted, then the search for extraterrestrial intelligent beings should not be confined to the neighborhood of visible stars. The most likely habitat for such beings would be a dark object having a size comparable to the Earth's orbit, and a surface temperature of 200 to 300°K. Such a dark object would be radiating as copiously as the star which is hidden inside it, but the radiation would be in the far infrared, at about 10μ wavelength.

If this were not the case, then the radiation produced by the star inside the shell would accumulate, and produce catastrophically high temperatures.

Since an extraplanetary civilization surrounded by a Dyson sphere would be a very powerful source of infrared radiation, and since the atmosphere of the Earth is transparent to radiation between 8 and 13μ, it would be possible to search for such infrared stars with existing telescopes on the Earth's surface. ▽ The sensitivity of contemporary infrared detectors is such that with the use of large telescopes, Dyson spheres could be detected over distances of hundreds of light-years even today. However, there is not necessarily any way of distinguishing a Dyson sphere detected at $8-13\mu$ from a natural object such as a protostar, contracting towards the main sequence, and emitting infrared radiation with the same intensity. If the sky were mapped in the infrared for possible Dyson spheres, each radiation source could then be investigated by other techniques for characteristic radiation of an intelligent species—for example, at the 21 cm radio frequency. △

It is also possible that Dyson civilizations might be detected by existing optical techniques.

> Such radiation might be seen in the neighborhood of a visible star, under either of two conditions: A race of intelligent beings might be unable to exploit fully the energy radiated by their star because of an insufficiency of accessible matter, or they might live in an artificial biosphere surrounding one star of a multiple

system, in which one or more component stars are unsuitable for exploitation and would still be visible to us. It is impossible to guess the probability that either of these circumstances could arise for a particular race of extraterrestrial intelligent beings, but it is reasonable to begin the search for infrared radiation of artificial origin by looking in the direction of nearby visible stars, and especially in the direction of stars which are known to be binaries with invisible companions.

Dyson's idea is notable for the fact that it presents a specific example of how the activity of an intelligent society might change a planetary system to such an extent that the transformation would be detectable over interstellar distances. But a Dyson sphere is not the only way a civilization can utilize the available energy resources of its planetary system. There are other sources which may be even more effective than the complete utilization of local solar radiation.

First we shall consider using the mass of the large planets as a fuel for thermonuclear reactors. The Jovian planets consist primarily of hydrogen. The mass of Jupiter is 2×10^{30} gm, and the store of energy which would be released from the conversion of this quantity of hydrogen into helium would be approximately 10^{49} ergs, a vast amount of energy comparable to that released in a supernova explosion. If this energy were liberated gradually, over a long period of time—for example, at a rate of 4×10^{33} erg sec^{-1}, comparable to the present solar luminosity—it would last for nearly 300 million years, a time span most likely greater than the life of the technical civilization itself.

Perhaps a highly developed civilization could also use a fraction of its own star as an energy source. For example, it might be possible to "borrow" a few percent of the solar mass without any significant decrease in luminosity. Certainly, we do not yet know the methods for arranging such a loan, but it would probably be accomplished gradually. The conversion of, say, 5×10^{31} gm of solar hydrogen —25 times more than the mass of Jupiter—would provide some 3×10^{50} ergs, an energy supply adequate to satisfy the requirements of a technical civilization for several billion years.

It is also conceivable, but much less likely, that such utilization of the mass of a star would occur at a more rapid pace, perhaps regulated so that the lifetime of the star would correspond to the lifetime of the civilization. The spectral characteristics of such a star would slowly vary. At the time that the star finally was turned off, the civilization would cease to exist. ▽ But while we can imagine such a cosmic Götterdämmerung, it is not likely to be staged often. △

If intelligent use is made of the enormous stores of energy available in the solar system, it would not be necessary to construct a Dyson sphere about the Sun. Assume, for example, that half the mass of the Jovian planets were used to construct artificial satellites, the "space cities" of Tsiolkovskii. These cities would be established in orbits close to the Sun. We may imagine thermonuclear reactors installed in these satellites and fueled by the remaining material in the Jovian planets. This picture preserves the essential direction of the development of a technical civilization envisioned in *Dreams of the Earth and Sky,* but it adds controlled thermonuclear reactions as an energy source.

Now, given these enormous controlled energy sources, civilizations could expand their activities on a much larger scale. We shall presently consider several additional ways in which a civilization might announce its presence over interstellar distances. These methods seem fantastic. We wish to emphasize that we are not saying that such methods are actually in existence; but the probability of their existence is not zero. ▽ And what we have encompassed as "fantastic" has declined progressively with the centuries. △ The fundamental point is that the possibilities open to advanced technical civilizations are almost unlimited.

▽ First, let us reconsider the possibility broached in Chapter 28, that a technical civilization may make its presence known by changing the spectrum of its star. We found there that the dumping of 10^5 tons or less of atoms not normally found in the star might be detectable over interstellar distances as anomalous absorption lines. A short-lived radioisotope such as technetium -43 was discussed. △ We should point out that due to convection in the upper layers of a stellar atmosphere, any artificial technetium introduced would be rapidly conveyed to deeper layers, where it would no longer be detectable. Therefore, the technetium would have to be dumped periodically, ▽ or placed in orbit about the star. △

▽ The production and transportation of such quantities of rare isotopes is of course expensive, from our point of view. But we have just been considering the nuclear conversion and transportation of much larger masses. △ It is even possible that coded information could be incorporated by this process. Thus, the massive dumping of unstable atoms into a stellar atmosphere would be a powerful way of transmitting signals isotropically throughout interstellar space.

Let us now give an even freer rein to our imaginations. We shall assume that a certain highly developed civilization finds itself in need of materials, especially heavy elements. In principle, these materials could be obtained by exploiting a nearby star in a colossal experiment—the production of an artificial supernova. How could this be accomplished?

The British astrophysicist Geoffrey Burbidge, of the University of California at San Diego, has made an exciting, although unsubstantiated, speculation concerning the possibility of a supernova chain reaction. He postulated that if a supernova were accidentally exploded in the nucleus of a galaxy, where the density of stars was millions of times greater than in the solar neighborhood, the resulting gamma-ray flux to nearby stars would be so great that exceedingly high temperatures would be generated in the outer layers of these stars. Such high temperatures might trigger a supernova explosion which would then be transferred to other neighboring stars, and a supernova chain reaction would be initiated. In this way, over a period of several hundred years, perhaps hundreds of millions of stars making up the nucleus of a galaxy might become supernovae.

We must also consider the possibility that an artificial supernova might be induced in a single star. Let us assume that a technical society possessed a highly advanced and extremely powerful laser, operating at gamma ray frequencies—with wavelengths about 10^{-10} cm, 1 Ångstrom unit. With an aperture diameter of 10 meters, such a laser would have a beam width only 5×10^{-9} of a second of arc. If the star in this experiment were 10 light years from the gamma ray source, the laser beam on the surface of the star would have a diameter of only 10 km. According to Burbidge's hypothesis, the flow of gamma radiation at the surface of the star must be approximately 10^{10} erg cm^{-2} sec^{-1}, in order to initiate a supernova explosion. To produce this gamma ray flux with a source 10 light years away, the power output of the laser installation would have to be 10^{12} kilowatts. This is 1000 times greater than the total power consumption of contemporary civilization. But for the Type II civilizations we have been discussing, this does not seem an excessively large figure.

We must bear in mind that life forms greatly in advance of ourselves may possess capabilities which are unknown to us. Perhaps they can channel other types of penetrating radiation, both electromagnetic and corpuscular, into extremely narrow beams. Since each star is a vast potential source of nuclear energy, such beams might serve as the match which ignites the powder keg.

Let us speculate further. Would it be possible, through the controlled use of radiation, to modulate the course of stellar nuclear reactions, increasing or decreasing the pulse of the stars? A star regulated by remote control could become an effective source of energy for a Type II civilization. The supernova could be a quarry, where heavy elements are made and mined for the use of the civilization. Might there in fact actually be any connection between supernovae and the activities of highly developed technical civilizations? No—it is very likely that supernovae, even supernovae of Type I, result from natural phenomena which are still unknown to us. This example merely serves to illustrate the boundless ways in which intelligent life might manifest itself in the universe.

Could a highly developed civilization ▽ —one which we have called a Type III civilization— △ change the characteristics of entire galaxies? For example, could the emission of the radio galaxies ▽ and quasars [see Chapters 3 and 9] △ be ultimately of biological origin? This brings us to a critical question: Are any of the phenomena which we observe in the universe inexplicable in terms of the physics of non-living matter? Can some phenomena be understood only if we invoke the intervention of living organisms in technical civilizations? We cannot yet answer this question. If none of the many unexplained phenomena known today can be traced to some form of intelligent life, it might follow that life has not yet reached an extremely high level of development ▽ —say, between Type II and Type III civilizations— △ anywhere in the universe. ▽ But if other civilizations are common, many of them must be much older than our own; △ the absence of unexplained phenomena could then be a serious argument in favor of the melancholy theory that we are alone in the universe. ▽ Any such anomalous phenomena will be carefully investigated, because they are promising leads to new physical phenomena; the quasars, for example, may be due to an aggregation of matter so dense that only the theory of general relativity can be used to describe it. But the failures at purely physical understanding will perhaps be of even greater interest. △

Now let us consider the interesting ideas of the Soviet astrophysicist N. S.

Kardashev, of the Sternberg Astronomical Institute ∇ —ideas which we have already touched upon in Chapter 27. △ Assume that a highly developed civilization which has achieved mastery over all its interplanetary space—either by the construction of a Dyson sphere, or by thermonuclear-powered space cities— decides to broadcast isotropic signals into interstellar space. Dyson proposed that ∇ infrared radiation would necessarily be emitted by △ the sphere surrounding the central star. This, however, would be a most uneconomical means of signaling. For a given amount of power, the most efficient medium would be radio waves, since they would be detectable over greater distances. As we mentioned in Chapter 27, a radio signal can be very narrow-banded, and also easily modulated, so that an almost unlimited potential is available in terms of information transmittance.

Let us assume that such a civilization decides to use a portion of its energy resources for the purpose of contacting extraplanetary civilizations; and further, that this radiation is transmitted isotropically. It would be extremely difficult to construct a large transmitter for conveying radio waves to all directions. It would be much more reasonable to construct a number of smaller transmitters and place them throughout the planetary system.

Such an isotropic signal could be detected over a range $d = (WA/4\pi kT)^{1/2} \times (\tau/\Delta f)^{1/4}$, where W is the power output of the transmitters; A is the surface area of the receiver antenna; T is the noise temperature of the receiver; τ is the integration time of the recording device; $k = 1.38 \times 10^{-16}$ erg $(K°)^{-1}$ is Boltzmann's constant; and Δf is the bandwidth of the receiver, which depends in turn on the bandwidth of the transmitter. This formula is very similar to the expression for d mentioned in Chapter 27, where the transmitter antenna had a high directivity. The wavelength does not enter into the formula, but is assumed to be close to 21 cm. We shall further assume that a highly organized civilization will use about 0.1 percent of its power resources for interstellar communication. For example, let us suppose that a Type II civilization is distributed on a Dyson sphere surrounding a star similar to our Sun. Then $W = 4 \times 10^{30}$ erg sec^{-1}. Setting $A = 400$ meters^2, $\Delta f = 10^6$ c.p.s., $\tau = 1$ sec, and $T = 100°K$, we find that $d = 4 \times 10^{22}$ cm, or about 13,000 parsecs. This is considerably in excess of the distance from the solar system to the Galactic center.

Thus, an isotropic radio signal of the power we have assumed could reach out to the limits of the Galaxy. Furthermore, by making the bandwidth Δf sufficiently narrow, it would be possible in principle to establish intergalactic radio communications.

For this purpose, it would be expedient to use a highly directional beam width. For example, assume that such a civilization in our Galaxy wished to send a signal to M 31, the great galaxy in Andromeda, using the same over-all power, $W = 4 \times 10^{30}$ erg sec^{-1}. The angular dimension of M 31, seen from our Galaxy, is about 2°. Therefore, it would be useful to use a system of antennas with an angular dimension of 2° in the main lobe [see Figure 27-2]. With this antenna, the power gain, G, would be 10,000 times that of an isotropic radiator. Therefore, the effective contact distance would be increased by a factor of 100. Using the same values for A, T, τ, and Δf as given above, we find that $d = 1.3 \times 10^6$ parsecs, or twice the distance to the great galaxy in Andromeda.

INTELLIGENT LIFE AS A FACTOR ON THE COSMIC SCALE   477

For contacting remote galaxies, even more highly directional antennas could be used. It is possible to diminish Δf still further. Thus, there is the possibility of sending narrow-beam, narrow bandwidth signals of detectable power to the very limits of the metagalaxy. ▽ For isotropic broadcast of radio signals over such distances, the power level would have to be very much greater, and a Type III civilization in the sense of Kardashev [Chapter 27] would be required. △

Will the receiving civilizations respond by showering us with replies? We recall that a two-way radio contact with M 31 would take 3 million years. Only a very long-lived civilization would be in a position to send a query and intercept a reply. However, intergalactic radio contact does have a singular advantage over interstellar contact: the signal would be directed simultaneously at several hundred billion stars, rather than at one particular star. The probability of contacting a civilization out of this vast number of stars would be much greater than if we were to send signals toward but one star.

In a short time, Kardashev and Paschenko, of the Sternberg Astronomical Institute, Moscow, will be attempting to detect signals of artificial origin, using a highly sensitive receiver which operates in the 21 cm waveband and which is capable of a smooth frequency variation. The anticipated power of the signals should be relatively great. Consequently, large, highly directional antennae are not required. A negative result from this search could possibly mean that our Galaxy does not contain highly developed civilizations with power resources $\sim 10^{33}$ erg sec^{-1}. Particular interest will be centered on attempts to detect signals from M 31. ▽ No similar plans for the extension or elaboration of Project Ozma have been announced in the United States. △

35

Artificial intelligence and galactic civilizations

Gilgamesh, whither rovest thou?
The life thou pursuest thou shalt not find.
When the gods created mankind,
Death for mankind they set aside,
Life in their own hands retaining . . .
Do we build a house for ever?

Epic of Gilgamesh (third millennium B.C.)

In our final chapter, we shall consider several questions, some of a philosophical nature. The discussion will continue to be speculative in intent.

▽ We have mentioned several times the possibility that the lifetime of a technical civilization, is not indefinitely long. △ It has been suggested that the thesis of a finite lifetime of technical civilizations is a sermon on pessimistic materialism. However, I believe that the combination of the words "pessimistic" and "materialism" is a contradiction in terms. Materialism is an objective analysis of the material world outside of and independent of our own consciousnesses. It is an attempt at an objective coping with the complexities of the universe. It is meaningless to label any particular law of nature as either pessimistic or optimistic. Even an attempt to comprehend the language of nature is a reason for genuine optimism; but ignorance and apathy go hand in hand with pessimism and obscurantism.

The acceptance of our individual mortality is no cause for pessimism. Why should it be any more pessimistic to assume that even societies of intelligent beings do not live forever? Just as the death of one individual does not obstruct the progress of society, the death of civilization on one small planet does not imply the end of intelligent life in the universe. Just as the activity of each individual can introduce a definite, although small, contribution to society, a given planetary civilization may make a contribution to the general development of intelligent life in the universe. And finally, just as the participation of the individual in society would be impossible without some sort of communication, the contribution of one planet to the development of intelligent life in the universe as a whole cannot take place without interstellar communications.

▽ Perhaps many young technical societies, like young men, are unmindful of the end of life because it seems so distant in time, and because there is so much yet to do. But when men are older, the thought of death is not so fearsome, and the unfinished tasks are somehow fewer. We live in a time when the thought of violent and accidental death of our civilization is a legitimate cause for anxiety. But perhaps an elder civilization, long past the problems of infantile societies, will willingly embrace the Elysian dreams of the lotus-eaters, and sink into an eternal sleep. △

In the *Dialectics of Nature,* Frederick Engels concluded, in the last century, that the lifetime for intelligent life on any particular planet is finite, and that this is an inevitable consequence of the development of the universe. He wrote:

> It is an eternal cycle in which matter moves, a cycle that certainly only completes its orbit in periods of time for which our terrestrial year is no adequate measure, a cycle in which the time of highest development, the time of organic life and still more, that of the life of beings conscious of nature and of themselves, is

just as narrowly restricted as the space in which life and self-consciousness came into operation; a cycle in which every finite mode of existence of matter, whether it be sun or nebular vapour, single animal or genus of animals, chemical combination or dissociation, is equally transient, and where nothing is eternal but eternally changing, eternally moving matter and the laws, according to which it moves and changes. But however often and however relentlessly this cycle is completed in time and space, however many millions of suns and earths may arise and pass away, however long it may take before the conditions of organic life arise, however innumerable the organic beings that have to arise and to pass away before animals with a brain capable of thought are developed from their midst, and for a short span of time find conditions suitable for life only to be exterminated later without mercy, we have the certainty that matter remains eternally the same in all its transformations, that none of its attributes can ever be lost, and therefore also that with the same iron necessity that it will exterminate on the earth its higher creation the thinking mind, it must somewhere else and at another time again produce it.

If the lifetime of a technical civilization is limited only by astronomical factors, then civilizations might continue for several billions of years—a period which we might be tempted to describe as "eternal"—and the probability would be high that intelligent life is almost ubiquitous. But as we have seen in previous chapters, the lifetimes of technical civilizations may well be limited. The majority of investigators believe that this timescale may be very short $\triangledown$ compared with the age of the Galaxy. $\triangle$ However, we believe that this question must be reevaluated in the light of recent advances in cybernetics and in molecular biology.

In Part III of this book, we have repeatedly used the words "intelligent life," taking it for granted that a definition of this term was self-evident. But what in fact do we mean by "intelligent life"? Is a being intelligent if it possesses the ability to think? If so, what do we mean by "thinking"?

Human thought has been considered, $\triangledown$ until very recently, $\triangle$ the only form of creative thinking known to mankind. Thus, any definition of "thinking" and "intelligence" inevitably leads to a description of the activities of men, or of the specific functions of the human brain.

But the Soviet physicist A. N. Kolmogorov has emphasized that such a definition is unsatisfactory in the light of current knowledge for two reasons: As astronomical and space exploratory investigations progress, there is the distinct possibility that we shall encounter on other planets entities which have all the essential attributes of life and thought but which are nonetheless essentially different from terrestrial forms of life. Second, there is now the possibility of the duplication of any complex material system, $\triangledown$ and in particular, the artificial construction of a thinking machine. $\triangle$ There is, accordingly, a great need for a functional definition of the term "thought" which is not confined to our preconceived notions about the physical nature of this process.

A systematic approach to such a functional view of life and thought leads us to a startling conclusion which, in our opinion, is of substantial significance to the problem of intelligent life in the universe. Kolmogorov writes:

. . . A model of the operational processes and organization of a material system must be constructed of other material elements in a new system which possesses the same essential characteristics of organization as the system which is being modeled. Therefore, a sufficiently complete model of a living being, in all fairness, must be called a living being, and a model of a thinking being must be called a thinking being. . . . The following questions are of general interest:

Could machines reproduce themselves? And in the course of such reproduction, could progressive evolutionary changes occur which would lead to the production of new machines which are progressively more perfect ▽ [that is, better adapted to their environment] △ than their predecessors?

Could these machines experience emotions? Would they feel desires; would they be capable of solving original problems which their creators did not build into them?

Negative answers to questions of this nature are frequently the result of the following misconceptions: (a) a too-limited definition of the concept of "machine"; (b) an idealistic interpretation of the concept "thought," by which it is easy to prove that not only machines, but also human beings could not think.

. . . However, it is important to understand that within the framework of materialist ideology there are no well-founded arguments against a positive answer to our questions. Such a positive answer is in accord with contemporary views on the origin of life, and on the physical basis of consciousness. . . .

The possibility that complete living beings can be constructed out of discrete units capable of information processing and control does not contradict the principles of dialectic materialism.

Kolmogorov cautions against oversimplified specifications of the basic requirements for the synthesis of artificial intelligent beings. At present, we understand but a small portion of man's conscious activity. Only the mechanisms of conditioned reflex and of formal logic are understood to any degree. Much further work remains to be done on an objective definition in terms of information theory of the intricacies of the creative activity of man and other aspects of his highly developed nervous system.

Kolmogorov continues:

. . . A serious objective study of the higher neural activity of man is a necessary link in the development of such mathematical humanism. As science has developed, the illusions of mankind have been progressively eroded. At the stage of half-truths and half-knowledge, these so-called "destructive conclusions" often become arguments against science itself, in favor of irrationalism and idealism. Thus, Darwin's insights into the origins of species, and Pavlov's studies of the higher nervous system have been described as degrading the higher capacities of man, debasing his ability to create moral and aesthetic ideals. Analogously in our time, fear that man is no better than a "cold-hearted" machine has produced a psychological argument for vitalism and irrationalism.

Artificial mechanical beings—robots—are a favorite subject of science fiction writers. They are usually pictured as an assemblage of nuts and bolts with the external shape of a man, but powered by electron tubes. In his play *R.U.R.*, the remarkable Czechoslovakian writer Karel Čapek coined the word "robot" to describe an artificial, manlike being, made of organic molecules. ▽ In Western science fiction, the word "robot" has evolved into an inorganic, usually metallic artificial being, while the word "android" has been used for an organic simulacrum of a human being. Actually, Čapek's original conception of the robot and the contemporary idea of an android have both been anticipated by the golem, an artificial human being which, according to Jewish folk legend, was created by the Rabbi of Prague to perform labors on the Sabbath from which Jews were forbidden by Biblical law. △ It is probable that after mankind has knowledge and control of the synthetic pathways for the production of proteins, under the guidance of the nucleic acids, artificial living organisms will have a natural external appearance. But it is premature to predict just how such artificial beings will look. We reemphasize that contemporary terrestrial science and technology cannot yet synthesize even the simplest living beings.

▽ In Chapter 14, we estimated that the number of possible combinations of the approximately 4×10^9 nucleotide pairs in human chromosomes was $4^{4 \times 10^9}$. This corresponds to approximately 10^{10} bits of information contained in the genetic code, and required for the construction of a human being. We can show that the information content of the human brain is probably even greater than the information content of the genetic material. There are something like 10^{10} neurons in the brain, each of which has probably more than 100 connections (dendrites) with other neurons. It is believed that the information content of the brain is at least in part stored through the intermediation of such neurons, although additional non-electrical information repositories—for example, proteins, or RNA, or even the configuration of membranes of cells in the brain—may be more significant. The number of possible arrangements of 10^{10} neurons, each with 100 dendrites, is $10^{2 \times 10^{10}}$, corresponding to an information content of some 10^{13} bits. Even if the great majority of the neurons in the brain are redundant or inactive, the information content of the human brain is far in excess of the information content of the genetic material. This is another way of saying that we are not born with all we know, and that the great bulk of our knowledge is acquired during our lifetimes.

▽ The characteristic mass of a human brain is ~ 1300 grams. We may consider a typical neuron to be cylindrical in shape, with a radius of a few microns, and a length of perhaps 1 mm. The volume of a typical neuron is therefore about $\pi(3 \times 10^{-4} \text{ cm})^2 (10^{-1} \text{ cm}) \simeq 3 \times 10^{-8} \text{ cm}^3$. Since neurons, like other biological material, have a density of about 1 gm cm^{-3}, each neuron has a mass of about 3×10^{-8} gm. 10^{10} neurons have, therefore, a mass of about 300 gm, and we see that a major fraction of the total mass of the brain is composed of neurons.

▽ The transistors which, in modern computing machines, are the analogues of the neurons in our brains, have masses considerably larger than 3×10^{-8} gm. Therefore, a computing machine with the same number of connecting units as the human brain would have to be much more massive. For example, if each transistor had a mass of $\frac{1}{100}$ of a gram, the total mass of an equivalent computing machine would be 10^8 grams, or 100 tons. We see that the human brain is marvelously microminiaturized.

▽ Many scientists believe that the complexities of human thinking are simply the consequence of the complexities of the interactions among 10^{10} units. Among organisms on Earth, there is a general, although by no means complete, correspondence between brain mass and intelligence; an even more striking correlation exists between intelligence and the ratio of brain mass to total body mass. It is in this context that the large mass of the dolphin brain—comparable to the mass of the human brain—is notable (see Chapter 29). If the information content of intelligent beings on other planets is stored in units of mass comparable to our neurons, then it is clear that they must be approximately as massive as we, or even larger. There is no general tendency for neurons to be of smaller mass in what we like to think of as the more advanced species on the planet Earth.

▽ But we can imagine other possibilities. Suppose, for example, that information is coded not on the level of neurons, but on the molecular level, and that provisions are made for the long-term stability of these information-carrying molecules. In the genetic material, such molecular information stores are of course used, and we have already mentioned that there is some evidence that molecules such as RNA are involved as a molecular basis of memory in animals and perhaps in human beings. We can imagine a crystal lattice, in which the information is stored by atoms, in terms of the position they occupy within the lattice. If there are 10 possible atoms for each position, we require about 2×10^{10} total atoms to reproduce the information content of the human brain. A cube containing 2×10^{10} atoms has about $(2 \times 10^{10})^{1/3} = 5000$ atoms on a side. The atoms in a crystal are usually a few Å apart. Therefore, such a cubical crystal could be 10^{-4} cm, or about 1 micron on a side. Some examples of coding miniaturization in contemporary technology—not yet up to the efficiency of our cube—are displayed in Figures 35–1 and 35–2.

▽ This example of the cube, due to Philip M. Morrison, is probably the extreme in the compression of information. It would be very difficult to extract information contained within the crystal without disrupting the information contained in the exterior atoms of the crystal. But such examples do illustrate that organisms can conceivably be considerably smaller than we and yet contain a vastly greater quantity of information. If our intelligence is characterized by an information storage capability of, say, 10^{13} bits, what will we have to say to a member of an advanced civilization with a storage capability of 10^{20} bits?

▽ These considerations suggest not only that beings may exist elsewhere in the universe with intelligence substantially beyond our own, but also that we may be able to construct such a being ourselves. △ Of course, many difficulties would have to be overcome before an artificial intelligent being could be constructed. The greatest difficulty is not the storage of information, but the development of the very complex program that represents the actual operation of the brain and associated nervous system, which in turn represents thought. It is possible in principle to build a complex machine which would solve problems through the use of smaller, ancillary machines, into which simpler problems could be introduced. However, such cascaded machines appear to be cumbersome and slow. At present, it is not clear just how these difficulties will be overcome.

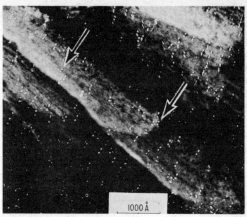

FIGURE 35–1. *A photograph taken with an electron microscope of special films of mica, a single crystal thick. The magnification is 800,000 times. The holes to which the arrows point are produced in the mica by radioactive decay. Each hole is 50–100 Å in diameter. Similar techniques may be extremely useful in microminiaturizing information coding. (Courtesy: Dr. H. Fernandez-Moran, University of Chicago.)*

▽ Great progress has already been made in the construction of machines sufficiently complex to learn by experience and to show signs of creative thinking. Computing machines today can perform in a few seconds mathematical problems which previously would have taken a team of mathematicians decades. There is every reason to believe that artificial intelligence will be increasingly pervasive in the future development of our civilization. △ Cybernetics, molecular biology, and neurophysiology together will some day very likely be able to create artificial intelligent beings which hardly differ from men, except for being significantly more advanced. Such beings would be capable of self-improvement, and probably would be much longer-lived than conventional human beings.

One proposed cause for the aging process of organisms is the gradual accumulation of imperfections in the genetic code over the lifetime of the individual. ▽ As time progresses, more and more nonsense information is transmitted to the cytoplasm (see Chapter 14), and the proper functioning of the cell is impaired. But the information repositories and coding procedures of artificial organisms could be much more durable and stable than those of contemporary organisms. △

The division of intelligent life into two categories—natural and artificial—may eventually prove to be meaningless. We may anticipate the synthesis of body parts. For example, we all know that some artificial body parts, such as teeth, are widely used today. ▽ Partial substitutes for the lenses of our eyes have been common for some centuries, and today we are witnessing the very rapid development of artificial hearts, lungs, kidneys, and other organs. △ The intelligent beings of the future may be made largely of artificial organs. ▽ Is it therefore out of the

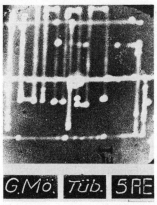

Figure 35–2. *Upper: Photograph taken with an electron microscope of an ultra-miniaturized electronic circuit pattern. Is is produced by photo-engraving with an electron microbeam on special ultra-fine photographic film. The widths of the lines are 500–1,000 Å in diameter, and the magnification is 10,000 times. Lower: Miniaturized letters less than 1 micron high engraved on thin collodion film, using electron microbeam probes. The writing is produced with an electron microscope (after G. Möllenstedt and R. Speidel, Physik. Bl. 16, 192, 1960).* (*Courtesy: Dr. H. Fernandez-Moran, University of Chicago.*)

question that the brains of our descendants may also be artificial, so that vast quantities of information may be made accessible without a tortuous learning process? Perhaps in the future we shall be able to plug in modular units containing the entire body of knowledge of specialized areas, which we may then unplug and return to our library when no longer of immediate use. △ In principle, we can anticipate the construction of highly organized, intelligent, self-improving, and non-anthropomorphic forms of life.

We have mentioned the possibility that the artificial intelligent beings of the future may be very long-lived. ▽ Their civilizations might be vastly longer-lived than civilizations like our own. △ Such long lifetimes could be very advantageous for interstellar contact among advanced communities. The sluggishness of two-way radio communication over interstellar distances tends to make such contact unsatisfactory for beings with lifetimes measured in decades. But for very long-lived beings, such communication would be much more interesting. Further, such beings would be able to undertake interstellar flights over vast distances at sub-relativistic velocities ▽ without the use of metabolic inhibitors. △ Perhaps highly specialized beings could be constructed specifically for such flights of long duration. These beings would be capable of enduring the hardships of the flight, and of implementing the tasks awaiting them at the end of the journey. It would be impossible to draw a clear distinction between such specialized automatic machines, artificial intelligent living beings ▽ and natural advanced organisms of an exotic type. △

It is possible for intelligent life in the universe to make fundamental qualitative transformations of itself. ▽ Major improvements in the lifetimes of advanced technical civilizations and of the organisms which compose them, and qualitatively different advances in their intelligence, make the prospect of successful interstellar contact much larger. △

▽ Let us now consider the possibilities more in consonance with the discussion of the beginning of this chapter. Perhaps technical civilizations are nowhere able to construct long-lived artificial beings of vast intelligence; or perhaps, while they are capable, the lifetimes of the initial technical civilizations are so short that a society of intelligent artificial beings is never able to develop. △ Under these circumstances, could an advanced civilization create a large artificial satellite containing electronic equipment capable of transacting interstellar radio communications for periods of millions of years or longer? Such a satellite, launched into circular orbit high above the planet of origin, could have a life span of hundreds of millions of years. It is possible that we have an example of such a moon in our own solar system (see Chapter 26); and in fact, when I first developed the hypothesis that the moons of Mars may be of artificial origin, I had such a function in mind. The energy source for the equipment aboard the satellite could be either the radiation flux of the local sun or controlled thermonuclear fusion. The radio transmitters aboard the satellite would transmit modulated signals according to a pre-programmed plan; answers to these signals could be recorded, ▽ and appropriate responses automatically devised, according to program. △ In this way, two-way automatic radio contact among Galactic civilizations could be established.

There are, of course, formidable technical problems which must be solved before such a satellite would be feasible. The automatic equipment must function stably and be protected against meteors over immense periods of time.

There are three primary advantages for interstellar contact that an artificial satellite has over a station on a planetary surface. ▽ First, the satellite is capable of transmission at frequencies which are absorbed by the planetary atmosphere or ionosphere. △ Second, the lifetime of the satellite could be much longer than the lifetime of the civilization which constructed it. Such a satellite might orbit its planet for millions of years after the local civilization had perished. Finally, in the epoch of decay and destruction of the parent civilization, very likely the safest place for such a station would be aboard a satellite. Here, the instruments would be protected not only from wars, but also from the destructive action of wind and water, and from geological changes on the surface of the planet. A large instrumented artificial satellite might be able to transmit the treasures of science and the heritage of culture of a dead civilization into the cosmos for hundreds of millions of years. We draw upon the knowledge and insights of men long dead through the books which they once wrote. Is it not possible that civilizations throughout the universe also draw upon the knowledge and insights of civilizations long vanished? If some technical societies have devised methods for transmitting information to space for extremely long periods of time, longer than their own life spans, the probability of contact among Galactic civilizations is immeasurably enhanced.

Bibliography

The following references are given in an order which approximates the introduction of the topics in this book. Only a few of these are written primarily for specialists in the field, and the more difficult ones are starred.

1. A masterly discussion of a wide range of topics in introductory chemistry, physics, biology and astronomy—highly recommended to the reader with little previous science background—is *Knowledge and Wonder* by Victor Weisskopf (Anchor Books, 1962).

2.* Many of the most exciting contemporary scientific research endeavors are described in a collection of papers presented at a meeting commemorating the 100th anniversary of the founding of the United States National Academy of Sciences: *The Scientific Endeavor* (Rockefeller Institute Press, 1965).

3. An intriguing essay on pseudoscience, including a short description of the flying saucer cult is *Fads and Fallacies in the Name of Science* by Martin Gardner (Dover Publications, New York, 1957).

4. Flying saucers are comprehensively discussed and concluded to be exclusively misapprehended natural objects in *The World of Flying Saucers: A Scientific Examination of a Major Myth of the Space Age,* by Donald H. Menzel and Lyle B. Boyd (Doubleday, 1963).

5. Some of Chapter 2 of the present work is based upon the article "Unidentified Flying Objects," by Carl Sagan, written for the 1967 edition of the *Encyclopedia Americana.*

6. Perhaps the most restrained book, despite occasional errors of fact and interpretation, which concludes that some flying saucers may be extraterrestrial space vehicles is *Anatomy of a Phenomenon: Unidentified Objects in Space—A Scientific Appraisal,* by Jacques Vallee (Henry Regnery Co., Chicago, 1965).

Part I—The Universe

7. An excellent introduction to astronomy, particular to stellar and galactic studies, is the introductory college textbook, *Exploration of the Universe* by George Abell (Holt, Rinehart and Winston, 1964).

8. A very clear introductory discussion of the same subject, designed for the layman and including a discussion of quasars, is *The Universe,* Isaac Asimov (Walker and Company, New York, 1966).

9. Somewhat more detailed and semi-quantitative is *The Universe* by Otto Struve (M. I. T. Press, Cambridge, Massachusetts, 1962).

10. Another excellent introductory astronomy textbook is *Elementary Astronomy* by Otto Struve, Beverly Lynds, and Helan Pillans (Oxford University Press, 1959).

11. A clear exposition of a variety of astronomical topics, only slightly out of date, is contained in *Frontiers of Astronomy* by Fred Hoyle (Harper, 1955).

12. The historical aspects of astronomy are treated in *The History of Astronomy* by A. Pannekoek (John Wiley & Sons, 1961).

13. The interstellar medium is treated in comprehensive, popular fashion in *Physics of Interstellar Space* by S. B. Pikelner [Foreign Languages Publishing House, Moscow, 1961]. This book is published in English.

14. An up-to-date discussion of the origin of the elements is contained in the article by W. H. Fowler, in reference 2.

15.* Many of Shklovskii's contributions to radio astronomy are summarized in *Cosmic Radio Waves* by I. S. Shklovskii (Harvard University Press, 1960).

16.* The best contemporary book on stellar evolution is *Structure and Evolution of the Stars,* by Martin Schwarzschild (Princeton University Press, 1958).

17.* A good introductory text on stellar atmospheres is *Introduction to Astrophysics: The Stars* by Jean Dufay, translated by Owen Gingerich (Dover, 1964).

18. A superb picture folio of galaxies photographed at Mt. Wilson and Palomar Observatories with an accompanying discussion of their evolution is contained in *The Hubble Atlas of Galaxies* by Alan Sandage, Publication 618 of the Carnegie Institution of Washington, D.C., 1961.

19.* Stimulating and recent discourse on many of the later topics of Part I can be found in *Galaxies, Nuclei and Quasars* by Fred Hoyle (Harper, 1965).

20. Perhaps the best popular discussion of cosmology, which very successfully explains sophisticated concepts to the layman, is *The Mystery of the Expanding Universe* by William Bonner (Macmillan, 1964).

21. A novel discussion of both special and general relativity which begins with elementary algebra and works up to quantitative discussions of the curvature of space, etc., is *The Einstein Theory of Relativity: A Trip to the Fourth Dimension* by Lillian R. Lieber and Hugh Gray Lieber (Holt, Rinehart and Winston, New York, 1945).

22. A charming popular excursion into cosmology, relativity and quantum theory is *Mr. Tompkins in Paperback* by George Gamow (Cambridge University Press, 1965).

23. Googols, googolplexes and other mathematical delights can be discovered in *Mathematics and the Imagination* by Edward Kasner and James R. Newman (Simon and Schuster, 1953).

24.* A convenient source of both historical and modern views on the origin of the solar system is the symposium proceedings: *Origin of the Solar System* by Robert Jastrow and A. G. W. Cameron (Academic Press, New York, 1963).

25. A Soviet view in English on the origin of the solar system can be found in *Origin of the Earth and Planets* by B. J. Levin (Foreign Languages Publishing House, Moscow, 1956).

26. A fascinating pictorial discussion of the scale of the universe is *Cosmic View: The Universe in Forty Jumps* by Kees Boeke (John Day, 1957).

Part II—Life in the Universe

27. An up-to-date discussion of extraterrestrial life, written over a period of two years by 66 scientists in various disciplines is *Biology and the Exploration of Mars* (U.S. National Academy of Sciences, Washington, D.C. 1966). The discussion includes questions of the origin and nature of life, environments in the solar system, evidence for life on Mars and the strategy of Martian exploration.

28. Many important articles on the origin of life and related topics are collected in *Extraterrestrial Life: An Anthology and Bibliography* (U.S. National Academy of Sciences, Washington, D.C., 1966). It includes a classic paper by J. B. S. Haldane, and the most complete bibliography in print on the subjects of Parts II and III of the present book.

29. Questions of organic chemistry used in contemporary molecular biology are well introduced in *A Direct Entry to Organic Chemistry,* by John Read (Harper Torchbooks, 1960).

30.* A modern classic on molecular biology by one of the leaders in the field is *Molecular Biology of the Gene,* by James D. Watson (W. A. Benjamin, Inc., 1965).

31. A more elementary treatment of the same subject is *The Genetic Code,* by Isaac Asimov (Signet Science Library, 1962).

32. One of the best introductions to cell biology is *Cell Structure and Function* by A. G. Loewy and Philip Siekevitz (Holt, Rinehart, and Winston, 1963).

33. Highly recommended is *The Molecular Basis of Evolution* by C. R. Anfinsen (John Wiley, 1963).

34. Physical and biological aspects of living systems, including the question of fitness of the environment, are treated in *Time's Arrow and Evolution* by Harold Blum (Princeton University Press, 2nd edition, 1961).

35. A recent introductory discussion by a pioneer in the field is *Life: Its Nature, Origin and Development,* by A. I. Oparin (Oliver and Boyd, London, 1961). See also references 27 and 28.

36. Another popular discussion of the origin of life is *The Dawn of Life,* by J. H. Rush (New American Library, 1962).

37.* The proceedings of a lively symposium on the origin of life, at which the pioneers, A. I. Oparin and J. B. S. Haldane, both participated, is *The Origins of Prebiological Systems,* edited by S. W. Fox (Academic Press, 1965).

38. A basic popular discussion of evolution which provides an excellent modern companion to Darwin's "Origin of Species" is *The Meaning of Evolution* by George Gaylord Simpson (Yale University Press, 1949).

39. Two exciting excursions into biology and evolution are *The Immense Journey,* by Loren Eiseley (Random House, 1957), and

40. *Nature and Man's Fate* by Garrett Hardin (Mentor, 1959).

41. The standard popular introductory text on the planets is *Earth, Moon and Planets,* revised edition, by Fred L. Whipple (Harvard University Press, 1963).

42.* A more technical interdisciplinary discussion, now slightly out of date, is *The Atmospheres of Mars and Venus,* edited by W. W. Kellogg and Carl Sagan (National Academy of Sciences, National Research Council, Publication 944, Washington, D.C., 1961).

43.* An up-to-date recent symposium, including results of the Mariner IV mission, is *Proceedings of the Caltech-J.P.L. Lunar and Planetary Conference,* edited by Harrison Brown (available from the Jet Propulsion Laboratory, Pasadena, California, 1966). This conference also covers studies of the moon.

44. An introduction to the earth as a planet can be found in *The Earth and Its Atmosphere,* edited by D. R. Bates (Basic Books, 1957).

45.* On a more technical level, see *Study of the Earth: Readings in Geological Science,* edited by J. F. White (Prentice Hall, 1962).

46.* The origin of some features of our own environment, related to other planets in the solar system, is covered in the symposium volume *The Origin and Evolution of Atmospheres and Oceans,* edited by P. J. Brancazio and A. G. W. Cameron (John Wiley, 1964).

47.* A comprehensive discussion of lunar problems, including questions of its origin, is *Measure of the Moon* by Ralph Baldwin (University of Chicago Press, 1963).

48.* An earlier discussion of the moon and planets, with particular attention to questions of origin is *The Planets* by Harold C. Urey (Yale University Press, 1952).

49. An exceptionally well-illustrated layman's introduction to planetary astronomy is *Planets* by Carl Sagan and Jonathan Leonard (Life Science Library, 1966).

50. See also, *Pictorial Guide to the Planets,* Joseph H. Jackson (Thomas Y. Crowell, 1965).

51.* An excellent technical anthology on the solar system is *Planets and Satellites,* edited by G. P. Kuiper and B. M. Middlehurst (University of Chicago Press, 1961).

52. A superb collection of photographs of Mars including some which purportedly show canals is *A Photographic History of Mars* by Earl C. Slipher (Lowell Observatory Publications, Flagstaff, Arizona, 1962).

53. An introductory discussion on the debris of the solar system is *Meteors, Comets and Meteorites* by Gerald S. Hawkins (McGraw-Hill, 1964).

54. See also *Between the Planets,* revised edition, by Fletcher G. Watson (Doubleday, 1962).

55. A Soviet book which combines discussions of biology and astronomy and includes the question of extraterrestrial life is *Life in the Universe,* by A. I. Oparin and V. G. Fessenkov (Foreign Languages Publishing House, Moscow; also available from Twayne and Company, 1961).

56. A recent discussion of methods for the detection of extraterrestrial life is *Concepts for Detection of Extraterrestrial Life,* edited by Freeman H. Quimby (NASA Document SP56, U.S. Government Printing Office, 1964).

Part III—Intelligent Life in the Universe

57.* A useful collection of papers referred to in the present work, and which were previously published in the scientific literature is *Interstellar Communication,* edited by A. G. W. Cameron (W. A. Benjamin, Inc. 1963). This includes papers by Shklovskii, Huang, Dyson, von Hoerner, Cocconi and Morrison, Bracewell, Schwartz and Townes, and a short summary by J. P. T. Pearman of the Space Science Board meeting on intelligent extraterrestrial life.

58. A stimulating popular discussion of some of these topics is *We Are Not Alone* by Walter Sullivan (McGraw-Hill, 1964).

59.* Some of the discussion of Chapters 29, 32 and 33 follows "Direct Contact Among Galactic Civilizations by Relativistic Interstellar Space Flight" by Carl Sagan, published in the journal, *Planetary and Space Science,* Vol. 11, p. 485 (1963).

60.* N. S. Kardashev's views on Type I, Type II, and Type III civilizations are contained in "Transmission of information by extraterrestrial civilizations," in *Soviet Astronomy—A. J.,* Vol. 8, p. 217 (1964). [This is an English translation of the Soviet journal *Astronomicheskhi Zhurnal.*]

61.* A further discussion of Dyson civilizations is "The infrared detectability of Dyson civilizations," by Carl Sagan and Russell G. Walker, *Astrophysical Journal* (June, 1966).

62. Intelligent extraterrestrial life and a wide variety of other topics are touched on in *Of Stars and Men,* by Harlow Shapley (Beacon Press, Boston, 1958).

63. A similar range of subjects discussed with a similar philosophical outlook is the similarly titled *Of Men and Galaxies* by Fred Hoyle (University of Washington Press, 1964).

64.* An interesting discussion of the frequency of extra-solar planetary systems is *Habitable Planets for Man* by Stephen Dole (Blaisdell, 1964).

65. An exciting, but not always reliable, discussion of the origin and nature of man is *The Human Animal,* by Weston LaBarre (University of Chicago Press, 1954).

66. See also: *The Primates,* by Sarel Eimerl and Irven Devore (Life Nature Library, 1965),

67. *Early Man* by F. Clark Howell (Life Nature Library, 1965), and

68. "The biological nature of man," by George Gaylord Simpson, in the journal *Science,* Vol. 152, p. 472 (1966).

69. A discussion of a variety of evolutionary topics which concludes in the last chapter that animals similar to human beings are unlikely to be found anywhere but on earth is *This View of Life* by George Gaylord Simpson (Harcourt, Brace and World, 1965).

70. Many of the topics of Part III used to be the exclusive province of science fiction. An able science fiction excursion into the question of interstellar radio contact co-authored by a well-known astronomer is *A For Andromeda* by Fred Hoyle and John Elliott (Harper, 1962).

71. An excellent discussion of the origins and nature of Mesopotamian civilization is the book *The Intellectual Adventure of Ancient Man* by H. Frankfort, H. A. Frankfort, J. A. Wilson and T. Jacobsen (University of Chicago Press, 1946). The book has been reprinted by Penguin Books as *Before Philosophy.* The quote from Jacobsen in Chapter 33 is contained in Chapter 5, "The Cosmos as a State," of this work.

72. A profound essay on the philosophy of science which covers in great detail many questions touched on in this work is *The Language of Nature* by David Hawkins (W. H. Freeman and Co., 1964).

73. The magazine *Scientific American* contains excellent popular discussions of the entire subject matter of science. Offprints of these articles can be obtained from W. H. Freeman Co., San Francisco. A very short sample of such articles relevant to the present volume follows:

"The Smallest Living Cells" by Harold Morowitz and Mark E. Tourtellot (March 1962).

"Antimatter," by Geoffrey Burbidge and Fred Hoyle (April 1958).

"The Fine Structure of the Gene," by Seymour Benzer (January 1962).

"Messenger RNA" by J. Hurwitz and J. J. Furth (February, 1962).

"Paleobiochemistry" by P. H. Abelson (July 1956).

"The Genetic Basis of Evolution" by Theodosius Dobzhansky (January 1950).

"The Ages of the Elements in the Solar System," by John H. Reynolds (November 1960).

"The Evolution of Intelligence" by M. E. Bitterman (January 1965).

Subject Index

497

Brain, artificial (see artificial intelligence)
——, human, 482
Brightness curve, of binary star system, 146
Brownian motion, 208

Canonical changes, 367
Carbon-14, 106, 230
Carbonaceous chondrites, 206–7, 335–40
Cargo cults of New Guinea, 436
Carotenoids, 274
Cassiopeia A (radio source), 95–6
Catalysts, 215
Celestial mechanical perturbations as source of satellite secular acceleration, 367, 372
Centauri, Alpha and Proxima (See Alpha Centauri)
Centaurus A (radio galaxy), 121, 137–8
Centigrade temperature scale, 51
Ceti, tau (nearby star), 349, 392
Chemical Elements, origins of, 105–09
Chinese civilization, 412
Chironoumus (midge), 195
Chlorophyll, 222, 274
Chloroplasts, see photosynthesis
Chromatic aberration of telescopes, 273
Chromosomes, 189, 194–5
Civilization, terrestrial, relative state of development of, 360
Civilizations, advanced, origin of life by, 211–12
——, Types I, II, and III, 476
Civilizations, galactic, colonial, 451
——, conceivable hostile intentions of, 463–64
——, direct contact among, 438–47, 439–64
——, interval between direct contacts, 449–51
——, large-scale activities of, 467–77
——, lifetimes of, 412–14, 449
——, postulated network of, 435–6, 449
——, properties of planets of from radio transmission, 390–91
——, radio contact among, 379–97, 422, 439–41
——, relative advantages of direct contact among, 434–5
——, space vehicle contact among, 432–7
Civilizations, technical, distance to nearest, 413, 451
——, number and distribution in galaxy, 408–18, 451
Civilizations, tendency to control their environments, 360–61, 466–477
Cloud-bound planet, astronomy of hypothetical inhabitants of, 121
Clusters of stars, ages of, 81–3
Coacervate, 239–41
Codex Galactica, 451

Collision hypothesis of the origin of the solar system, 165–66
Collisions among stars, 165–66; see also Quasars
Colonization, interstellar, 451
—— of the solar system by man, 469–74
Color index, 51
Comets, 332–34
Communications, interplanetary, by laser, 407
Computing machines (analogy to living systems), 197–200
Column, Indian rust resistant, 455
Conquistadores, 412
Conservation of angular momentum (See Angular Momentum)
Contamination, biological (See Biological contamination)
Contraction of stars to the main sequence (See Protostars, stellar evolution)
Contact myths, 453–62 (See also Chapter 2)
Coral growth rings, 295–6
Cory's "Ancient Fragments," 456–9
Cosmic abundance of the elements, 57, 106–07
Cosmic Rays, 66, 93, 95, 96, 99, 100, 210
——, connection with supernovae, 95
——, induced by relativistic interstellar space flight, 446
"Cosmological principle," 139
Cosmology, 127–42
Cosmonauts, 9
Crab Nebula, 89–96
Cygnus A (radio source), 43–5, 48, 92–3, 121
Cylinder seals, 458, 460–62
"Cytherean," 317
Cytoplasm, of cells, 186, 193
Cytosine (C), 190

Darkness of the sky at night, 127–29
Deimos (See Mars, moons of)
Detection of life on other planets, techniques for *in situ,* 289–93
Dextrorotary (See Molecular Asymmetry)
Dialectical materialism, 136
Diameters of planets and satellites, method for determining, 365
Diffraction, limitation on resolution by, 154–5
Dinosaurs, possible causes of extinction of, 100
Directivity of radio telescope, 382–83
Direct rotation, 324–25
Disks, condensation of intergalactic gas clouds into, 113
DNA, 188–91, 194, 196, 236–8, 241
Dolphins, 411–12, 483
Doppler Effect, 43–45

Double stars (See Multiple stars)
Drosophila Melanogaster, 194–5
Dwarf stars, 55–6
Dyson spheres, 471–3

"Early" type stars, 61
Earth, age of, 70–71
——, albedo of, 399
——, atmosphere of, microbiological profile, 208
——, changing length of day on, 295–6
——, conditions on primitive, 217, 234
——, early history of, 220–21, 223–24
——, escape of gases from, 217–19
——, impact craters on, 301–302
——, possible reasons for absence of direct interstellar contact with, 437
——, possible visits of extra-terrestrial civilizations to, 452–64 (See also Chapter 2)
——, present atmosphere, secondary origin of, 220–21
——, radio emission of, 255–6, 360, 421
Earthshine, 399
Earth, ultimate fate of, 86
Eating, as function of living systems, 185
"Eavesdropping" on advanced technical civilizations, 393, 421, 463
Ecosphere, 344
18 cm line of hydroxyl, 65–66
Electromagnetic braking, as source of satellite acceleration, 367, 371–2
Electronic computing machines, lifelike, 185, 483–7
Electron microbeam photoengraving, 485
Electron microscope, 484–5
Elementary particles, number of in universe, 130
Elements, synthesis of in stars by advanced technical civilizations, 475
Elliptical galaxies, 66
——, formation of, 114–15
Energy, conservation of, 163
Energy sources for future terrestrial civilizations, 469–70
Entropy, 199
Entry probes, atmospheric, 284
Enzymes, 194, 243
——, origins of, 238–9
Epicurean school, 3
Erg, definition, 55
Eridani, epsilon (nearby star), 392
Escape velocity, 218
Euclidean geometry, 130
European Space Research Organization, 334
Evolution and genetic code, parable on, 192–94
Evolutionary cosmology, 140
Evolution, biological, 99, 186, 196–7, 205

——, effect of historical accidents on, 183
Evolution, by natural selection, 135
—— of galaxies, 110–124
—— of matter, 104–09
Exosphere, 218
—— temperature, connection with origin of life, 247
Extra-focal blue light, of refracting telescopes, 273
Extraterrestrial life, see Life, extraterrestrial
Eyes, color sensitivity of, 51

Fahrenheit temperature scale, 51
"Fitness of the environment," 228–9
Flood, the Great, 459
Flying saucers, 13–21
Four-dimensional universe, 130–31
1420 Mc/sec line (See 21 cm line of hydrogen)
Freezing, deleterious biological effects of, 441
Frequency of light, 41, 42
Frequency selections, for interstellar radio communication, 380–81
F2 Discontinuity in stellar rotational velocities, 170–71, 175–6
Fuels, fossil, 414, 470

"Gain" of radio telescope (see Directivity)
Galactic civilizations, see Civilizations, galactic
Galaxies, elliptical, 40
——, elliptical, formation and origins of, 114–16
——, evolution of, 111–24
——, irregular, 40
——, motions and distributions of, 48
——, origins of, 111–14
——, radio, possible artificial origin of, 475–6
——, spiral, 40
——, spiral, formation and origins of, 114–16
——, violent events in the nuclei of, 118–24
Galaxy, age of, 83
——, dimensions and shape of, 28–33
——, halo or corona of, 27
——, nucleus of, 30
——, outflow of gas from center of, 119
——, position of sun in, 28
——, rotation of, 33
Galilean satellites of Jupiter, 330–32
Gamma rays, 42
"Garbage" theory of origin of life, 211–12
Gauss (unit of magnetic field strength), 59
Genes, 194 (See also Chromosomes, DNA)
Genesis, 205
Genetic code (See DNA)
Genetic material, see self-replication, DNA

Geocentricism, practical, 9
Giant stars, 55–6
Globular clusters in galaxy, 28, 40, 47, 78
——, origins of, 112–13
Glucose (See Sugar)
Gold and uranium, synthesis of, 107
Golem, 482
Googol, 129–30
Googolplex, 130
Gram, definition of, 55
Gravitational binding of light to a star, 123
Gravitational potential energy as energy source for stars and galaxies, 71, 73, 75, 76, 78, 122
Gravity, acceleration due to, 443
Greenhouse effect, 222
Guanine (G) 190
"Gulliver," Mars life detection experiment, 291–2
Gulliver's Travels, 363

Hale telescope (See Mt. Palomar Observatory)
Halley's comet, 332–4
h and χ Persei (open star cluster), 83
Harvard University, 20
Heredity (See self-replication, DNA)
Hertzsprung-Russell Diagram, position of stars on, 78
—— of star clusters, 82–83
Hexose, see Sugar
Hieroglyphics, Egyptian, 440
"Hillbillies, Beverly," 394
Hindu cosmology, 135, 136
Hoarfrost on Mars, 261–2
"Hot dilute soup," origin of life in, 233
H II regions, 40, 64, 65, 209
Hubble's Constant, 132
—— Law, 132, 133, 136–7
Hyades (open star cluster), 83–4
Hydrogen atom, structure of, 34
Hydroxyl radical (OH), 389
Hygroscopic salts, 280

Ice II, 442
Inclination of satellite and planetary orbits, 365
Inferior conjunction, 319
Infinity, 129–30
Information compression, 482–3
Information content, of genetic material, 195–6
—— of interstellar radio communication, 427–8
—— of the human brain, 482
Infrared detection of Dyson civilizations, 472–3
Infrared light, 42

Intelligence, definition of, 480–81
——, evolution of, 358–9, 411–412
Intelligent life as a factor on the cosmic scale, 466–77
Intelligent life on earth, radio detection of, 255–57, 360, 421
Interstellar dust grains, 63
Interstellar medium, 63–67
——, changing composition of, 107–108
——, connection with galactic evolution, 115
——, early density of, 108
Interstellar space, emptiness of, 35, 63–64
Interstellar spaceflight (See Spaceflight, interstellar)
Ions, 52
Irish monasteries, 412
Irregular galaxies, 66
——, origin of, 114–15
Isotopes, 105–06
Isotropic radiation, 382

"Jabbaren," 455
Java Man, 451–2
Jovian planets, 217, 327–9
——, source of methane on, 254
——, utilization of as energy sources by advanced civilizations, 473
Jupiter, 152, see also Jovian planets
——, mass of, 165
——, radio emission from, 436
——, satellites of, 329–32

Kelvin temperature scale, 51
Krypton, 219

Lalande 21185 (nearby star with dark companion), 151
Land, process of color photography, 274
Laputa, 363
Lasers, 360–61, 400–07
Laser, gamma ray, 475
"Late" type stars, 61
Levorotary (See Molecular asymmetry)
Libration, 313
Life, common origin of on earth, 216–17
——, conditions needed for development of, 228–9, 247
——, consequences of contraction of the universe for, 135–6, 142
——, detection of by infrared observations, 253–4
——, diversity of extraterrestrial forms of, 350–52
——, existence of, connection with Olber's paradox, 128–9
——, extraterrestrial, early views, 3–8
——, extraterrestrial, significance of discovery of, 358

——, in other solar systems, 342–52
——, intelligent, required size of brains of, 482–3
Life on earth, mass of, 248
——, oldest known forms of, 221–4
Life, on the definition of, 182–200
Life, origin of, 188, 197, 202–45
——, influence of planetary mass on, 347–8
——, Jupiter as a laboratory for, 328–9
——, lunar evidence for, 306–7
—— on earth, date of, 224
—— on other terrestrial planets, 247
—— role of metabolism in, 197, 199, 240–41
Life, possible influence of nearby supernovae explosions on, 99–100, 158
——, possible influence of quasar explosions on, 124
——, possible influence of red giant evolution on, 86
——, sensory receptors in possible extraterrestrial forms of, 351–2
——, size ranges of, 342, 350–51
——, spontaneous generation of, 188, 197, 202–45
——, survival of under extreme conditions, 209–10
——, temperature restrictions on origin of, 344
——, unity of, on earth, 183, 216–17
"Light bucket," 406
Lightning, role of, in origin of life, 230–34
Light, velocity of, 129
Light year, 29
Limb brightening, 321
Limb darkening, 321
Limb of a planet, 259
Limonite, 233, 270, 281–2
"Lincos," language for interstellar communication, 428–30
Lobes of a radio telescope, 382–3
Long distance calls in interstellar radio contact, 421
Los Angeles, possibility of life in, 267
Lowell Observatory, 374
Lucifer, 325
Luna III, 284, 304–5, 306–7, 434
Luna IX, 304, 434
Luna X, 434
Lunar spacecraft, 308

M1 (See Crab Nebula)
M3 (globular cluster), 82–3
M 13 (globular cluster), 32
M 20 (diffuse nebula), 92, 94
M 31 (nearest spiral galaxy), 35–39, 48, 123
M 67 (open star cluster), 83

M 82 (spiral galaxy), 118–19
M 104 (spiral galaxy), 40
M stars, possible development of life on planets of, 410–11
Magellanic Clouds, 35, 40, 111, 114
Magnetic fields, interstellar, 66, 173–6, 445–6
Magnetohydrodynamics, 163, 167
Magnitude, absolute, 56
——, apparent, 56
——, scale of brightness, 35, 56
Main sequence, 59, 77–8
Maintaining reactions, 198–200
Man, recent evolution of, 451–2
Mare Humorum (lunar feature), 300–01
Mare Imbrium (lunar feature), 298, 305
Mariner II, 321–23, 384, 434
Mariner IV, 21–2, 266, 284–9, 290, 368–9, 434
"Markers" for interstellar communication, 406–7, 474
Mars, biological contamination of, 211, 267–70
——, blue haze of, 260, 266
——, bright areas of, 264–5
——, canals on, 275–9, 289–90
——, chemical composition of atmosphere of, 265
——, color changes on, 274
——, craters on, 21, 287–89
——, dark areas of, 265
——, dark areas, dark nuclei of, 264–7, 275
——, dust storms on, 264
——, elevations on, 264
——, erosion on, 287–9
——, escape of oxygen and other gases from, 219
——, "green" color of dark areas, 273–4
——, inclination of axis of, 259–60
"Mars Jars," 268
Mars, length of year on, 260
——, life on, possible locales for, 281, 289, 290–91
——, magnetic field of, 285
——, maps of, 263, 264
——, moons of, 362–76
——, organic molecules on, 283–4
——, physical environment of, 258–68
——, polar caps of, 260–61, 261–2
——, polar cap, dark collar to, 280–81
——, possible ancient technical civilization on, 373–76
——, possible primitive environment of, 270–71
——, radio detection of life on, 256–7
——, rotation of, 259
——, satellites of, possible artificial nature of, 373–6

Mars, seasonal variations on, 279–81, 283, 289
——, secular changes on, 281, 283
——, surface pressure on, 266
——, survival of terrestrial microorganisms on, 267–70
——, temperatures, 267
——, ultraviolet light on, 265–6
——, upper atmosphere, 268–9
——, visco-elastic properties of, 370–71
——, visual and photographic appearance, 259–64
——, water on, 261–2, 279
——, wave of darkening, 279–80, 289
"Martian gods," 455–6
Marxist philosophy, 135–6
Maser, 385
Mass-luminosity relation, 60–61
Materialism, 479
Matter, origin of, 207
Mean free path, 64
Mechanism in biology, 182–4
Mediocrity, assumption of, 356–61
Megacycle per second, radio frequency, 380
Megaparsec, 127
Mercury, 313–15
——, anomalies in motion of, 131
——, escape of atmosphere from, 219
——, possibilities of life on, 247
——, ultimate fate of, 86
Mesons, Mu, 442
Metabolic inhibitors, 441–2, 449
Metagalaxy, 35
Meteorites, 333–40 (See also Carbonaceous chondrites)
——, ages of, 70
Methane bacteria, 254
Micromegas, 363
Micron, 42
Milky Way (see Galaxy)
Mitochondria, see Respiration
Molecular asymmetry, 336–7
Moon, absence of atmosphere on, 302
——, biological contamination of, 308
——, *continentes* of, 296
——, craters on, 296–311
——, craters on, origin of, 298–302
——, craters on rays, 300, 302–3
——, dark halo craters on, 310–11
——, early history of, 306
——, far side of, 304–5
——, gas clouds on, 308–11
——, history of surface of, 304
——, laser beam reflection off, 400–401
——, lava flow on, 302
—— *maria* of, 296, 300–301
——, mountains on, 297–8
——, permafrost on, 308

——, physical environment of, 295–311
——, possibility of life and organic matter on, 306–11
——, possibility of observatory on, 155
——, rills on, 299
——, surface conditions on, 307–8
——, temperature on, 306
——, connection with panspermia hypothesis, 211
——, vulcanism on, 310–11
Morgan-Keenan-Kellman Atlas, 52–55
Mortality of men and civilizations, 478–87
Mt. Palomar Observatory, 40, 284
Multivator, device for detection of life on Mars, 291, 293
Mutation, 99–100, 188–89, 194, 200

National Aeronautics and Space Administration, 154
National Radio Astronomy Observatory, 386, 392, 409
Natural selection, 99, 186 (See also Evolution, biological)
Neanderthal man, 451–2
Nebulae, spiral (See Galaxies, Spiral Galaxies)
Nebular hypothesis, 162–67
Nebula, solar, in origin of solar system, 162
Neon, 219
Neptune, 374 (See also Jovian planets)
Neptune and the Panspermia hypothesis, 210
Neurons, number of in brain, 482
Neutral hydrogen, 21 cm line of, 388–89
New York Times, 21
Nimbus meteorological satellite, 248–53, 283
NGC 205 (galaxy), 35–36, 39
NGC 221 (galaxy), 36
NGC 2237 (gaseous nebula), 74–75
NGC 4725 (spiral galaxy), 89, 90
NGC 5128 (See Centaurus A)
NGC 5364 (spiral galaxy), 30
NGC 5457 (See M 101)
NGC 7293 (planetary nebula), 85
Noble gases, 219
Noise, background, in interstellar radio communication, 381
——, extraction of signal from, 384, 391–3
Noise temperature of a radio receiver, 385–6
Non-thermal radiation, 93
Novae, 149
Nuclear weapons, 71, 253, 335, 412–13, 467
Nucleoside Phosphates, 189, 190
Nucleus, of cells, 186, 193

Oannes, 457–9, 461
Obligate anaerobes (See Anaerobes)
Observatories, location on mountains, 259
Occlusion of gases, 220–21

Olber's paradox, 128–29, 141
Optical activity and origin of life, 244
Optical activity of organic molecules (See Molecular asymmetry)
Optical contact among galactic civilizations, 398–407
Orbiters, 284
Orbiting Astronomical Observatories, 154, 266
Organic matter, 215
—— as index of planetary biological activity, 253–4
—— in meteorites, 335–7, 340
——, prebiological synthesis of, 214–17
Orgeuil meteorite (See Carbonaceous chondrites)
Origin of life (See Life, origin of)
—— on earth from outside (See Panspermia hypothesis)
Origin of solar system, 144–178
——, lunar evidence on, 306
——, planetary evidence on, 334
Outgassing, 218, 220
Oxygen as a poison, 215–16
—— as sign of planetary biological activity, 254–55
—— on earth, origin of, 221
Oz, 391
Ozma, Project, 386, 391, 392–3, 416, 477
Ozone, absence of on primitive earth, 234
——, ultraviolet absorption by, 98–99

Panspermia Hypothesis, 3, 7–8, 207–12
Paper chromatography, 230–31
Parallelepiped, steel, 454–55
Paranthropus, 451
Parkes Observatory, Sydney, Australia, 313
Parsec (pc), 29
Payloads for "conventional" interstellar space vehicles, 445
Pentose (see Sugar)
Perfect Cosmological Principle (See Cosmological Principle)
Petroleum, origin of, 217
Phobos (See Mars, moons of)
Photodissociation of gases by ultraviolet light, 221
Photographic and visual observations, relative merits of, 278, 281
Photons, 42
Photosynthesis, 221, 241
Phytane, 221–2
Pic du Midi Observatory, 259, 277, 313
Pilgrim's Progress, 342
Pithecanthropus, 451–2
Planetary atmospheres, escape into space, 217–20
——, spectroscopic determination of composition of, 265, 283–4

Planetary nebulae, 84–5
Planetary systems (See Solar systems)
Planets, angular momentum of, 164–5
——, diversity of, 350
——, habitable in galaxy, 343–50
——, Jovian, 152 (See also Jovian planets)
——, methods for discovery of extra-solar, 149–55
—— of other stars, 151–55
——, original chemical composition of, 166, 177
——, possible representation of on cylinder seals, 460–61
——, relative sizes and distances of, 28–9
Plants, source of green color of, 274
Pleiades (open cluster), 31, 83–4
Pleuropneumonia-like organism (PPLO), 350
Pluto, 329, 331, 374
——, discovery of, 151
——, planets more distant than, 28
Polymerization, 237
Polypeptides, 235, 238 (See also Proteins)
Population increase of earth, 471
Positive curvature, 131
Poynting-Robertson effect, 372
Primary of a double star system, 145
Probes, automatic interstellar, 432–7
Proconsul, 451–2
Project *Westford,* 360
Projective tests, psychological, 13–22, 94
Proteins, 186, 188, 189
Proto-galaxies, 112–14, 115
Protostars, 73, 76–77
Proxima Centauri (nearest star), 150, 165, 346–47

Quanta, 42
Quantum yield, 231–32
Quasars, 120–24, 395
——, possible artificial origins of, 475–76

Racemic mixture of molecules (See Molecular asymmetry)
Radar, determination of planetary rotation, 313–14, 324–5
—— investigations of planets, 384
—— test of general theory of relativity, 131
Radial velocity, 153
Radian, 400
Radiation pressure, 121–22
—— as source of satellite secular acceleration, 367, 372
Radioactivity, 70
Radio communication, intergalactic, 477
Radio communication, interstellar, 379–97, 422, 439–41
——, frequency assignment for 388–9
——, range of, 384, 387–8, 393, 476–7

Venus, phases of, as argument against Ptolemaic cosmology, 4–5

——, physical environment of, 315–25

——, possible alteration of environment of, 467–8

——, rotation of, 324–5

——, III, Soviet space vehicle, 434

——, ultraviolet markings in clouds of, 317

Violet shift, 142

Virgo cluster of galaxies, 111

Visual and photographic observations, relative merits of, 278, 281

Vital force, 184

Vostok, Soviet space vehicle, 28, 218

Wavelength of light, 41, 42

White dwarfs, 56, 60, 61, 84–5

"Windows" in atmospheric transmission, 351

Wolf Trap, device for detection of life on Mars, 293

WZ Sagittae (eclipsing binary), 147

Xenon, 219

Xi Ursae Majoris (visual binary star), 145–6

X-rays, 42

Zeta Ursae Majoris (star), 108–9

Zodiacal light, 303

Zond II, 286

Zond III, 306, 434

Name Index

Doyle, Sir Arthur Conan, 2
Drake, Frank, 381, 391, 393, 397, 406, 409, 423–27, 462
Dyce, Rolf, 314
Dyson, Freeman J., 469–74, 476

Eddington, Sir Arthur Stanley, 71, 121
Einstein, Albert, 130–32, 442
Eiseley, Loren, 25, 182, 356, 432
Eliade, M., 453
Empedocles, 205
Emmons, G. T., 453
Engels, Frederick, 479–80
Eratosthenes, 357
Ezer, G., 77

Fermi, Enrico, 448
Fernandez-Moran, H., 484–85
Feynman, Richard P., 184–5
Fitch, Frank, 337–8
Flammarion, Camille, 6
Focas, J. H., 279
Fogg, Phileas, 27
Fontenelle, Bernard de, 6
Fox, Sidney W., 235, 241, 242
Frankfort, H., 458, 461, 462

Gagarin, Y. A., 9, 28
Galileo Galilei, 4, 296, 357
Galper, Ruth Ellen, 463
Gilgamesh, 478
Giraudoux, Jean, 12, 378
Glenn, John, 9
Gold, Thomas, 123, 139, 211, 302
Graham, Billy, 22
Green, Elinore, 231
Groth, W., 231

Haldane, J. B. S., 217, 233, 350, 463
Hall, Asaph, 364, 366, 374
Hardy, Thomas, 182
Hawkes, Jacquetta, 452
Hedén, Carl-Gören, 442
Herschel, William, 6, 110, 308–9
Hertz, Heinrich, 379
Hertzsprung, Einar, 59
Hesiod, 205
Hoerner, Sebastian Von, 357, 409, 413, 414–18, 421–2, 451
Horowitz, Norman H., 239
Hoshi, R., 80
Hoyle, Fred, 86, 121, 139, 173–6, 318, 414, 441
Huang, Su-Shu, 345–6, 409
Hubble, Edwin, 44, 132
Huxley, T. H., 214
Huygens, Christianus, 6, 26, 160, 181, 202, 312, 356, 362, 420, 448

Jacchia, Luigi, 316
Jacobsen, Thorkild, 459–60
Jeans, Sir James, 8, 165–7
Jeffreys, Sir Harold, 369–70
Job, 144, 168

Kafka, Franz, 464
Kant, Immanuel, 6, 160–62, 165, 166–7
Kardashev, N. S., 115, 394, 395, 476–77
Kasner, Edward, 129
Kellerman, Kenneth, 313
Kepler, Johannes, 5, 96, 294
Kerr, Frank J., 368
Kijé, Lt., 193
Kolmogorov, A. N., 200, 480–81
Kornberg, Arthur, 236
Kosachevskii, M. P., 372
Kozyrev, N. A., 309–11
Kuiper, G. P., 176, 297–8, 301

Langley, Samuel P., 246
La Perouse, 453
Laplace, Pierre Simon, Marquis de, 161–3, 165, 166–7, 175
Lear, Edward, 408
Lederberg, Joshua, 211, 293
Leighton, Robert B., 289
Levin, Gilbert, 292
Levinthal, Elliott, 293
Lhote, Henri, 455–6
Liapunov, A., 197–200
Lilley, John C., 409, 411
Loeb, Jacques, 182
Lomonosov, M. N., 6
Lowell, Percival, 275–9, 281, 318, 364, 365
Lucretius, 3, 161–2, 205
Lynds, C. R., 118–19, 146–7
Lysenko, Trofim, 135

Macdonald, G. J. F., 370
MacGregor, A. M., 222
Magellan, Ferdinand, 27, 35
Maltby, P., 395
Malthus, Thomas, 471
Mamedov, 339
Marconi, G., 380
Martel, Charles, 412
Marx, Karl, 437
Maxwell, James Clerk, 162, 176, 379
Mayer, Cornell H., 319
McCrea, W. H., 178
Mendel, Gregor, 188–89
Mendelyeev, 430
Menzel, Donald H., 20, 219, 318
Metrodoros, 3
Miller, S. L., 231, 233–4, 243
Moffet, A. T., 395
Mollenstedt, K. G., 485

Morgan, Thomas Hunt, 194
Moroz, V. I., 284, 314
Morrison, Philip, 358, 380, 388, 391, 397, 409, 422, 433, 483
Muller, H. J., 196
Murray, B. C., 289

Nagy, Bartholomew, 336–8
Newton, Sir Isaac, 5, 6, 17, 162, 363

Ochoa, Severo, 236
Ogdai Khan, 412
Oliver, Bernard M., 409
Oort, Jan, 334
Oparin, A. I., 197, 217, 239–41
Oró, John, 234
Ostroumov, G. N., 454

Page, Thornton, 163
Palade, S. E., 187
Pariiskii, N. N., 166, 370
Pascal, Blaise, 27
Paschenko, 477
Pasternak, Boris, 26
Pasteur, L., 206–7, 242–3
Pavlov, I., 481
Pearman, J. P. T., 409
Pettengill, Gordon H., 314
Pickering, W. H., 277, 306
Piddington, J. S., 115
Pikelner, S. B., 118
Pillans, H., 146–7
Pimentel, George, 229
Plato, 168
Pliny, 411
Plutarch, 466
Pol, van der, 436
Pollack, James B., 264–6, 283, 324
Polyhistor, Alexander, 456–57, 459
Ponnamperuma, Cyril, 235
Popovich, P. R., 9
Prokofiev, Sergei, 193
Pythagoras, 363

Redi, Francesco, 206
Russell, Henry Norris, 59, 219

Sagan, Carl, 207, 251, 264–66, 283, 324, 409, 413, 424, 450, 467
Sandage, A. R., 81, 83–4, 114–15, 118–19, 395
Schiaparelli, Giovanni, 275, 278, 313
Schatzmann, Evry, 178
Schilling, Gerhard, 368
Schirra, Walter, 9
Schmidt, Maarten, 410
Schmidt, O. Y., 155, 178
Schwartz, R. N., 401–03, 405–06, 433
Shajn, G. A., 169
Shapiro, Irwin I., 131

Sharpless, B. P., 366–7, 373, 375–6
Shklovskii, I. S., 65–6, 93, 95, 100, 135, 136, 177, 208, 361, 373–5, 394–5, 405–6, 414, 437, 450, 471, 479
Sholomitskii, G. B., 395–7
Simplicius, 104
Sinton, William, 283–4
Sisler, Frederick D., 339–40
Slipher, V. M., 45, 132
Smelianov, I., 272
Smith, Adam, 437
Sophocles, 2
Speidel, R., 485
Spitzer, Lyman, 123, 166
Strand, K. A., 149–50
Struve, Hermann, 366
Struve, Otto, 153, 169–70, 171, 392, 409
Stryor, Lubert, 243
Subutai Khan, 412
Tereshkova, V., 9
Tesla, N., 380
Thales, 3
Tikhov, G. A., 275
Titov, G., 9, 28
Tombaugh, Clyde, 151, 374
Townes, C. H., 401, 402, 403, 405, 406, 433
Troitskii, V. I., 307
Trouvelot, E., 280
Tsiolkovskii, K. E., 8, 469, 472
Tyler, Stanley, Figure 16–7

Urey, Harold C., 176, 229–34, 374

Van Biesbroeck, George, 277
Van de Kamp, Peter, 150–52
Verne, Jules, 27
Vishniac, Wolf, 293
Voltaire, 6, 12, 363

Walker, M., 81
Watson, James D., 189
Weiner, Norbert, 197
Wells, H. G., 401
Wells, John W., 295–6
Weyssenhoff, H. von, 231
Whewell, William, 6, 326, 356
Whipple, Fred L., 318, 333, 368
Whitman, Walt, 104
Whittaker, Ewen, 297, 304–5, 307
Wildt, Rupert, 328
Wilkins, G. A., 375–6
"Winkler, Helmut," 13–18
Woltjer, T., 123
Woodruff, L. L., 203
Wyndham, J. D., 395, 396

Xenophanes, 12

Yeats, William Butler, 294
Yuyuma, S., 242
Zigel, F., 374